BTEC national

2nd Edition

Sport

Book 1

Ray Barker • Adam Gledhill
Chris Lydon • Andy Miles
Chris Mulligan • Graham Saffrey
Rob Saipe • Louise Sutton

Series editor: Mark Adams

www.harcourt.co.uk

✓ Free online support
✓ Useful weblinks
✓ 24 hour online ordering

01865 888118

Heinemann is an imprint of Harcourt Education Limited, a company incorporated in
England and Wales, having its registered office: Halley Court, Jordan Hill, Oxford OX2 8EJ.
Registered company number: 3099304

www.harcourt.co.uk

Heinemann is the registered trademark of Harcourt Education Ltd

Text © Adam Gledhill, Chris Mulligan, Graham Saffery, Louise Sutton, Ray Barker, Andy Miles,
Chris Lydon and Rob Saipe 2007

First published 2007

12 11 10 09 08 07
10 9 8 7 6 5 4 3 2 1

British Library Cataloguing in Publication Data is available from the British Library on request.

ISBN 9780435465148

Edited by Melanie Gray and Ros Davies
Typeset by Tek-Art, Surrey, UK
Illustrated by Tek-Art, Surrey, UK
Cover design by Pentacor Big Ltd
Picture research by Cath Bevan
Cover photo/illustration © Stockbyte
Printed by Scotprint

Websites
The websites used in this book were correct and up to date at the time of publication. It is
essential for tutors to preview each website before using it in class so as to ensure that the URL
is still accurate, relevant and appropriate. We suggest that tutors bookmark useful websites and
consider enabling students to access them through the school/college intranet.

Contents

Acknowledgements   v
Introduction   vi

Unit 1 The body in action   2

1.1 Understand the structure and function of the
skeletal system and how it responds to exercise 4
1.2 Understand the structure and function of the
muscular system and how it responds to
exercise   17
1.3 The structure and function of the cardiovascular
system and how it responds to exercise   29
1.4 The structure and function of the respiratory
system and how it responds to exercise   36
1.5 Understand the different energy systems and
their use in sport and exercise   42

Unit 2 Health and safety in sport   50

2.1 Know the key factors that influence health and
safety in sport   52
2.2 Be able to carry out risk assessments   68
2.3 Know how to maintain the safety of participants
and colleagues in a sports environment   74
2.4 Be able to plan a safe sporting activity   81

Unit 3 Training and fitness for sport   90

3.1 Understand the fitness requirements of
different sporting activities   92
3.2 Understand the different methods of physical
fitness training   102

3.3 Be able to plan a fitness training programme   112
3.4 Be able to monitor and evaluate a fitness
training programme   125

Unit 4 Sports coaching   134

4.1 Understand the roles, responsibilities and
skills of sports coaches   136
4.2 Understand the techniques used by coaches
to improve the performance of athletes   154
4.3 Be able to plan a sports coaching session   162
4.4 Be able to deliver a sports coaching session   170

Unit 5 Sports development   180

5.1 Understand key concepts in sports
development   182
5.2 Know about key providers of sports
development   193
5.3 Understand how quality is measured in
sports development   208
5.4 Know about sports development in practice   216

Unit 6 Fitness testing for sport and exercise   228

6.1 Understand a range of laboratory-based and
field based fitness tests   230
6.2 Understand the practice of health screening   244
6.3 Be able to prepare for and conduct
appropriate fitness tests   258
6.4 Be able to analyse the results of fitness
tests   265

Unit 10 Sports nutrition   274

10.1 Understand the concepts of nutrition and digestion   276

10.2 Understand energy intake and expenditure in sports performance   289

10.3 Understand the relationship between hydration and sports performance   298

10.4 Be able to plan a diet appropriate for a selected sports activity   302

Unit 16 Psychology for sports performance   316

16.1 Understand the effect of personality on sports performance   318

16.2 Understand the relationships between stress, anxiety, arousal and sports performance   327

16.3 Understand group dynamics in sports teams   337

16.4 Be able to plan a psychological skills training programme to enhance sports performance   344

Unit 26 Technical and tactical skills in sport   364

26.1 Understand the technical skills and tactics demanded by selected sports   366

26.2 Be able to assess the technical and tactical ability of an elite sports performer   381

26.3 Be able to asses their own technical and tactical ability   400

Unit 27 The athlete's lifestyle   420

27.1 Understand how lifestyle can affect athletes   422

27.2 Understand the importance of appropriate behaviour for athletes   431

27.3 Understand how to communicate effectively with the media and significant others   442

27.4 Understand factors involved in career planning   451

Index   462

Acknowledgements

The authors and publisher would like to thank Mark Adams for his help and support in developing the BTEC National Sport resources.

The authors and publisher would like to thank the following individuals and organisations for permission to reproduce photographs:

Front cover: Stockbyte
Feature icons: Getty Images / PhotoDisc, Jupiter Images / Photos.com, Corbis

Alamy / Dominic Burke – page 2
Pa Photos / John Giles – page 9
Corbis / Gideon Mendel – page 15
Science Photo Library / Prof P. Motta / Dept Of Anatomy / University "La Sapienza", Rome – page 19
Masterfile / Hiep Vu – page 23
Pa Photos / AP / Natacha Pisarenko – page 45
Alamy / Bill Bachman – page 50
Crown / Office of Public Service Information – page 54
Photofusion / David Tothill – page 60
Alamy / Ian McKinnell – page 61
Action Plus / Neil Tingle – page 63
Action Plus / Glyn Kirk – page 74
Alamy / David Lawrence – page 76
Action Plus / Mike King – page 81
Action Plus / Glyn Kirk – page 83
Getty Images / Mike Powell – page 90
Action Plus / Glyn Kirk – page 92
Alamy / Image Source – page 103
iStockPhoto / Eliza Snow – page 106
Getty Images / PhotoDisc – page 115
Action Plus / Neil Tingle – page 126
Pa Photos / AP / Thomas Kienzle – page 134
Pa Photos / EMPICS / Adam Davy – page 136
Action Plus / Chris Brown – page 140
Action Plus / Glyn Kirk – page145
Getty Images / AFP / Odd Anderson – page 147
Getty Images – page 149
Pa Photos / Peter Byrne – page 151
Pa Photos / EMPICS / Neal Simpson – page 155
Pa Photos / Toby Melville – page 180
Corbis / Reuters / Handout / EDAW Consortium – page 185
Pa Photos / AP / Marc Bence – page 189
Getty Images / John Peters – page 191
Action Plus / Glyn Kirk – page 211
Pa Photos / AP / Sergio Dionisio – page 216
Alamy / Richard Naude – page 218
Author supplied – page 219
Corbis / ZEFA / Frank Bodenmueller – page 228
Science Photo Library / Philippe Psaila – page 242

Alamy / Photofusion Picture Library – page 248
Action Plus / Mike King – page 264
Action Plus / Mike Shearman – page 266
Action Plus / Steve Bardens – page 274
Masterfile / Mark Tomalty – page 277
Science Photo Library / Gustoimages – page 277
Getty Images / PhotoDisc – page 279
Tudor Photography – page 294
Science Photo Library / Gustoimages – page 300
Action Plus / Glyn Kirk – page 316
Action Plus / Glyn Kirk – page3 20
Getty Images / AFP / Hassan Ammar – page 323
Action Plus / Glyn Kirk – page 337
Getty Images / NBA / Andrew D Bernstein – page 345
Getty Images / AFP / Francois-Xavier Marit - page 364
Action Plus / Glyn Kirk – page 389
Pa Photos / EMPICS / Adam Davy – page 390
Pa Photos / Gareth Copley – page 393
Action Plus / Neil Tingle – page 398
Action Plus / Neil Tingle – page 420
Pa Photos / AP / Jasper Juinen – page 424
Pa Photos / Stefan Rousseau/ – page 425
Action Plus / Glyn Kirk – page 425
Pa Photos / Owen Humphreys – page 426
Pa Photos / Panoramic – page 429
UK Sport – page 430
Pa Photos / EMPICS / Neal Simpson – page 433
Getty Images / AFP / Carl de Souza – page 436
Action Plus / Glyn Kirk – page 438

The authors and publisher would like to thank the following individuals and organisations for permission to reproduce copyright material:

1. Unit 2 pg 65. Donaghue v Stevenson (Paisley snail). Adapted from information from the following webpage:
   http://www.leeds.ac.uk/law/hamlyn/donoghue.htm
2. Unit 6 tables 6.2, 6.5, 6.6, 6.7 and 6.8 (pages 231-238) are adapted from information from the following website:
   www.1st4sport.com/1st4sportsite/
3. Unit 10 tables 10.6 (pg 284), 10.8 (pg 285) and 10.9 (pg 286) are adapted from The Composition of Foods 6th edition 2002: McCane and Widdowson.
4. Unit 10 table 10.11, pg 296 is adapted from: The 1991 COMA Report on Dietary Reference Values (DRVs)
5. Unit 10 tables 10.5 (pg 283) and 10.12 (pg 298) are adapted from The IOC Consensus Statement on Sports Nutrition 2003 http://multimedia.olympic.org/pdf/en_report_723.pdf

Introduction

Welcome to this BTEC National Sport course book one, specifically designed to support students on the following programmes (with the number of units required to gain the qualification identified):

- BTEC National Award in Sport
  3 core and 3 specialist units
- BTEC National Award in Sport (Performance and Excellence)
  3 core and 3 specialist units
- BTEC National Certificate in Sport (Performance and Excellence)
  8 core and 4 specialist units
- BTEC National Certificate in Sport (Development, Coaching and Fitness)
  7 core and 5 specialist units
- BTEC National Diploma in Sport (Performance and Excellence)
  8 core and 10 specialist units
- BTEC National Diploma in Sport (Development, Coaching and Fitness)
  7 core and 11 specialist units

It is important to highlight the fact that some of the units you will study on your course are included in the 2nd BTEC National Sport course book.

The following table shows the units included in Sport Book 1 and Sport Book 2 which you can use to support you in your studies. The table indicates whether it is a **core (bold)** or *specialist (italic)* unit. Those units in blue appear in this title, those in green will appear in BTEC National Sport Book 2.

If nothing is indicated in a box that means the unit is not included in your qualification.

Unit	BTEC National Award in Sport	BTEC National Award in Sport (Performance and Excellence)	BTEC National Certificate in Sport (Performance and Excellence)	BTEC National Certificate in Sport (Development, Coaching and Fitness)	BTEC National Diploma in Sport (Performance and Excellence)	BTEC National Diploma in Sport (Development, Coaching and Fitness)
1 The Body in Action	**1**	**1**	**1**	**1**	**1**	**1**
2 Health and Safety in Sport	**1**	**1**	**1**	**1**	**1**	**1**
3 Training and Fitness for Sport	**1**	**1**	**1**	**1**	**1**	**1**
4 Sports Coaching	*1*		*1*	**1**	*1*	**1**
5 Sports Development	*1*			**1**		**1**
6 Fitness Testing for Sport and Exercise	*1*	*1*	**1**	**1**	**1**	**1**

Unit	BTEC National Award in Sport	BTEC National Award in Sport (Performance and Excellence)	BTEC National Certificate in Sport (Performance and Excellence)	BTEC National Certificate in Sport (Development, Coaching and Fitness)	Diploma in Sport (Performance and Excellence)	BTEC National Diploma in Sport (Development, Coaching and Fitness)
10 Sports Nutrition		1	1	1	1	1
11 Sport and Society			2	2	2	2
12 Instructing Physical Activity and Exercise				2	2	2
16 Psychology for Sports Performance	1	1	1	1	1	1
17 Sports Injuries			2	2	2	2
18 Analysis of Sports Performance			2		2	2
19 Talent Identification and Development in Sport					2	2
20 Sport and Exercise Massage			2	2	2	2
21 Rules, Regulations and Officiating in Sport			2	2	2	2
23 Working with Children in Sport				2	2	2
24 Sport as a Business				2	2	2
25 Work-based Experience in Sport			2	2	2	2
26 Technical and Tactical Skills in Sport		1	1		1	
27 The Athlete's Lifestyle		1	1		1	

The revised specification has been structured to allow learners maximum flexibility in selecting specialist units, so that particular interests and career aspirations within sport can be reflected in the choice of unit combinations. This series of books effectively reflect the specification and will help the tutor and the student to successfully direct their learning in a specific path enabling them to develop essential skills required for gaining employment or securing career progression.

You should also note that Exercise, Health and Lifestyle in addition to Exercise for Specific Groups are included in the BTEC National Sport and Exercise Sciences Book.

The aim of this book is to provide a comprehensive source of information for your course. It follows the BTEC specification closely, so that you can easily see what you have covered and quickly find the information you need. Examples and case studies from Sport are used to bring your course to life and make it enjoyable to study. We hope you will be encouraged to find your own examples of current practice too.

You will often be asked to carry out research for activities in the text, and this will develop your research skills and enable you to find many sources of interesting Sports information, particularly on the Internet. The book is also a suitable core text for students on HND, foundation degree and first-year degree programmes. To help you plan your study, an overview of each unit and its outcomes is given at the beginning of each unit.

Features of the book

This book has a number of features to help you relate theory to practice and reinforce your learning. It also aims to help you gather evidence for assessment. You will find the following features in each unit.

Key terms

Issues and terms that you need to be aware of are summarised under these headings. They will help you check your knowledge as you learn, and will prove to be a useful quick-reference tool.

Theory into practice

These practical activities allow you to apply theoretical knowledge to Sport tasks or research. Make sure you complete these activities as you work through each unit, to reinforce your learning.

Case studies

Interesting examples of real situations, for example fitness testing results are described in case studies that link theory to practice. They will show you how the topics you are studying affect real people and businesses.

Assessment practice/Activities

Activities are also provided throughout each unit. These are linked to real situations and case studies and they can be used for practice before tackling the preparation for assessment. Alternatively, some can contribute to your unit assessment if you choose to do these instead of the preparation for assessment at the end of each unit.

---

your activities are appropriate and safe. This data can be found in accident books and RIDDOR documentation (see page XX), as well as from your own records on individual participants and any significant injuries or accidents they have had. It is important to note any near misses that have occurred and the situation that led to the near miss. Subsequent action to prevent further near misses and dangerous occurrences is a sign of a good sports organiser.

Key term

Accident book A book where all accidents and incidents are recorded so that they can be investigated.

Suitability of group for activity and effectiveness of briefings

Any good sports leader or coach reviews the effectiveness of each session to find out if the session's goals were achieved and whether the activity was suitable for the participants.

Most sessions should start with a briefing to the participants. This should outline the key safety factors including what to do in case of an emergency and a brief outline of what the session will entail, as well as any discipline and behavioural rules.

The review as to whether the participants have understood what has been said should take place during the session and not at the end. At the end of the session an overall review of suitability to the activity should take place.

Suitability of equipment

Before the session starts it is important to select the appropriate equipment for the participants you are working with, such as the correct size basketball and height of ring for the given age group. Guidelines on this would be available from the English Basketball Association. Once again, the review should take place during the activity through observation and asking participants to ensure they are using the equipment safely.

Support of other agencies

You may have sought support from agencies such as governing bodies, local authorities or line managers and it is a useful exercise to see if that advice and support was effective.

Remember!

If you have received support from someone who was helpful, remember to contact them and tell them what the outcome was.

Case study: Keeping your players healthy

The Danny Leisure Centre hockey team, which plays in the local league, has undergone pre-season training and is now preparing for its first competitive league game of the season. There are two more coaching sessions before the first game and the focus is on improving the team's overall strategies and tactics, with special emphasis on short corners. However, you aware that several players are missing through injury.

1 Why is it important to keep clear records of coaching activities and injuries?

2 What information should the coach give to the players in relation to health and safety?

Your tutor should check that you have completed enough activities to meet all the assessment criteria for the unit, whether from this book or from other tasks.

Tutors and students should refer to the BTEC standards for the qualification for the full BTEC grading criteria for each unit (www.edexcel.org.uk).

I do hope that you enjoy your course and find this book an excellent support for your studies. Good luck!

Graham Saffery

Assessment practice

Pre-season training is about to commence at the rugby club for all the teams. As the assistant coach, you meet with the head coach to plan the first few training sessions. You identify your aims for pre-season including improving fitness, technical individual skills, team skills and plays as well as identifying each player's most suitable position. You are keen to ensure this is done as safely as possible.

1 Identify what information you require before you commence any activities. Plan a sports activity that will help achieve your aims. This should identify the facilities and equipment you require and it should have a warm-up, a main session and a cool-down. **P5 M4**

2 You should review the plan and identify what the strengths and weaknesses are, saying how these could be improved. **D3**

Grading tips

Grading Tip P5

Your plan should indicate the methods used to ensure the group's safety. You could use a plan from a session that you are taking or for a group you are observing. The plan should identify the equipment and facilities that are needed. It should ensure that the activities are safe, challenging and have variety. You should also look to include information on insurance requirements and first aid.

Grading Tip M4

You should explain why you have chosen the selected equipment and activities. You should explain the purpose of your warm-up and cool-down and why the main activities are appropriate.

Grading Tip D3

You need to analyse your plan to identify the strengths of the plan and where you could make improvements. You should clearly identify any suggestions you have for improvements.

Knowledge check

1 Describe three key legislative factors for sports organisers that are required of them from the Health and Safety at Work Act (1974). Provide practical examples of how they should be implemented.

2 What are the key differences between civil law and statutory law? Provide two examples of each.

3 Select a regulatory body and describe their main roles and responsibilities in relation to managing sports activities.

4 When should a risk assessment be carried out? When should action be taken after you have completed the assessment?

5 Identify five procedures of good practice in relation to maintaining the safety of participants and colleagues in a sports environment.

6 What are the advantages of providing safety equipment, training and supervision for participants?

7 Provide five examples of safe practice in sports provided by a selected governing body of sport.

8 Who are the key people in organisation who can provide support in relation to health and safety in sport?

9 What are the key factors when identifying a suitable site for sports activities?

10 What are the key areas to consider when reviewing the effectiveness of your risk management?

11 Where might you find information to help you undertake your review?

Preparations for assessment

Each unit concludes with a full unit assessment, which taken as a whole fulfils all the unit requirements from Pass to Distinction. Each task is matched to the relevant criteria in the specification. If you are aiming for a Pass, make sure you complete all the Pass (P) tasks. If you are aiming for a Merit, make sure you complete all the Pass (P) and Merit (M) tasks. If you are aiming for a Distinction, you will also need to complete all the Distinction (D) tasks. P1 means the first of the Pass criteria listed in the specification, M1 the first of the Merit criteria, D1 the first of the Distinction criteria, and so on.

Think it over

These are points for individual reflection or group discussion. They will widen your knowledge and help you reflect on issues that impact on Sport and Exercise Science.

Knowledge checks

At the end of each unit is a set of quick questions to test your knowledge of the information you have been studying. Use these to check your progress, and also as a revision tool.

Taking it further

Facilitating the knowledge from each unit and extending your thinking is what Taking it further is all about. Questions will be posed that will stretch the learning and build on what has already been explained.

The body in action

Introduction

This unit introduces you to the basic structures and functions of the skeletal, muscular, cardiovascular and respiratory systems of the human body. You will explore and learn how each of these body systems responds and adapts to exercise.

The unit begins by examining the structure and function of the skeletal and muscular systems and their role in bringing about movement in physical activity, sport and exercise. It will explore the structure of skeletal muscles and how they contract to move the body. It will then move on to focus on the structure and functions of the cardiovascular and respiratory systems and investigate the short- and long-term adaptations of these body systems in response to sport and exercise. The unit concludes with a look at the different energy systems and their use in sport and exercise.

Each section will concentrate on the structure and function of a particular system and provide a summary of the short- and long-term adaptations of these separate systems to exercise.

A variety of activities will help you to understand and appreciate the body in action. Through analysing case studies, considering thought-provoking questions, undertaking practical activities and researching the body in action, you will develop a sound understanding of the complex functioning of these systems in bringing the body in to motion. Throughout the unit there are tasks that will introduce you to key themes and concepts that you need to understand when doing your assessment activities. These range from individual tasks and investigations, to working in pairs, to working as part of a small group.

After completing this unit you should be able to achieve the following outcomes:

- Understand the structure and function of the skeletal system and how it responds to exercise.

Think it over

There are 11 systems in the human body, many of which interact in a complex way to bring your body in to motion.

Imagine you have been selected to run the London Marathon. In order to participate safely in such an event you need to undertake a regular training programme. As you are relatively unaccustomed to training, you are a little apprehensive about taking on the challenge.

What activities would it be appropriate to include in your training programme? What body system changes are you likely to experience during your first training session? What might you expect to see as long-term responses to your regular programme of training? How might you investigate and measure these responses?

- Understand the structure and function of the muscular system and how it responds to exercise.

- Understand the structure and function of the cardiovascular system and how it responds to exercise.

- Understand the structure and function of the respiratory system and how it responds to exercise.

- Understand the different energy systems and their use in sport and exercise.

In this section you will learn about the structure and function of the skeletal system, the positions and names of the major bones of the skeleton and the types, structure and functions of joints and their movement.

Skeletal system

The human skeletal system is made up of bones, cartilage and joints. It consists of 206 bones, 80 of which form your axial skeleton – the long axis of your body. The other 126 bones form the appendicular skeleton – the bones that are attached to this axis.

Key terms

Axial skeleton Provides the main area of support and protection for the body. It includes the cranium (skull), the thorax (rib cage) and the vertebral column (spine).

Appendicular skeleton Consists of the bones of the limbs. It includes the femur, fibula and tibia in the legs, and the humerus, radius and ulna in the arms, together with the girdles that join on to the axial skeleton.

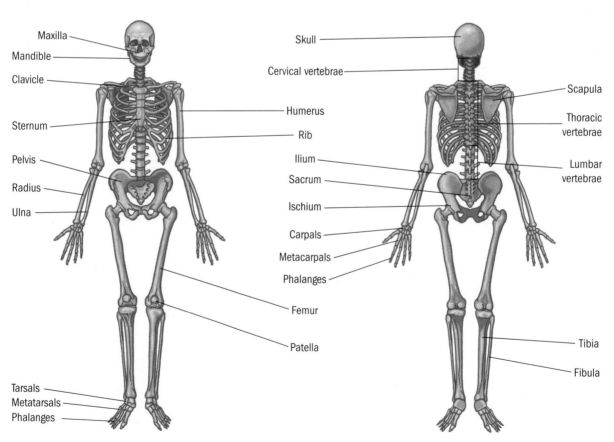

Bones of the skeleton

Structure

■ Axial skeleton

The axial skeleton forms the main axis or core of your skeletal system and consists of the:

- skull (cranium and facial bones)
- thorax (sternum and ribs)
- vertebral column.

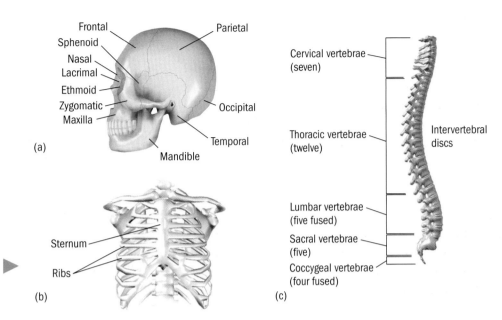

The axial skeleton: (a) the skull, (b) the thorax and (c) the vertebral column

■ Appendicular skeleton

This consists of the following:

- Upper limb bones: 60 bones form the upper limbs. Each upper limb is made up of one humerus, one radius, one ulna, eight carpals, five metacarpals and fourteen phalanges.

- Lower limb bones: 60 bones form the lower limbs. Each lower limb is made up of one femur (thigh bone), one tibia (shin bone), one fibula, one patella (kneecap), seven tarsals, five metatarsals and fourteen phalanges. The bones of your lower limbs

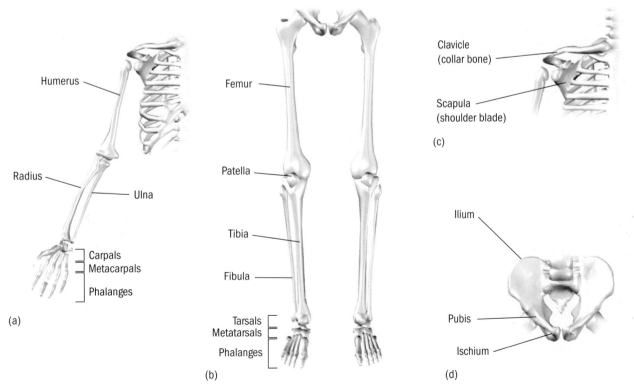

The appendicular skeleton: (a) the upper limbs, (b) the lower limbs, (c) the shoulder girdle and (d) the pelvis

are designed for weight bearing, locomotion and maintaining an upright posture. As a result they are required to have a higher degree of strength and stability than the bones of the upper limbs.

- Shoulder girdle: this consists of four bones – two clavicles and two scapula – which connect the limbs of the upper body to the thorax.
- Pelvic girdle: this is made of three bones: the ilium, ischium and pubis. These three bones fuse together with age and are collectively known as the innominate bone. The principal function of the pelvic girdle is to provide a solid base through which to transmit the weight of your upper body. It also provides attachment for the powerful muscles of your lower back and legs, and protects the digestive and reproductive organs.

Key term

Innominate bone The hip bone, consisting of the ilium, ischium and pubis.

Assessment practice

Draw two large tables to describe the structure and function of the axial and appendicular skeletons. Your descriptions should include all the major bones. **P1**

Grading tips

Grading Tip **P1**

Describe the axial and appendicular skeletons and locate and name all of these major bones: cranium, clavicle, ribs, sternum, humerus, radius, ulna, scapula, ilium, pubis, ischium, carpals, metacarpals, phalanges, femur, patella, tibia, fibula, tarsals, metatarsals, vertebral column, vertebrae – cervical, thoracic, lumbar, sacrum and coccyx.

The skeleton performs a number of mechanical and physiological functions.

■ Support

The skeleton gives your body shape. It provides the supporting framework for the soft tissues of the body that prevent it from collapsing in a heap on the floor.

■ Protection

The bones of the skeleton surround and protect vital tissues and organs in the body.

- The skull protects the brain.
- The thorax protects the heart and lungs.
- The vertebral column protects the spinal cord.
- The pelvis protects the abdominal and reproductive organs.

■ Attachment for skeletal muscle

Parts of the skeleton provide the surface for skeletal muscles to attach, allowing movement to occur.

■ Leverage

The skeletal system affords movement by the coordinated action of the muscles on the bones. Tendons attach muscles to bones, which provides leverage. When the muscles pull on the bones, they act as levers and movement occurs at the joint.

Source of blood cell production

The bones are not completely solid as this would make the skeleton heavy and difficult to move around. Blood vessels feed the centre of the bones and stored within them is bone marrow. The marrow of the long bones is continually producing red and white blood cells – an essential function as large numbers of blood cells, particularly red cells, die every minute.

Key term

Bone marrow Fat- or blood-forming tissue found within bone cavities.

Store of minerals

The skeleton acts as a mineral reservoir for important minerals such as calcium and phosphorus, essential for bone growth and the maintenance of bone health. These minerals are stored and released to tissues as required. They are transported in the bloodstream to sites of growth or injury.

Major bones

The bones of the skeleton are classified according to their shape and size. They can be divided into the following categories.
- Long bones are found in the limbs. These act like levers, such as the femur in the thigh and the humerus in the upper arm. They have a shaft known as the diaphysis and two expanded ends known as the epiphysis.

Key terms

Diaphysis The shaft of a long bone.

Epiphysis The rounded end of a long bone.

- Short bones are small, light, strong, cube-shaped bones. They are like a sweet with a hard shell and a

soft centre. Examples are the carpals of your wrist and the tarsals of your foot.
- Flat bones are thin, flattened and slightly curved. They have a large surface area, such as the bones of the pelvis, scapulae and cranium.
- Sesamoid bones are found in tendons, such as the patella in the knee.
- Irregular bones have complex shapes and cannot be classified under any of the other categories. The hip bone and vertebrae are good examples.

Remember!

Exercise increases the strength of bones. They adapt to the stress imposed during exercise by laying down more calcium.

Location

Many terms are used to describe the position and location of anatomical structures of your body, some of which are described in Table 1.1.

Term	What it means
Anterior	To the front or in front
Posterior	To the rear or behind
Medial	Towards the mid-line
Lateral	Away from the mid-line
Proximal	Near to the root or origin
Distal	Away from the root or origin
Superior	Above
Inferior	Below

Table 1.1 Main anatomical terms

Key term

Origin A muscle's origin is attached to the immovable (or less movable) bone.

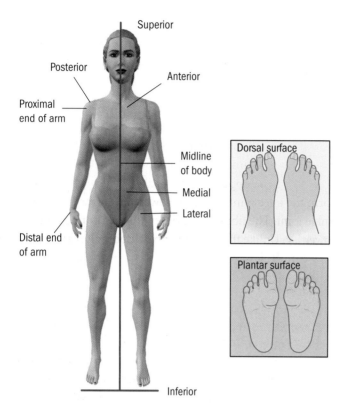

Superior

Posterior

Anterior

Proximal
end of arm

Midline
of body

Medial

Lateral

Dorsal surface

Distal end
of arm

Plantar surface

Inferior

▲ Anatomical positions

Cranium

The cranium is a box-like cavity that contains and protects the brain. It consists of interlinking segments of bone that gradually fuse together during the first few years of life.

Clavicle

The clavicles (collar bones) are the long, slim bones that form the anterior part of the shoulder girdle. This provides a strong and mobile attachment for the arms and is designed for the performance of complex movements.

Ribs

The ribs are long, flat bones. There are twelve pairs in all. The first seven are known as true ribs, as each is joined directly to the sternum. The remaining five pairs are known as false ribs.

Sternum

Commonly referred to as the breast bone, this is the elongated, flat bone that lies at the centre of the chest.

It extends from the base of the neck to the abdominal wall and can be divided into three sections. The top section, known as the manubrium, is the widest part of the sternum and articulates with the clavicle and first rib. The mid-section, referred to as the body, articulates with the costal cartilage linking the ribs to the sternum. The lower section, known as the xiphoid, provides an attachment point for the diaphragm and the muscles of the abdominal wall.

Key terms

Costal cartilage The bars of cartilage that connect the sternum to the ends of the ribs. Its elasticity allows the thorax to move during respiration.

Articulation The meeting of two or more bones.

Dorsal This refers to the back or upper surface.

Humerus

The humerus is the largest bone in the upper limbs. It is a long bone, the head of which articulates with the scapula to form the shoulder joint. The distal end articulates with the radius and ulna to form the elbow joint.

Radius and ulna

The ulna is the longer of the two bones of the forearm. The ulna and radius articulate distally with the wrist. The convex shape of the radius allows it to move around the ulna to bring about pronation (turning) of the hand. One way of remembering which is which is to turn your palm upwards – the ulna is the bone nearest to you.

Scapula

The scapulae (shoulder blades) are large, triangular, flat bones that form the posterior part of the shoulder girdle.

Ilium

The pelvis is the bony structure located at the base of the spine that provides the sockets for the hip joints and supports the lower abdominal organs. There are three fused irregular pelvic bones collectively known as the innominate bone on each side of the pelvic girdle.

The ilium is the upper and largest of these three bones. The upper edge of the ilium is known as the iliac crest.

■ Pubis

The pubis, also known as the pubic bone, forms the lower part of the innominate bone.

■ Ischium

The ischium is situated below the ilium and forms the middle part of the innominate bone.

■ Carpals

These are the bones that make up the wrist. They consist of eight irregular, small bones arranged in two rows of four. These small bones fit closely together and are kept in place by ligaments.

■ Metacarpals

In the palm of the hand there are five long cylindrical metacarpal bones, one corresponding to each digit. These run from the carpal bones of the wrist to the base of each digit in the hand.

■ Phalanges

These are the small bones that make up the skeleton of the thumbs, fingers and toes. In most fingers and toes there are three phalanges. The thumbs and big toes have two phalanges, which accounts for their shorter length. The phalanges at the tips of the fingers and toes are known as distal phalanges, whereas those that articulate with the bones of the hands and feet are referred to as proximal phalanges.

■ Femur

The femur is the longest and strongest bone in the body, the head of which fits into the socket of the pelvis to form the hip joint. The lower end joins the tibia to form the knee joint.

■ Patella

The patella (kneecap) is the large, triangular sesamoid bone found in the quadriceps femoris tendon. It protects the knee joint.

■ Tibia and fibula

The tibia and fibula form the long bones of the lower leg. The tibia is the inner and thicker bone, also known as the shin bone. The upper end of the tibia joins the femur to form the knee joint, while the lower end forms part of the ankle joint. The fibula is the outer, thinner bone of the lower leg. Unlike the tibia, the fibula does not reach the knee but the lower end does form part of the ankle joint.

■ Tarsals

The foot and heel are formed from seven bones known collectively as the tarsals and often referred to as the midfoot and hindfoot. Along with the tibia and fibula, they form the ankle joint. They are short and irregular bones. The calcaneous, or heel bone, is the largest tarsal bone. It helps to support the weight of the body and provides attachment for the calf muscles via the Achilles tendon.

■ Metatarsals

Five metatarsals form the dorsal surface of the foot, with 14 phalanges forming the toes. These collectively

The metatarsals are often broken by football players ▶

make up the forefoot. The base of each metatarsal bone articulates with one or more tarsal bones and the head of one phalange. The forefoot is responsible for bearing a great deal of weight and balances pressure through the balls of the feet. The metatarsal bones are a common site of fracture in sport.

■ Vertebral column

The vertebral column, also known as the spine or backbone, extends from the base of the cranium to the pelvis, providing a central axis for the body. It is made up of 33 irregular bones called vertebrae.

The vertebral column accounts for around 40 per cent of your overall height. The vertebrae of your spine are held together by strong, powerful ligaments. These allow little movement between your adjacent vertebrae but afford a considerable degree of flexibility along the spine as a whole.

The vertebral column has many functions. These include protection of the spinal cord and supporting the rib cage (maintaining the balance between it and the abdominal cavity). The larger vertebrae of the lumbar region are designed to support a large amount of body weight. The flatter thoracic vertebrae afford attachment for the large muscles of the back and the curves of the spine – four in all. These, along with the intervertebral discs, receive and distribute impact associated with the dynamic functioning of your body in action, reducing shock.

■ Vertebrae

These increase in size from the top down, and can be divided into the following groups:

- cervical vertebrae in the neck
- thoracic vertebrae in the chest region
- lumbar vertebrae in the small of the back
- sacral vertebrae (fused vertebrae that form the sacrum)
- coccygeal vertebrae (fused vertebrae that form the coccyx).

There are 24 movable vertebrae in all, separated by intervertebral discs. These padded discs act as shock absorbers and give the vertebral column a certain degree of flexibility. The cervical and lumbar regions of the spine are the most vulnerable to injury as a result of sport and exercise.

Cervical

These are the vertebrae in the neck. The first two are known as the atlas (C1) and the axis (C2). These two vertebrae form a pivot joint that allows the head and neck to move freely. These form the smallest and most vulnerable vertebrae of the vertebral column. The axis sits on top of the first intervertebral disc of the vertebral column.

Thoracic

These are the vertebrae of the mid-spine, which articulate with the ribs. They lie in the thorax, a dome-shaped structure that provides protection for the heart and lungs. The thoracic vertebrae are larger than the cervical vertebrae and increase in size from top to bottom.

Lumbar

These are situated in the lower back and are the largest of the movable vertebrae. They are required to support more weight than other vertebrae and provide attachment for many of the muscles of the back. The discs that lie between these vertebrae produce a concave curve in the back.

Sacrum

Five sacral vertebrae are fused to form the sacrum. This is a triangular bone located below the lumbar vertebrae and it forms the back wall of the pelvic girdle sitting between the two hip bones. The upper part connects with the last lumbar vertebra and the bottom part with the coccyx.

Coccyx

At the bottom of the vertebral column there are four coccygeal vertebrae, which are fused to form the coccyx or tail bone.

Joints

You have seen that your skeleton is made up of a series of bones that support and protect your body. However, in order for movement to occur, the bones must be linked. Joints provide the links between the bones. A joint is formed wherever two or more bones meet – this is known as an articulation. Your bones act as levers bringing about movement while your joints act as the fulcrum (pivot point) in the process, steadying the movement and allowing your bones to move in specific directions.

There are three types of joint, each classified according to the degree of movement they allow. These joints and their respective ranges of movement are described below, concentrating on synovial joints and their basic structure and introducing anatomical terms used to describe movement.

Fixed

A fixed joint is also known as a fibrous or immovable joint. It occurs where the margins of two bones meet and interlock, held together by bands of tough, fibrous tissue. An example of this type of joint is between plates in the cranium.

Fixed joints

Cranium

▲ Fixed joints in the cranium

Slightly movable

Slightly movable or cartilaginous joints allow some slight movement. The ends of the bone are covered in articular or hyaline cartilage (a smooth, shiny covering that reduces friction) which is separated by pads of white fibrocartilage (a tough cartilage capable of

absorbing considerable loads). Slight movement is made possible because the pads of cartilage compress. An example of this type of joint is between most vertebrae.

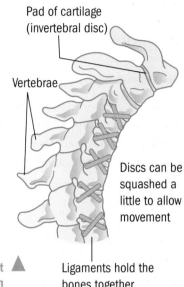

Pad of cartilage (invertebral disc)

Vertebrae

Discs can be squashed a little to allow movement

A slightly movable joint ▲ in the vertebral column

Ligaments hold the bones together

Key terms

Articular (hyaline) cartilage The most abundant type of cartilage in the body that forms the smooth, shiny covering of the ends of bones that reduces friction and has the ability to bear large compressive loads.

Fibrocartilage Compressible cartilage that is found where strong support and the ability to withstand heavy pressure is required. For example, the intervertebral discs (the resilient cushions between vertebrae).

Synovial

Synovial joints offer the highest level of mobility at a joint. They consist of two or more bones, the ends of which are covered with articular cartilage, which allows the bones to move over each other with the minimum degree of friction. They make up most of the joints of your limbs. They are completely surrounded by a fibrous capsule, lined with a synovial membrane, the purpose of which is to secrete fluid known as synovial fluid into the joint cavity to lubricate and nourish the joint. The joint capsule is held together by tough bands of connective tissue known as ligaments. This provides the strength to avoid dislocation, while being flexible enough to allow movement.

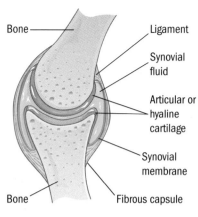

▲ A synovial joint in the knee

Bone — Ligament
Synovial fluid
Articular or hyaline cartilage
Synovial membrane
Bone — Fibrous capsule

Synovial joints can be divided into the following groups, according to the type of movement they allow.

■ Hinge

These allow movement in one direction only. Your elbow and knee joints are typical examples of hinge joints.

■ Ball and socket

The round end of one bone fits into a cup-shaped socket in the other bone, allowing movement in all directions. Examples include the hip and shoulder joints.

■ Ellipsoid

Also known as condyloid joints, these are a modified version of a ball and socket joint, in which a bump on one bone sits in the hollow formed by another. Movement is backwards and forwards and from side to side. Ligaments often prevent rotation. An example is the wrist joint.

■ Gliding

These allow movement over a flat surface in all directions, but this is restricted by ligaments or a bony prominence, for example in the carpals and tarsals.

■ Pivot

These allow rotation only about a single axis. The ring of one bone fits over a peg of another. An example is in the neck, where the atlas and axis join.

■ Saddle

These are similar to ellipsoid joints but the surfaces are concave and convex. Movement occurs backwards and forwards and from side to side, as at the base of your thumb.

All synovial joints contain the following features:

- An outer sleeve or joint capsule: to help to hold the bones in place and protect the joint.
- A synovial membrane: the capsule lining that oozes a slippery, viscous liquid called synovial fluid. This acts as a lubricant to the knee joint.
- A joint cavity: the gap between the articulating bones. This is where the synovial fluid pools to lubricate the joint so that the bones can move more easily.
- Articular cartilage on the end of the bones: to provide a smooth and slippery covering to stop the bones knocking or grinding together.
- Ligaments: to hold the bones together and keep them in place.

Types of movement

When studying your body in action it is important to understand the range of movements that joints are capable of performing. The degree of movement at joints varies between individuals and depends on many factors, including:

- the shape and contour of the articulating surfaces
- the tension of the supporting connective tissue
- the tension of muscles and tendons that surround the joint
- the amount of soft tissue surrounding the joint
- the age of the individual.

Joint movements possible at synovial joints can be classified as gliding, angular or circular movements. These movements are often combined to produce a variety of movements at any one joint, as described below.

■ Flexion

Bending a limb to reduce the angle at the joint, such as bending your arm in a bicep curl action.

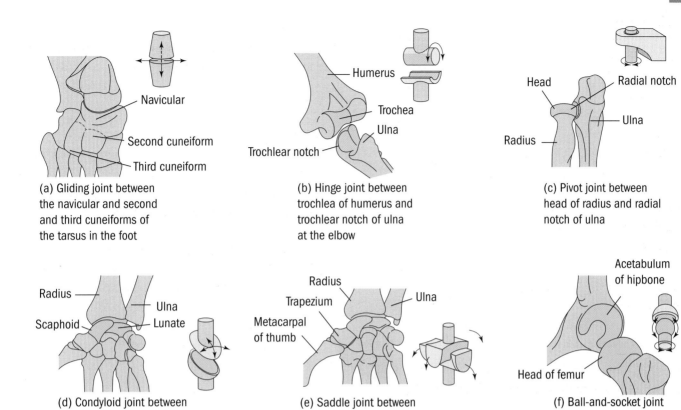

(a) Gliding joint between the navicular and second and third cuneiforms of the tarsus in the foot

(b) Hinge joint between trochlea of humerus and trochlear notch of ulna at the elbow

(c) Pivot joint between head of radius and radial notch of ulna

(d) Condyloid joint between radius and scaphoid and lunate bones of the carpus (wrist)

(e) Saddle joint between trapezium of carpus (wrist) and metacarpal of thumb

(f) Ball-and-socket joint between head of the femur and acetabulum of the hipbone

▲ Types of synovial joint

■ Extension

Straightening a limb to increase the angle at the joint, such as straightening your arm to return to your starting position in a bicep curl action.

■ Abduction

Moving a limb away from the mid-line of the body, such as lifting your arms from the sides of your body.

■ Adduction

Moving a limb towards the mid-line of the body, such as lowering your arms back to your sides.

■ Circumduction

Moving a limb through a full 360º circle, such as circling your shoulder.

■ Rotation

Turning about the vertical axis of your body, medially (inwards) and laterally (outwards) such as at the shoulder and hip.

■ Pronation

The inward rotation of the forearm so that the palm of the hand is facing backwards and downwards. This occurs at the wrist joint during a table tennis forehand topspin shot.

■ Supination

The outward rotation of the forearm so that the palm of the hand is facing forwards and upwards. This occurs at the wrist joint during a table tennis backhand topspin shot.

■ Plantar flexion

This is a movement that points the toes downwards by straightening the ankle. This occurs at the ankle when jumping to shoot in basketball.

■ Dorsiflexion

An upward movement, as in moving the foot to pull the toes upwards towards the knee.

(a) Flexion

(b) Extension

(c) Abduction, adduction and circumduction

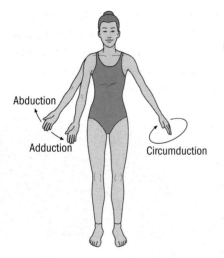

Abduction

Adduction

Circumduction

(d) Rotation

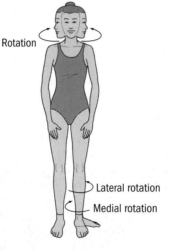

Rotation

Lateral rotation

Medial rotation

(e) Pronation and supination

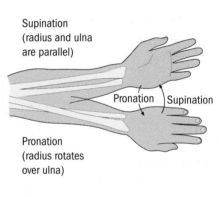

Supination
(radius and ulna
are parallel)

Pronation

Supination

Pronation
(radius rotates
over ulna)

(f) Plantar flexion and dorsiflexion

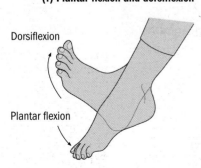

Dorsiflexion

Plantar flexion

(g) Inversion and eversion

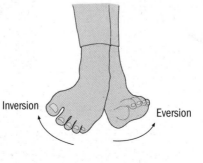

Inversion

Eversion

(h) Hyper-extension

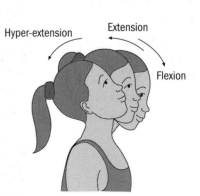

Hyper-extension

Extension

Flexion

▲ Anatomical and biomechanical terms relating to muscle action

■ Inversion

Moving the foot and ankle inwards.

■ Eversion

Moving the foot and ankle outwards.

■ Hyper-extension

This involves movement beyond the normal anatomical position in a direction opposite to flexion. This occurs at the spine when a cricketer arches his or her back when approaching the crease to bowl.

Assessment practice

1 Produce a large table to describe the structure and function of the different classifications of joints and the range of movement each provides. **P1**

2 In your table, explain clearly why different classifications of joint allow different ranges of movement. **M1**

Grading tips

Grading Tip P1

You must be able to describe all three classifications of joint and the movement available at each, including the movement allowed at each of the synovial joints.

Grading Tip M1

Examine each of the three classifications of joints, including all six synovial joints, and explain how and why the range of movement allowed at these joints differs. Use sporting examples to support your explanation.

Response to exercise

The short-term effects of exercise on the skeletal system are demonstrated by changes within the joint. Movement of joints stimulates the secretion of synovial fluid. This fluid becomes less thick and the range of movement at the joint increases.

Key terms

Physical activity Any skeletal muscle contraction that results in an increase in energy expenditure.

Exercise Repetitive physical activity or movement designed to improve or maintain health and fitness.

Sport Physical activity or movement that is defined by rules and competition.

Regular physical activity and exercise increases the strength of your bones ▶

With regular exercise, connective tissue improves in flexibility. Long-term responses of the skeletal system to exercise include maintenance of the improved range of movement around your joints.

Your bones are not static. They can become stronger and denser as a result of the demands you place on them through physical activity and exercise. Physical activity and exercise can increase the mineral content of your bones. The key factor regulating this is the mechanical force you apply during the activities you undertake. The types of exercise that help build stronger bones are strength training and weight-bearing exercises that work against gravity with differing degrees of impact, such as tennis, netball, basketball, aerobics, dancing, walking and running. Your bones are strengthened as a result of the stress exercise imposes on them, which results in greater quantities of calcium and collagen being deposited within them. This helps to reduce the risk of osteoporosis. A strengthening in the supportive connective tissue surrounding your joints also occurs.

Key term

Osteoporosis This literally means 'porous bones'. Our bones are made up of a thick outer shell and a strong inner honeycomb mesh of tiny struts of bone. Osteoporosis means some of these struts become thin or break. This makes the bone more fragile and prone to breakage.

Thickening of the hyaline cartilage

Hyaline (articular) cartilage becomes thicker with regular exercise. This is the most common type of cartilage in the body. It is found mainly on the articulating surfaces of the bones and protects the bone surfaces from wear and tear. It also provides a certain amount of elasticity to absorb shock. It connects the ribs to the sternum and is found in certain structures of the respiratory system. This type of cartilage can become calcified with advancing age.

Slight stretch of ligaments

Ligaments and tendons increase in flexibility and strength with regular exercise.

Remember!

- Tendons attach muscle to bone.
- Ligaments attach bone to bone.

Assessment practice

1 Describe how the skeletal system responds to exercise. **P2**

2 Using a practical sporting example, explain what happens to the skeleton during exercise. **M2**

3 Using another sporting example to support your answer, analyse how the skeletal system responds to exercise. **D1**

Grading tips

Grading Tip P2

Describe how the skeletal system responds to both short- and long-term exercise. You should use practical examples to support your answer.

Grading Tip M2

Explain what happens to the skeleton during exercise and how it responds to both short- and long-term exercise. A detailed explanation would include reasons or examples to support the statements you make.

Grading Tip D1

Investigate and analyse how the skeletal system responds to exercise. Analysing requires you to take a more critical approach in your account.

Muscular system

Approximately 40 per cent of your body mass is made up of muscle, the key function of which is to move the bones of your skeleton. In this section you will learn about the principal skeletal muscles of your body and their associated actions, the structure of skeletal muscle and muscle fibre types. You will investigate muscle movement and the short- and long-term responses of your muscular system to exercise.

Types of muscle

Three different types of muscle tissue are found in the body:

- cardiac muscle
- skeletal (voluntary) muscle
- smooth (involuntary) muscle.

Key terms

Cardiac muscle Specialised muscle of the heart.

Skeletal muscle Voluntary muscle with obvious striations that attaches to the body's skeleton.

Smooth muscle Muscle with no visible striations found mainly in the walls of hollow organs.

Striations Skeletal muscle is striated. This means that the fibres contain alternating light and dark bands (striations) that are perpendicular to the long axes of the fibres.

All three muscle types can stretch with the application of force and return to their usual size after undergoing a stretch or contraction.

■ Cardiac

This forms the walls of the heart and works continuously. It is involuntary (not under conscious control) and composed of a specialised type of striated tissue that has its own blood supply. Cardiac muscle contains actin and myosin filaments similar to that of skeletal muscle cells and is highly resistant to fatigue. Each contraction and relaxation of the heart muscle as a whole represents one heart beat.

■ Skeletal

Skeletal muscle is also known as striated or striped muscle because of its striped appearance when viewed under a microscope. This type of muscle is voluntary,

Remember!

Skeletal muscles only pull on your bones – they do not push.

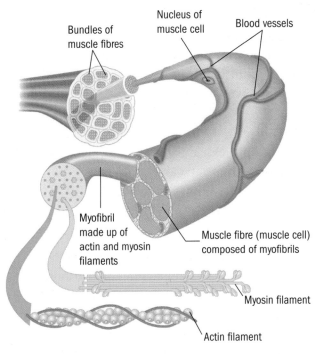

Bundles of muscle fibres

Nucleus of muscle cell

Blood vessels

Myofibril made up of actin and myosin filaments

Muscle fibre (muscle cell) composed of myofibrils

Myosin filament

Actin filament

▲ Cross-section of skeletal muscle

which means it is under conscious control and you control the contraction when you decide to bring your body in to action, such as by walking, running or jumping. Skeletal muscles are attached to the bones of your skeleton by tendons and they usually work in pairs.

Smooth

Smooth muscle is an involuntary muscle that works without conscious thought, functioning under the control of the nervous system. It is located in the walls of the digestive system and blood vessels and helps to regulate digestion and blood pressure.

Fibre types

All skeletal muscles contain a mixture of fast- and slow-twitch fibres. Fast-twitch fibres are generally larger than slow-twitch fibres. The mix of fibres varies from individual to individual, and within the individual from muscle group to muscle group. To a large extent this fibre mix is inherited, so if you want to become the next Olympic marathon champion or the world record holder at the 100-metre sprint, you need to choose your parents carefully! However, training can influence the efficiency of these different fibre types.

During activity the types of muscle fibre recruited and the order in which they are recruited depends on the level of force required to be exerted by the muscle or muscles involved.

Two main types of striated skeletal muscle can be distinguished on the basis of their speed of contraction: type 1 (slow twitch) and type 2 (fast twitch). The human body consists of both types of fibre.

Characteristics of Type 1 muscle fibres

Type 1 (slow-twitch) fibres contract slowly with less force. They are slow to fatigue and suited to longer duration aerobic activities. They have a rich blood supply and contain many mitochondria to sustain aerobic metabolism. They are recruited for lower intensity, longer duration activities such as long-distance running and swimming.

Key terms

Mitochondria Organelles responsible for adenosine triphosphate (ATP) production for energy use.

Adenosine triphosphate (ATP) Stores and releases chemical energy for use in body cells.

Remember!

Type 1 fibres:

- contract slowly and with minimal power
- do not tire easily
- suit activities that need endurance, such as long-distance running and swimming.

Characteristics of Type 2a muscle fibres

Type 2a fibres (also called fast-twitch or fast-oxidative fibres) are fast-contracting and able to produce a great force, but are also resistant to fatigue. These types of fibres are suited to middle-distance events.

Characteristics of Type 2b muscle fibres

Type 2b fibres (also called fast-twitch or fast-glycolytic fibres) contract rapidly and have the capacity to produce large amounts of force, but they fatigue more readily making them better suited to anaerobic activity. They depend almost entirely on anaerobic metabolism and are recruited for higher intensity, shorter duration activities. They are important in sports that include many stop-go or change-of-pace activities.

Key terms

Aerobic Reactions that require oxygen.

Anaerobic Reactions that do not require oxygen.

Remember!

Type 2b fibres:

- contract quickly with fast, powerful contractions
- tire easily
- suit activities that require sudden bursts of power, such as weightlifting or sprinting.

Remember!

Muscle fibres differ in speed of contraction, force and resistance to fatigue.

Table 1.2 outlines the characteristics of each fibre type.

Type 1	Type 2a	Type 2b
Red	Red	White
Contract slowly	Contract rapidly (but not as fast as type 2b)	Contract rapidly
Aerobic	Aerobic	Anaerobic
Endurance-based	Middle-distance	Speed- and strength-based
Can contract repeatedly	Fairly resistant to fatigue	Easily exhausted
Exert minimal force	Exert medium force	Exert great force

Table 1.2 Characteristics of each fibre type

■ Types of sports each is associated with

Table 1.3 identifies the sports associated with the different fibre types.

Type 1	Type 2a	Type 2b
Endurance sports such as running, cycling, swimming, skiing	Middle-distance running such as 800m and 1500m	Explosive sports such as sprinting, jumping, throwing, weight lifting

Table 1.3 Sports associated with each fibre type

Activity

Consider the range of favourite sporting or fitness activities you and your fellow students take part in and consider the types of muscle fibres involved in these activities. Draw up a table or chart to record your findings.

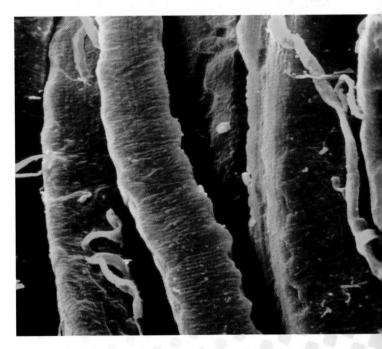

▲ The three muscle fibre types

Case study: Exploring energy systems

Peter is the lead-off member of your college's sprint relay team. Before the race he spends time warming up. During his warm-up he walks around the start area, shakes off his arms and legs, and does a few strides and stretches. The starter calls the athletes to the line. He settles into his starting blocks, the starter announces the set position and he waits for the gun to sound. The gun fires and he bursts out of the blocks and runs as hard as he can all the way to changeover, recording a personal best time for the start leg.

1 Which muscle fibres were creating the force required while Peter was walking around the start area?

2 During the entire warm-up, were all muscle fibres recruited acting maximally?

3 When Peter burst out of the blocks and sprinted towards the finishing line, which muscle fibres were recruited?

Think it over

Consider what types of activities Peter might want to undertake in training to ensure that he continues to improve his personal best time.

Major muscles

There are more than 640 named muscles in the human body. Your muscles are generously supplied by arteries to convey nutrients and oxygen, and veins to remove

Remember!

To bring your body in to action, different parts of your muscular skeletal systems work under the influence of your nervous system to produce voluntary movements. Your skeletal muscles contract when stimulated via impulses from your nervous system. At the point of contraction your muscles shorten and pull on the bones to which they are attached. When a muscle contracts, one end normally remains stationary while the other end is drawn towards it. The end that remains stationary is known as the origin, and the end that moves is referred to as the insertion.

waste products. Your skeletal muscles work either to move parts of your body or your body as a whole. Most sporting movements involve the coordinated action of muscles rather than muscles working in isolation.

Trying to remember all the names, locations and actions of the major muscles is a huge task. Therefore, from a sports perspective, the main ones you should remember are outlined in Table 1.4.

Key terms

Origin A muscle's origin is attached to the immovable (or less movable) bone.

Insertion A muscle's insertion is attached to the movable bone.

Olecranon process Forms part of the elbow; located at the proximal end of the ulna.

Acromion Roughened triangular projection atop of the scapula.

Xiphoid process Forms the inferior (or sword-like) end of the sternum.

Pubic crest An inferior and anterior portion of the pelvis located next to the pubic arc.

Calcaneus Major portion of the heel bone.

Occipital bone Forms most of the skull's posterior wall and base.

Iliac crest When you rest your hands on your hips, you are resting them on the iliac crests.

Muscle	Function	Location	Origin	Insertion	Exercise
Biceps	Flexes lower arm	Inside upper arm	Scapula	Radius	Arm curls, chin-ups
Triceps	Extends lower arm	Outside upper arm	Humerus and scapula	Olecranon process	Press-ups, dips, overhead pressing
Deltoids	Abducts, flexes and extends upper arm	Forms cap of shoulder	Clavicle, scapula and acromion	Humerus	Forward, later and back-arm raises, overhead lifting
Pectorals	Flexes and adducts upper arm	Large chest muscle	Sternum, clavicle and rib cartilage	Humerus	All pressing movements
Rectus abdominis	Flexion and rotation of lumbar region of vertebral column	'Six-pack' muscle running down abdomen	Pubic crest and symphysis	Xiphoid process	Sit-ups
Quadriceps -- rectus femoris -- vastus lateralis -- vastus medialis -- vastus intermedius	Extends lower leg and flexes thigh	Front of thigh	Ilium and femur	Tibia and fibula	Knee bends, squats
Hamstrings -- semimembranosus -- semitendinosus -- biceps femoris	Flexes lower leg and extends thigh	Back of thigh	Ischium and femur	Tibia and fibula	Extending leg and flexing knee (running)
Gastrocnemius	Plantar flexion flexes knee	Large calf muscle	Femur	Calcaneus	Running, jumping and standing on tip-toe
Soleus	Plantar flexion	Deep to gastrocnemius	Fibula and tibia	Calcaneus	Running and jumping
Tibialis anterior	Dorsiflexion of foot	Front of tibia on lower leg	Lateral condyle	By tendon to surface of medial cuneiform	All running and jumping exercises
Erector spinae	Extension of spine	Long muscle running either side of spine	Cervical, thoracic and lumbar vertebrae	Cervical, thoracic and lumbar vertebrae	Prime mover of back extension
Teres major	Rotates and abducts humerus	Between scapula and humerus	Posterior surface of scapula	Intertubercular sulcus of humerus	All rowing and pulling movements
Trapezius	Elevates and depresses scapula	Large triangular muscle at top of back	Continuous insertion along acromion	Occipital bone and all thoracic vertebrae	Shrugging and overhead lifting
Latissimus dorsi	Extends and adducts lower arm	Large muscle covering back of lower ribs	Vertebrae and iliac crest	Humerus	Rowing movements
Obliques	Lateral flexion of trunk	Waist	Pubic crest and iliac crest	Fleshy strips to lower eight ribs	Oblique curls
Gluteus maximus	Extends thigh	Large muscle on buttocks	Ilium, sacrum and coccyx	Femur	Knee-bending movements, cycling

Table 1.4 Major muscles and their functions

Activity

Physical activity and exercise require your body to move, which is accomplished by the action of your skeletal muscles.

1 List all the movements you can recall that your muscles have contributed to in the past 30 minutes.

2 Using your past experience of sport and exercise and what you have learnt about muscle fibre types, consider whether your muscles are better able to sustain low-intensity activities such as walking or high-intensity activities such as sprinting or weight training.

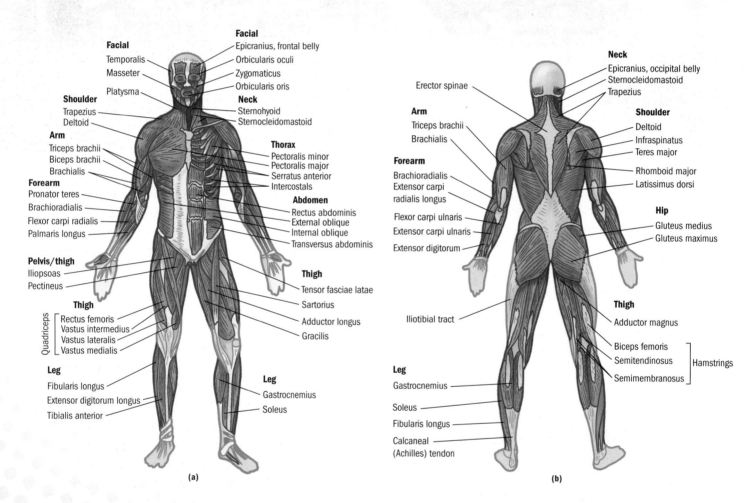

Facial
Epicranius, frontal belly
Orbicularis oculi
Zygomaticus
Orbicularis oris

Facial
Temporalis
Masseter
Platysma

Shoulder
Trapezius
Deltoid

Arm
Triceps brachii
Biceps brachii
Brachialis

Forearm
Pronator teres
Brachioradialis
Flexor carpi radialis
Palmaris longus

Neck
Sternohyoid
Sternocleidomastoid

Thorax
Pectoralis minor
Pectoralis major
Serratus anterior
Intercostals

Abdomen
Rectus abdominis
External oblique
Internal oblique
Transversus abdominis

Pelvis/thigh
Iliopsoas
Pectineus

Thigh
Quadriceps
  Rectus femoris
  Vastus intermedius
  Vastus lateralis
  Vastus medialis

Thigh
Tensor fasciae latae
Sartorius
Adductor longus
Gracilis

Leg
Fibularis longus
Extensor digitorum longus
Tibialis anterior

Leg
Gastrocnemius
Soleus

(a)

Neck
Epicranius, occipital belly
Sternocleidomastoid
Trapezius

Erector spinae

Arm
Triceps brachii
Brachialis

Forearm
Brachioradialis
Extensor carpi radialis longus
Flexor carpi ulnaris
Extensor carpi ulnaris
Extensor digitorum

Shoulder
Deltoid
Infraspinatus
Teres major
Rhomboid major
Latissimus dorsi

Hip
Gluteus medius
Gluteus maximus

Iliotibial tract

Thigh
Adductor magnus
Biceps femoris
Semitendinosus
Semimembranosus
Hamstrings

Leg
Gastrocnemius
Soleus
Fibularis longus
Calcaneal (Achilles) tendon

(b)

▲ (a) Anterior muscular system and (b) posterior muscular system

▲ Health and fitness equipment targets specific muscle groups

Taking it further

Visit your local leisure centre or health club to analyse its range of fitness equipment. Draw up a table of your findings to include information on:

- the range of equipment available
- the muscle groups targeted by each piece of equipment and the actions they bring about.

Assessment practice

Using a large piece of paper with the outline of a human drawn on it, identify all of the muscles listed in Table 1.4. Then describe the function of the muscular system.　　　　**P3**

Muscle movement

To bring the body in to action, muscles must cross the joint they move. Some cross joints to produce movements in more than one joint, for example the bicep crosses the elbow and shoulder joint, causing flexion at both joints. When a muscle contracts, a pulling force is exerted on the bones, causing them to move together around the joint. The bones act like levers and the joint like the fulcrum. If a muscle did not cross a joint, no movement could occur.

Under normal circumstances muscles are always in a state of partial contraction, ready to react to a stimulus from your nervous system. Without this muscle tone, the body would collapse. When a stimulus from the nerve supply occurs, muscle fibres work on an 'all or nothing' basis – either contracting completely or not at all.

The strength of muscle contraction in response to the stimulus depends on the number of muscle fibres brought into use, a process known as muscle fibre recruitment. To bring about contraction, the muscle requires oxygen and a fuel source, either fat or glucose. Muscle cells use up much more energy than other cells in the body and convert chemical energy into mechanical energy. When you exercise, your muscles use energy at a rate that is directly proportional to the intensity of the exercise. If this energy is not replaced as it is used up, your muscles are unable to maintain their work rate and you have to reduce the intensity of the activity or stop it.

Theory into practice

1 When your body is in action during sport and exercise, your muscles either shorten, remain the same length or lengthen. Pick up a dumb-bell (or a bag of sugar or a heavy book). Bend your arm at the elbow to bring your forearm up towards your shoulder in a bicep curl action.

2 Think about what your bicep muscle appears to be doing as you bring the weight closer to your shoulder. Has the muscle shortened, remained the same length or lengthened?

3 Return the dumb-bell to the starting position and consider what has to happen to your muscle to allow this action to take place. Do you think the bicep shortened, remained the same length or lengthened?

4 Curl the arm again, but this time only to a 90° angle. Hold your object in this position for a sustained period of time. What does the bicep muscle appear to be doing now? Do you think it is shortening, remaining the same length or lengthening?

Antagonistic muscle pairs

The muscles do not work in isolation. They are assembled in groups and work together to bring about movement. They act only by contracting and pulling. They do not push, although they are able to contract without shortening, and so hold a joint firm and fixed in a certain position. When the contraction passes off the muscles become soft but do not lengthen until stretched by the contraction of the opposing muscles. They can act in the following ways to bring your body in to action.

■ Agonist

The muscle that shortens to move a joint is called the agonist or prime mover. This is the muscle principally responsible for the movement taking place – the contracting muscle.

■ Antagonist

The muscle that relaxes in opposition to the agonist is called the antagonist. This is the muscle responsible for the opposite movement, and the one that relaxes as the agonist works. If it did not relax, movement could not take place. Antagonists exert a 'braking' control over the movement.

■ Synergist

Synergists are muscles that work together to enable the agonists to operate more effectively. They work with the agonists to control and direct movement by modifying or altering the direction of pull on the agonists to the most advantageous position.

Think it over

Take a complex movement like riding your bike. In this example, it is your quadriceps and your calf muscles that are the agonists, the contracting muscles. The antagonists are the muscles of your hamstrings and shin. Other muscles of your leg may act as synergists and the muscles of your back and abdomen will act as fixators to stop you falling off. Try to identify these muscle groups at work during your next bike ride.

▲ Riding a bike involves a complex series of muscular movements

■ Fixator

These muscles stop any unwanted movement throughout the whole body by fixing or stabilising the joint or joints involved. They also help to maintain posture.

Remember!

Each agonist must contract just sufficiently, and each antagonist must relax equally to allow movement to take place smoothly without jerking. This concerted action of many muscles is called muscle coordination.

Types of contraction

There are three main types of muscle contraction: isometric, concentric and eccentric.

■ Isometric

In this type of contraction, no change in muscle length takes place. It occurs when a muscle is actively engaged in holding a static position, for example when stopping halfway up in a press-up or squat, or holding an abdominal plank position. With this type of contraction, the origin and insertion do not move and no movement occurs at the respective joint. This type of muscle work is easy to undertake but rapidly leads to fatigue and can cause sharp increases in blood pressure as blood flow is reduced. Strength gains achieved are also limited to the range in which the training has occurred.

■ Concentric

This occurs when a muscle shortens against a resistance, for example in a bicep curl. The brachialis and bicep shorten, bringing your forearm towards your upper arm. Another example is the knee extension, perhaps straightening the leg on a leg extension machine in the gym. The quadriceps are the muscles that contract to extend the leg. Concentric contractions are sometimes known as the positive phase of muscle contraction.

■ Eccentric

This occurs when a muscle returns to its normal length after shortening against a resistance. Using the bicep curl as an example, this is the controlled lowering of your arm to the starting position. At this point your muscles are working against gravity and act like a breaking mechanism. In the leg extension example, this is the lowering of the weight back to the bent-leg starting position. This contraction can be easier to perform but it does produce muscle soreness. Eccentric contractions occur in many sporting and daily activities. Walking down the stairs and running downhill involve eccentric contraction of your quadriceps muscles. Eccentric contraction can be a significant factor in the stimulus that promotes gains in muscle strength and size. Eccentric contractions are sometimes known as the negative phase of muscle contraction.

Remember!

There are three main types of muscle action:

- isometric, during which your muscle contracts but the angle at the joint remains unchanged
- concentric, during which your muscle shortens
- eccentric, during which your muscle lengthens.

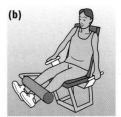
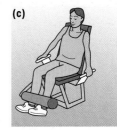

▲ Muscle contractions: (a) isometric, (b) concentric and (c) eccentric

Activity

Look at the diagrams of the leg extension machine on the previous page.

1 Which muscle contracts to cause flexion bringing the leg upwards?

2 What will its opposite muscle be doing, and why, to bring about flexion at the knee joint?

3 Are there any other muscle groups not identified in this diagram that are also involved in the successful execution of this exercise? If so, what are their functions?

Theory into practice

1 Lie on your back with both knees bent and both feet on the floor in a curl-up position. Place your hands on your thighs and slowly raise your head and shoulders, sliding your hands up your thighs until they touch your knees. Slowly return to the floor. Repeat this action six to eight times.

  a Consider the type of movement you have just performed. What forms the resistance for this activity?

  b There are two phases to this movement. Which phase can be described as the positive phase?

  c Which joints and muscles are involved in this movement?

2 Use a set of light dumb-bells or two small books. Start by holding the weights at the sides of your body. Keeping your elbows slightly bent but the arms long, with the palms facing downwards, raise your arms until your hands are at eye level. Slowly return the weights under control to your sides. Repeat this action six to eight times.

  a Consider the type of movement you have just performed. What forms the resistance for this activity?

  b Name the muscle groups targeted by this exercise. Are there any other muscles that are working to bring about this movement?

Taking it further

Working with a partner as subject and researcher, investigate the effects of isometric and isotonic exercise on your heart rate. For this activity you will need a stop watch and a heart-rate monitor. If a heart-rate monitor is not available, the researcher can take the subject's pulse at the radial artery for a 10-second period and multiply it by six to establish beats per minute.

1 *Isometric squatting exercise*

  a Attach the heart-rate monitor to the subject and record resting heart rate after the subject has been sitting in a relaxed state for two to three minutes.

  b Ask the subject to perform a ski squat by assuming a squat position against a wall. The back should be upright and fully in contact with the wall and the legs at a 90° angle. The subject should hold this position to the point of fatigue.

  c Record the heart rate at 30 seconds during the activity, immediately after the point of fatigue, and at one, two, three and five minutes thereafter.

  d Plot a graph to show heart-rate response against time while the subject rests.

2 *Isotonic squatting exercise*
  Istononic movements have two phases, a concentric or shortening phase and an eccentric or lengthening phase.

  a Ask the subject to perform as many squats as possible, standing with the feet one-and-a-half times shoulder-width apart, flexing at the knees and hips, and taking the thighs to a point parallel to the floor at the bottom of the movement.

  b Record heart rate at 30 seconds during the activity, immediately after the point of fatigue, and at one, two, three and five minutes thereafter.

  c Plot a graph to show heart-rate response against time.

Compare and explain your findings.

Sliding filament theory of muscular contraction

Your individual muscle fibres are long, cylindrical, multinucleated cells that vary in length and breadth. The structures of an individual muscle fibre, working from the outside inwards, include:

- Endomysium: this forms the fibrous sheath around the outside of the fibre.
- Sarcolemma: the cell membrane that binds the muscle fibre. It lies below the endomysium just above the nuclei of the cell.
- Sarcoplasm: the cytoplasm of the muscle cell. This is where the mitochondria are housed.
- Myofibrils: tiny thread-like structures. These run the length of the muscle fibre and make up much of its bulk. These are the elements that contract and relax.
- Myofilaments: these contain thin filaments called actin (small thread-like structures) and thick filaments called myosin. These myofilaments are contained in functional units called sarcomeres. When the stimulus to contract is received by the muscle fibre, actin and myosin slide over each other, decreasing sarcomere length.

Each muscle fibre contains several hundreds or thousands of myofibrils. The sarcomeres of the myofibrils within a single muscle fibre are aligned. When viewed under a microscope, stripes or striations can be seen along the length of the fibre. These alternate light and dark bands overlap.

When the muscle contracts, the degree of overlap between the thick filaments (myosin) and thin filaments (actin) increases, causing the filaments to creep along each other via tiny cross bridges that extend from the myosin filaments. The sliding of the actin filaments results in a reduction in the length of each myofibril. This process takes place within all fibres, causing the whole muscle to shorten.

Remember!

Single muscle cells are referred to as muscle fibres. Sarcomeres form the smallest functional units of a muscle. They are comprised of the protein filaments actin and myosin, which are responsible for muscle contraction.

Response to exercise

Short term

The short-term effects of exercise on the muscles include an increase in temperature and metabolic activity. As a result of this increase in metabolic activity, there is a greater demand for oxygen met by an increase in blood supply through capillary dilation.

■ Muscle damage

The warming of your muscles during activity makes them more pliable and reduces the risk of muscle damage and injury.

Long term

The long-term responses and adaptations of the muscles to exercise depend on the type and frequency of sport and exercise training undertaken and the overload achieved.

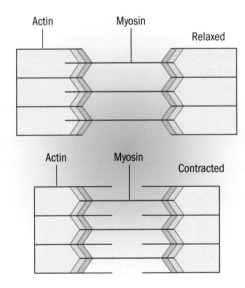

▲ Sliding filament theory

Hypertrophy

The strength and bulk (hypertrophy) of the muscles increase in response to a programme of progressive resistance training. This is largely due to an increase in the actin and myosin filaments in the muscle cell, making the muscle fibres thicker. Flexibility training leads to an increased range of movement around your joints. The endurance of the muscles also improves, allowing them to contract for longer while resisting fatigue and facilitating better muscle tone, shape and posture. The muscles need to be kept in continuous use for them to remain in good condition. If they are not exercised regularly, they become weak and their capacity for work is reduced.

Increased strength of tendons

Tendons are tough bands of fibrous connective tissue that are designed to withstand tension. Like muscles, tendons adapt to the mechanical loading of regular exercise. A general adaptation is in the increased strength of the tendons but different types of training result in different effects.

Assessment practice

1 Taking a sport of your choice, write an account to describe how the muscular system responds to exercise. **P4**

2 In your account, explain how the muscular system responds to exercise using two other practical examples to support your explanation. **M3**

3 Develop your account further to analyse how the muscular system responds to exercise. **D2**

Grading tips

Grading Tip P4

Make sure you describe the short- and long-term effects of exercise on the muscular system.

Grading Tip M3

Explain in detail the short- and long-term effects of exercise on the muscular system.

Grading Tip D2

Investigate and analyse how the muscular system responds to exercise. Analysing requires you to take a more critical approach in your answer. You might find it useful to undertake some practical research to support your answer.

Taking it further

1 Working in small groups, use a video recorder to film a range of sports people in action. Suitable sports to choose include gymnastics, football, track and field events and golf. If access to sports people is difficult, visit your local leisure centre or gym and film people using resistance equipment. Note that before starting to film you need to gain the written consent of those being filmed.

2 Review the data you have captured and analyse the sports people in action. To do this, devise a simple movement analysis checklist concentrating on the bones, joints and muscle responsible for bringing the body into action in the sporting activities you have chosen.

In this section you will learn about the structure and function of the cardiovascular system and the way in which it responds to exercise.

Structure of the cardiovascular system

The cardiovascular system (also referred to as the circulatory system) consists of the heart, blood vessels and blood. This system is the major transport system in the body by which food, oxygen and all other essential products are carried to the tissue cells, and their waste products and carbon dioxide carried away. Oxygen is transported from the lungs to the body tissues, while carbon dioxide is carried from the cells to the lungs for excretion. Life-sustaining nutrients are transported from the intestines to the liver and body cells, and waste products from the tissues are transported to the kidneys. Protective white blood cells, antibodies, hormones and medicines are also transported in your blood.

Heart

The heart is the centre of your cardiovascular system. It is a hollow organ situated in the left-hand side of the chest beneath the sternum. An adult heart weighs approximately 255 g and is about the size of a closed fist. It is a muscular pump, the purpose of which is to drive blood into and through the arteries in order to deliver blood to your tissues and working muscles.

The heart is surrounded by a sac known as the pericardium. This is a twin-layered sac with its cavity filled with pericardial fluid, the purpose of which is to prevent friction as your heart moves through beating. The heart wall itself is made up of three layers: the epicardium (the outer layer), myocardium (the strong

Remember!

The components of the cardiovascular system are:

- Blood: the fluid in which materials are carried to and from your tissues. This is the transport medium of the cardiovascular system. Blood cells comprise approximately 45 per cent of your total blood volume. The remainder is plasma that carries nutrients, hormones and all other essential elements required to support life.
- Heart: the muscular pump that contracts rhythmically at the centre of the system, pushing blood out through the vascular system to the working muscles.
- Blood vessels: a range of vessels (venules, veins, arteries, arterioles and capillaries) that are the routes by which your blood travels to and through your tissues, and back to your heart.

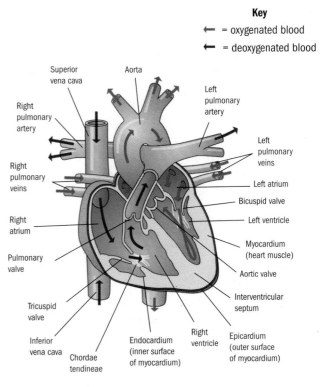

Key
← = oxygenated blood
← = deoxygenated blood

Superior vena cava
Aorta
Right pulmonary artery
Left pulmonary artery
Right pulmonary veins
Left pulmonary veins
Left atrium
Bicuspid valve
Right atrium
Left ventricle
Pulmonary valve
Myocardium (heart muscle)
Aortic valve
Interventricular septum
Tricuspid valve
Inferior vena cava
Chordae tendineae
Endocardium (inner surface of myocardium)
Right ventricle
Epicardium (outer surface of myocardium)

▲ The heart

middle layer that forms most of the heart wall), and the endocardium (the inner layer).

The right side of the heart is separated from the left by a solid wall known as the septum. This works to prevent the blood on the right side of the heart coming into contact with the blood on the left side.

The heart can be thought of as two pumps: the two chambers on the right-hand side and the two chambers on the left function separately from one another. The two chambers on the right side supply blood at a low pressure to the lungs via the pulmonary arteries, arterioles and capillaries, where gaseous exchange takes place. Here carbon dioxide passes from the blood to the alveoli of the lungs and oxygen is taken on board. This blood is then returned to the left side of the heart via the capillaries, venules and veins.

Key term

Gaseous exchange Loading oxygen and unloading carbon dioxide at the lungs.

When the two chambers of the left side of your heart are full, it contracts simultaneously with the right side,

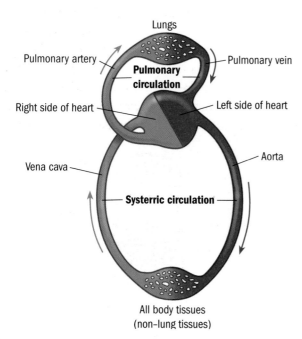

▲ **Double circulation of blood through the heart**

acting as a high-pressure pump. It supplies oxygenated blood via the arteries, arterioles, and capillaries to the tissues of the body such as muscle cells. Oxygen passes from the blood to the cells and carbon dioxide (a waste product of energy production) is taken on board. The blood is then returned to the right atrium of the heart via the capillaries, venules and veins.

■ Atria

The atria are the upper chambers of the heart. They receive blood returning to the heart from either the body or the lungs. The right atrium receives deoxygenated blood from the superior and inferior vena cava. The left atrium receives oxygenated blood from the left and right pulmonary veins.

■ Ventricles

The ventricles are the pumping chambers of the heart. They have thicker walls than the atria. The right ventricle pumps blood to the pulmonary circulation for the lungs and the left ventricle pumps blood to the systemic circulation for the body.

■ Bicuspid valve

The bicuspid (mitral) valve is one of the four valves in the heart. It is situated between the left atrium and the left ventricle. It allows the blood to flow in one direction only, from the left atrium to the left ventricle.

■ Tricuspid value

The tricuspid valve is situated between the right atrium and the right ventricle. It allows blood to flow from the right atrium to the right ventricle.

■ Chordae tendineae

These are cord-like tendons that connect to the bicuspid and tricuspid valves. They prevent the valves from turning inside out and ensure the correct flow of blood through the heart.

■ Aortic valve

Another of the four valves in the heart, this valve lies between the left ventricle and the aorta. It prevents backflow from the aorta into the left ventricle.

Pulmonary valve

The pulmonary valve lies between the right ventricle and the pulmonary artery. It prevents backflow from the pulmonary artery.

Aorta

The aorta is the main artery in the body. It originates in the left ventricle and carries oxygenated blood to your body tissues except the lungs.

Superior vena cava

The superior vena cava receives deoxygenated blood from the upper body to empty into the right atrium of the heart.

Inferior vena cava

The inferior vena cava receives deoxygenated blood from the lower body to empty into the right atrium of the heart.

Pulmonary vein

The pulmonary vein carries oxygenated blood from the lungs to the left atrium of the heart.

Pulmonary artery

The pulmonary artery carries deoxygenated blood from your heart back to your lungs. It is the only artery in the body that carries deoxygenated blood.

Blood vessels

As the heart contracts, blood flows around the body in a complex network of vessels. Around 96,000 km of arteries, arterioles, capillaries, venules and veins maintain your blood's circulation throughout the body. The structure of these different vessels within your cardiovascular system is determined by their different functions and the pressure of blood exerted within them.

Blood flowing through the arteries appears bright red in colour due to its oxygenation. As it moves through the capillaries it drops off oxygen and picks up carbon dioxide. By the time it reaches the veins it is much bluer in colour.

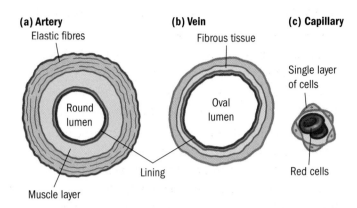

(a) Artery — Elastic fibres, Muscle layer, Round lumen, Lining
(b) Vein — Fibrous tissue, Oval lumen
(c) Capillary — Single layer of cells, Red cells

▲ Major blood vessels

Arteries

Arteries carry blood away from the heart and with the exception of the pulmonary artery they carry oxygenated blood. These vessels have two major properties: elasticity and contractility. They have thick muscular walls to carry blood at high speeds under high pressure. When the heart ejects blood into the large arteries, the arteries expand to accommodate the extra blood. They do not require valves as the pressure within them remains high at all times, except at the point where the pulmonary artery leaves the heart.

The contractility of your arteries comes from the smooth muscle surrounding them, which enables the diameter of these vessels to be decreased and increased when required. This contractility of the arteries helps to maintain blood pressure in relation to changes in blood flow. The arteries are largely deep except where they can be felt at a pulse point. These vessels branch into smaller arterioles that ultimately deliver blood to the capillaries.

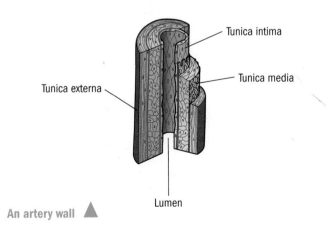

Tunica intima, Tunica media, Tunica externa, Lumen

An artery wall ▲

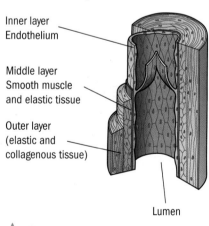

Arterioles

Arterioles have thinner walls than arteries. These vessels control blood distribution by changing their diameter. This mechanism facilitates adjustment of blood flow to the capillaries in response to differing demands for oxygen. During exercise, muscles require an increased blood flow in order to get the extra oxygen they need. To accommodate this, the diameter of arterioles leading to the muscles dilates to allow for extra blood flow. Other areas, like the gut, temporarily have their blood flow reduced to compensate for this, and the diameter of the arterioles in these sites is decreased. Arterioles are essentially responsible for controlling blood flow to the capillaries.

Capillaries

Capillaries form an extensive network that connects arteries and veins by uniting arterioles and venules. They are the smallest of all the blood vessels, narrow and very thin. They form an essential part of the vascular system as they bathe the tissues of your body with blood and allow the diffusion of oxygen and nutrients required by the cells of your body. Capillaries that surround muscles ensure they get all the oxygen and nutrients they require to produce energy. The walls of capillaries are only one cell thick. This allows nutrients, oxygen and waste products to be transferred. The number of capillaries in the muscle may be increased through frequent and appropriate exercise. The pressure of blood within the capillaries is higher than that in veins, but not as great as in the arteries.

Veins

Veins facilitate venous return – the return of deoxygenated blood to the heart. They have thinner walls than arteries and have a relatively large diameter. By the time blood reaches the veins, it is flowing slowly and under low pressure. Contracting muscles push the thin walls of the veins inward to help squeeze the blood back towards the heart. As muscle contractions are intermittent, there are a number of pocket valves in the veins that assist in preventing any backflow when the muscles relax. Veins are mainly close to the surface and can be seen under the skin. Veins branch into smaller vessels called venules, which extend to the capillary network.

The structure of a vein

Venules

These have thinner walls than arterioles. They collect blood leaving the capillaries and transport it to the veins.

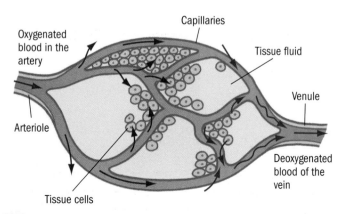

The capillary system

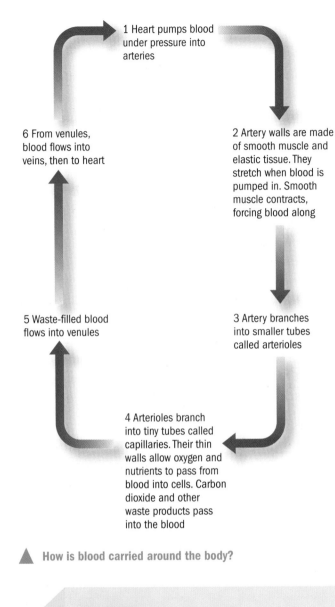

1 Heart pumps blood under pressure into arteries

2 Artery walls are made of smooth muscle and elastic tissue. They stretch when blood is pumped in. Smooth muscle contracts, forcing blood along

3 Artery branches into smaller tubes called arterioles

4 Arterioles branch into tiny tubes called capillaries. Their thin walls allow oxygen and nutrients to pass from blood into cells. Carbon dioxide and other waste products pass into the blood

5 Waste-filled blood flows into venules

6 From venules, blood flows into veins, then to heart

▲ How is blood carried around the body?

Activity

Draw a table to help you to remember the functional and anatomical differences between arteries, arterioles, capillaries, veins and venules.

Functions of the cardiovascular system

The sino atrial node (SAN) is the natural pacemaker for the heart. Nestled in the upper area of the right atrium, it sends the electrical impulse that triggers each heartbeat. The impulse spreads through the atria, prompting the cardiac muscle tissue to contract in a coordinated, wave-like manner.

The impulse that originates from the sino atrial node strikes the atrio ventricular node (AVN), which is situated in the lower section of the right atrium. The atrio ventricular node in turn sends an impulse through the nerve network to the ventricles, initiating the same wave-like contraction of the ventricles.

The electrical network serving the ventricles leaves the atrio ventricular node through the right and left bundle branches. These nerve fibres send impulses that cause the cardiac muscle tissue to contract.

Delivery of oxygen and nutrients

The key function of the circulatory system is to supply oxygen and nutrients to the tissues of the body. It achieves this function via the bloodstream. Blood has many essential roles in the proper functioning of your body. It carries nutrients absorbed from the intestine to the tissues of the body, along with oxygen and water.

Removal of waste products

As well as providing oxygen and nutrients to all the tissues in the body, the circulatory system is responsible for the removal of waste products from cells. It carries waste products from the tissues to the kidneys and the liver and returns carbon dioxide from the tissues to the lungs.

Thermoregulation

The cardiovascular system is also responsible for the distribution and redistribution of heat within the body to maintain thermal balance.

Key term

Thermoregulation The ability to maintain body temperature within certain boundaries, even when the surrounding temperature is very different.

Assessment practice

1 Draw detailed diagrams of the heart and blood vessels and then add labels to your diagrams.

2 Describe the structure and function of the cardiovascular system.

3 Describe the function of the heart.   **P5**

Grading tip

Grading Tip **P5**

You must be able to label the constituent parts of the cardiovascular system and relate them to the exercise where appropriate.

Response to exercise

During exercise, the muscles that are contracting require a continual supply of nutrients and oxygen to support energy production. These requirements are over and above those required to support normal activities at work or rest. As a result, the heart has to beat harder and faster to meet these increased demands. If these demands are repeated frequently as a result of a systematic training programme, over time the heart becomes stronger. The heart and blood vessels of the circulatory system adapt to repeated bouts of exercise.

Theory into practice

Record your pulse at various points throughout the day and draw a table to show how your pulse responds to different activities and situations. Include the following activities:

- on waking
- after eating and drinking
- after walking to college
- during participation in sport and exercise
- after sport and exercise
- watching television
- after a bath or shower.

Short term

■ Anticipatory heart rate

Nerves that directly supply the heart and chemicals within the blood can rapidly alter heart rate. Before starting exercise your pre-exercise heart rate usually increases above resting levels. This is known as anticipatory heart rate. The greatest anticipatory heart rate response is observed in short sprint events.

■ Heart rate at onset of exercise

This is the heart rate as exercise commences.

■ Redirection of blood flow

At the start of exercise, or even slightly before, nerve centres in the brain detect cardiovascular activity. This results in adjustments that increase rate and pumping strength of the heart. At the same time, regional blood flow is altered in proportion to the intensity of the activity to be undertaken.

■ Vasodilation

This is when the blood vessels widen in an attempt to increase blood flow.

■ Vasoconstriction

This is when the blood vessels constrict to reduce blood flow.

Long term

■ Cardiac hypertrophy

Cardiac hypertrophy is when the heart increases in size and blood volume. The wall of the left ventricle thickens, increasing the strength potential of its contractions. This has an important effect on stroke volume, heart rate and cardiac output.

■ Increased stroke volume

This is when the heart pumps more blood per beat, increasing stroke volume. Stroke volume at rest has been shown to be significantly higher after a prolonged endurance training programme. The heart can therefore pump more blood per minute, increasing cardiac output during maximal levels of exercise. Blood flow increases as a consequence of an increase in blood vessel size and number. This allows for more efficient delivery of oxygen and nutrients.

Key term

Stroke volume The volume of blood that the heart pumps out with each beat.

■ Increased cardiac output

Cardiac output is the volume of blood pumped out by the heart in one minute. During participation in sport and exercise, cardiac output is raised as a result of increases in either heart rate, stroke volume or both. Stroke volume does not increase significantly beyond the light work rates of low-intensity exercise, so the increases in cardiac output required for moderate- to high-intensity work rates are achieved by increases in heart rate. Maximum attainable cardiac output decreases with increasing age, largely as a result of a decrease in maximum heart rate. Maximum heart rate can be calculated using the formula below:

maximum heart rate = 220 – age in years

Theory into practice

Calculate your maximum attainable heart rate using the formula given.

Remember!

Cardiac output can increase five to seven times in order to accelerate the delivery of blood to your exercising muscles and to meet their demand for increased oxygen.

■ Decreased resting heart rate

This is when the resting heart rate falls, reducing the workload on the heart. Your heart rate returns to normal after exercise more quickly.

Remember!

It would not matter how efficient your circulatory system was at supplying blood to your tissues during exercise if your respiratory system could not keep pace with the demand for oxygen. In common with the cardiovascular system, your respiratory system undergoes specific adaptations in response to a systematic training programme which help to maximise its efficiency.

Assessment practice

Imagine you are trying to promote sport and exercise participation. You have been asked to explain the effects of sport and exercise on the cardiovascular system to a group of participants.

1 Describe how the cardiovascular system responds to exercise. **P6**

2 Using simplified diagrams, explain how the cardiovascular system responds to exercise. **M4**

3 Analyse how the cardiovascular system responds to exercise using two different sport or exercise activities. **D3**

Grading tips

Grading Tip **P6**

Make sure you describe how the cardiovascular system responds to exercise in both the short and the long term.

Grading Tip **M4**

Explain how the cardiovascular system works and how each part of the system is designed to meet its function. Say how it responds to short- and long-term exercise. You should provide appropriate examples where appropriate.

Grading Tip **D3**

Investigate and analyse how the cardiovascular system responds to exercise.

1.4 The structure and function of the respiratory system and how it responds to exercise

The respiratory system is also known as the pulmonary or ventilatory system. This system is responsible for the provision of oxygen and the removal of carbon dioxide, heat and water vapours.

All living creatures require oxygen and give off carbon dioxide. Oxygen is required for every cell in the body to function. The mechanism of respiration is the process by which cells receive a constant supply of oxygen and carbon dioxide is removed.

The respiratory system consists of your nose, lungs and breathing tubes. Its job is to take in oxygen for your body cells and to get rid of carbon dioxide. This system also has a role to play in regulating the body's acid-base balance.

Structure of respiratory system

Air is usually drawn into the body via the nose, but sometimes the mouth, and passes through a series of airways to reach the lungs. This series of airways is referred to as the respiratory tract, and can be subdivided into two main parts. The upper respiratory tract includes the nose, nasal cavity, mouth, pharynx and larynx, while the lower respiratory tract consists of the trachea, bronchi and lungs.

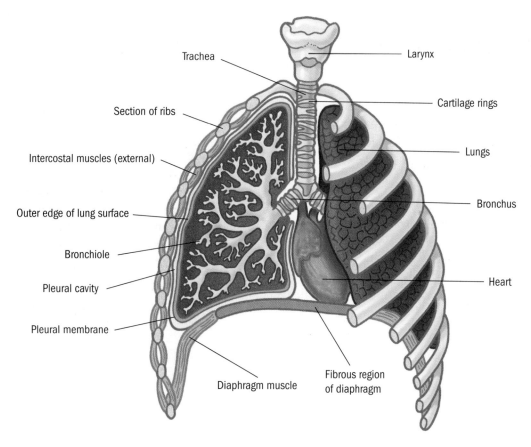

▲ **Cross-section through the thorax to show the respiratory organs**

Nasal cavity

The nasal cavity is the air passage above and behind your nose. Air enters the body through the nostrils. Small hairs within the nostrils filter out dust and foreign particles before the air passes into the two nasal passages of the nasal cavity. Here the air is further warmed and moistened before it passes into the nasopharynx. A mucous layer within this structure traps smaller foreign particles, which tiny hairs known as cilia transport to the pharynx to be swallowed.

Remember!

The nasal cavity has an important role in warming and cleaning air as it is inhaled.

Pharynx

The funnel-shaped pharynx connects the nasal cavity and mouth to the larynx and oesophagus. Commonly called the throat, the pharynx is a small length of tubing that measures approximately 10 to 13 cm from the base of the skull to the level of the sixth cervical vertebra. The muscular pharynx wall is composed of skeletal muscle throughout its length. It is a passageway for food as well as air, meaning special adaptations are required to prevent choking when food or liquid is swallowed.

Larynx

The larynx has rigid walls, formed of muscle and cartilage, contains the vocal cords and connects the pharynx to the trachea.

Trachea

The lower respiratory tract starts at the trachea (windpipe). It is about 12 cm long by 2 cm in diameter and contains rings of cartilage to prevent it from collapsing. It travels down the neck in front of the oesophagus and branches into two bronchi: the right and left bronchus.

Bronchus

The main role of the two bronchi is to conduct air into the lungs. The right bronchus is shorter and wider than the left. By the time inhaled air reaches the bronchi, it is warm, clear of most impurities and saturated with water vapour.

Once inside the lungs, each bronchus subdivides into lobar bronchi: three on the right and two on the left. The lobar bronchi branch into segmental bronchi, which divide again into smaller and smaller bronchi. Overall, there are approximately 23 orders of branching bronchial airways in the lungs. Because of this branching pattern, the bronchial network within the lungs is often known as the bronchial tree.

Key terms

Lobar bronchi Second-order bronchus. A subdivision of the primary bronchus that branches further into segmental bronchi.

Segmental bronchi Third-order bronchus. A subdivision of the lobar bronchi that further divides into small bronchioles.

Bronchioles

Bronchioles are small airways that extend from the bronchi. They are about 1 mm in diameter and are the first airway branches of the respiratory system that do not contain cartilage. Bronchioles terminate in clusters of thin-walled air sacs known as alveoli in the lungs.

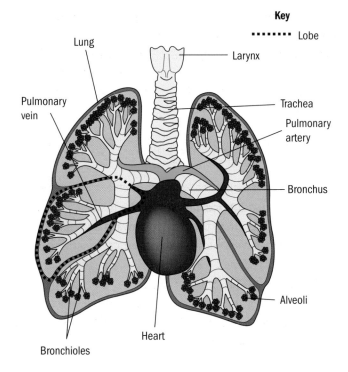

Key
········· Lobe

Lung
Larynx
Pulmonary vein
Trachea
Pulmonary artery
Bronchus
Alveoli
Heart
Bronchioles

▲ **The lungs**

Lungs

The right and left lungs hang suspended in the right and left pleural cavities straddling the heart. Each lung is divided into lobes – the right lung has three lobes and the left two. The lungs are surrounded by pleural membranes known as pleura. These contain a cavity with fluid that lubricates the pleural surfaces as your lungs expand and contract, so preventing friction.

Alveoli

The bronchioles end in air sacs called alveoli. The 300 million gas-filled alveoli in each lung account for most of the lung volume and provide an enormous area for gaseous exchange – roughly the size of a tennis court. A dense network of capillaries surround the alveoli to facilitate this process.

Diaphragm

The diaphragm separates the chest from the abdomen and is the most important muscle involved in breathing.

When you breathe out, the diaphragm moves upwards forcing your chest cavity to become smaller, which forces air out of the lungs. When you breathe in, the diaphragm moves downwards to assist in enlarging the chest cavity, which draws air into the lungs via the nose and mouth.

Internal and external intercostal muscles

The intercostal muscles are located between the ribs.

- The internal intercostal muscles lie inside the ribcage They draw the ribs downward and inwards, decreasing the volume of the chest cavity and forcing air out of the lungs during expiration.
- The external intercostal muscles lie outside the ribcage. They pull the ribs upwards and outwards, increasing the volume of the chest cavity and drawing air into the lungs during inspiration.

Function of the respiratory system

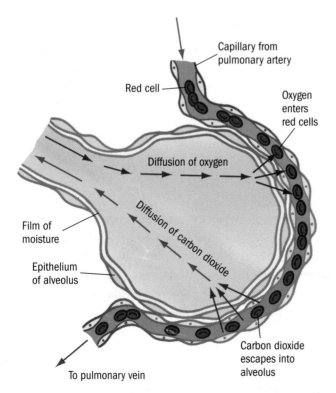

Capillary from pulmonary artery

Red cell

Oxygen enters red cells

Diffusion of oxygen

Diffusion of carbon dioxide

Film of moisture

Epithelium of alveolus

Carbon dioxide escapes into alveolus

To pulmonary vein

▲ Gaseous exchange in the alveoli

Diffusion of oxygen into the blood stream

The respiratory system is the first link in the process of oxygen delivery to the body's tissues. The transport of oxygen in the air you breathe to the alveoli in your lungs allows for the diffusion of oxygen into the blood stream.

Diffusion of carbon dioxide out of the blood stream

As well as playing a key role in the delivery of oxygen to your working muscles, your respiratory system also works to regulate and remove carbon dioxide levels within your body.

Mechanisms of breathing

Pulmonary ventilation, or breathing, is the process by which air is transported into and out of the lungs, and it can be considered to have two phases. Breathing is regulated by the respiratory centres in the brain and stretch receptors within the air passages and lungs. It requires your thorax to increase in size to allow air to be taken in followed by a decrease to allow air to be forced out.

Breathing in is referred to as inspiration and breathing out as expiration.

Inspiration

With inspiration the intercostal muscles contract to lift the ribs upwards and outwards while the diaphragm is forced downwards and the sternum forwards. This expansion of the thorax in all directions causes a drop in pressure below that of atmospheric pressure, which encourages air to flood into the lungs. At this point, oxygen is exchanged for carbon dioxide through the capillary walls.

Expiration

Expiration follows inspiration as the intercostal muscles relax, the diaphragm extends upwards and the ribs and sternum collapse. At that point pressure within the lungs is increased and air is expelled. When the body is in action, greater amounts of oxygen are required to produce energy, requiring the intercostal muscles and diaphragm to work harder.

Respiratory volumes

The respiratory rate is the amount of air breathed in one minute. For a typical 18-year-old, this represents about 12 breaths per minute at rest, during which time about six litres of air passes through the lungs. Respiratory rate can increase significantly during exercise – by as much as 30 to 40 breaths per minute.

Tidal volume

Tidal volume is the term used to describe the amount of air breathed in and out with each breath, and at rest represents about 500 cm³ of air. Of this, only two thirds (350 cm³) reaches the alveoli in the lungs where gaseous exchange occurs. The remainder fills the pharynx, larynx, trachea, bronchi and bronchioles. This is an inefficient use of air as these parts of the respiratory system have few blood capillaries, so little gaseous exchange occurs. This 150 cm³ of air is known as dead or stationary air.

During exercise, tidal volume increases to allow more air to pass through the lungs. The volume of air passing through the lungs each minute is known as the minute volume and is the product of breathing rate and the amount of air taken in with each breath.

The lungs normally contain about 350 cm³ of fresh air, 150 cm³ of dead air and 2,500 cm³ of air that has already undergone gaseous exchange with the blood.

Inspiratory reserve volume

By breathing in deeply, it is possible to take in more than the usual 350 cm³ of fresh air that reaches the alveoli. This is especially important during exercise. In addition to the tidal volume, you can also breathe in up to an additional 3,000 cm³ of fresh air. This is known as the inspiratory reserve volume.

Expiratory reserve volume

This can be up to 1,500 cm³ and is the amount of additional air that can be breathed out after normal expiration. At the end of a normal breath, the lungs contain the residual volume plus the expiratory reserve volume. If you then exhale as much as possible, only the residual volume remains.

Vital capacity

The maximum amount of air produced after you breathe out as hard and as deeply as you can is known as vital capacity. The volume is around 4,800 cm³.

Residual volume

The lungs are never fully emptied of air, otherwise they would collapse. The air that remains in the lungs is referred to as residual volume. It is the amount of air remaining in the lungs after you have breathed out as hard as you can. The volume is around 1,200 cm³. Residual volume decreases in response to increased fitness through training.

Total lung capacity

Your total lung capacity after you have inhaled as deeply and as maximally as you can is normally around 6,000 cm³ for an average-sized male.

Lung volume and capacities of a ▶ healthy adult

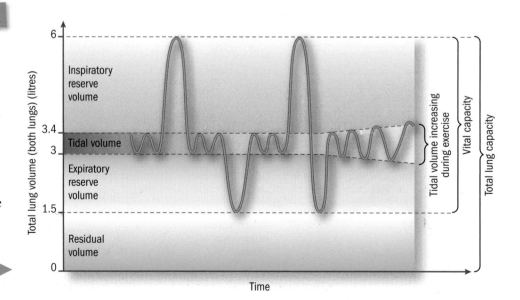

When it comes to sport and exercise, it appears that the efficiency of the exchange of oxygen and carbon dioxide between the lungs and the blood and between the blood and muscle fibres is more important in determining performance than total lung volume.

Taking it further

Draw up a table to help you to remember the definitions relating to the different types of lung volumes and their changes during exercise.

Remember!

The amount of oxygen required and the quantity of carbon dioxide given off vary with the amount of activity your body undergoes. During sleep, your body requires comparatively little oxygen, but it requires much more during strenuous exercise, such as running, football or stair-climbing. During exercise, ventilation increases in direct proportion to the rate of work being undertaken, up to the ventilatory break point. Once this point is surpassed, ventilation increases at a disproportionate rate as your body attempts to clear carbon dioxide.

Response to exercise

The respiratory system adapts to exercise in the following ways.

Short term

■ Increased breathing rate

Exercise results in an increase in the rate and depth of breathing. During exercise your muscles demand more oxygen and the corresponding increase in carbon dioxide production stimulates faster and deeper breathing. The capillary network surrounding the alveoli expands, increasing blood flow to the lungs.

Remember!

Athletes or highly trained individuals can tolerate higher breathing rates during exercise.

■ Tidal volume

Tidal volume is elevated by both aerobic and anaerobic exercise. During exercise oxygen is depleted from the body, triggering a deeper tidal volume to compensate.

Long term

■ Increased vital capacity

Vital capacity increases in response to physical training to provide an increased and more efficient supply of oxygen to working muscles. During strenuous exercise, oxygen diffusion may increase by as much as three times above the resting level.

■ Increased strength of intercostal muscles

The muscles of the diaphragm and intercostals increase in strength, allowing for greater expansion of the chest cavity.

Remember!

When you exercise, your breathing rate increases in order to take in more oxygen and expel more carbon dioxide.

Assessment practice

1 Create a short Microsoft PowerPoint® presentation to describe the structure and function of the respiratory system, the mechanisms of breathing, respiratory volumes and how the respiratory system responds to exercise. **P7**

2 Explain the functions of the respiratory system, including the mechanisms of breathing, and how the body responds to exercise using an exercise or sport as an example. **M5**

3 Undertake a practical analysis of your body's response to exercise and write up your findings in a short report. **D4**

Grading tip

A detailed explanation should include reasons or examples to support the statements you are making. Analysing requires you to take a more critical approach in your answer.

1.5 Understand the different energy systems and their use in sport and exercise

All movement requires energy. The methods by which the body generates energy is determined by the intensity and duration of the activity being undertaken. Activities that require short bursts of effort like sprinting or jumping require the body to produce large amounts of energy over a short time period, whereas activities like marathon running or cycling require the body to provide continued energy production over a longer period and at a slower rate. It is the energy systems of the body that facilitate these processes.

Energy systems

The body's ability to extract energy from food and transfer it to the contractile proteins in the muscles determines your capacity to exercise for different durations at differing intensities. Thousands of complex chemical reactions are responsible for this energy transfer. The body maintains a continuous supply of energy through the use of adenosine triphosphate (ATP), which is often referred to as the energy currency of the body.

Remember!

Energy can be defined as the capacity to do work.

Key term

Contractile proteins This means the actin and myosin filaments.

ATP consists of a base (adenine) and three phosphate groups. It is formed by a reaction between an adenosine diphosphate (ADP) molecule and a phosphate.

ATP is a versatile molecule that can be used for many things. Energy is stored in the chemical bonds in the molecules. When a bond is broken, energy is released. When a bond is made, energy is stored. When ADP binds with another phosphate, energy is stored that can be used later. When a molecule of ATP is combined with water, the last group splits off and energy is released.

The energy systems of the body can function aerobically (with oxygen) or anaerobically (without oxygen). Movements that require sudden bursts of effort are powered by energy systems that do not require oxygen – anaerobic systems – whereas prolonged activities are aerobic and require oxygen.

Remember!

The aerobic and anaerobic breakdown of food nutrients provides the source of energy for the production of chemical energy to fuel work.

Energy is required in order to make the muscle fibres contract. This energy is obtained from the oxidation of foods in the diet, particularly carbohydrate and fat.

- Carbohydrate is broken down to a simple sugar called glucose, which if not required immediately by your body is converted into glycogen and stored in the liver and muscles.
- Fat is broken down to form free fatty acids.

When these substances are burned in the muscle cell ATP is formed, which is rich in energy. When ATP is broken down, it gives energy for muscle contraction. It is the only molecule that can supply the energy used in the contraction of muscle fibres and can be made in three ways: the creatine phosphate energy system, the lactic acid energy system and the aerobic energy system.

Creatine phosphate energy system

ATP and creatine phosphate (or phosphocreatine, or PCr) make up the ATP-PCr system. It is the immediate energy system. Creatine phosphate (PCr) is a high-energy compound. When exercise intensity is high, or energy needs are instantaneous, creatine phosphate stored in muscle is broken down to provide energy to make ATP. When the high-energy bond in PCr is broken, the energy it releases is used to resynthesise ATP.

In this process, ATP is usually made without the presence of oxygen. Explosive work can be achieved, but only for short periods of time (up to about ten seconds) at maximum intensity as the supply of PCr is very limited.

Lactic acid energy system

This is the short-term energy system. To meet energy requirements of higher intensity over a longer period, such as during a 400-metre race, ATP can be made by

(a) ATP is formed when adenosine diphosphate (ADP) binds with a phosphate

(b) A lot of energy is stored in the bond between the second and third phosphate groups, which can be used to fuel chemical reactions

(c) When a cell needs energy, it breaks the bond between the phosphate groups to form ADP and a free phosphate molecule

ATP and energy released from the breakdown of ATP

the partial breakdown of glucose and glycogen. This is an anaerobic process that does not require oxygen and therefore is not sustainable over a long duration. Around 60 to 90 seconds of maximal work is possible using this system.

■ Anaerobic glycolysis

When the ATP-PCr system begins to fade at around ten seconds, the process of anaerobic glycolysis begins to occur. This system breaks down liver and muscle glycogen stores without the presence of oxygen, which produces lactic acid as a by-product. This limits energy production via this process.

■ Lactic acid production

Lactic acid is the limiting factor of the anaerobic system. Lactic acid accumulates and diffuses into the tissue fluid and blood. If this substance is not removed by the circulatory system, it builds up to impede muscle contraction and cause fatigue. You may have experienced this during intense exercise as an uncomfortable burning sensation in your muscles.

Remember!

Glycolysis is the breakdown of glucose or glycogen to produce ATP.

Aerobic energy system

This is the long-term energy system. If plenty of oxygen is available, as it is during everyday movements and light exercise, glycogen and fatty acids break down to yield large amounts of ATP. This produces carbon dioxide and water, which do not affect the ability of muscles to contract.

Aerobic energy production occurs in the mitochondria of the cells. These are the power stations of the cells, responsible for converting the food ingested by the cells

into energy. The production of energy within the aerobic system is slow to engage because it takes a few minutes for the heart to deliver oxygenated blood to working muscles. Long, continuous and moderate exercise produces energy using this system.

During exercise the body does not switch from one system to the other – energy at any time is derived from all three systems. However, the emphasis changes depending on the intensity of the activity relative to the efficiency of your aerobic fitness, i.e. your ability to deliver and utilise oxygen.

Activity

Survey the exercise and sporting pursuits of your fellow students and consider the principle energy systems involved in fuelling the range of activities undertaken. Draw up a table to summarise your findings.

Amounts of ATP produced by each system

- Creatine phosphate energy system:
  ADP + creatine phosphate $\rightarrow$ ATP + creatine
- Lactic acid energy system:
  Glucose $\rightarrow$ 2 ATP + 2 lactic acid + heat
  Glycogen $\rightarrow$ 3 ATP + 2 lactic acid + heat
- Aerobic energy system:
  Glucose + oxygen $\rightarrow$ 38 ATP + carbon dioxide + water + heat
  Fatty acids + oxygen $\rightarrow$ 129 ATP + carbon dioxide + water + heat

Types of sports that use each system

All three energy systems are active at any given time, but depending on the intensity and duration of activity undertaken different energy systems will be the primary energy provider. Table 1.5 shows the types of sport and the relative contributions made by the different energy systems.

Sport	Creatine phosphate energy system	Lactic acid energy system	Aerobic energy system
Archery	High	Low	
Basketball	High	Moderate	Low
Hockey	High	Moderate	High
Netball	High	Moderate	Low
Soccer	High	Moderate	High
Track and field distance		Moderate	High
Track and field jumping	High		
Track and field sprinting	High	Moderate/high	
Track and field throwing	High		

Table 1.5 Energy systems used for different sports

Remember!

Imagine you start running. Here's what happens:

- The muscle cells burn off the ATP they already contain in about three seconds.
- The creatine phosphate system kicks in and supplies energy for eight to ten seconds. This would be the major energy system used by the muscles of a 100-metre sprinter or weight lifter, where rapid acceleration, short-duration exercise occurs.
- If exercise continues longer, then the lactic acid energy system kicks in. This would be true for short-distance exercises such as a 200- or 400-metre run or 100-metre swim.
- If exercise continues, then the aerobic energy system takes over. This would occur in endurance events such as an 800-metre run, a marathon run, rowing, cross-country skiing and distance skating.

▲ Team sports of a high-intensity intermittent nature place demands on all of your energy systems

Theory into practice

1 Complete the health status questionnaire below.

2 Choose your favourite sporting or fitness activity, such as aerobics, running, cycling, swimming or playing a team sport such as football, hockey, netball or basketball.

3 Take five or six minutes to warm up and then do your favourite activity at a relatively moderate to high intensity for about 15 to 20 minutes. At the end of the session, be sure to finish with a five-minute cool-down. At each stage of the fitness session (warm-up, main activity, cool-down) pay close attention to how the different parts of your body respond and adapt to the activity.

4 List the bodily changes you have experienced. How did your body adapt to the different stages of the workout?

5 Although you were asked to perform the activity at a relatively high intensity, you could have chosen to walk at a low intensity, or run at a high intensity, or play a high-intensity intermittent activity such as football or netball. How does exercise intensity appear to affect your body's reaction?

6 In small groups, discuss the changes that occurred during the variety of activities undertaken by different group members. Do you note any similarities in responses?

7 Taking account of your body's reaction to this bout of activity, how would you rate your current level of fitness?

8 Explain the roles of the different energy systems in the activities you have undertaken.

Health status questionnaire

Name: _____   Date: _____

The following questions are designed to find out whether you can participate in the practical exercise and physical activities outlined above. If you answer Yes to any of the questions in this questionnaire, you should have a thorough medical examination prior to participating in the practical tasks.

1 Have you ever had a heart condition or experienced chest pains or a sensation in your chest associated with exercise?   Yes/No

2 Do you have a family history of heart disease below the age of 55?   Yes/No

3 Have you ever suffered from high or low blood pressure?   Yes/No

4 Are you taking any prescribed medication?   Yes/No

5 Do you suffer from any respiratory problems such as asthma or shortness of breath with minimal exertion?   Yes/No

6 Have you ever had any condition or injury affecting your joints or back that could be aggravated by exercise?   Yes/No

7 Do you suffer from diabetes or epilepsy?   Yes/No

8 Has your GP ever advised you not to participate in exercise?   Yes/No

When undertaking the exercise and physical activities described above, start at a slow pace and listen to your body. If you experience any signs of discomfort or stress, end the activity immediately and seek medical advice as soon as possible.

Recovery periods

Any exercise represents a stress to your body and creates a disturbance in your body's natural balance. The amount of disturbance depends on the intensity and duration of the activity or exercise undertaken. Your total recovery from exercise depends on a number of factors including the restoration of your immediate energy system, the removal of lactic acid and the restoration of muscle glycogen.

The creatine phosphate system can be restored almost as quickly as energy is released from the system. As a result, it is possible to repeat several short bursts of activity without becoming exhausted. However, once lactic acid is produced it will take around 45 to 60 minutes for it to be removed from the system. The rate of muscle glycogen restoration depends on the choice, speed and amount of carbohydrate consumption after exercise.

Taking it further

Using the Internet and a selection of textbooks, investigate how an understanding of energy systems can help to facilitate the achievement of optimal sporting performance.

Assessment practice

1 Using the research you have undertaken in this section of the unit, describe the different energy systems and their use in sport and exercise activities. **P8**

2 Using sport and exercise activities, examine the different energy systems and explain their use in sport and exercise. **M6**

Grading tips

Grading Tip **P8**

Make sure you describe each energy system and link each one to their use in different sport and exercise activities.

Grading Tip **M6**

Examine each energy system and explain its use in sport and exercise. Try to provide more complex sporting examples and consider the implications of training.

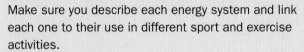

Knowledge check

1 Draw and label a simple diagram of the axial skeleton.

2 Describe five functions of the skeleton.

3 Draw and label a simple diagram of a synovial joint.

4 Describe the different types of muscle found in the body.

5 Describe the location and action of the following muscles:
   a rectus abdominis
   b erector spinae
   c quadriceps
   d gastrocnemius.

6 Draw a diagram to explain the sliding filament theory.

7 Define the functional roles of the following in relation to muscle movement:
   a agonist
   b antagonist

   c synergist
   d fixator.

8 Identify the main muscles working to bring about a bicep curl movement and analyse the type of muscle contraction taking place.

9 Describe the major functional differences between arteries and veins.

10 Describe the short- and long-term effects of exercise on the cardiovascular system.

11 Identify the key structure of the respiratory system and describe its function.

12 Briefly describe the mechanics of breathing.

13 Describe and define four respiratory volumes.

14 Identify two short-term responses of the respiratory system to exercise.

15 Describe the three energy systems.

Preparation for assessment

Imagine your college wants to raise the profile of health and fitness among staff and students and increase uptake of the sport and exercise opportunities it has to offer. You have been commissioned to produce a range of promotional materials such as leaflets, posters, videos and web pages that aim to promote exercise and sport. Decide on the most appropriate format for your promotional materials. These materials should take an educational focus and should include the following information.

1 Describe the structure and function of the key body systems involved in bringing the body in to action, namely:

a the skeletal system **P1 P2 M1 M2 D1**

b the muscular system **P3 P4 M3 D2**

c the cardiovascular system **P5 P6 M4 D3**

d the respiratory system. **P7 M5 D4**

2 Describe the different energy systems and their use in sport and exercise. **P8 M6**

To achieve a pass grade the evidence must show that the learner is able to:	To achieve a merit grade the evidence must show that, in addition to the pass criteria, the learner is able to:	To achieve a distinction grade the evidence must show that, in addition to the pass and merit criteria, the learner is able to:
P1 Describe the structure and function of the axial and appendicular skeleton, including all the major bones, and the different classifications of joints and the range of movement at each **Assessment practice Pages 6 and 15**	**M1** Explain why different classifications of joints allow different ranges of movement **Assessment practice Page 15**	
P2 Describe how the skeletal system responds to exercise **Assessment practice Page 16**	**M2** Explain how the skeletal system responds to exercise **Assessment practice Page 16**	**D1** Analyse how the skeletal system responds to exercise **Assessment practice Page 16**
P3 Describe the muscular system, including all the major muscles, and how the muscles move **Assessment practice Page 23**		
P4 Describe how the muscular system responds to exercise **Assessment practice Page 28**	**M3** Explain how the muscular system responds to exercise **Assessment practice Page 28**	**D2** Analyse how the muscular system responds to exercise **Assessment practice Page 28**

To achieve a pass grade the evidence must show that the learner is able to:	To achieve a merit grade the evidence must show that, in addition to the pass criteria, the learner is able to:	To achieve a merit grade the evidence must show that, in addition to the pass criteria, the learner is able to:
P5 Describe the structure and function of the cardiovascular system **Assessment practice Page 34**		
P6 Describe how the cardiovascular system responds to exercise **Assessment practice Page 36**	**M4** Explain the function of the cardiovascular system and how it responds to exercise **Assessment practice Page 36**	**D3** Analyse how the cardiovascular system responds to exercise **Assessment practice Page 36**
P7 Describe the structure and function of the respiratory system, the mechanisms of breathing, respiratory volumes, and how the respiratory system responds to exercise **Assessment practice Page 42**	**M5** Explain the function of the respiratory system, including the mechanisms of breathing, and how it responds to exercise **Assessment practice Page 42**	**D4** Analyse how the respiratory system responds to exercise **Assessment practice Page 42**
P8 Describe the different energy systems and their use in sport and exercise activities **Assessment practice Page 47**	**M6** Explain the different energy systems and their use in sport and exercise activities **Assessment practice Page 47**	

Health and safety in sport

Introduction

Sporting activities and events provide enjoyment and general health benefits. However, recent tragedies and serious incidents at sporting events have highlighted the need for safe practice in sporting activity. As with many sporting activities, it is virtually impossible to be risk free, but providing a healthy and safe environment should be an integral feature of all aspects of the services and facilities provided by everyone working in and organising sport.

This unit describes the legal responsibilities of those organisations and individuals that provide sports activities or sports events for others, including local authority leisure centres, private health and sports clubs, national governing bodies, clubs and societies. In particular, it highlights the key legislative and legal factors that apply to health and safety in sport and the need for risk assessments to be undertaken for all sports activities and events before they take place. The unit outlines the process of risk assessment, and how to maintain, manage and reduce any risks to acceptable levels.

After completing this unit you should be able to achieve the following outcomes:

- Know the key factors that influence health and safety in sport.
- Be able to carry out risk assessments.
- Know how to maintain the safety of participants and colleagues in a sports environment.
- Be able to plan a safe sporting activity.

Think it over

Imagine you have just accepted a post as a leisure centre assistant at your local sports centre. Your duties include lifeguard on poolside, setting up activities for sports clubs and leading children's after-school sports sessions. You have received your induction training, which included health and safety, and you want to ensure that you are prepared for your responsibilities.

Where would you find more information on what legal factors influence health and safety in sport? What are the main factors regarding health and safety you would need to know prior to starting your shift? What would you do in the event there is an emergency while you are on duty? What are the main hazards that you should be aware of in the swimming area and in the sports hall? What documentation relating to health and safety needs to be completed before you commence your duties?

Legislative factors

The laws on health and safety come from a number of sources and each can be applicable to different areas of sport.

Employers and employees have direct responsibilities under the Health and Safety at Work Act (1974), while employers, employees and volunteers have a common law 'duty of care' to other people. All national governing bodies, clubs and societies, therefore, have specific requirements to implement safe practices and procedures, to operate with safe equipment and to provide guidance on how to manage the risks associated with their activities.

It is essential that managers of clubs and societies understand their legal responsibilities with respect to health and safety management.

Several sources of information can be used to keep up to date with any changes or new regulations, including governing body of sport websites, Sport England, journals and representing bodies of sport and leisure organisations such as the Institution of Leisure and Amenity Management. These organisations help to produce codes of practice that are generally issued with regulations and give practical guidance on how to comply with the law.

Theory into practice

Choose a sport and obtain guidelines or codes of practice for your chosen sport. You could use the Internet to help you.

- Briefly describe what the codes of practice and guidelines cover.
- Identify those that are particular to the sport and ones that could be applied to other sports.
- Suggest any other guidelines that might create a safer sporting environment.

A good example can be provided by the gambling industry.

- Those working in football, rugby union, cricket and horse racing have all agreed to adopt a mutual code of practice designed to prevent betting cheats.
- The government's ten-point scheme is intended to increase cooperation between governing bodies and the gambling industry.

Guidance is sometimes issued which acts as a support mechanism providing advice on how to comply with the regulations.

Think it over

Can too many guidelines for safety in sport take the fun away from the activity?

Health and Safety at Work Act (1974)

The main piece of health and safety legislation is the Health and Safety at Work Act (1974). This sets out the general duties that employers, self-employed people and those in control of premises have towards their employees and others who could be affected by the work activities. It also gives employees the general duty to ensure the health and safety of themselves and each other.

Key term

Legislation Making or enforcing laws.

The Act was expanded in European legislation and became known as the Management of Health and Safety at Work (Regulations) (1992). This has since been replaced by the Management of Health and Safety at Work Regulations (1999).

However the principles of the Health and Safety at Work Act still remain. They are to:

- secure the health, safety and welfare of people at work
- protect people other than those at work against risks to health and safety arising from the activities of people at work
- control the handling and storage of dangerous substances
- control the emission into the atmosphere of noxious or offensive substances from premises.

The main aim of the Act is to involve everyone – management, owners and employees – in making them aware of the importance of health and safety.

It is the duty of the employer, as far as is reasonably practicable, to safeguard the health, safety and welfare of the people who work for them as well as that of non-employees (e.g. customers, visitors and members of the general public) while they are on the premises.

The term 'reasonable and practicable' indicates that in any situation each associate must use his or her own judgement before embarking on a particular course of action. At that particular time, the individual needs to decide what they consider to be reasonable and practicable. The seriousness and subjectivity of this means careful consideration of all the available options with respect to the consequences, the immediacy of making a decision and the available resources at the time.

These provisions are:

- the provision, use and maintenance of equipment and systems that are safe and without unnecessary and unacceptable risk to health
- taking action to ensure safety and absence of unnecessary and unacceptable risk to health in connection with the use, handling, storage and transport of articles and substances
- the provision of information, instruction, training and supervision as necessary to ensure the health and safety of clients, employees and contracted staff at work, and the health and safety of any other person

- the maintenance of all premises in use by the organisation, whether they own them or not, in a condition that is safe and without unnecessary and unacceptable risk to health including the maintenance of safe means of access to and from it (entry and exit)
- the provision of a working environment for clients, employees and contracted staff that is safe, without unnecessary and unacceptable risk to health, and has adequate facilities and arrangements for their welfare at work
- to operate within the current health and safety policy
- the review of all health and safety issues, material and policies at any time, in response to differing opinion, incidents and accidents, and at regular intervals to ensure that the policies and procedures are in force, understood, effective, implemented and up to date.

Remember!

These provisions not only need to be adhered to but clearly communicated to staff and visitors in all sports environments by the use of notices and posters, for example.

Activity

Design a poster for a health club that informs staff and users that health and safety is the responsibility of everyone not just the management.

Under the Health and Safety at Work Act the employee also has responsibilities. This is an attempt to reduce the risk of accident or injury to everyone in the workplace and to promote responsible behaviour. Employees must:

- take reasonable care of their own health and safety

- take reasonable care of the health and safety of others who may be affected by their actions
- cooperate with the employer and other relevant organisations to ensure that the requirements of the Act are met (this includes notifying supervisors of unsafe equipment or practices)
- not misuse equipment provided to maintain health and safety.

Most organisations have an accident record book that all staff are aware of and where any incident, accident or injury can be recorded. This is useful for people who are changing shifts and should be used by management and safety representatives to identify trends or recurrence of similar incidents. This may then bring about the need for change in policy and procedure.

In the sports environment, these record books may be more specialised such as a log of the water in a swimming pool. This is not only important to help identify when incidents have taken place but also in the light of the possibility of litigation.

Key term

Litigation A legal dispute between parties that is brought before a court.

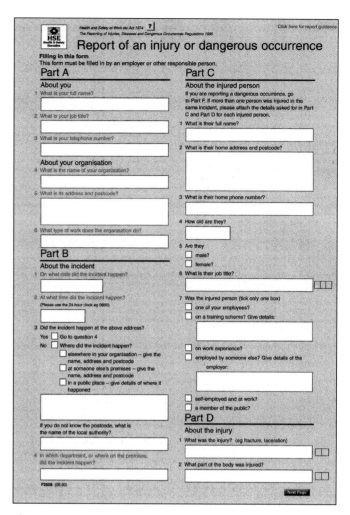

An example of a RIDDOR form

Additions since the 1974 Health and Safety at Work Act

■ Reporting of Injuries, Diseases and Dangerous Occurrences Regulations (RIDDOR)

The regulations relating to reporting accidents and incidents are covered under the Reporting of Injuries, Diseases and Dangerous Occurrences Regulations (1995). These regulations are also known as RIDDOR.

RIDDOR basically allows the following.

- The Health and Safety Executive (HSE), a government body, to follow-up on, report and check safety practices and operational procedures.

Key term

Health and Safety Executive (HSE) The organisation responsible for proposing and enforcing safety regulations throughout the UK.

- A standardised report form to be used.
- Officers from the HSE to advise organisations on prevention of further accident and illness.
- An investigation to prosecute, prohibit and make improvements where necessary.

RIDDOR regulations require employers to record and report to the HSE whenever one of the following events arise:

- a fatal accident, whether or not they are an employee, visitor or participant
- a major injury involving someone at work
- an injury to someone who is not at work such as a participant in a sports activity
- a dangerous occurrence that may not have caused harm but has the potential to
- an injury to someone at work that has come from an accident that has prevented them from doing their normal work for three days.

■ Personal Protective Equipment 2002 (PPE)

The Personal Protective Equipment (2002) regulations cover all aspects concerned with the use of personal protective equipment. These regulations revoke the previous legislation known as the Personal Protective Equipment at Work (1992) and subsequent three amendments.

Personal protective equipment (PPE) means any device or appliance designed to be worn or held by an individual for protection against one or more health and safety hazards.

It requires that employers undertake the following:

- assess risks and identify and provide appropriate protection for employees
- ensure that all personal protective equipment is clean, protected from damage or loss and kept in good working order
- provide training and information about PPE for employees and how it should be maintained.

It is a regulation that any training is provided free of charge to employees. For those working in sport, this could take a variety of forms such as gloves for handling substances hazardous to health or ear protectors when working within an environment with loud noise such as plant areas.

Think it over

What jobs in sport require PPE? Why do they need the PPE and what is the nature of the PPE?

■ Control of Substances Hazardous to Health (COSHH)

Hazardous substances include all substances or mixtures of substances classified as dangerous to health under the Chemicals (Hazard Information and Packaging for Supply) Regulations 2002 (CHIP), such as:

- substances used directly in work activities (e.g. adhesives, paints and cleaning agents such as markings used for sports pitches)
- substances generated during work activities (e.g. fumes from soldering and welding)
- naturally occurring substances (e.g. grain dust)
- biological agents (e.g. bacteria and other micro-organisms such as those in swimming pools or spas).

The COSHH regulations can be enforced by following an eight-step process.

1 Assess the risks: undertake a risk assessment to decide whether there is a problem with the substance(s) being used. This includes:

- identifying the hazardous substances present in the place of work
- considering the risks these substances present to people's health.

The assessment should be carried out by the employer but anyone with the appropriate knowledge can do some or most of the work of preparing it on the employer's behalf.

2 Decide what precautions are needed: if during the risk assessment there have been significant risks identified, then this step covers what action needs to be taken. This includes identifying whether or not the substance could be absorbed through the skin.

3 Prevent or adequately control exposure: if it is reasonably practicable to do so, the COSHH regulations require the prevention of exposure to substances hazardous to health. This may include:

- changing the process or activity so that the hazardous substance is not needed or generated
- replacing the hazardous substance with a safer alternative
- using it in a safer form, e.g. cones instead of markings

4 Ensure that control measures are used and maintained: this involves taking reasonable steps to ensure that control methods are being used and maintained. This could include staff training, displaying notices and regular checks.

5 Monitor exposure: it is the responsibility of the employer to measure the concentration of hazardous substances in the air breathed in by workers, if this has been identified as a serious risk to health.

6 Carry out appropriate health surveillance: it is also the responsibility of employers to carry out a health surveillance if an employee is exposed to a hazardous substance.

Key term

Health surveillance A strategy and method for employers to detect and assess systematically the adverse effects of work on the health of workers.

7 Prepare plans and procedures to deal with accidents, incidents and emergencies: this involves the preparation of procedures and setting up warning and communication systems in order to have an immediate response if the work activity gives rise to a risk of an incident involving substances hazardous to health.

8 Ensure that employees are properly informed, trained and supervised: the COSHH regulations state that all employers should provide 'suitable and sufficient information, instruction and training', which should include:

- the names of the substances they work with or could be exposed to and the risks
- the main findings of the risk assessment
- the precautions that should be taken to protect themselves and others
- how to use personal protective equipment and clothing
- the results of any exposure monitoring and health surveillance (without giving individual employees' names)
- any emergency procedures that need to be followed.

An example is a swimming pool, which contains different chemicals. One area a pool manager must ensure under COSHH is that bacteriological testing is regularly carried out. In public leisure centres, such tests are checked by the HSE while in private leisure pools this responsibility often falls on the Environmental Health Officer to take random bacteriological tests.

▲ It is important to display appropriate warning signs

Remember!

Ideally, these checks should be taken regularly. In most swimming pools, this is several times a day to ensure the correct levels of disinfection and pH.

■ Health and Safety (First-Aid) Regulations (1981)

This is an extremely important area for those working in sport and providing sports activities. These regulations are found under the general duty of care found in Section 2 of the Health and Safety at Work Act. This duty of employers extends to the duty to provide first aid. The regulations cover the following broad areas.

- It is the duty of the employer to provide first aid. These provisions must be 'adequate and appropriate' to the organisation. This depends on the number of employees, the type of work, the size and location of employees. A general ruling is to have at least one first aider for every 50 employees. Most leisure recreation organisations have more than this to cover different sites, outdoor, indoor and wet and dry provisions as well as shift rotations. First-aid boxes and first-aid rooms are identified. The overall aim is to ensure every employee has reasonably quick access to basic medical care.
- It is the duty of the employer to inform the employees of the first-aid arrangements. This includes a clear notice of the regulations and procedures involving first aid, as well as identification as to which people are qualified first aiders and where first-aid equipment is located.
- It is the duty of the self-employed person to provide first-aid equipment. In most leisure centres there should be a first-aid room because sports centres are considered to be more likely to have a higher occurrence of injuries.

■ Manual Handling Operations Regulations (1992)

The Manual Handling Operations Regulations (1992) apply to any situation where employees are carrying, lifting or moving loads. Loads are not identified with a maximum weight; each requires a risk assessment of the task, the weight to be lifted or carried and the working environment.

Employers are required to 'avoid hazardous manual handling operations' as far as is reasonably practicable. This can be done in several ways.

- By redesigning the task to avoiding moving the load or using some kind of equipment that reduces the risk.
- By undertaking a risk assessment where there is no obvious alternative than moving the load by hand.

(a) Keep the feet apart for a stable base. Point toes out. Bend the knees. Don't bend at the waist. **(b)** Tighten the stomach muscles to support the spine when lifting. Lift with the legs not the weaker back muscles. Keep the back upright. **(c)** Keep the load close to your body to keep the force of the load off your back.

 Why is it important to use good posture when lifting a heavy load?

- By taking all efforts to reduce the risk, where reasonably practicable.
- By ensuring that employees receive training and information about manual handling operations such as lifting techniques. Guidance is available that contains details on aspects such as lifting loads from floor level, using back supports and the increased risk to pregnant women.

■ Management of Health and Safety at Work Regulations (1999)

These regulations replaced previous 1992 regulations as well as incorporating legislation on pregnant women and young workers. One of the main requirements of the regulations is to make sure that all employers undertake risk assessment.

Every employer and anyone who is self-employed, such as a soccer coach, should make a suitable and sufficient assessment of:

- the risks to the health and safety of employees or himself/herself while at work
- the risks to the health and safety of people not in employment such as visitors to a community centre.

The regulations state that a risk assessment should be 'suitable and sufficient' and therefore should:

- clearly identify hazards
- determine the likelihood of injury or harm that may arise from the hazard (i.e. the risk)
- identify the actual legal duty relating to the hazard
- acknowledge the time frame of the risk assessment, e.g. is it appropriate to undertake one annually or twice a day?
- identify any control measures that may be needed to reduce the level of risk.

Specific information is given on young people who are in employment in relation to risk assessment. You should take into consideration a young person's experience, awareness of risks, maturity, the nature of the work activities and the training provided.

If the employer has five or more employees it is necessary to record any significant findings of the risk assessment and the groups identified. However, it is good practice to do this regardless of the size of the organisation.

Further provisions include the following measures.

- Health and safety arrangements: every employer should make appropriate arrangements with regard to the nature of his activities and the size of the undertaking for the effective planning, organisation, control, monitoring and review of the preventative and protective measures. This is to be written down if an employer has more than five employees.
- Health surveillance: every employer should ensure that the employees are provided with any items that are identified by the assessment, such as eye tests for those working closely with computer screens. This is the case if:
  o there is an identifiable condition related to the work
  o the condition is clearly detectable
  o the condition is likely to occur
  o continued observation as further health protection for employees is likely.

Think it over

What jobs in sport would require health surveillance?

- Preventative and protective measures: this requires employers to put into practice any preventative and protective measures based on the following principles:
  o risk avoidance
  o measuring and evaluating risks that cannot be avoided
  o reducing risks at source
  o changing the working environment and/or equipment to suit the needs of the individual and work methods, such as reducing monotonous work
  o changing dangerous conditions to safe or safer alternatives
  o developing a policy of prevention that covers work organisation, technology, working environment, working conditions and social relationships
  o giving appropriate instructions to employees.

Key term

Risk avoidance The most effective way of managing risk. It means making a decision not to enter into a new way of working because of the risks this would introduce.

Many sporting activities have inherent risks, for example ski jumping. However, there are still aspects that can be managed that reduce the risks such as monitoring the weather conditions.

- Health and safety arrangements: these state that every employer should have in place such arrangements that demonstrate how the organisation is providing for health and safety. This includes:
  o effective planning
  o organisation
  o control
  o monitoring
  o review of the preventative and protective measures.

The HSE states that these safety arrangements should be the main focus of the management structure and should be applied to all areas of the organisation. This may mean identifying someone in management that has responsibility for health and safety.

- Health and safety assistance: employers are required to appoint someone competent to assist in undertaking any measures required to ensure that all protective and preventative measures are put in place. The person appointed must have access to all the appropriate information and have the time made available to them to ensure they can fulfil their functions. Within the code of practice it makes suggestions that this should ideally be someone within the organisation rather than a consultant and someone who is willing to develop their experience and knowledge.

- Procedures for serious and imminent danger: this requires the employer to establish appropriate procedures to be followed in the event of serious and imminent danger. For many leisure and sports facilities, this means having a number of procedures such as in case of fire, bomb threat, crowd disturbance and evacuation procedures.

The employer should nominate a number of competent people to ensure that these procedures are in place. Employees have the right to stop work and proceed to a place of safety if they are exposed to 'serious, imminent and unavoidable danger'. There should be a notice displayed with contact information for external emergency services such as the fire brigade, emergency medical care and rescue assistance. Many organisations such as outdoor activity centres have quick-dial links to emergency services set up on the phone, carry direct contacts of medical personnel on outings and meet regularly with such service providers to ensure their procedures for serious and imminent danger are in place.

Think it over

The regulations state that a competent person is required for dealing with procedures for serious and imminent danger. What skills and personal characteristics are required of such a person?

- Information and training: this regulation focuses on information and training that must be provided by employers to all their employees. This information must be 'comprehensive and relevant'. This includes all information relating to the risks to employees' health and safety identified by risk assessment, all preventative and protective measures and clear identification of those people who have positions of responsibility for health and safety.

The training given to employees should take place during work hours, according to the code of practice and be regularly updated if there are changes with equipment or work procedures. This is very much in evidence with life saving techniques at swimming pools, where changes in good practice require regular training and updating of skills.

Regulations 11, 12 and 15 deal with sharing premises and contracted and temporary staff. This has clear implications for those working in sport, such as seasonal workers. There is still a requirement for employers to provide information on health and safety especially about risks and health and safety measures taken.

- New and expectant mothers and young workers: employers need to pay particular attention to new and expectant mothers and young workers. It is rightly believed that employers must protect such people from risks to health and safety. Any risk assessment should pay particular attention to new and expectant mothers and young workers.

■ Fire Safety and Safety of Places of Sport Act (1987)

This legislation was brought into effect as a result of the Popplewell Inquiry, which examined the safety of sports grounds following the devastating fire at Bradford City Football Club in May 1985 in which 56 people died. One of the most relevant parts of the Act is that a safety certificate is required where sports grounds have permanent covered stands for over 500 spectators.

■ Adventurous Activities Licensing Act

These regulations arose from the tragedy at Lyme Bay in 1993 when four teenagers died while on a kayaking trip. This event accelerated governmental discussions until

Generally, licensing only applies to these activities when they are done in remote or isolated environments. For example, climbing on natural terrain requires a licence, climbing on a purpose-built climbing wall does not.

A licence is not required for:

- voluntary associations offering activities to their members (e.g. Scout groups, local canoe clubs)
- schools and colleges offering activities only to their own students
- activities where youngsters are each accompanied by their parent or legally appointed guardian.

A licence is required for:

- climbing: rock climbing, abseiling, ice climbing, gorge walking, ghyll scrambling and sea-level traversing
- watersports: canoeing, kayaking, dragon boating, wave skiing, white-water rafting, improvised rafting, sailing, sailboarding and windsurfing
- trekking: hillwalking, mountaineering, fell running, orienteering, pony trekking, off-road cycling and off-piste skiing
- caving: pot-holing and mine exploration.

Activity

Use the AALA's website at www.aala.org to find out how much a licence costs.

▲ If the AALA is satisfied that the provider complies with nationally accepted standards of good practice, it will issue a licence

the Activity Centres (Young Persons' Safety) Act (1995) was passed through parliament in January 1995 and an independent licensing authority, the Adventurous Activities Licensing Authority (AALA) (see page 66), was created to bring the Act into reality.

It is a legal requirement under the Activity Centres (Young Persons' Safety) Act (1995) for providers of certain adventure activities to undergo inspection of their safety management systems and become licensed. This licensing scheme only applies to those who offer activities to young people under the age of 18 years and who operate these activities commercially.

Legal factors

Law

■ Statutory

Legislation has become the common source of new laws or law reform since the seventeenth century. When we think of laws in modern times, we often think of sections in an Act of Parliament such as the Health and Safety at Work Act (1974). Statutes can be applied to all or any combination of jurisdictions within the UK, whereas common law jurisdictions are more limited. Acts of Parliament which apply to everyone throughout one or more jurisdiction are called public general Acts.

But Acts may also be limited to geographical locations within a jurisdiction (such as local byelaws) or to specific people or companies.

Key terms

Jurisdiction The right and power to apply the law.

Act of Parliament These originate from a bill, which is considered by both houses of parliament. Once the content of the bill has been agreed, it receives Royal Assent and becomes an Act of Parliament.

They are designed to regulate the behaviour of organisations and individuals and are enforced by representatives of the government (mainly the police).

▲ The law affects everyday life and society in many ways – can you think of some?

The courts, magistrates and crown courts impose penalties on those found to have criminal liability, such as fines, improvement and remedial liabilities.

Statutory legislation comes with a number of instruments that relate closely to the Act. These are put forward by the Health and Safety Commission following discussions and advice provided by relevant organisations that represent the industry such as national governing bodies of sport and local authorities. These take the form of regulations such as the Control of Substances Hazardous to Health (COSHH) and the Management of Health and Safety at Work Regulations (1999). Guidelines and codes of conduct often produced by specialists and governing bodies of sport also play a major role in providing a healthy, safe and secure environment by determining standards and approved codes of practice.

Remember!

These codes of practice are not legislation but are often considered by the law to be developed by experts in their field and hence are often referenced when people take civil action.

Any person who commits a crime does so against the state. This means they have made a breach of criminal law. The police will make a criminal charge and have to prove that the person accused is guilty beyond reasonable doubt. If the person is guilty, the courts impose a punishment that could be in the form of a fine or a prison sentence.

■ Civil law

There is an increasing awareness of individuals' legal rights and willingness to seek compensation for damages caused by acts or omissions of others. This is especially so within a sporting environment where one person suffers a sports injury caused by another player. For example, there are several cases where a professional footballer has won a case for injuries caused by the poor tackle of another player. In 1980 civil action commenced against a council in West Yorkshire by an ex-pupil of one of their schools who had used an unattended trampoline left in an unlocked sports hall and became paralysed following an accident. This action was settled out of court.

These cases are normally heard in county and high courts. An individual (plaintiff) brings an action against another party (defendant) to claim damages for losses incurred. The penalties that can be imposed by the courts are known as civil liability and the action taken by the plaintiff is called civil action.

The most important common law duty for providers of sport and leisure in terms of health and safety is the duty of care. For employers this means that they have to take reasonable care to protect their employees from the risk of foreseeable injury or death at work.

■ Case law

The legal system within the UK was based largely on judge-made law (law developed through decisions by judges necessary to decide cases brought before them – called common law or case law) until around the seventeenth century. Each jurisdiction developed its own forms of common law. Since that time, new laws and law reform have increasingly been brought about through Acts of Parliament. A statement of law made by a judge in a case can become binding on later judges and can in this way become the law for everyone to follow.

This is called a precedent and has an important role in case law. It ensures certainty, consistency, logical progression and development in the law. At the same time it can be rigid and complex. Nevertheless, common law has advantages over codified systems. It is more flexible and practical as it is derived from real-life dramas played out before the courts.

Loco parentis

According to the courts, when parents send a child to school or college they delegate their authority to the teacher or lecturer (so far as is necessary for the child's welfare and so far as is reasonable to maintain discipline) both in the interests of the school or college as a whole and (above all) of the individual student.

Therefore, a teacher or lecturer supervising or accompanying a student on a school or college trip has overall responsibility for her or his health and safety and is said to act 'in loco parentis'.

The teacher is expected to apply the same standard of care as would a 'reasonable parent' acting within a range of reasonable responses. The standard of care that a court expects might vary according to the type of activity, the age and maturity of the students and changing conditions.

A teacher who takes a party away from school or college remains 'in loco parentis' throughout the trip – the responsibility cannot be delegated to anyone else. Teachers could be liable for negligence if a student or other person suffers injury or damage as a consequence of their carelessness or their failure to act within the range of reasonable responses. This applies primarily to PE teachers and club leaders, who often organise outdoor activities, field trips, sports fixtures and other events.

Duty of care

All those involved in sport have a duty of care for the health and safety of others who may be affected by their actions. These include owners, event organisers, staff, agents, contractors, officials, coaches, administrators and participants. All these groups need to have some understanding of the law of negligence (see page 64) and how it applies to them.

The principle is based on common sense, reason and foresight. For a successful negligence claim, the claimant (plaintiff) must show that the defendant was at fault to meet a reasonable standard of care.

The principles for duty of care were laid down in the case of *Donoghue v. Stevenson* (1932). These principles still form the basis for establishing a duty of care under UK law. The general principles for duty of care were highlighted in this case as follows.

- Does a duty of care exist? This depends on the relationship between the parties, as a duty of care is not owed to the world at large but only to those who have a sufficiently close relationship. The courts have found that there is no liability if the relationship between the parties is too remote.

- Is there a breach of that duty? Liability will only arise if the action breaches the duty of care and causes a loss or harm to the individual which would have been reasonably foreseeable in all the facts and circumstances of the case.

- Did the breach cause damage or loss to an individual's person or property? When this case was decided it was thought that duty of care would only be applicable to physical injury and damage to property. However, this has now been extended in some circumstances to include pure economic loss.

All those involved in sport, including participants, need to comply with legislation as a minimum standard and be aware of relevant codes of practice, regulations and the issue of 'forseeability'. This extends to those involved on the field of play such as players, coaches and officials.

sports coach UK provides the following guidance for a coach in relation to duty of care. As a coach, you have a duty to be safe.

- In any coaching environment where there is a foreseeable risk of harm, you must carry out a risk assessment of the activity to be carried out within the environment and be able to provide documentary evidence to support that assessment.

- No one can completely eliminate the risk of harm but you must show evidence of having acted reasonably to minimise the risks as far as is humanly possible.

- Make your participants fully aware of the risks involved in particular activities. This needs to be done repeatedly, clearly and thoroughly. Remember that a novice may not necessarily have the same comprehension or appreciation of the risks as an expert.

- It is important to plan and deliver appropriate coaching sessions to meet the needs of your participants. This means selecting appropriate activities for the age, physical and emotional maturity, experience and ability of participants.

Why does duty of care apply to everyone, regardless of their role?

- Ensure participants are made aware of the health and safety guidelines that operate in your sporting environment and within the governing body of sport.
- Encourage fair play and penalise incidences of foul play in your sport.
- Ensure participants stick to the rules and take as few risks as possible on their way to achieving their goals.

Higher duty of care

It is recognised that there is a higher duty of care owed to children and young people and this is something that those working in sport with children and young people must reflect. An example of this is the Occupier's Liability Act (1957). This requires that 'an occupier must be prepared for children to be less careful than adults would be in a similar situation'. This consideration should be even greater if a child is known to have learning difficulties or a medical condition that may make them more vulnerable than the average child to foreseeable risk of harm.

Negligence

If someone thought you had acted negligently, your legal representatives would attempt to put together your defence. This would have to be based on one of the following.
- There was no duty of care owed by you (the defendant) to the person who claimed to have suffered damages (the plaintiff).
- The injury that occurred was an accident and could not have been foreseen. It was a genuine accident.
- You were following 'standard and approved practice' such as governing body guidelines or codes of practice.
- The injured person had voluntarily consented to the risk involved.
- The cause of the injury was not caused by the actions of the defendant but by another reason. An example is a woman who complains of back pain after a fitness class when she had previously had back problems that were made worse by a recent visit to the physiotherapist.

Regulatory bodies

Appropriate to all activities

A regulatory body or competent authority is an organisation recognised by a national government as being the body responsible for the regulation and/or approval of processes in a specific area. There are many regulatory bodies that are appropriate to sport and safety, some of which may work together to ensure safety in sports activities is achieved.

■ Health and Safety Executive (HSE)

This body looks at people's health and safety at work, such as serious injuries that have happened to people at work or in a sports facility. It also:
- inspects workplaces
- publishes and provides information such as guidance booklets
- undertakes research
- investigates accidents and causes of ill health
- enforces good standards by advising and requesting organisations to improve their standards in the workplace
- prosecuting if improvements or standards have been ignored.

The HSE visits properties and facilities owned by local authorities such as sports arenas and swimming pools, as well as larger properties such as theme parks.

■ Other regulatory bodies

Local authorities

A typical local authority deals with most non-industrial workplaces such as catering, wholesale and retail premises, consumer services, leisure and cultural sites, offices, religious premises, cosmetic treatment businesses and various other types of workplace. This includes:
- carrying out inspections of workplaces to promote good practice and making sure businesses keep to health and safety law
- providing advice and guidance for employers so they can meet their health and safety obligations

- giving advice to employees, the self-employed and members of the public on work-related issues affecting health, safety and welfare
- investigating work-related accidents, certain dangerous incidents such as 'near misses' and cases of occupational ill health
- investigating complaints about working conditions and hazards in the workplace
- licensing and registration of skin piercing premises, reservoirs, Sunday trading activities and cooling towers
- training, information provision and promotional work to raise awareness on a wide range of health and safety topics
- developing and using relationships with other organisations with an interest in health and safety such as business associations and occupational health groups.

An environmental health officer has the power to close a restaurant in a sports facility that has failed to reach required standards of health and hygiene. It is normal practice that improvement notices would be issued first and therefore the centre would be able to correct any problems.

Your local licensing authority is responsible for granting licences such as those required to hold events at a sports ground. A licence application is obtained from the licensing authority, which decides the type and scope of licence that is most appropriate for the premises and their location. Your local authority should be the first point of contact for initial licence application questions or queries. Local authorities and police share information with licensing authorities about premises and their locations and advise on the potential impact on the community that surrounds the premises.

Local authorities and the HSE are responsible for the enforcement of health and safety under the general direction of the Health and Safety Commission (HSC). They work in partnership to secure HSC's objectives.

Local education authorities

There are 150 local education authorities (LEAs) in England. They are part of a local council or local authority and are responsible for education within that council's area.

LEAs have responsibility for all state schools in their area. They organise funding for the schools, allocate the number of places available and employ all teachers. LEAs have three roles.

- To guarantee the infrastructure of a universal school system. This means ensuring that every child has a school place, that children with special needs receive appropriate education and support, that changes in the school population are planned for, that children entitled to free school travel receive it, and that large school building projects can be managed and funded.
- To lead the local education community, to set a vision for education, and to bring different partners together to achieve change and improvement.
- To offer support to heads, governors and teachers and to monitor and challenge performance in schools.

Police

The main purpose of the police force is to uphold the law fairly and firmly, to prevent crime, to pursue and bring to justice those who break the law. For many people working in the sporting community, having a good working relationship with the local police force is essential. For example, a voluntary sports soccer club wanting to put on a charity run would certainly contact the police for advice and cooperation if roads were involved in the run.

The assessment of the need for police attendance and action at an event is mainly based on the need to discharge the police service's core responsibilities, which are as follows:

- protecting life and property
- preventing and detecting crime
- preventing or stopping breaches of the peace
- traffic regulation (within the legal powers provided by statute)
- activating a contingency plan where there is an immediate threat to life and coordinating the resulting emergency service activities.

The level of police resources committed to any event and the action undertaken should be proportionate to the assessment of risks posed by the event. Normally, police involvement will be restricted to these core areas of responsibility.

■ Adventurous Activities Licensing Authority (AALA)

The Adventurous Activities Licensing Authority (AALA) is an independent, cross-departmental public authority funded by the Department of Education and Skills and operating under the written guidance of the Health and Safety Commission (HSC). It is an independent watchdog on the delivery of outdoor adventure activities for young people.

The aim of the licensing scheme is to provide assurances to the public about the safety of those activity providers who have been granted a licence. In this way it is hoped that young people can continue to enjoy exciting and stimulating activities outdoors without being exposed to avoidable risks of death or disabling injury.

A licence indicates that the provider has been inspected by the organisation, with particular attention being paid to their safety management systems, and has been able to demonstrate compliance with nationally accepted standards of good practice in the delivery of adventure activities to young people.

Governing bodies of sport

Each sport is represented by a governing body of sport that defines the way in which the sport operates through its affiliated clubs and societies. Employed and/or voluntary workers within governing bodies of sport, clubs and societies accept a responsibility to take reasonable steps to identify and control the risks associated with the sport. These responsibilities, however, do not extend to providing an absolute guarantee to all participants, spectators and members of the public that accidents or injuries will not occur. Most activities involve a certain level of risk, even when the risks have been identified and all reasonable precautions have been implemented. Governing bodies must, however, be able to demonstrate that they have identified these risks and provided adequate guidance to associated clubs and societies on how to assess and control them in order to meet their legal obligations. Governing bodies

should develop and implement a management system within their sport that:

- provides a statement of the governing body's philosophy on health and safety
- defines the organisational structure for managing the sport's activities
- provides laws or rules and procedures for controlling the risks associated with the sport
- reviews the efficacy of the laws or rules and procedures and revises them when appropriate.

Governing bodies do not have sole responsibility for health and safety within their sports. Individual clubs and societies organise most activities and events and they are responsible for the health and safety risks associated with them. It is important, however, to differentiate between those activities where a governing body, society or club is responsible and those activities that fall outside of their responsibility such as training sessions undertaken by individuals at locations that are not controlled by a governing body, club or society. Participants, officials and spectators also have responsibilities to comply with the laws and rules specified for the sport in general and for specific activities and events in particular.

The primary responsibility of all governing bodies is to establish procedures that will enable clubs and societies to manage their activities and events safely. However, because of the potential financial implications of an accident, it is essential that governing bodies, clubs and societies take out insurance to cover potential third-party liabilities and to encourage participants to carry appropriate insurance.

Taking it further

In small groups, select a governing body of sport. Identify all the provisions they have in place for health and safety including policies, advice and guidelines.

The Football Licensing Authority's mission is to ensure that all spectators regardless of age, gender, ethnic origin, disability or the team they support are able to attend sports grounds in safety, comfort and security.

Case study: Planning safety for a new sports facility

Parisa is the manager of a new leisure facility at the Taylor Hotel in the Midlands. This thriving hotel has achieved planning permission to construct a gym, a multi-purpose activity room, a small swimming pool and a sauna. The gym will contain a range of ergometers including treadmills, bikes and cross trainers as well as a small section containing free weights, benches and mats. The activity room is to hold fitness classes including aerobics, step, boxercise, yoga and karate. There will be two full-time members of staff required and five to eight part-time staff including instructors and a receptionist.

Parisa has been asked to prepare a health and safety document that outlines all the relevant legislation and regulations that the proposed venue and activities will have to adhere to.

1 Identify the key health and safety legislation and regulations that are appropriate for Parisa.

2 What are the key responsibilities of the employers?

3 Identify five signs that would be required for the building and where they should be placed.

4 What key actions does Parisa need to take before the facility is built?

5 Who are the key people and organisations that you should speak to for advice and support with your document?

The authority has agreed the following objectives with the government.

- To ensure by means of guidance, assistance and monitoring that local authorities perform their functions to a consistent and acceptable standard and, in the long term, to give these authorities the opportunity to reduce their level of involvement as clubs take greater responsibility for safety.
- To maintain and build on the achievements of the government's policies on spectator accommodation.
- To bring about, through advice and persuasion, a permanent change of culture whereby consistently high standards of safety are maintained at every premiership, football league and international football ground by the clubs or ground management taking responsibility on their own initiative rather than in response to requirements imposed by other bodies.
- To maintain and enhance its position as the leading authority on ground safety and standards both at home and overseas and as the prime source of advice and assistance to the government, local authorities, clubs and other bodies.

Assessment practice

Imagine you have been appointed as an assistant coach to the youth rugby team at your local club. The first team plays in the national league. The rugby club has just been awarded a lottery grant and has moved to a new facility. It has a number of full-time members of staff, including coaches, a groundsman and two administrators. The facilities include a club house, changing rooms, a fitness gym, a small indoor hall and several rugby pitches.

It is the off season and the club is having a meeting with all the coaching staff to prepare for the forthcoming season. The club has achieved club mark status and is reviewing all its policies and any action that needs to be taken to ensure the welfare and safety of its members.

You have been asked to gather information on health and safety legislation and present it to the rest of the coaching staff. This can be in the format of your choice but should clearly identify the key legislation that the club and staff need to know and how it applies to them. **P1 P2 M1**

Grading tips

2.2 Be able to carry out risk assessments

Risk assessments

Despite the existing legislation and regulations, there are many cases each year of accidents and injuries in the workplace.

- In the UK, 1.6 million injuries occur in the workplace every year, as well as 2.2 million cases of ill health caused or made worse by work.

- 30 million working days are lost annually, 24 million as a result of work-related ill health and 6 million due to workplace injury.

- Health and safety failures currently cost employers up to £6.5 billion every year.

Most sports participants have experienced injury, often because of the inherent risk of the sport. Obvious examples include downhill skiers who push themselves for greater speed and consent to the likelihood that they may fall. However, all sports participants like to know that the sports organisers have undertaken every step to help reduce the likelihood of injury occurring. In the case of skiers, this may involve checking weather conditions, the physical state of the course, location of support netting to help fallers and first-aid provisions. These steps and measures for sports organisers, employees and owners are formally undertaken by means of a risk assessment.

	No. of injuries recorded by HASS	No. of injuries recorded by LASS	Total
Household activity	216,234	4,941	221,175
DIY/maintenance	218,510	15,785	234,295
Shopping	1,968	65,395	67,363
Education/training	595	167,403	167,998
Sport (excluding education)	16,790	693,228	710,018
Play/hobby/leisure	569,470	638,944	1,208,414
Basic needs	758,008	206,845	964,853
Travelling/touring	44,465	436,199	480,664
Other	875,309	647,575	1,522,884
Total	2,701,349	2,876,315	5,577,664

Table 2.1 Data for the Home Accident and Leisure Activities Surveillance Systems, 2002

The Home Accident Surveillance System (HASS) and the Leisure Accident Surveillance System (LASS) were funded and maintained by the Department for Trade and Industry from 1976 to 2003. The systems contain records of non-fatal accidents occurring in the home or at leisure, which caused a serious enough injury to warrant a visit to hospital, since the start of 1978. The purpose of the systems was to collect information to underpin accident prevention policy and thus to improve consumer safety. The database holds records of accidents to consumers involving injury or suspected injury.

Table 2.1 summarises the findings of the surveys in 2002.

Activity

1 Using the students in your class as your sample, in groups design a questionnaire that asks questions relating to sporting injuries. You should identify what injuries people have had, where any injuries have taken place and what caused them.

2 Once you have collected this information, prepare it in a table format and comment on your findings.

Aims

Risk assessment is a tool to help individuals and organisations prevent accidents and ill health from occurring. The requirement for risk assessment was first legally introduced in 1992 with the Management of Health and Safety at Work (Regulations) (1992), even though the concept was contained within the Health and Safety at Work Act (1974). The current regulations are covered in the Management of Health and Safety at Work Regulations (1999) (see page 57).

The regulations require all employers and self-employed people to undertake risk assessment of their workers and any others who may be affected by their work or business and 'to ensure as far as reasonably practicable that exposure to the risks are reduced to an acceptable level'. The risk assessment process should be systematic and logical. It is essential to keep accurate records using forms similar to the one below.

The risk assessment must be appropriate to the proportion of risk. This includes making the venue safe so that all activities can be accurately assessed and controlled (e.g. rugby coaches taking their teams on fields and table tennis coaches taking sessions in sports facilities).

Risk assessment form

Department: _____

Work/project title: _____

Location(s): _____

Description of work: _____

Persons involved: _____

Hazard identification (state the hazards involved in the work)

Risk assessment (make an assessment of the risks involved in the work and, where possible, state high, medium or low risk)

Control measures (state the control measures that are in place to protect staff and others from the above risks. Put in place adequate control measures for any risks that have been identified as uncontrolled)

Declaration
I the undersigned have assessed the work, titled above, and declare that there is no significant risk/the risks will be controlled by the methods stated on this form (delete as applicable) and that the work will be carried out in accordance with the company's codes of practice.

Name: _____

Signed: _____

Date: _____

There is a high level of responsibility on owners, managers and organisers of sports activities and events to ensure the health and safety of all those involved in their provision. EU regulations stipulate that each employer has to assess the health and safety hazards and risks and take action, where appropriate, to remove or control the risk. Understanding what a risk and a hazard are is critical to be able to undertake any risk assessment.

■ Eliminate

Hazards are something that have the potential to cause harm. These may well be known by the employers, such as water in a swimming pool. Tragically, people have died in swimming pools from drowning and therefore the hazard needs to be monitored and controlled by appropriate staffing ratios based on the number of swimmers. Other hazards may be unknown and arise from actively seeking to identify hazards, such as a loose collar on a bar with free weights. These must be eliminated as so far as possible.

■ Minimise

The term 'risk' refers to the likelihood of harm from a particular hazard. This tends to be more subjective and involves the probability of future events taking place. A trampoline can be viewed as a hazard. Putting a novice on a trampoline without safety mats or 'spotters' and without anyone with coaching qualifications supervising increases the risk of injury. Providing these precautions will help to minimise the risk to an acceptable level.

Theory into practice

When you undertake your next sports activity, try and arrive a few minutes before the session starts and identify any hazards and risks that you can.

■ Protect participants from harm

This is the most important aim of risk assessment and can be achieved by following the risk assessment process.

There are many variations and formats of risk assessments, which should be adapted to meet the needs of the situation, the sports environment and the employer. However, the following steps are a good guide to help eliminate or minimise hazards and risk and to protect sports participants from harm.

1 Look for different types of hazards within the workplace: these could include chemicals, work equipment, animals and work activities.

2 Decide who might be harmed and to what extent: consider participants, employees, visitors, contractors and members of the public. Pay particular attention to young workers, trainees and new or expectant mothers.

3 Assess the risk of the hazard causing harm: this will help to determine whether or not anything else can be done to reduce the likelihood further. This will usually involve monitoring and reviewing existing control measures and practices. A risk of harm will always exist and the risk assessment process will help you decide whether any further action needs to be taken to reduce the risk. A useful way of carrying out a risk assessment is to prioritise these remaining risks. They could be categorised as high, medium or low. The risk assessments need to be suitable and sufficient in order to address the category of risk. Staff should be made aware of and trained in the procedures in place for controlling the hazard.

4 Undertake a written risk assessment: this ensures that the process is systematic and consistent and gives you a record of the process you have used to reach your conclusions. This also helps you to monitor the systems in place to reduce the likelihood of injury occurring. A method of doing this might include a daily checklist for a particular piece of sports equipment or activity, especially in sports halls where the equipment being used can be constantly changing.

5 Review the risk assessment: the hazards associated with your sports environment or the nature of your business may change from time to time, and it is therefore important to periodically review your risk assessment to see if it is still appropriate. If any changes occur, staff should be made aware of the detail of the changes. This may also result in additional training being required.

Objectives

■ Identify hazards

A hazard is something with the potential to cause harm. This can include equipment, the environment and activities as well as methods of work. Having a good understanding of the areas where hazards are likely to occur will help to prevent accidents and improve safety awareness.

Think it over

What do you think is the key to help ensure the health and safety of yourself and sports participants?

It is often preferable to undertake hazard identification as a group rather than individually as it increases the likelihood of hazards being isolated.

Identifying those at risk

This clearly identifies which people may be at risk from the hazards identified. These could include:

- employees
- young people
- contractors
- the public
- visitors
- participants
- people with special needs
- cleaners
- night security staff.

Some risk assessment systems also consider how many people may be at risk and how potential incidents could happen. A simple example of a gym with glass doors situated at either end of the room is a hazard. For footballers participating in a five-aside-match in the gym, the risk of someone smashing the glass is quite high.

Assess chance of hazard causing harm and grade risks

This process develops the degree of risk that is perceived. It involves looking at each hazard and attempting to foresee the potential risks that could happen. This is sometimes given in numerical scores or simply as low, medium or high risk. Table 2.2 shows a typical system that could be used.

Likelihood of risk occurring	Grade
Certain	5
Probable	4
Possible	3
Remote	2
Unlikely	1

Table 2.2 Grading the likelihood of a risk occurring

A thorough process would also include a grading on the severity of injury that may occur from the risk.

Any risks that have been identified as being high risk require immediate action to be taken to put the risk at an appropriate level. This action will form the risk management proposal, which needs to be recorded. The measures proposed should have clear allocation of people and resources. In the case of glass doors in the gym, this could be a likelihood risk of level 4 as there is the probability that serious injury could be caused to one of the participants.

Do not do activity

In this example, this would involve stopping all competitive sports in the gym, putting together costs for replacing the glass with shatterproof material, and drawing up a time frame for replacement.

Modify activity

This can be done in several ways such as moving the activities away from unsafe areas or conditioning sports activities to make them non-contact.

Protect participants from hazard

Once a hazard has been identified, action should be taken to protect participants wherever possible. For example, if a light is not working in an area of a sports hall, that area should not be used.

Provide appropriate safety equipment

These needs should have been identified following the risk assessment. For example, a hockey player has the obvious hazard of a hard ball hitting them and the person most likely to be injured is the goalkeeper. Therefore, the goalie should be provided with the appropriate safety equipment before starting the activity.

Activity

When visiting a sports venue, try to find the information that instructs you on what the emergency procedures are in the event of a serious or imminent danger such as a fire.

Provide appropriate training

A risk assessment for an event obviously needs to be repeated for each subsequent event depending on the type, length and number of people involved. A risk assessment for a health club, cinema, theatre or outdoor activities centre, where factors such as environment and activities are constantly changing, may be carried out daily. Regular training of all staff and reviewing risk assessments are all part of the risk assessment process. All employees should be aware of changes in conditions that might affect the risks.

If it is found that systems and procedures need to be revised, this must be communicated to any internal and external customers who may be affected.

Provide appropriate supervision for participants

When leading or coaching activities or supervising field trips, local authorities and sports governing bodies have guidelines on the ratios of leaders to the number of participants. This depends on the age, ability, number and disability of the participants and the nature and location of the activity. An obvious example would be that the number of lifeguards should increase if more people are using the pool.

Case study: Managing health and safety

A football team is in the sports hall for five-a-side football. The players notice that benches are still out on the floor and there appear to be used drinks bottles on the floor with water lying in several areas of the hall. The team manager notices that some players do not have shin pads on and some of the players are bringing glass drinks bottles into the gym.

1 **What immediate action must be taken?**

2 **What are the systems that need to be in place to ensure that the sports centre is managing its health and safety responsibilities?**

Assessment practice

You have presented your information on health and safety to the rugby club staff and they are clear on their responsibilities. Risk assessment also forms part of each coach's duties but they have only a basic understanding of their responsibilities. Each coach will be leading activities both in the fitness area and on the pitch as well as taking teams to away games.

The coaching staff need to be brought up to speed with the requirements of risk assessment and where, when and what they should be doing in order to help prevent and reduce the likelihood of injury to their players.

1 Write a statement that can be prominently displayed in the club that identifies the aims of risk assessment. **P3**

2 Carry out two risk assessments to show as examples of what should be done by the coaches. One should be of a fitness area and one on an outdoor pitch. **M2**

3 Clearly identify any risk controls that should be used and explain three procedures that could be used to promote a healthy and safe environment at the rugby club. **D1**

Activity

In small groups, select three sports and identify the ratio of supervisors to participants suggested for a given age group and activity.

Taking it further

Working in small groups, plan a visit to a sporting event such as a local rugby match. Ideally you should contact the club secretary in advance and ask for their support in undertaking a risk assessment of the event. You should plan to have all your forms prepared in advance and the system you are going to use to assess any hazards and risk. These findings should be reported back to the rest of the class, accompanied by suggestions on how the risks may be eliminated or minimised to an acceptable level.

Grading tips

Grading Tip **P3**

You must be able to show two completed risk assessments for sports activities. This can be done through working with a local club or fitness centre. You should ensure you have a blank risk assessment form you can use and are clear on the criteria and grading you are going to implement.

Grading Tip **M2**

All risk assessments should be done autonomously and you should be including any risk controls that come out of your assessments.

Grading Tip **D1**

You should clearly review all the risk controls in order to manage any hazards that you have identified. You should ensure you evaluate their effectiveness in reducing or eliminating the risk and how that will protect people from coming to any harm.

2.3 Know how to maintain the safety of participants and colleagues in a sports environment

We have seen the various legislation and regulations that affect sports providers, organisers and facility managers. The Management of Health and Safety at Work Regulations (1999), for example, identifies that the organisation must work to meet certain requirements and have clear systems, policies and procedures for managing health and safety in the workplace. For example, a

▶ All organisations need to be able to maintain the safety of participants and employees in a sports environment

health club that employs five or more people must have a written statement of their health and safety policy that explains how the health and safety of their employees is assessed. The policy will often be drawn up by a safety committee and an appointed safety representative who has responsibility for ensuring the policy is enforced.

Procedures

Operating procedures and good practice

Many sports facilities produce a set of operating procedures known as standard/normal operating procedures (S/NOPs). These procedures will contain the safety programme as well as health and safety issues such as daily alarm testing. They will also cover operational procedures for maintenance and dealing with customer complaints.

A safety programme is a document produced by the organisation in accordance with relevant legislation and approved guidelines and practices. It should contain methods of raising the awareness of the importance of health and safety to all staff and customers. This involves having clear methods of communicating essential information to employees as well as allowing time for the safety programme to be effective.

Individuals such as coaches and instructors also have to be aware of the correct operating procedures. It is their responsibility to seek and employ measures to ensure the health and safety of their participants. Due to many tragic events at sports stadiums and elsewhere, people are quite rightly eager to prevent further similar tragedies. A clear and well-considered safety programme is essential and must be adhered to.

Activity

Part of any safety programme is an effective communication system. In pairs, identify all the communication methods that could be used when managing health and safety issues at a sports facility, such as notice boards and walkie-talkies. What are the advantages and disadvantages of each method?

■ Staff training

Under the Health and Safety at Work Act (1974) employers are required to consult and inform safety representatives of issues regarding health and safety. In many situations legislation, regulations and codes of practice change and employers and safety representatives need to keep up to date with all new relevant information.

Staff training is a method that is used and involves sending staff on appropriate courses, seminars and conferences, or holding internal training such as on the manual handling of loads. All safety representatives have the right to be paid for time taken off work in order to carry out their safety duties.

For example, the Health and Safety (First-Aid) Regulations (1981) require that, in order to provide first aid to their employees who are injured or become ill at work, employers must have adequate and appropriate equipment, facilities and personnel.

■ Staff development

Employers have a responsibility to provide safe and healthy workplace conditions as well as safe systems and methods for workplace activities. An essential element of any safe system is the knowledge and attitude of employees, and this demands proper training in the basics of health and safety as well as specific training for individual tasks. Opportunities should therefore be provided for staff to develop their skills and knowledge in relation to health and safety. This may involve attending courses or gaining qualifications.

■ Risk assessments

The Management of Health and Safety at Work Regulations (1999) outline a set of principles to apply when you are deciding on what action to take to reduce risk in the workplace.

- Wherever possible, avoid risks altogether: this is the most important principle in good health and safety management.
- Always try to combat risks at their source: for example, if you have a slippery changing room floor, drying it immediately is better than putting up a warning sign.

- Ensure all staff understand what they must do: communication is vital to ensure the successful implementation of health and safety measures to protect everyone.

Remember!

When it comes to implementing measures to control risks in the workplace or sports environment, it is important to understand that different types of controls vary in terms of how effective they are at reducing risks.

■ Emergency procedure protocols

Most people playing sport or working in sport have experienced or witnessed some kind of injury. A bloody nose from a ball may be easy to deal with on the premises by asking the injured person to pinch the nose until it stops bleeding. On the other hand, a dislocated shoulder may need more specialist help and an ambulance should be called for.

The Health and Safety at Work Act (1974) encompasses the requirement to provide first aid and employers have to justify their decision. In order to do this they should consider:

- the nature of the workplace, and any hazards and risks
- the size of the premises, the organisation and where workers are situated
- previous information on accidents
- annual leave of first aiders and cover required
- the proximity to emergency services.

The regulations also state that an organisation must provide the following.

- First-aid equipment, including first-aid boxes, a list of controls and their locations and supplementary equipment such as a spine board and resuscitation kit.
- A first-aid room. The regulations also specify the size, design and location.
- First aiders and any training programmes that should be provided. This includes a list of those people who have received a certificate from an authorised training body. Certificates are normally valid for three years.

Think it over

Do you think that anyone leading or coaching sports activities should have an appropriate first-aid qualification before starting work?

■ First aid

How badly the person is injured depends on whether first aid can be administered on the premises or a visit to hospital is required.

It is the employer's duty to provide an adequate number of trained and qualified first aiders. Certificates to

▲ What are a first aider's primary duties?

identify who those people are and where they are located should be clearly visible and accessible to all staff.

The duties of someone administering first aid are to:

- preserve life
- prevent the condition worsening
- promote recovery
- provide information to more qualified people, such as the patient's history, symptoms and treatment.

Taking it further

Research what equipment should be available in a first-aid kit.

Remember!

If you are not qualified to handle first-aid incidents, get someone who is. Do not attempt to carry out actions you are not qualified to do.

■ Communications cascade system for notification of incidents

If an incident has occurred, in most cases the first course of action is to ensure that no further incidents can occur. For example, if a footballer is injured during a game, the match should be stopped in order to deal with the incident and to prevent no further accidents.

Once the incident has been dealt with, the next stage is to report it. This can be done verbally at first to a supervisor. This may then have to be more formally documented in written form in an accident or incident book. You should always make a note of the time and location as well as the nature of the incident, who was involved and what action was taken. It is good practice to identify any reliable witnesses who can support your statement.

Depending on the nature of the incident, a RIDDOR form may need to be completed (see page 54).

(see page 54)

Safety procedures and protocols

Safety procedures and protocols are often recorded in the organisation's operating procedures. The procedures should cover many different areas of work and focus on establishing and maintaining a safe environment to work in. This should ensure the safety of everyone. Here are two examples.

- When you make a call to the emergency services, it is useful to have the following information to hand and to speak clearly and slowly. Ask for the emergency service you want. They will want to know the following information:
- the telephone number and address from where you are calling
- where the incident has taken place
- any information on the incident, such as who may be involved, how serious it is and who is on the scene
- other useful information, such as ambulance accessibility point

Remember!

Before starting work for an organisation, familiarise yourself with their safety and operating procedures.

- What to do in the event of a fire should be part of any organisation's normal operating procedures. Staff should have regular training so they can act under pressure to deal with the threat of fire. Here is a standard operating procedure for dealing with fire:
  o activate the nearest alarm
  o dial 999 and ask for the fire brigade
  o inform the line manager and those with responsibility for security
  o inform colleagues, including administration support
  o assist the public by clearly informing them of the emergency procedure and location of the nearest exits
  o extinguish the fire, but only after ensuring the above steps have been taken and if safety permits

- ensure windows and doors are closed before leaving the building and to help contain the fire if it is safe to do so
- check the numbers of customers and employees to account for their safety.

Established to maintain a safe environment

The first step to establishing safety procedures and protocols is to produce a written commitment to providing a safe and inviting sports environment. Copies of the policy should be distributed widely and distributed throughout the organisation.

Information about the procedures should flow from all those who work and enjoy the use of the sports facilities. Preventative measures are essential but they cannot keep all dangerous situations from occurring. Everyone must work hard to create a safe sports environment. However, if problems arise, the response should be immediate.

Governing body guidelines

The governing bodies of sport with the support of **sports coach UK** have provided guidelines to help support sports leaders and coaches. Here is an example from the Football Association.

Code of conduct for coaches

Coaches are key to the establishment of ethics in football. Their concept of ethics and their attitude directly affects the behaviour of players under their supervision. Coaches are, therefore, expected to pay particular care to the moral aspect of their conduct.

Coaches have to be aware that almost all of their everyday decisions and choices of actions, as well as strategic targets, have ethical implications.

It is natural that winning constitutes a basic concern for coaches. This code is not intended to conflict with that. However, the code calls for coaches to disassociate themselves from a 'win-at-all-costs' attitude.

Increased responsibility is requested from coaches involved in coaching young people. The health, safety, welfare and moral education of young people are a first priority, before the achievement or the reputation of the club, school, coach or parent.

Set out below is the FA Coaches Association Code of Conduct (which reflects the standards expressed by the sports coach UK and the National Association of Sports Coaches), which forms the benchmark for all involved in coaching.

1. Coaches must respect the rights, dignity and worth of each and every person and treat each equally within the context of the sport.
2. Coaches must place the well-being and safety of each player above all other considerations, including the development of performance.
3. Coaches must adhere to all guidelines laid down by governing bodies.
4. Coaches must develop an appropriate working relationship with each player based on mutual trust and respect.
5. Coaches must not exert undue influence to obtain personal benefit or reward.
6. Coaches must encourage and guide players to accept responsibility for their own behaviour and performance.
7. Coaches must ensure that the activities they direct or advocate are appropriate for the age, maturity, experience and ability of players.
8. Coaches should, at the outset, clarify with the players (and, where appropriate, parent) exactly what is expected of them and also what they are entitled to expect from their coach.
9. Coaches must cooperate fully with other specialists (e.g. other coaches, officials, sports scientists, doctors, physiotherapists) in the best interests of the player.
10. Coaches must always promote the positive aspects of the sport (e.g. fair play) and never condone violations of the Laws of the Game, behaviour contrary to the spirit of the Laws of the Game or relevant rules and regulations or the use of prohibited substances or techniques.
11. Coaches must consistently display high standards of behaviour and appearance.
12. Coaches must not use or tolerate inappropriate language.

■ Equipment manufacturers' guidelines

Most sports equipment is simple to use and needs few instructions. However, there are many items of sports equipment that may need to be assembled such as a basketball post or football posts. Each of these items will have instructions of assembly and guidelines for use that should have the EU approval mark. You will also find instructions and guidelines of use on smaller items such as balls, which will have inflation pressure suggestions and instructions on how to insert the needle to inflate the ball.

Remember!

It is essential that as a sports leader or coach you should familiarise yourself with all manufacturers' guidelines and instructions before using any sports equipment.

■ When to consult with others and who to consult with

Even the most experienced people working in a sports environment are still learning how to improve the performance, enjoyment and safety of their participants. There are many aspects of sports and people working within the industry who have knowledge in those specialist areas. The key things to know are where you can obtain support and who to consult with. Do not be afraid to ask for guidance and help if you feel you need it.

Remember!

The best people to consult with are often those who have specific experience in the areas you are working in, such as a previous coach or leader.

The best time to consult with other people is when they have time to spend with you and prior to undertaking your activity. For example, if you know you have to undertake a risk assessment for a sports activity and need support, support can be available from the HSE or your line manager. If it is a specific sport you are interested in, the governing body of that sport will be happy to provide the support required.

Activity

Select a sport or activity that you would like to work in. Write a list of organisations and people that should be able to provide you with help you may need. Identify what areas they may be able to support you in and what their contact details are.

■ Local and national requirements

On pages 52–68 we identified the major legal and legislative factors that influence health and safety in sport as well as the role of many national governing bodies. However, it is important to note that local requirements may differ from region to region in relation to the safety of sports participants. It is important to check with your local authority and regional governing body of sport before starting any activity to ensure you are following approved guidelines.

Remember!

There are plenty of places to access useful information, such as from governing bodies of sport. However, keep a look out for other organisations that may be able to help, which sometimes appear on instructions or guidelines on assembly from equipment manufacturers.

Case study: Applying first aid

During a boxercise class at a health and fitness club, the instructor sees a participant appear to faint. The instructor, a trained first aider, assesses the situation. The class is halted to avoid any further accidents and a known member of the class is sent to get assistance and report back that she has done so.

The patient quickly awakes and it is discovered that he ate shortly before exercising and fainted. He is now complaining of a pain in his arm where he must have fallen. The instructor makes sure the patient and his arm are supported and his legs are raised above his head to allow blood to return to the head.

1 **What type of report should be completed if it is later discovered that the arm is broken? List the details that should go in it.**

2 **What further action does the instructor need to take?**

Assessment practice

The rugby club is undertaking regular risk assessments and is maintaining key safety procedures. It is essential that any new personnel are up to speed with their safety responsibilities as well as providing further support to all staff. You have been asked by the club to put together a document that identifies key safety procedures, including staff development and how incidents are to be communicated. You realise how important first-aid training is and want to encourage all staff to attend first-aid training courses.

Provide examples of procedures that should be used by the rugby club staff. This should include training and development, emergency procedures and communicating incidents. **P4 M3 D2**

Grading tips

Grading Tip P4

You should describe the procedures used to promote a healthy and safe environment. These procedures could be provided using an example from another organisation and must be clearly headed. You may also find it useful to gather information through observing procedures such as at a local leisure centre that is having a practice fire drill.

Grading Tip M3

You need to explain three procedures that will help promote a healthy and safe environment such as using manufacturers' guidelines when using equipment.

Grading Tip D2

For this grade your procedures are written using more analysis and here you must identify why your procedures will be successful in relation to achieving your stated aims.

Plan

Roles and responsibilities

When working with sports participants as a coach or leader you may have to take on several roles such as educator, trainer, first aider, equipment manager and role model. You must be aware of your health and safety responsibilities.

All these roles have responsibility for the environment and facilities where any sporting sessions take place. Any potential hazards and safety aspects like first aid, fire exits and fire drills should be identified and the participants made aware of what action should be taken to ensure a safe environment.

Planning for a sports activity should take place a long time before the session starts, including booking the facilities, planning training schedules and knowing details of your participants.

Remember!

To become a qualified coach in your chosen sport you will need to take the relevant coaching qualifications offered by the governing body of your sport. You can apply to become an assistant coach as young as 16 in some sports, with qualifications available for you to progress to a full coach.

■ Leader

A sports leader helps participants to develop vital skills for life and to make real and lasting differences to the groups they work with. A good sports leader is able to teach people, organise and plan, motivate others, communicate effectively and work as a team. The Community Sports Leader Award aims to produce responsible, motivated and confident people who can lead safe, purposeful and enjoyable sporting and recreational activities.

◄ Why should coaches be aware of current health and safety regulations?

Coaches

Here are some basic tips on becoming a successful coach.

- Know yourself: why do you want to coach and what do you want to achieve?
- Understand your sport: the better your understanding of the techniques and skills of the sport, the better equipped you are to pass these on.
- Be positive: patience and praise work a lot better than criticism and shouting.
- Variety is the key: avoid games where children have to sit out and don't make all your sessions competitive.
- Teach skills and demonstrate: demonstrating a skill works much better than talking about it. If you cannot do it, find someone who can.
- Involve everyone: always make sure there is enough equipment or kit for all. Create small groups of children rather than one big group.
- Communicate well: actions speak louder than words. Body language is important. Smiles and positive gestures work wonders.
- Work with mind and body: a grasp of how the body responds to exercise and training and an ability to adopt safe practices and prevent injury are important. So too is confidence building, goal setting, emotional control, concentration skills – coaches work on the mindset as well as the body.
- Sense and sensitivity: some children take longer than others to learn so adopt your style accordingly. It helps to be consistent, set achievable goals and give frequent feedback.
- Take it from the top: lead by example and gain trust and respect. Children's coaches are role models and this carries responsibility. How you behave and dress, and your attitude, all set an example. If you adhere to consistent high standards, this will rub off.

First aid

First aid is the care given to a casualty before professional help arrives. The aims of a first aider are to:

- preserve life
- prevent the condition worsening
- promote recovery
- provide information to more qualified people, such as the patient's history, symptoms and treatment.

Planning for first aid takes place a long time before the commencement of any activities. It is standard practice to have a qualified first aider on hand when leading or coaching any sports activities.

Equipment

Nearly all sports have recommended dress codes, some involving safety equipment to prevent illness and injury. Recommendations can be found through texts, online resources, sports organisations and professionals.

- Proper dress may range from the usual sturdy, loose-fitting clothing made of breathable fabric to heat-preserving wetsuits or running shoes with a list of essential features. This depends on the type of sport and the environmental conditions in which it is played.
- Protective equipment for contact sports – or those with a high risk of falling – is also specific to the activity. It may include guards or pads for specific body areas and may need to be professionally fitted. It should be worn at all times during participation, including practice and matches.

Type

The type of equipment to be used should also be considered. The following questions should be asked:

- What is the age of the equipment?
- What is its quality and condition?
- Is the equipment being maintained correctly, including regular services and inspections?
- How suitable is it for use by the age group involved?

All equipment should, of course, meet the requirements of the relevant legislation and relevant British standards.

Use

Equipment should be appropriate for what it is to be used for. This relates to the guidelines of sports equipment and recommendations such as size of footballs and goals in relation to the age group.

Think it over

Why is it important to wear appropriate clothing and to use the right equipment for specific sports?

Suitability of site

The nature of the activity is possibly the most important matter to consider. Some things are simply more inherently dangerous than others and the inherent risks need to be fully assessed before any further contributing factors are taken into account.

- There are a number of important considerations to do with suitability. Whether the sports area was actually designed for the activity being undertaken in the circumstances in which it is being undertaken will have a substantial influence on the risk of accident or injury.
- Was the area designed or adapted for the type of activity being undertaken?
- How many participants was it designed for? Some spaces, particularly laboratories and workshops, were designed for certain group sizes. Putting larger groups into these spaces can create overcrowding, which could affect safety standards.
- Are the facilities provided in the space adequate for the activity?
- Is there adequate space for people to enter, move around and leave safely?
- Are there any potential problems caused by layout, lines of sight, acoustics and noise?
- Have fire precautions been drawn up that specifically reflect the activities undertaken and the numbers involved?
- Does the area make necessary provision for people with disabilities?

If you feel the setting may not be safe, raise the issue with the appropriate senior member of staff and get advice from the person in charge.

Under section 7 of the Health and Safety at Work Act (1974), employees are required to take reasonable care for the health and safety of themselves and others who may be affected by their acts or omissions at work. This means that sports leaders can legitimately refuse to participate in activities that risk their own health and safety and/or that of their class. Advice should be sought from the sport's governing body.

Suitability of participants to activity

Most sports coaches in charge of practical sessions are trained specialists and accident levels are low in such classes. Next there are the participants themselves:

- How familiar is the leader with the class?
- How familiar are the participants with the activity?
- Have they been given training on the use of the equipment in question and in use of safety precautions?
- How old are they?
- How many of them have special educational needs? What are those needs and are they likely to cause a risk to themselves and/or others?

▲ It is important to ensure the correct equipment is used for each participant

- Are any of them likely to be disruptive and thereby cause a risk to themselves and/or others?
- How many are there of them? The number of participants affects the teacher's ability to supervise effectively. It may also be relevant in terms of the suitability of the teaching area and possible overcrowding.

Remember!

A coach is a role model who can socially, morally, emotionally and technically influence the people he or she is coaching, especially the young. The role of a coach is changing constantly to meet the needs of the team or individuals. Being able to communicate, analyse, solve problems and evaluate performance are just some of the key skills required for a successful coach. The more knowledge a coach has, the better the decisions he or she will be able to make when using their skills.

Insurance

It is essential that all coaches have insurance. If you are a member of the national governing body you may well have insurance cover as part of this membership. However, it is strongly recommended that you check this to cover the following areas.

- Public liability: bodily injury or damage to third persons or property, e.g. to spectators or participants.
- Products: legal liability arising out of products supplied, e.g. food and drink supplied at an event or equipment you have sold.
- Professional indemnity: errors or omissions in advice given, e.g. inappropriate guidance on safety precautions.
- Officers and officials: protects against their own personal liability by reason of a wrongful act committed in their capacity as officers of the association, e.g. failure to provide appropriate insurance to affiliated players and coaches.

- Libel and slander: for example, your association may issue a newsletter that contains defamatory material or it may be accused of discrimination.

Review

Effectiveness of risk management

Sports organisers must consider action that is preventative and is documented in the risk assessment. However, the risk assessment should be reviewed to find out how effective it has been. For example, the following preventative action needs to be reviewed to ensure it has resulted in safe practice.

- Avoid the risks altogether, e.g. water leaking in a sports hall and cancelling any sports activity.
- Evaluate risks that cannot be avoided.
- Combat risks at source, e.g. is it possible for experienced workmen to repair the leaking roof?
- Adapt the work to an individual, e.g. layout of workplace, choice of work equipment and methods of working.
- Take advantage of technological and technical progress, which often offers opportunities for improving working methods and make them far safer.
- Replace work equipment with less dangerous equipment or change methods of working, e.g. perhaps use one-piece weights in a gym rather than those that need weights to be added.
- Ensure employers are aware of what they need to do and how they need to do it.
- Provide adequate training, instruction, information and appropriate supervision and pay particular attention to young and pregnant workers.
- Provide suitable and appropriate personal protective equipment as a last resort where the exposure to the risks cannot otherwise be controlled.

Injuries, near misses and dangerous occurrences

It is important to have health and safety on your mind on an ongoing basis. You must allow time for evaluating the effectiveness of the risk management strategies you have put in place. Collecting data on the type, frequency and nature of any injuries will help you to evaluate if your activities are appropriate and safe. This data can be found in accident books and RIDDOR documentation (see page 54), as well as from your own records on individual participants and any significant injuries or accidents they have had. It is important to note any near misses that have occurred and the situation that led to the near miss. Subsequent action to prevent further near misses and dangerous occurrences is a sign of a good sports organiser.

Key term

Accident book A book where all accidents and incidents are recorded so that they can be investigated.

Suitability of group for activity and effectiveness of briefings

Any good sports leader or coach reviews the effectiveness of each session to find out if the session's goals were achieved and whether the activity was suitable for the participants.

Most sessions should start with a briefing to the participants. This should outline the key safety factors including what to do in case of an emergency and a brief outline of what the session will entail, as well as any discipline and behavioural rules.

The review as to whether the participants have understood what has been said should take place during the session and not at the end. At the end of the session an overall review of suitability to the activity should take place.

Suitability of equipment

Before the session starts it is important to select the appropriate equipment for the participants you are working with, such as the correct size basketball and height of ring for the given age group. Guidelines on this would be available from the English Basketball Association. Once again, the review should take place during the activity through observation and asking participants to ensure they are using the equipment safely.

Support of other agencies

You may have sought support from agencies such as governing bodies, local authorities or line managers and it is a useful exercise to see if that advice and support was effective.

Remember!

If you have received support from someone who was helpful, remember to contact them and tell them what the outcome was.

Case study: Keeping your players healthy

The Danny Leisure Centre hockey team, which plays in the local league, has undergone pre-season training and is now preparing for its first competitive league game of the season. There are two more coaching sessions before the first game and the focus is on improving the team's overall strategies and tactics, with special emphasis on short corners. However, you aware that several players are missing through injury.

1 Why is it important to keep clear records of coaching activities and injuries?

2 What information should the coach give to the players in relation to health and safety?

Assessment practice

Pre-season training is about to commence at the rugby club for all the teams. As the assistant coach, you meet with the head coach to plan the first few training sessions. You identify your aims for pre-season including improving fitness, technical individual skills, team skills and plays as well as identifying each player's most suitable position. You are keen to ensure this is done as safely as possible.

1 Identify what information you require before you commence any activities. Plan a sports activity that will help achieve your aims. This should identify the facilities and equipment you require and it should have a warm-up, a main session and a cool-down. **P5 M4**

2 You should review the plan and identify what the strengths and weaknesses are, saying how these could be improved. **D3**

Grading tips

Grading Tip P5

Your plan should indicate the methods used to ensure the group's safety. You could use a plan from a session that you are taking or for a group you are observing. The plan should identify the equipment and facilities that are needed. It should ensure that the activities are safe, challenging and have variety. You should also look to include information on insurance requirements and first aid.

Grading Tip M4

You should explain why you have chosen the selected equipment and activities. You should explain the purpose of your warm-up and cool-down and why the main activities are appropriate.

Grading Tip D3

You need to analyse your plan to identify the strengths of the plan and where you could make improvements. You should clearly identify any suggestions you have for improvements.

Knowledge check

1 Describe three key legislative factors for sports organisers that are required of them from the Health and Safety at Work Act (1974). Provide practical examples of how they should be implemented.

2 What are the key differences between civil law and statutory law? Provide two examples of each.

3 Select a regulatory body and describe their main roles and responsibilities in relation to managing sports activities.

4 When should a risk assessment be carried out? When should action be taken after you have completed the assessment?

5 Identify five procedures of good practice in relation to maintaining the safety of participants and colleagues in a sports environment.

6 What are the advantages of providing safety equipment, training and supervision for participants?

7 Provide five examples of safe practice in sports provided by a selected governing body of sport.

8 Who are the key people in an organisation who can provide support in relation to health and safety in sport?

9 What are the key factors when identifying a suitable site for sports activities?

10 What are the key areas to consider when reviewing the effectiveness of your risk management?

11 Where might you find information to help you undertake your review?

Preparation for assessment

You have recently acquired a job with your local authority as a youth sports development officer. This post has been newly created with the help of new funding. Your remit is pretty broad but essentially it is working with partners such as leisure centres, youth clubs, and primary and secondary schools to help set up sports clubs for young children.

You have been asked to create a development plan that clearly identifies your goals and how they are to be achieved. One of the most important aspects of the document is the identification of the health and safety needs of the programme.

To help you produce this information, you have decided to produce a document that all the partners and people working on the project can use as a reference. Here are the headings that you will use in order to complete the document.

1 *Legislative factors*

   a Identify four key legislative factors that influence health and safety in sport and describe the legal factors and regulatory bodies. **P1 P2**

Grading tips

Grading Tip P1

Describe the legislation required and try to summarise why the legislation is so important.

Grading Tip P2

When defining the legislation, you need to make it clear what behaviour and actions people working in a sporting environment should take. Provide examples of how the regulatory terms will apply.

   b Compare and contrast the influences of legislation, legal factors, regulatory bodies on health and safety in sport. **M1**

2 *Risk assessment*

   a Show examples of two risk assessments for two different activities and review the risk assessment controls as well as evaluating their effectiveness. **P3 M2 D1**

Grading tips

Grading Tip M1

You should demonstrate good knowledge of the differences between statute and case law this can be done through providing examples of each and how they relate to a sports leader.

Grading Tip P3

When you complete your two risk assessments for the sports activities, you must include the controls you are going to use to minimise and protect your participants from harm.

Grading Tip M2

All your risk assessments must clearly identify any controls you have for reducing or eliminating risks.

Grading Tip D1

Your risk assessments should have a review ensuring you can demonstrate how you have implemented controls that manage any identified hazards.

3   *Promoting and maintaining a healthy and safe environment*

a   Describe three examples of good practice of procedures that should be used to maintain a healthy and safe environment. Try to explain these procedures.   **P4 M3 D2**

4   *A safety plan*

a   Produce a plan as an example on how to undertake a safe delivery of a sports activity. Explain the plan and identify the strengths and areas for improvement.   **P5 M4 D3**

Grading tips

Grading Tip   P4

You must describe the procedures used to promote and maintain a healthy and safe sporting environment. You could research what other organisations' policies and practices are.

Grading Tip   M3

You should explain three procedures used to promote health and safety in a sports environment. Again, these should be provided with examples related to a coach or sports leader.

Grading Tip   D2

You have to analyse three procedures in relation to any aims you have set. These procedures, such as first aid and staff training, must identify why they are required for the coach or sports leader.

Grading tips

Grading Tip   P5

Think carefully about your plan, which can be taken from one of your own activities or when you observe somebody else's activity session.

Grading Tip   M4

Your plan should include a review, which should be undertaken in relation to the aims and goals of the session.

Grading Tip   D3

You must identify the strengths and weaknesses of your planned sports activity session. This should have any suggestions you may have for improving the session in relation to health and safety.

To achieve a pass grade the evidence must show that the learner is able to:	To achieve a merit grade the evidence must show that, in addition to the pass criteria, the learner is able to:	To achieve a distinction grade the evidence must show that, in addition to the pass and merit criteria, the learner is able to:
P1 Describe four legislative factors that influence health and safety in sport **Assessment practice Page 67**	**M1** Compare and contrast the influences of legislation, legal factors and regulatory bodies on health and safety in sport **Assessment practice Page 67**	
P2 Describe the legal factors and regulatory bodies that influence health and safety in sport **Assessment practice Page 67**		
P3 Carry out risk assessments for two different sports activities, with support **Assessment practice Page 73**	**M2** Carry out risk assessments for two different sports activities **Assessment practice Page 73**	**D1** Review the risk assessment controls and evaluate their effectiveness **Assessment practice Page 73**
P4 Describe three procedures used to promote and maintain a healthy and safe sporting environment **Assessment practice Page 80**	**M3** Explain three procedures used to promote and maintain a healthy and safe sporting environment **Assessment practice Page 80**	**D2** Analyse three procedures used to promote and maintain a healthy and safe sporting environment **Assessment practice Page 80**
P5 Produce a plan for the safe delivery of a selected sports activity and review the plan **Assessment practice Page 86**	**M4** Explain the plan for the safe delivery of a selected sports activity and review the plan **Assessment practice Page 86**	**D3** Identify strengths and areas for improvement in the plan, suggesting how it could be improved **Assessment practice Page 86**

Training and fitness for sport

Introduction

Regardless of your ability in sport, it is vital that you have a certain level of fitness to perform at your best. Beginners need fitness to carry out basic activities such as running for the ball in football. In comparison, an elite-level athlete needs to be at peak fitness to win major competitions such as the Olympics. It is the role of the fitness trainer or personal instructor to improve or maintain an athlete's fitness level.

The first two sections in this unit explore the different components of fitness, such as strength, and their importance for a variety of sporting activities. Discussion will be focused on activities for all areas of sport including athletics, dance, gymnastics and combat sports such as boxing. To support your knowledge of the components of fitness, we will be looking at the different methods of training such as stretching to improve flexibility.

The last two sections are based around planning, monitoring and evaluating a training programme as you will need to go through this with a selected athlete for your assessment. We will use the term 'athlete' throughout this unit, but remember that this term can mean an athlete at elite level or a beginner to a sport who is trying it out for the first time.

After completing this unit you should be able to achieve the following outcomes:

- Understand the fitness requirements of different sporting activities.
- Understand different methods of physical fitness training.
- Be able to plan a fitness training programme.
- Be able to monitor and evaluate a fitness training programme.

Think it over

Look at the photo on these pages. What reasons can you think of to explain why these women are taking part in this fitness training session?

You should have thought of several possible reasons, but some of them are not related to fitness. The women may be training for the following reasons:

- to support friends who are in the same class
- to have some time to themselves, away from family commitments
- to enjoy socialising with other women in the class.

Remember that people start training for a variety of reasons. It is hoped that this training will have physical, psychological and social benefits.

In this section you will consider the different components of fitness such as flexibility or aerobic endurance. Within each component of fitness, the importance of having the component for sporting performance is explained. We will also be looking at the fitness required for different sporting activities.

There is a wide range of sports covered including athletics, swimming and gymnastics. Although the sport you play may not be included, if you have a good understanding of the components of fitness you can apply this knowledge to your chosen sport.

Think it over

Think about definitions of the term 'fitness' and then discuss your definitions in small groups.

Components of fitness

Fitness is a complex term as it contains a number of different elements. It can be classified as follows.

- Total fitness: this relates to an optimal quality of life and includes social, spiritual and physical well-being.
- Physical fitness: this is a level of fitness based on fitness test scores, with good scores meaning the individual has a small chance of developing health problems (this is also known as health-related fitness).
- Motor fitness: this is a level of fitness that allows the individual to perform an activity, task or sport.

◄ As with all sports, a footballer needs a blend of different components of fitness to maximise performance

Physical fitness involves seven components of fitness: aerobic endurance, muscular endurance, flexibility, speed, strength, power and body composition.

Key terms

Aerobic endurance The ability of the cardiovascular system to supply the exercising muscles with oxygen to maintain the aerobic exercise for a long period of time, for example over two hours during a marathon.

Muscular endurance The ability to maintain a high level of muscular contractions, which is vital for a number of sporting activities. Muscular endurance is closely related to the ability of the athlete to perform in his or her chosen sport. For example, the 400m sprinter produces a high level of force in the leg muscles repeatedly over a number of minutes.

Flexibility The ability of a specific joint, for example the knee, to move through a full range of movement. As with muscular endurance, an athlete can have different flexibility levels in different joints.

Speed The ability to cover a specific distance within the shortest possible time.

Strength The ability of a specific muscle or muscle group to exert a force in a single maximal contraction to overcome some form of resistance.

Power The ability to generate and use muscular strength quickly over a short period of time.

Body composition The percentage of fat-free mass (i.e. muscle) compared to fat within the body.

Activity

1 An athlete starting a training or exercise programme might have many reasons or long-term goals. In small groups, devise a list of possible reasons why an athlete might start a programme. You may wish to draw on your own experience to start your list.

2 When you have prepared your list, with the aid of your tutor produce a whole-group spider diagram on the whiteboard. You should discover that there are many reasons for starting a training programme.

■ Aerobic endurance

Aerobic endurance also known as stamina can help with daily tasks such as walking to work or doing the gardening and housework. A good level of aerobic endurance allows the athlete to take part in sport, leisure and recreational activities. There are a number of events that rely almost exclusively on aerobic endurance, such as marathon running, long-distance swimming and cycling. Aerobic endurance is the ability of the cardiovascular system (the heart and lungs) to supply the exercising muscles with oxygen to maintain the exercise.

Activity

In pairs, produce a list of six other sports that require a high level of aerobic endurance.

The benefits of having good aerobic endurance for the athlete through training and exercise are:

- decreased body fat
- increased oxygen to the muscles
- decreased stress levels
- increased removal of waste products such as lactic acid.

Aerobic endurance forms the basis of fitness for most sports. If an athlete has a reduced aerobic endurance, possibly due to a long-term injury, this leads to a decrease in other fitness components such as muscular endurance. Therefore, poor aerobic endurance inevitably leads to poor sporting performance.

Think it over

Elite-level cross-country skiers have the largest aerobic endurance capacity of all athletes. Why do you think this is the case?

Muscular endurance

Muscular endurance is needed where a specific muscle or muscle group makes repeated contractions over a significant period of time (possibly over a number of minutes). Examples include:

- a boxer making a repeated jab
- continuous press-ups or abdominal curls
- the 400m sprint in athletics.

Taking it further

For each example given above, carry out some research into the key muscle groups required for these repeated contractions.

Flexibility

Flexibility is important for all sports and for health. It relates to the amount of movement possible around a joint or a number of joints. Poor flexibility may lead to:

- a decrease in the range of possible movement
- an increased chance of injury and stiffness
- a decrease in sporting performance.

However, possible improvements in flexibility are limited by an athlete's:

- body composition: e.g. the percentage of body fat
- genetics: characteristics inherited from parents
- age: flexibility levels generally decrease with age
- gender: females tend to be more flexible than males
- muscle and tendon elasticity: the capacity to stretch before injury occurs.

It is important that any joint does not become too flexible because an excessive range of movement can lead to injury. For example, a dislocated shoulder is likely to recur in rugby because of an excessive range of movement.

Speed

Speed is a central component of physical fitness. Team-based sports and certain athletic sports such as the long jump require a high degree of speed. Speed is the ability to move a short distance in the quickest possible time. For more information on speed, see page 109.

Strength

There is a clear distinction between muscular strength and muscular endurance. Strength is the ability of a specific muscle or muscle group to exert a force in a single maximal contraction. For example, if weightlifter A lifts 80 kg and weightlifter B lifts 100 kg, weightlifter B is said to have greater strength than weightlifter A (although perhaps only in the muscle groups used in this particular lift). Strength is often thought of as being related to athletes such as weightlifters or boxers, but it is required in most sports.

Activity

In pairs, try to explain in relation to the following sporting examples why and where the athlete needs to display strength:

- a gymnast performing a vault
- a defender in footballer trying to head the ball to safety
- a judo player executing a throw.

Power

Athletes who are stronger tend to be able to produce a greater amount of power during the action, for example during the tennis serve a more powerful serve will be a lot harder to return. This is because power is closely related to muscular strength in combination with speed of movement. Power is the ability to generate and use muscular strength quickly.

Body composition

Body composition is the amount (normally expressed as a percentage) of body fat and lean body tissue the athlete possesses. Lean body tissue is water, blood, skin, muscle and bone. From a health point of view, it is important to have low levels of body fat. Increased levels of fat can usually happen through injury or during the off-season period and can lead to a decrease in performance. You can see this when footballers return to pre-season training in July and are carrying extra weight, which has

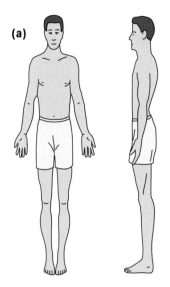 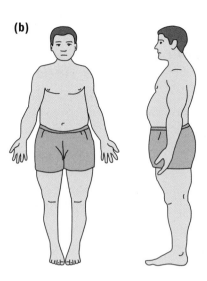 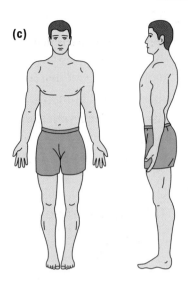

▲ The three types of body frame: (a) ectomorph, (b) endomorph and (c) mesomorph

to be lost. The increase in body fat can reduce the fitness of the player by making them slower.

Skill-related fitness

The following skill-related components of fitness are required by the athlete to maximise performance: speed, agility, balance, coordination, power and reaction time.

Key terms

Agility The ability to change direction quickly at speed.

Balance This is when the athlete remains steady while either moving dynamically (sprinting for the ball) or in a stationary position such as a handstand.

Coordination The skilful and balanced movement of different body parts at the same time.

Power The ability to generate and use muscular strength quickly over a short period of time.

Reaction time The ability to react (movement) to a given stimulus (e.g. a starting pistol) as quickly as possible.

■ Speed

Team-based sports and certain athletic sports require a high degree of speed. Speed is the ability to move a short distance in the quickest possible time.

A high level of speed can have a significant influence on the result in team-based sports, sprinting and jumping activities. It is also important for certain positions in team-based sports such as a winger in rugby. Speed endurance is the ability of the athlete to make repeated sprints over a long period of time. A midfield player in football often has to make 10–15m sprints continuously throughout the game.

■ Agility

Agility means the ability of an athlete to change direction many times quickly and accurately during sporting performance. For example, a rugby winger sprinting for the try line may have to dodge a number of defending players by side-stepping them while moving quickly.

■ Balance

Balance is often overlooked when considering the requirements of an activity. It means being able to maintain stability or equilibrium while performing. There are two forms of balance:

- static balance, where the athlete is stationary, e.g. in a handstand in gymnastics
- dynamic balance, where the athlete is moving, e.g. a footballer sprinting with the ball.

Balance is also important in activities that require precise movements with a high degree of accuracy, such as archery or snooker. A lack of balance often has a dramatic result on sporting performance.

Activity

1. In small groups, draw up a list of ten sporting activities that need good balance.
2. Decide which of these activities require static balance and which require dynamic balance.

■ Coordination

Most sporting movements require the athlete to use a number of joints and muscles in a specific order or sequence. Consider the tennis serve, which involves movement of the ankles, knees, hips, upper body, shoulder, elbows and wrist. These complex movements require a high degree of coordination. Good coordination means the tennis player moves the correct body parts at the correct time, while transferring force from the ankles through the body to the wrist joint.

■ Power

Power is closely related to muscular strength in combination with speed of movement. It is the ability to generate and use muscular strength quickly. Athletes who are stronger tend to be able to produce a greater amount of power during the action. Generally, an athlete interested in health-related fitness does not train for power as it is specific and is needed only by an elite athlete. Power is important for many track and field athletes in the following:

- sprinting: the legs and arms need power to sprint as fast as possible
- jumping (e.g. triple jump): the legs need power to gain a greater distance and/or height

- throwing (e.g. shot put): strength is needed in the upper body and arms to propel the shot.

■ Reaction time

Reaction time is the time between the start of the movement and the stimulus, such as a starting pistol in sprint events. After the stimulus, the sprinter needs to react as quickly as possible to leave the starting blocks. Reaction time is vital for a number of sports. For example:

- in tennis, a player needs to react to a shot that has changed direction and speed because the ball has clipped the top of the net
- in football, the goalkeeper needs to react quickly to clear a shot
- when a basketball has hit the rim of the basket, the players need to react quickly to regain possession of the ball.

Taking it further

It is important that you know which fitness test is used to assess which fitness component. Research a variety of tests and complete a table like the one below by inserting the name of a suitable test for each fitness component.

Component of fitness	Name of test
Aerobic endurance	
Muscular endurance	
Flexibility	
Strength	
Body composition	
Speed	
Agility	
Balance	
Coordination	
Power	
Reaction time	

Sporting activities

Different sports require the development and training of different components of fitness. A 100m sprinter requires a high level of strength and speed, whereas a marathon runner requires excellent aerobic endurance. It is important to understand the fitness requirements for a variety of sports because:

- the coach or trainer needs to be able to train the correct components of fitness
- when working with athletes as a fitness trainer, it is important to show that you understand the sport they play by being aware of the fitness requirements
- fitness tests should be matched with the component of fitness used in the sport or the position played; for example, a 2.5 km run can be used to test for aerobic endurance.

Remember!

A number of the sports discussed in this unit require a high degree of tactical awareness and skilled execution, although we are concentrating on fitness components.

▼ **The correct technique for putting the shot needs coordination and flexibility**

Athletics covers both track and field events:

- track events include the 100m sprint, the 800m and the 5,000m races
- field events include the shot put, javelin and the long jump.

In track events, the aim is to run as fast as possible over a short, specified distance, reaching the finishing line before your opponents. The components of fitness required for sprinting differ greatly from those for longer-distance races such as 10,000m. Sprinting requires good:

- reaction time: the sprinter must leave the block as quickly as possible after the pistol has sounded
- muscle strength: this is needed especially at the start of the sprint to get the body moving from a stationary position in the blocks
- coordination: through good coordination, the athlete can use the correct technique for sprinting and not waste energy and power
- speed: good leg and arm speed is required to move the body over the distance as quickly as possible
- power: this is required in the legs and arms
- body composition: a high percentage of fast-twitch muscle fibres (see Unit 1: pages 18–19) is needed in the sprinter's legs. Fast-twitch fibres can exert a great force over a short period of time, which is vital for producing high levels of power in the legs
- flexibility: this is vital because of the range of movement shown by the athlete.

As you would expect, field events require a different blend of fitness components. For the shot put, the athlete has to push, rather than throw, the shot as far as possible. It requires good:

- body composition: shot putters normally have large amounts of lean muscle and fat tissue to increase the power generated
- strength: this is required in the legs to generate the force needed to propel the shot

- coordination: the correct technique involves the use of the legs, waist, arms and hands, which must be coordinated correctly (see diagram)
- power: this is needed to apply to the shot to gain a good distance
- balance: dynamic balance is required for the athlete to remain within the designated area while putting the shot

Theory into practice

In small groups, produce an information booklet on the various field events in athletics, which a trainer could use in a training session. The booklet should be six pages long, with one page for each of the following field events:

- triple jump
- pole vault
- hammer throw
- javelin
- discus
- long jump.

Details of the following should be included for each event:

- the components of fitness required
- the importance of the components required
- a diagram to show the technique.

Swimming

In competitive swimming there are a number of events over distances from 50m to 1,500m. Four swimming styles are used: freestyle, backstroke, butterfly and breaststroke.

The components of fitness and muscle groups required differ significantly for each style because of the different techniques and distances covered. For example, for the 50m sprint freestyle event, the following are required:

- reaction time: the swimmer must react quickly to the start of the event, normally a bleep or pistol
- strength: a large amount of force is required in the leg muscles to push off the block and generate horizontal speed
- coordination: all muscle groups need to work together in the correct order
- muscular endurance: the swimmer must make continuous and repeated arm and leg movements over a significant period of time
- power: this is generated through the arms and legs to propel the swimmer through the water.

As the distance swum increases, there is a greater reliance on aerobic endurance.

Gymnastics

Gymnastics has a number of disciplines such as the rings, the beam and the floor. It is unique in sport because it requires a combination of most health- and skill-related components of fitness.

Case study: Training different components of fitness

Holly, 16, has recently been promoted to the county swimming squad because of her excellent performances in the 100m freestyle event. She has a new swimming coach, who has started to train different components of fitness. This has left Holly confused, and she would like some clarification on the following questions.

1 Is the coach right in trying to reduce Holly's body fat?

2 The coach says he is trying to improve Holly's power through training strength. Is this correct?

3 The coach says Holly should not train reaction time. Is this correct?

Activity

In small groups, investigate the fitness components for gymnastics. Draw a mind map showing the links between the fitness components and the different disciplines. You may need to research the different disciplines to further your understanding before you produce the mind map. Disciplines include beam, floor, vault, rings and bars.

Dance

Dance includes a number of disciplines and styles, such as salsa, tap, ballet, ballroom and line. Although they differ in their routines, moves and tempo, there are some common features in the fitness requirements of these different dance types:

- flexibility: this is vital for all forms of dance because the dancer has to move the body quickly into many different positions
- strength: dancing often involves lifting or carrying a partner, e.g. in ballet
- balance: the dancer sometimes has to hold a position for a number of seconds (static balance); dynamic balance is required while making complex moves
- coordination: in competition, judges will be looking for good coordination in executing a move correctly and with style
- aerobic endurance: dance routines are physically demanding and can often last up to an hour, therefore requiring aerobic endurance.

Combat sports

Combat sports normally involve a contest between two athletes. They include sports such as boxing, Olympic wrestling, sumo and some martial arts like karate. Professional boxing is normally contested over 12 three-minute rounds. Boxing requires the following components of fitness:

- strength: this is to produce power in a punch with the aim of delivering a knock-out blow; it needs to be sustained for 36 minutes, and so it is strength endurance (the ability to produce power over a period of time)
- balance: poor balance increases the chances of being knocked down, but good balance is required to deliver a solid punch to the opponent
- muscular endurance: a boxer will throw up to 500 punches in a fight that lasts the full 36 minutes, so poor muscular endurance in the later stages of the fight is likely to lead to defeat if the boxer is unable to punch the opponent consistently
- speed: a good level of hand speed is required; good boxers are said to have quick hands, which ensures that their shots reach the target before the opponent can react
- aerobic endurance: the boxer is constantly moving around the ring, so aerobic endurance is important and is often trained through road running
- flexibility: boxers need good flexibility around the waist and hips to dodge a punch and to launch their own punches.

Invasion games

Invasion games include football, netball, basketball, hockey and polo. The aim of the game is to score with the ball in the opponent's field of play, which has a net, basket, hoop or other designated target.

Rugby has two codes: rugby league and rugby union. League has 13 players while union has 15. Because of their different rules, the two games differ in style. Rugby league is more flowing and rugby union less so with its mauls and line-outs.

As with other invasion games, each positional role has different physical demands. A winger requires a great deal of speed, whereas a forward requires strength. The basic components of fitness for a rugby player are:

- upper and lower body strength: due to the contact nature of the sport, this is required in situations such as the scrum
- speed: when breaking with the ball and sprinting for the try line, it is important for players to have a good degree of speed
- power: both codes require jumping for the ball, so power in the legs is important

- agility: it is vital for a player running with the ball to avoid being tackled by the opposition, which means changing direction quickly
- balance: this is needed in order to change direction at speed
- aerobic endurance and muscular endurance: a game lasts 80 minutes and players need to keep running throughout and make repeated sprints.

When considering which components of fitness are required, you should consider the sport or activity and the position played.

Net/wall games

Most net or wall games involve the use of a racquet and a divided court area, as in tennis or badminton, or a shared wall, as in squash. Games include badminton, tennis, table tennis, volleyball and squash. All these games have the aim of getting the ball or shuttlecock into the opponent's area as often as possible without return.

Squash is one of the most physically demanding games, and requires these components of fitness:

- agility: the player must make rapid changes of direction constantly throughout the game to hit the ball
- strength: this is required in the arm muscles to hold and use the racquet over a long period of time
- acceleration: when moving around the court, speed is needed so the player can reach the ball before it hits the floor for the second time

- muscular endurance: required in both the upper and lower body, as the player has to make high-intensity intermittent sprints throughout the game
- flexibility: sometimes, the ball must be played from the corner of the court, which requires a high level of flexibility
- balance: this is required when playing the shots and sprinting for the ball
- aerobic endurance: as some squash games can be more than an hour long, a good level of aerobic endurance is required.

Striking and/or fielding games

The basic principle behind striking and fielding games is that one team is attempting to score what are normally termed runs, while the other is trying to get them out and stop them scoring. Examples of striking and/or fielding games are baseball, rounders and cricket.

Cricket contains three main disciplines: fielding, batting and bowling. They each require a mix of different fitness components. Batting involves the player striking the ball with the aim of scoring runs and not getting out.

As with all sports, the athlete needs good mental discipline to succeed at top level. The mental attributes necessary for successful batting include concentration, focus, decision-making skills and alertness.

Batters are expected to run between the wickets to register a run, so they require:

- balance: poor balance when playing a shot leads to a loss in power that might cause the batter to be out

Case study: Andrew 'Freddie' Flintoff

Some players are classed as all-rounders: they are good at batting, bowling and fielding. An all-rounder would be expected to bat, bowl and field and sometimes keep wicket. Andrew 'Freddie' Flintoff is an all-rounder who plays for England. Flintoff consistently produces world-class bowling, batting and fielding performances.

1 **What components of fitness are required for bowling?**

2 **What components of fitness are required for fielding?**

3 **What influences do you think the demands of being an all-rounder have on Flintoff's training regime?**

- speed: when running between the wickets, it is important to have good speed to reduce the chance of being run out
- strength: as the cricket bat can be heavy, the batter requires good strength in the arms, which also adds power to the shot
- aerobic endurance: some innings can last for six hours or more, so a good level of aerobic endurance is required
- coordination: playing a shot in cricket requires a complex movement including most body parts; when hitting the ball it is important to have good hand-eye coordination.

Target games

Although the basic principle behind target games is the same – to hit or reach a target – target games can be different in nature. They include golf, bowls, curling and ten-pin bowling.

Golf is sometimes regarded as a game requiring little fitness, but this is not true. The components of fitness for golf are:

- balance: good balance is central to any shot in golf
- flexibility: good flexibility is needed in the ankle, knee, hip, shoulder and wrist joint as these form the basis of the golf shot
- coordination: this is required to ensure the shot is executed in a skilful manner
- strength: this is required in the upper body to propel the golf ball further
- aerobic endurance: although golf requires a number of short explosive movements during the driving shots, there is a need for a good level of aerobic endurance because it involves walking for 6.5–8 km depending on the course.

Remember!

Each sport requires a different blend of health-related and skill-related components of fitness.

Outdoor activities

There is a wide range of sporting and recreational activities, such as walking, orienteering, climbing, canoeing and white-water rafting. The basis for all of these outdoor activities is the need for a solid level of aerobic endurance as they often take many hours to complete.

Assessment practice

1 Plan and prepare a presentation that describes the fitness requirements of three different sporting activities. You need to consider both physical and skill-related fitness. The sports may contrast because they:

- are individual or team based
- require the use of different muscle groups
- are from different sporting categories, such as athletics or target games.

For example, you could use football, tennis and dance as your three sporting activities. **P1**

2 In your presentation, explain why the components of fitness you have described are required. **M1**

3 Describe the similarities and differences between your three chosen sports in terms of:

- fitness requirements
- movement patterns
- length and intensity of play
- importance of the components of fitness
- joint and muscle involvement
- any other factors you have discovered. **D1**

Grading tips

Grading Tip P1

Using tennis as one of the examples, you would need to describe that a tennis player needs muscular endurance to sprint around the court while making the shots.

Grading Tip M1

You could explain that tennis players need muscular endurance in order to make repeated sprints over varying distances to make the shots. If fatigue sets in, they will not be able to make the shot and will lose the point.

3.2 Understand different methods of physical fitness training

In this section you will expand on your knowledge of the components of fitness by considering the different types of training for fitness. For each component of fitness, there is a variety of methods of training, as different athletes need to use the different methods. We will also look at the practicalities of using the methods.

Components of physical fitness

Flexibility

Flexibility refers to the amount of movement possible around a joint or a number of joints. It can be improved through these types of stretching:

- static (passive and active)
- ballistic
- PNF (proprioceptive neuromuscular facilitation).

Strength

Strength is the ability of a specific muscle or muscle group to exert a force in a single maximal contraction.

An athlete is likely to train a specific muscle group to aid performance, but there are basic requirements for training regardless of the muscle group.

Muscular endurance

It is important to remember that muscular endurance is different from strength because it relates to repeated contractions at a high intensity rather that a single maximal contraction. As strength and endurance are different, they require different types of training.

Power

The main elements of power are strength and speed of movement, so to improve an athlete's power you need to be aware of strength and speed training.

Aerobic endurance

Aerobic endurance is a central component of fitness for most sports and is the ability of the cardiovascular system (heart and lungs) to supply the exercising muscles with oxygen. It can be trained in many different ways.

Unlike the other components of fitness, it is fairly difficult to improve an athlete's speed, and it takes a long time (more than two months). As with the other components, we will consider a variety of methods of training.

Methods of training

This section looks at a number of methods of fitness training that relate to the different components of fitness. It highlights the different methods athletes may use to improve fitness, and analyses their effectiveness.

Flexibility

The general principle of flexibility training is to overload the specific muscle group by stretching the muscles beyond what they are normally used to. The aim is to increase the range of movement, and work must be targeted towards the joints and muscle groups that require improvement. Of course, the movement should not exceed the tolerance level of the tissue, which may cause injury. For improvements in flexibility, an athlete should increase the time (duration) of stretching and the number of repetitions to allow overload to take place.

Here are some general tips for stretching:

- warm up first to increase body temperature
- stretch all the major muscle groups
- remain in a stretch position for at least ten seconds
- to overload, increase the time spent holding the stretch
- the session duration should be 10–30 minutes
- for improvements in flexibility, train three times a week.

■ Static stretching

Static stretches are controlled and slow, and are of two types: passive and active. After stretching the muscle, the athlete remains in a constant position for a number of seconds. Once in position, the athlete then applies an internal force to overload the muscle so that it stretches beyond its normal range, thereby improving flexibility.

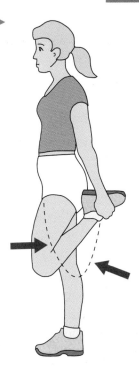

Active stretching gives increased flexibility and strength ▶

Jerky movements should be avoided and positions should be assumed slowly.

Passive stretching is also known as assisted stretching as it requires the help of another person or an object such as a wall. The other person would apply an external force (push or pull) to force the muscle to stretch.

Unlike passive stretching, active stretching can be achieved by the athlete alone. It involves voluntarily

▲ Flexibility is often overlooked as a component of fitness when training. However, for most sports it is a central component and should be trained for on a regular basis

contracting specific muscles. An example of this is where the athlete raises his or her lower leg by holding one foot behind the back, and stretches the leg in the new position.

■ Ballistic stretching

Ballistic stretching improves an athlete's flexibility. The athlete has to make fast, jerky movements, usually taking the form of bouncing and bobbing through the full range of motion.

Ballistic stretching should be specific to the movement pattern experienced in the relevant sporting activity. These stretches can lead to soreness or may even cause injury such as strains, so they must be undertaken carefully and with the correct technique.

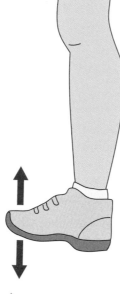

▲ Ballistic stretching involves fast, jerky movements

■ Proprioceptive neuromuscular facilitation (PNF) stretching

PNF stretching is slightly more complex than static stretching as it involves two clear stages and requires two people. The athlete holds the muscle in isometric contraction and then performs a slow static stretch as described above, aided by a second person. PNF stretches can be used to increase strength and flexibility while aiding muscle relaxation.

Key term

Isometric contraction The muscle develops tension but there is no shortening.

Activity

Produce an A3 poster that could be displayed at your local gym on 'Methods of flexibility training'. Your poster should explain the differences between the following forms of stretching:

- static passive
- static active
- ballistic
- PNF.

The poster should be colourful and include pictures. Try to be informative but not too technical. Include key words and diagrams to support your text.

Strength, muscular endurance and power

The aim of a fitness programme is to improve muscular strength, muscular endurance and power, so the number of repetitions in the training session is important. A repetition is equal to one movement – if an athlete does ten leg presses, they have done ten repetitions ('reps').

A set consists of a series of repetitions. Therefore, the athlete may leg press for ten reps followed by a rest period and then do another 10 reps. This is classified as two sets of ten reps.

The resistance in a training programme is the load the athlete has to move. For example, when performing a leg press, a 50 kg load has a greater resistance than a 25 kg load.

Athletes use a number of methods to improve their muscular strength, muscular endurance and power. When training for strength:

- the general concept is low reps and high loads
- three sessions a week with a rest day between sessions are best for optimal improvement
- the load should be increased gradually over a period of time
- high weights close to the athlete's maximum should be avoided at the start of the programme
- repetitions per set should be either ten down to six (making five sets) or six up to ten (again, five sets)

- apart from a general warm-up, aerobic exercise should be avoided on the same day as a strength session
- a record of sessions should be kept using an exercise card.

When training for muscular endurance:

- the general concept is high reps and low loads
- three sessions a week with a rest day between sessions are best for optimal improvement
- the number of reps and sets should be increased gradually over a period of time
- high numbers of reps should be avoided at the start (no more than ten)
- there should be a rest period before starting a new set to avoid a decrease in performance and build-up of lactic acid
- a record of sessions should be kept using an exercise card.

As power is a component of speed and strength, by definition to improve power you should look to improve strength or speed. See page 109 for more information on this type of training.

Theory into practice

Design a four-week training programme, with two sessions a week, to improve your strength using eight training cards and four different machines. The programme should show progression and overload while taking into account the health and safety factors such as gradual increases in resistance.

■ Resistance machines

Your local fitness centre should have a number of fixed resistance machines made by manufacturers such as Nautilus, which allow athletes to change the load based on their training programme schedule. The variable resistance ranges from 0–100 kg on most machines, allowing the programme to include overload and progression.

These machines are expensive, making them unsuitable for use at home. Also, due to their design they are limited to specialist exercises such as a bench or leg press. On the positive side, they have an increased safety element compared to free weights, and an athlete is able to change the range of movement at a specific joint by adjusting the machine's settings.

■ Circuit training

In a circuit training session, a number of different exercises (or stations) are organised normally in rotations. Athletes are usually set a time period to perform these exercises, such as one minute per station. Between the stations there should be a rest period of between 15 and 30 seconds.

A circuit can be specifically designed to improve aerobic endurance, muscular endurance, strength or a combination of all three. To avoid fatigue, the stations should be structured in a way that consecutive exercises use different muscle groups, for example repeated sprints (legs) may be followed by press-ups (upper body). To increase progression and overload, the athlete may wish to:

- decrease the rest period
- increase the number of stations
- increase the number of circuits
- increase the time spent at each station
- increase the number of circuit sessions per week.

Once the athlete has obtained a good level of fitness, the rest periods may become light work periods, such as jogging on the spot or skipping. Circuits are a good method of maintaining a level of aerobic endurance, possibly during the off-season period, and they offer the following benefits:

- they add fun and variety to the training
- they allow training of a combination of fitness components
- they allow the athlete to specialise in a specific movement pattern or muscle group
- they require minimal equipment
- they can involve a number of athletes
- they are designed to allow progression and overload.

▲ Fixed resistance machines and free weights are used to improve muscular strength. Both produce positive results

■ Free weights

Free weights, also known as barbells or dumb-bells, allow the athlete to have a constant resistance during a dynamic action. Free weights have these advantages:

- research data provides some support for claims of increases in strength in the short term
- they allow an increased range of movement
- they allow the athlete to specialise in certain movements or muscle groups
- some movements can aid the training of balance and coordination
- they are convenient for exercising at home.

However, there is a greater chance of injury while using free weights. For safety reasons when using larger weights, helpers are required to oversee (or 'spot') for the athlete.

There seems to be no clear advantage in using either fixed resistance machines or free weights in terms of results when training for strength. Each athlete will have his or her own preferences and experiences.

■ Plyometrics

Plyometrics is also known as jump training. It is designed to improve explosive leg power and has been used to improve athletes' jumping over the past three decades. The basic concept is that it uses the stretch reflex to aid recruitment of additional motor units during movement.

Plyometric exercise requires maximal force during the shortening stage of the muscle action (concentric contraction) and then immediate maximal force when the muscle lengthens (eccentric contraction). Plyometric training is ideal for sports and activities that involve explosive jumping such as basketball, netball and the high jump. It can be used to improve vertical jumping capacity.

Key terms

Concentric contraction The muscle gets shorter and the two ends of the muscle move closer together.

Eccentric contraction The muscle increases in length while still producing tension.

A hurdle or box may be used in plyometric training. The athlete jumps down from the box and immediately on impact jumps up. By jumping up after jumping down, the muscle is made to stop lengthening and is overloaded.

■ Medicine balls

Volleyball players throw and catch medicine balls (heavy balls weighing from 1–7 kg) to upgrade their spiking ability; basketball players use the balls to improve their passing and rebounding capacities; baseball players toss medicine balls to improve their throwing speed; and all-around athletes cavort with the balls in the hope of enhancing their 'core strength' (muscle strength in the hips, abdomen and back).

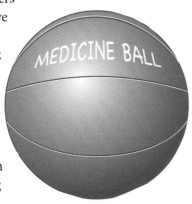

 Medicine-ball training is becoming increasingly popular with athletes

Theory into practice

In pairs, produce an A3 poster to highlight some medicine ball exercises you can use to improve the strength in your muscles. Add diagrams to illustrate your poster.

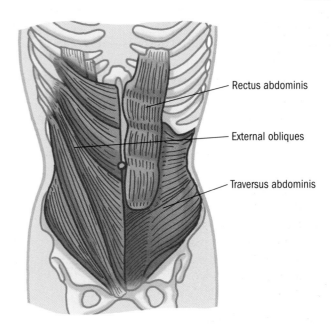

- Rectus abdominis
- External obliques
- Traversus abdominis

▲ The body's core muscles are the centre point for all movement within sport

■ Core stability

Core stability training is vital to most sports and for injury prevention.

The muscles of the torso stabilise the spine and provide a solid foundation for movement in the extremities (arms and legs). These core muscles lie deep within the torso and they generally attach to the spine, pelvis and muscles that support the scapula. Training the muscles of the core also corrects postural imbalances that can lead to injuries.

The main concepts of core strengthening programs involve using many muscles rather than isolating a specific joint as in most weight lifting. Stability exercises focus on working the deep muscles of the entire torso at the same time.

Aerobic endurance

Three methods used to improve aerobic endurance are continuous training, Fartlek training and interval training. There is not enough evidence to determine which method is the best for improving aerobic endurance, but with the correct implementation of training methods all three methods will lead to improvements in aerobic endurance.

■ Continuous training

Continuous training is also known as steady-state or long, slow, distance training. It involves the athlete training at a steady pace over a long distance. The intensity of steady-state training should be moderate to high (60 per cent to 80 per cent Vo_2 maximum) over a long distance and time. Using the principle of overload, the intensity should be high enough to lead to biological adaptation.

Key term

Vo_2 **maximum** The highest rate at which oxygen can be taken up and utilised during exercise by a person.

This method of training is suited to long-distance runners or swimmers. Because of the lower level of intensity, the athlete is able to train for a considerable period of time. This method of training at a lower intensity is ideal for:

- beginners who are starting structured exercise
- athletes recovering from injury
- 'special population' athletes such as children or elderly people.

To overload the system and show an improvement in performance, the athlete should increase the duration or distance of training.

■ Fartlek training

Fartlek training is another method designed to improve an athlete's aerobic endurance. It is based on running outdoors, and varies the intensity of work according to the requirements of the athlete. The intensity of the training is changed by varying the terrain. The athlete may run on:

- sand
- hills
- undulations
- soft grassland
- wooded areas.

Through increasing the intensity during training, the athlete will be switching from aerobic to anaerobic energy supplies. Through Fartlek training, the anaerobic endurance component leads to an improvement in aerobic endurance (Vo_2 maximum).

Key term

Anaerobic endurance component A component that does not use oxygen, such as speed.

In Fartlek training there is no rest period, but the athlete has more control and is able to decrease intensity at any given time to take informal rest periods. The benefits of Fartlek training are:

- athletes control their own pacing
- the boredom of conventional training is reduced
- it is suitable for off-season training to maintain aerobic endurance.

■ Interval training

The basic concept of interval training is that the athlete performs an exercise bout (work period) followed by a rest or recovery period before completing another work period.

Interval training can be used to improve anaerobic endurance components and aerobic endurance (Vo_2 maximum) by varying the intensity and length of the work periods. Here is an example of an interval for improving aerobic endurance components: run for two minutes (60 per cent Vo_2 maximum); rest for 30 seconds; run for two minutes (60 per cent Vo_2 maximum).

Remember!

Aerobic endurance can be improved by using various training methods such as continuous, interval and Fartlek training.

This method of training allows clear progression and overload to be built into the programme. Here are some ways of incorporating overload into the training session:

- increase the intensity of the work periods
- increase the number of intervals
- decrease the duration of the rest period
- make the rest period more intense, e.g. a slow jog rather than a brisk walk.

When designing a training programme, you need to consider:

- the number of intervals (rest and work periods)
- the intensity of the work interval
- the duration of the work interval
- the duration of the rest interval
- the intensity of the rest interval.

When designing a programme using interval methods, it is important that the rest intervals should be the same or greater than the work periods. However, the rest period can be shortened, especially if the athlete has a good level of fitness and will be able to meet the extra physical and psychological demands. For aerobic training, the intervals should exceed one minute in length with an intensity level above 80 per cent of the maximum heart rate.

For maximal improvements in aerobic endurance, the athlete should concentrate on exercising at a high intensity rather than for a long duration.

Key term

Maximum heart rate Calculated by deducting the athlete's age from 220. For example, someone aged 20 will have a maximum heart rate of about 200.

Activity

A beginner athlete is unsure about the different training methods to improve aerobic endurance and speed. Prepare and give a five-minute presentation outlining the differences between the various training methods. Make sure you distinguish between continuous, Fartlek and interval training. You may wish to use diagrams and pictures in your presentation, which could be supported by handouts.

Speed

Acceleration from a standing position is critical for success in sports such as sprinting. It is also important in team-based sports such as rugby league, where the player has to accelerate with the ball past opponents, changing

Case study: Improving aerobic endurance

Ali, 23, is a local 200m freestyle club swimmer. Imagine you are a local fitness training instructor. He wants you to devise a one-week training programme to improve his aerobic endurance. He has been told that interval training should improve his aerobic endurance.

1 **Devise a one-week training programme (three sessions of 45 minutes in duration) for Ali and use an appropriate method to display the programme such as a timetable or logbook.**

2 **Show overload, gradual progression and specificity between the sessions, which will allow Ali to improve his aerobic endurance.**

3 **Include interval training over a variety of distances, making sure you clearly indicate the duration of the rest and work periods.**

4 **Show the number of intervals clearly.**

5 **Show rest days, which should be taken to avoid over-training.**

Case study: Improving speed and acceleration

Helen plays for the local hockey team and wants to improve her speed and acceleration, which is important for hockey. She has been training for two weeks using uphill and downhill sprints.

1 Draw up a list of ways in which Helen can achieve overload and show progression, for example by increasing the number of reps.

2 Helen is concerned about the health and safety issues involved in this type of exercise. Draw up a list of the possible hazards while hill sprinting.

3 Which other components of fitness are important for hockey?

---

pace rapidly. A number of acceleration drills can be used, as follows.

- Parachute sprinting: the athlete attaches a small parachute to his or her back, which has the effect of increasing wind resistance. This helps to build leg-muscle strength. Once the parachute is removed, sprinting at a higher pace feels a lot easier.

- Stair drills: a flight of stairs (not house stairs, but ones with deeper treads) is used to train acceleration. The athlete has to sprint up a number of stairs for up to ten seconds, with the aim of improving leg power and strength. Stride length is also improved.

- Resistance drills: athletes can use some form of resistance, such as dragging a tyre, to improve acceleration. This is similar to the parachute method in improving muscle strength, which should aid acceleration.

- Hill sprints: athletes have used hill sprints to increase their speed, coordination and acceleration for many years. These sprints can be either up or down a hill, depending on the content and aims of the session.

There are many drills designed to improve the speed of the athlete. Here are some examples.

- Ladder sprints: many coaches use a ladder laid on the floor as a method of improving leg speed and coordination. The aim is to sprint through the ladder as fast as possible. The key to success is having a high knee lift, good technique and minimal ground contact.

- Basic sprint training: two sets of cones are placed 10–25m apart, depending on the training session.

The athlete should sprint between the cones then jog back to the start and sprint again.

- Bounds: these drills use a bounding principle and can increase an athlete's speed. The aim of the plyometric drill is to raise the free knee as high as possible while running. The knee should become parallel with and in line with the hip. The stride length should be increased compared to a normal running style. This method of training for speed will lead to an increase in the athlete's leg strength and power, while lengthening the stride.

■ Interval training

Interval training can be used to improve anaerobic endurance. The work intervals for aerobic endurance training would tend to be long in duration and low intensity in order to train the aerobic system. By contrast, for anaerobic endurance the work intervals will be much shorter but will be more intense (near to maximum). Interval training can help the athlete improve speed and anaerobic endurance (speed endurance).

The athlete should be working at a high intensity. The principles of overload and progression can be brought into the programme by making changes such as decreasing the rest period.

■ Sport-specific speed training

There are certain sports that require specific types of speed training to improve performance. For team-based sports you need to concentrate on different:

- distances: as players sprint over varying distances
- movement patterns: sprinting in different directions to aid agility.

Taking it further

There are some training methods that a 100m sprinter would need to follow, as he or she is training for a specialist sport. Carry out some research and produce written notes to describe some of these speed training techniques for sprinters. These notes can be added to your file and may be useful for your assessment.

Assessment practice

Produce a written report that explores the methods of training for these components of physical fitness:

- aerobic endurance
- muscular endurance
- flexibility
- speed
- strength
- power
- body composition.

1 Describe one method of fitness training for each of the above components, such as interval training for aerobic endurance. Include diagrams and illustrations to aid your descriptions. **P2**

2 Explain fully what an athlete needs to do to carry out the methods of training. You should include how the athlete can adapt the training to make it harder and show progression. **M2**

Grading tips

Grading Tip P2

For this criterion, you need to describe the training methods (which means you should give an overview). For example, 'Fartlek is a form of road-running or cross-country running in which the runner, usually solo, varies the pace significantly during the run. It is similar to interval training in that short, fast runs alternate with slow running or jogging recovery intervals. In Fartlek, the running is done on the road, on parkland or bush tracks. There is no predetermined schedule to follow, but instead athletes set their own interval lengths and pace in response to their own feeling of the workload.

Grading Tip M2

Within your explanation of the training methods, you need to explain the following:

- location and environment for exercise, e.g. on the track
- equipment and facilities required, e.g. sports hall, cones
- duration of exercise, e.g. one-hour run
- intensity the athlete is working at, e.g. 65 per cent maximum heart rate
- number of activities taking place, e.g. ten sprints
- specific movements required, e.g. how to perform a hamstring stretch (this is where your diagrams are needed)
- rest periods and what the athlete is doing between exercises
- the components of fitness and sports they can help you with
- how can the training method be made harder, e.g. by decreasing rest periods.

In this section you will plan a fitness training programme based on your knowledge of the components of fitness and training methods. However, before you start putting the programme together you need to complete the information regarding your athlete. This information will include the goals they have, such as to lose weight, together with any other factors like medical history and lifestyle. It is important that you collect this information so that the training programme fully considers the needs of the athlete.

The most important aspect of designing a training programme is that you incorporate the principles of training. These are vital for either a beginner or an elite-level athlete. The principles must be followed in order to maximise the training effects. It is good practice to encourage your athletes to keep a training diary, which charts progress and attitude to training.

Collect information

When you are planning the training programme, you need to gather the information that will make the programme appropriate to the athlete. As each athlete will have different goals, training history and fitness levels, you should never use the same programme on two athletes.

Short, medium and long-term goals

The first consideration should be the athlete's goals. The programme must be flexible while still being capable of meeting these goals and personal needs. Here are examples of different goals that you may encounter while working in a local fitness centre:

- an amateur rugby player wishing to regain fitness after injury
- a middle-aged person wishing to improve flexibility
- an elite performer wishing to use the facility for fitness maintenance during the off-season period.

Each athlete has different ambitions and aspirations, and your programme should reflect these. The athlete's goals should be broken up into short-term (one month), medium-term (three months) and long-term goals (one year).

For example, a football player who wants to improve his aerobic endurance may have the goals shown in the diagram when performing the multi-stage fitness test, which measures aerobic endurance.

Targets

■ SMART targets

When designing the training programme, it is important that you set goals that are based on SMART targets:

- **S – s**pecific: they say exactly what you mean (e.g. to improve flexibility in the hamstring muscle group)
- **M – m**easurable: you can prove that you have reached them (e.g. increase flexibility by 5 cm using the sit-and-reach test)
- **A – a**chievable: you can reach them in the next few weeks (e.g. the increase in flexibility must be manageable – a 20 cm increase in two weeks is not achievable)
- **R – r**ealistic: they are about action you can take (e.g. you can practise and improve flexibility through training)
- **T – t**ime-bound: they have deadlines (e.g. to reach the target within six weeks).

Short-term goal	Medium-term goal	Long-term goal
Level 11	Level 12, shuttle 2	Level 14

At the moment, the footballer's latest score was Level 10, shuttle 7. Therefore, you can see that the targets have logical progression and are achievable

Lifestyle

When designing a training programme, you need to understand the athlete's lifestyle, and specifically the time he or she has available to dedicate to the training programme. People have various commitments connected with work and family life, and the time available for most people is limited.

The training programme should be slotted into the time available and fit with the athlete's lifestyle. Elite athletes who receive lottery funding, sponsorship or prize money may not need to work, so they will have more time to devote to training or travelling. However, training for the working athlete may have to be concentrated nearer to home. Sessions may have to be as short as 20 minutes, and may involve performing basic exercises at home or using exercise videos.

Medical history

Before you design the programme, you need to find out about the athlete's medical history. Asking the athlete to complete a pre-exercise health questionnaire like the one shown here can do this.

If you choose to design you own questionnaire, you could include items related to heart conditions and asthma.

Activity

In small groups, produce a list of the types of questions you could include on a medical history questionnaire.

PAR-Q Physical Activity Readiness Questionnaire

For most people, physical activity should not pose any problems or hazards. PAR-Q has been designed to identify the small number of adults for whom physical activity might be inappropriate or those who should obtain medical advice concerning the type of activity most suitable for them. Common sense is your best guide in answering these questions. Please read them carefully and check the Yes or No opposite the question if it applies to you.

Yes	No	Question
☐	☐	Has your doctor ever said you have heart trouble?
☐	☐	Do you frequently have pains in your heart and chest?
☐	☐	Do you often feel faint or have spells of severe dizziness?
☐	☐	Has a doctor ever said your blood pressure was too high?
☐	☐	Has your doctor ever told you that you have a bone or joint problem such as arthritis that has been aggravated by exercise, or might be made worse by exercise?
☐	☐	Is there a good physical reason not to mention here why you should not follow an activity program even if you wanted to?
☐	☐	Are you over the age of 65 and not accustomed to vigorous exercise?

Use a PAR-Q questionnaire to ▶ assess athletes' medical history

Physical activity history

When designing a training programme, the fitness trainer must gain a picture of the athlete's history, including any health-related issues such as a punctured lung. Previous activity levels are part of this picture. If the athlete has previously been involved in a structured programme and has a good level of fitness, assessed through fitness tests, then the programme should reflect this. The exercises prescribed should be at a moderate to high intensity. Another athlete may not have exercised at all for a long time (one month or more) for a variety of reasons such as injury, illness or loss of motivation. In this case, the programme should be set at a lower level to start with, in terms of number of sessions per week, duration and intensity.

Principles of training

Any fitness programme is based on the principles of training. They apply to anyone embarking on a programme, ranging from an elite athlete to an unfit person aged 55. These principles are important because, if they are followed, athletes will see an improvement in their fitness levels. If the principles are not adhered to, athletes will not maximise their possible improvement in fitness. This means that fitness levels will remain fairly constant or possibly even decline. The principles of training are:

- overload
- specificity
- progression
- individual differences
- variation
- reversibility
- frequency, intensity, time and type (FITT).

These principles of training can be used to produce an improvement in a number of components of fitness:

- aerobic endurance
- strength
- muscular endurance
- flexibility
- body composition.

Remember!

When designing a training programme for an athlete, it is important to consider all the principles of training – they are vital for success.

Overload

Overload is an important principle of training. It involves exercising at an intensity (level of work) greater than before. An example of this can be seen in the graph, which shows overload being used in a middle-distance runner's training programme. The athlete increases the distance gradually over a six-week programme.

Constant overloading of the body's systems will cause it to respond and adapt. This is known as chronic adaptation. Acute responses to exercise, such as increased body temperature or heart rate, are short-

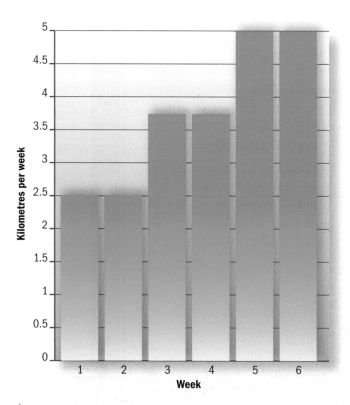

▲ **Overload in running**

term adaptations. Chronic changes, such as a decrease in resting heart rate, take from six weeks to a number of months to come into effect. The athlete is unlikely to see an improvement in performance unless overload is incorporated into the programme.

Key term

Chronic adaptation Refers to changes in the body that take place after six weeks of training, such as a decrease in resting heart rate.

The following are the components that can be adapted to lead to overload:

- frequency: the number of sessions a week, e.g. increasing from two to four
- intensity: the amount of energy needed to perform a particular exercise or activity
- duration: the total time an exercise session or activity takes, e.g. a 20-minute session could be increased to a 30-minute session.

Adaptations that result from chronic overload take place at cellular level. The trainer must link the metabolic/physiological responses and adaptations required with the training programme to ensure that the changes meet the athlete's needs.

Remember!

If the athlete does not overload the body, there will be no improvement in fitness and therefore probably none in performance.

Specificity

A common mistake that people make is not to train the specific muscles or muscle groups involved in the activity they perform. Change is also specific to muscle fibre type. For example, a 100m sprinter wishing to improve speed would use a speed-based programme that would train the fast-twitch muscle fibres required for sprinting.

The training programme should reflect the specific requirements of the sport or activity. An athlete who needs to improve strength in the biceps should not develop a programme around extensive resistance work for the legs.

The key to making training specific is to outline clear goals before starting the programme, which will allow the physical changes to match the desired outcome. An athlete who wants to decrease body fat percentage should engage in a training programme that maximises low-intensity, high-duration aerobic work (in conjunction with a possible change in diet and lifestyle).

◀ Although all these players are playing rugby, they have specific fitness needs. For example, a winger needs to concentrate on speed whereas a forward needs more strength

The local football team has been training for the past six weeks using the following training programme. Its aim is to improve aerobic endurance.

Week 1
- Swim 400m freestyle.
- Jog at 50 per cent of maximum heart rate for 1 km.
- Skills for one hour.

Week 2
- Swim 400m freestyle.
- Jog at 50 per cent of maximum heart rate for 1 km.
- Skills for one hour.

Week 3
- Swim 200m backstroke.
- Jog at 50 per cent of maximum heart rate for 1 km.
- Skills for one hour.

Week 4
- Swim 200m backstroke.
- Jog at 50 per cent of maximum heart rate for 1 km.
- Skills for one hour.

Week 5
- Swim 300m freestyle.
- Jog at 50 per cent of maximum heart rate for 1.5 km.
- Skills for one hour.

Week 6
- Swim 300m backstroke.
- Jog at 50 per cent of maximum heart rate for 0.8 km.
- Skills for one hour.

After a series of fitness tests, the team found that their aerobic endurance had not improved at all.

1 **What do you notice about the training programme in relation to the concepts of overload, progression and specificity?**

2 **Why do you think there has been no improvement in fitness?**

3 **Why is it important to consider the principles of training when designing a programme?**

Remember!

The training must be specific to the needs of the athlete and the sport. For example, a 100m sprinter should concentrate on speed drills, which will improve power in the legs.

Progression

Progression is achieved when there is a steady increase in the overload of the training programme to bring an improvement in fitness over a period of time.

Beginners often stop their training programmes because of lack of motivation when they fail to achieve progression. Poor performances may be due to too little progression in the programme or a training programme that overloads the system too much and has excessive intensity. Excessive overloading may lead to a number of acute or chronic injuries, or even illness.

The human body improves its efficiency gradually, adapting to a sensible level of overload. The frequency, intensity or duration of exercise should be increased gradually over a period of time.

Individual differences

The development and maintenance of fitness should be viewed as an ongoing project based on an adaptable programme specific to the athlete. A tailored programme should be incorporated into the athlete's lifestyle, with consideration given to the following factors:
- short-term goals: e.g. go to the gym twice a week
- medium-term goals: e.g. lose 2 kg in body weight within two months

- long-term goals: e.g. win the county tennis championship
- current activity and fitness levels, which may change over a short period
- age
- equipment availability
- access to facilities: e.g. opening times of the local swimming pool
- work commitments
- family responsibilities
- other leisure or social commitments.

The coach, personal trainer or fitness instructor should consider the athlete as a whole (this is called using a holistic approach) rather than trying to follow a standard approach. A tailored programme allows the athlete to increase his or her fitness levels to the maximum amount possible.

All athletes have different needs, abilities, goals, skills and physical attributes. Therefore, a training programme should be tailor-made for each athlete.

It is important not to overlook the athlete's preferences, such as the mode (the method or piece of equipment used) of training. If an athlete wishes to decrease body fat percentage using a bike rather than a treadmill, this is acceptable as both should allow the athlete to meet that goal.

Athletes with low levels of fitness will show a greater improvement than elite athletes because they have scope for larger amounts of improvement. However, even though elite athletes will show a minimal improvement, it could prove significant. An example of this would be weightlifting. A previously untrained athlete might increase his or her strength by 40 kg after a long period of training. An elite weightlifter, however, might increase his or her personal best by only 5 kg, but this could mean breaking the world record.

The potential for improvement is strongly linked to the athlete's genetic make-up. The trainer should expect the athlete to show continuing progress over a long period of time, but at some point each athlete will reach a genetic plateau for the specific muscle group or component of fitness.

Case study: Regaining motivation

Hassan, the local butcher aged 45, took up running a month ago with the aim of reducing his body fat. However, he has recently been missing some sessions through lack of interest. Hassan asks himself the following questions.

1 He is interested in using free weights to reduce his body fat percentage. Will they work or not?

2 What other aerobic exercises can he do to regain motivation?

3 For how long and how often does Hassan have to exercise to reduce his body fat percentage?

Case study: Weight loss and improved flexibility

Claire, 30, is the local librarian. She has joined the gym with the aim of losing a stone in body weight over an eight-week period. She also aims to improve her flexibility, as this is important for her job in the library.

1 Why would the standard training schedule at the gym, which focuses on strength, not be suitable for Claire? Base your answer on the principles of training.

2 When losing weight it is important to have short-term, medium-term and long-term goals, and that they are realistic. Set out three possible goals for Claire's weight-loss programme.

3 Why is it important to consider the athlete as a whole, in a holistic approach, when designing a programme?

Although goals are important, some athletes will start a fitness programme or join a club for social reasons and may not have distinct goals.

Variation

One of the biggest reasons for stopping a training programme is that the athlete becomes bored. This is because they are performing the same style of training on a regular basis. It is important that you offer some variety in the programme to add variation and reduce boredom. Add variation occasionally (once every two weeks) to reduce boredom.

Activity

In small groups, produce a list of possible exercises athletes can perform to improve their aerobic endurance, which is not continuous running.

Reversibility

Rest is essential within any athlete's training programme to allow for repair and renewal of the body's tissues. However, a marked decrease in training or complete inactivity will lead to a decrease in functional capacity, for example maximal cardiac output or aerobic capacity, and will be detrimental to performance. This decrease in performance is due to the principle of training called reversibility, which is also known as detraining.

Activity

In small groups, devise a wide-ranging list of possible types of athlete who might enter your fitness or health club requiring a tailored training programme. Discuss your answers with the other groups in your class.

If training is infrequent or not sufficiently intensive the effects will diminish, which can influence all components of fitness from flexibility to power.

There are many reasons for a training programme to be reduced in terms of frequency, duration or intensity:

- injury
- illness
- decrease in motivation
- ending of the season: June and July are the off-season in football
- loss of facilities or equipment: e.g. closure of the local fitness club
- personal or social reasons: e.g. bereavement, peer pressure.

Reversibility leads to a dramatic and rapid reduction in fitness levels – faster than the improvements gained through overloading over a period of time.

Elite athletes aiming to achieve a peak performance at, for example, an Olympic games, avoid exercise burnout by reducing the training intensity, frequency or duration just before the important performance. This is known as tapering (reducing) the training, and helps the athlete maximise performance.

Activity

Imagine you are going to be visited by a new coach who is interested in learning about the principles of training. Prepare a three-page summary, which includes the following, to aid the coach:

- An introduction to the concept of the principles of training, stating who can use them and how they form the basis of a training programme.
- A table or spider diagram showing the principles of training.
- A brief description of each principle of training (one brief paragraph for each principle). You may wish to use diagrams or figures to illustrate them.
- A discussion of how the principles of training influence two contrasting sports, such as football and gymnastics (this can be in bullet-point form). In football, for example, you would need to mention that the training should be specific and based on running, as this is what football involves.

Frequency, intensity, time and type (FITT principles)

When designing a training programme you can use the acronym FITT to help you remember the important points. FITT stands for:

- frequency
- intensity
- time
- type.

Put simply, the frequency of a training programme refers to the number of training sessions per week. Most evidence suggests that for increases in fitness levels, the intensity and duration of training are more important than the frequency.

In general, people should:

- exercise on three to five days each week
- warm-up for 5 to 10 minutes before aerobic activity
- maintain exercise intensity for 30 to 45 minutes
- gradually decrease the intensity of the workout, then stretch to cool down during the last 5 to 10 minutes
- for weight loss, undertake aerobic activity for at least 30 minutes on five days per week.

Remember!

For health and fitness reasons, the number of sessions per week should not exceed five. This will prevent over-training and burnout.

A beginner should not exceed two to three sessions per week to reduce the chance of injury and illness. After an increase in fitness over a long period (more than three months) the athlete should be encouraged to increase the frequency of sessions to allow further overloading and physiological adaptation.

People should not train for health and fitness reasons in excess of five sessions per week. The elite athlete may train on six or even seven days a week, but a number of these sessions will be light in terms of intensity or duration, and they may focus largely on skills or psychological training.

The concept of intensity in the programme is closely linked with the training principle of overload. Intensity is the most important factor for the fitness trainer to consider when designing a training programme.

There seems to be a widespread misconception that athletes must always be working at 100 per cent Vo_2 maximum to induce changes in fitness levels. However, if the programme incorporates the training principle of overload, an athlete who works near to 60 per cent Vo_2 maximum is likely to see some improvement in aerobic capacity over a long period of training. Furthermore some athletes, such as those recovering from injury, will gain health benefits for exercising below 60 per cent Vo_2 maximum.

Theory into practice

As a group, devise and carry out a basic aerobic workout which includes four clear levels of intensity. To assess the intensity levels, for each activity measure the heart rate (in beats per minute) and compare it against maximum heart rate (220 minus age).

Once you have collected the raw data, plot it on a line graph representing the heart rate in beats per minute or as a percentage of maximum heart rate. On completion of the graph you should be able to identify the four clear intensity levels of your chosen exercises.

The concept of time in connection with a fitness session is also known as duration. To improve an athlete's aerobic endurance through overload, the exercise period needs to exceed 20 minutes at the correct intensity level. Some studies have shown an improvement in aerobic endurance when training for only ten minutes a day at a high intensity (above 80 per cent Vo_2 maximum).

Aerobic endurance can be improved by high intensity/low duration or low intensity/high duration exercise.

The type or mode of exercise will depend on the athlete's choice, such as running, swimming or cycling. If the athlete wants to improve aerobic endurance, this can be achieved by using certain types of exercise such as steady-state training.

The choice of exercise method may be based on access to facilities and equipment, as not everyone has regular access to a swimming pool, for example. From a performance perspective, if the athlete is a runner he or she should concentrate a large percentage of training time on running, as swimming would train different muscle groups and movement patterns. When choosing the type of exercise, you should consider the:

- equipment/facilities available
- time available
- time of season
- sport of the athlete
- position played by the athlete
- personal preferences of the athlete.

Periodisation

Most professional and amateur coaches use a training programme based on a structured cycle. This is known as periodisation. The training cycle can be split into:

- macrocycles: one-year to four-year training cycles
- mesocycles: monthly training cycles
- microcycles: weekly or individually planned training sessions.

Key terms

Macrocycles One-year to four-year training cycles.

Mesocycles Monthly training cycles.

Microcycles Weekly or individually planned training sessions.

Periodisation is the cycling of work to provide the chance to improve the fitness of the athlete and maximise performance potential. The aim of periodisation is to divide the programme into smaller training cycles. For example, the period between October and December may be used to concentrate on speed training.

Periodisation offers the following benefits in a long-term training programme:

- time to recover from training
- increased chances of performance peaking at the correct time, e.g. in national championships
- reduced chances of over-training
- overload and progression included
- reduced chances of injury.

The nature of the sport or activity will dictate how long the training period is.

Macrocycle

The first layer of a training programme may be based on a one-year to four-year cycle, which is known as a macrocycle.

A football player will train based on a one-year cycle, from June to May, aiming to peak for a weekly or bi-weekly match. An Olympic athlete will have a training period based on a four-year cycle, aiming for peak performance to coincide with the Olympic games.

Mesocycle

The macrocycle is divided into a number of mesocycles. These normally consist of a number of months and depend on the structure of the season. A mesocycle in cricket would be the pre-season period and comprises the months January, February and March. The second mesocycle would follow in April, May and June.

The aim of mesocycles is to distinguish the focus of training for the athlete. In the pre-season stage there will be a focus on aerobic work, and in the second mesocycle there may be a change from aerobic exercise to speed and power work.

Microcycle

Each mesocycle is divided into a number of microcycles. The microcycle adds more detail, and can be one week in length. For one microcycle the athlete will be performing the same exercises with the same intensity, duration and type.

Table 3.1 shows part of the training cycle for football. The year is split into four mesocycles (each mesocycle is three months). In the pre-season months of June, July and August, the footballer will be concentrating on aerobic work to achieve a base level of fitness. This aerobic work will involve long runs and swimming. As the season starts in September, October and November, there is a change from aerobic work to more work on skills and drills.

Football training programme macrocycle		
June/July/August	September/October/November	*Mesocycles*
70% aerobic endurance 20% strength 10% skills	30% aerobic endurance 20% speed 10% strength 40% skills	*Microcycles*

Table 3.1 Extract from a football training macrocycle.

Activity

In small groups, devise a one-year training programme for a sport or activity of your choice. Use the football-training programme as a starting point. You should include:

- macrocycle
- mesocycles
- microcycles
- the components of fitness to be trained, e.g. aerobic endurance
- the percentage of training devoted to each component
- skills and drills work.

Once you have completed your programme, discuss it with the other groups in your class.

Taking it further

Due to the demands of training and ongoing competition, athletes are unable to produce their best performances (or 'peak') all the time. It is important for the athlete to match peak physical performance with the most important competitions, such as world championships. An Olympic athlete's training programme would be centred on producing the best possible performance on the day of the Olympic final. Carry out some further research and then answer the following questions.

1 What is meant by the term 'tapering', which is an important feature of an athlete's training programme?
2 Why is it important to taper the training programme?
3 Explain why it is difficult for an elite-level athlete to peak for every sporting performance.

Individual training sessions

It is generally accepted that a training session should include three basic components: the warm-up, the main workout and the cool-down.

The warm-up is performed before the main exercise period and is done for a number of reasons that are important to the health and safety of the athlete. The warm-up prepares the athlete for the more intense main section of the training session. A warm-up is needed to:

- increase cardiac output
- increase the blood flow to the working muscles
- increase vascular blood flow
- increase the muscle temperature
- reduce the chance of injury, e.g. pulls or strains
- prepare the athlete for the environment
- improve the elasticity (stretchiness) of the tendons and muscles
- prepare the athlete psychologically for the exercise (arousal).

Warm-ups consist of two clear stages. The general warm-up is performed before the specific warm-up, and consists of jogging, stretching and other general

Unit 3 | Training and fitness for sport [121]

exercises. The specific warm-up relates closely to the exercises to be done, and uses actions performed in the main workout section. Warm-ups should include:

- gentle loosening exercises, e.g. heel raises
- an aerobic phase (low intensity), e.g. light jogging, walking or cycling
- a stretching programme including specific stretches for the main activity.

Although the importance of a warm-up is generally known, a structured cool-down after the main workout is also important. The cool-down tends to be shorter than the warm-up and is based on low-intensity exercises. The main aim of the cool-down is to return the body to its resting state, and the main focus is on the aerobic component. There are a number of reasons why the athlete should perform a cool-down:

- to remove waste products from the working muscles, which are still receiving the oxygenated blood
- to stretch in order to decrease the chance of muscle stiffness
- to reduce the chances of fainting after an intense session.

Everyone should have a medical check-up before starting on a programme, but especially older people and those who have had cardiovascular complications. The fitness trainer should also take into account the following when considering health and safety factors:

- appropriate warm-up and cool-down
- implementation of the principles of training – gradual progression
- the exercise environment
- safe use of the equipment or facilities
- suitable clothing for the environment.

Regardless of the exercise being performed, there are a number of basic rules to follow in order to ensure the safety of the athlete. Within the fitness suite there are a number of considerations while exercising.

- Exercise machines should be well spaced out and in proper working order.
- Any loose equipment such as free weights should be stored correctly when not in use.
- Appropriate flooring should be provided for the exercise to be performed, e.g. gymnastics requires a sprung floor.

- There should be sufficient fluids available.
- There should be suitable ventilation to aid the cooling process.
- Always wear the appropriate clothing for the exercise, e.g. tracksuit bottoms not jeans.
- Make sure the footwear is correct for the exercise – failure to do this can lead to injury.
- If running outdoors, especially in the dark, make sure athletes wear bright, reflective clothing so they can be seen by traffic.

The personal safety of athletes who run outdoors, especially if running alone, requires careful thought. Runners should:

- run with a dog or running partner
- inform someone they are going running so that someone knows where they are
- avoid taking valuables with them, such as money or jewellery
- not wear headsets, as these can distract
- run on the same side of the road as oncoming vehicles, so that they can see approaching traffic
- vary their routes so that they do not develop a recognisable pattern
- make sure they know the route they are going to take
- only run in well-lit areas.

Theory into practice

In small groups, produce a three-minute video or an audiotape for the radio, which focuses on the health and safety aspects of running outside. Your project has the aim of reducing the numbers of injuries and deaths caused by running outside. Include the following in your video or tape:

- the importance of considering health and safety for the athlete
- the hazards associated with running outside
- the specific hazards for the female runner
- things to consider when running at night or in winter
- tips to reduce the chances of injury while running outside.

Remember!

If you feel dizzy, any pain, shortness of breath or excessive fatigue, stop or reduce your exercise immediately and see your GP before exercising again.

Training diary

When working with athletes it is important to maintain a training diary on a regular basis. The need to keep records of the training programme is often overlooked in the fitness industry, possibly because it is time-consuming. However, it is important for these reasons:

- health and safety: records can increase a trainer's awareness of previous injuries or illnesses
- progression: records allow the fitness trainer to see whether there is progression in the programme
- communication: records allow the trainer to gain an understanding of the athlete's history, which should aid communication
- evaluation: the information stored can be used as a part of the evaluation process
- professionalism: keeping records shows the fitness trainer has a level of competence and is following good practice.

Progression

It is important that the progress is logged so that you can monitor the programme on a regular basis. You may make comments on the following:

- How did you find the intensity?
- Could you have performed more reps and sets?
- What were your thoughts on the types of exercises you were performing?
- Do you feel you have progressed from the previous session?
- Any other relevant thoughts.

Attitude

A major part of a training session is based on your attitude or approach to training. You should use the diary on a regular basis to make comments on your attitude so that you can explain the reason for good or poor sessions. In addition, to gain a wider picture the fitness trainer should make comments on the attitude shown.

Motivation

Motivation is the most important ingredient for success when carrying out a training programme. The athlete will need to be motivated in the sessions to maximise the training effects. The motivation of the athlete may decrease due to:

- lack of improvement in fitness
- boredom due to repetitive exercise
- poor sporting performances
- external pressures, e.g. college work.

Links to goals

Within the diary you should try to comment on your goals, which you identified at the start of the programme. You could consider the following questions.

- How close are you to your goals?
- Are the goals still SMART targets?
- Do the goals need to be revised?
- Is the training too focused on one particular goal?

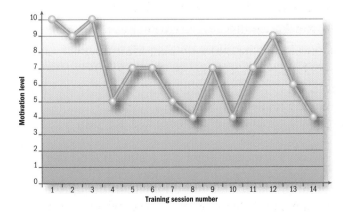

To monitor motivation, the athlete could complete a motivation chart like this

Assessment practice

1 Select an athlete and ask him or her to agree to engage in a six-week training programme with you. This may be a fellow student from your group, or an athlete you have previously identified, such as an older athlete you know.

   a Interview your client regarding the components of fitness he or she would like to improve through training. Decisions about this should be based on the needs and the goals of the client. For example, a football player may wish to improve speed and aerobic fitness.

   b Gather information from the client about his or her commitments relating to work, family or study. Produce a timetable showing the client's commitments such as study time. This will be important for identifying possible testing and training sessions.

   c Carry out fitness tests to establish a baseline score for the relevant components of fitness. These will form the basis of your evaluation. Look at Unit 6: Fitness Testing for Sport and Exercise for more information on fitness testing.

2 Devise a six-week training programme for your athlete based on the relevant components of fitness and using a range of training methods.

   Use the following methods to log your training programme using a training diary:

   - timetable
   - diary
   - database
   - spreadsheet.

   Remember to apply the principles of training such as overload during the six-week period.

Grading tips

Grading Tip

In the interview, ask your client about the sports they play and the position or role they have, for example winger in football. This will allow you to make the programme specific to them. In terms of their commitments, make sure you can identify a possible extra training session (as a back up) so that if they do not make a session you have flexibility in the programme. When reporting your fitness tests, make sure you include:

- the name of the test
- the component of fitness tested, e.g. body composition
- units of measurement, e.g. metres or kilograms
- normative data rating, e.g. very good.

Grading Tip

When producing your training diary, make sure it includes the following information (where appropriate):

- dates of training sessions
- locations of training sessions
- frequency
- intensity
- time (duration)
- type (method of training, e.g. speed drills)
- sets
- reps
- rest periods (in interval training)
- competition results
- fitness testing results (before and after training)
- missed sessions
- any changes made during the programme for any reason, e.g. if the athlete suffered from a cold for a couple of days.

In this section you will consider the important aspects of monitoring and evaluating the training programme. As a fitness trainer, the evaluation of a programme is an important job because you may need to change things for future training programmes. For example, you might have set the intensity too high with an athlete, which needs to be changed in the future. A major part of the evaluation process should be based around reviewing whether the goals have been met and how they need to be changed in future.

Monitor

Recording information specific to the training programme can be done using the following methods:

- basic programme cards
- brief note format
- training logs, e.g. a diary
- timetables
- calendars
- personal organisers
- audio tapes
- video recorders.

It is now commonplace for fitness trainers to record training details using ICT such as:

- databases
- spreadsheets
- word-processed documents such as tables
- online journals.

Training diaries

Regardless of the method used for recording information, it is important that this is done in a professional and systematic manner. Records should be updated on a regular basis and filed securely using a logical filing system. The following information should be logged:

- dates of training sessions
- locations of training sessions
- frequency

- intensity
- time (duration)
- type (method of training, e.g. speed drills)
- sets
- reps
- rest periods (in interval training)
- competition results
- fitness test results (before and after training)
- missed sessions
- any changes made during the programme for any reason, e.g. if the athlete suffered from a cold for a couple of days
- future needs, e.g. to concentrate on improving speed.

As well as the basic programme, the fitness trainer should keep a number of other records including:

- personal contact details in case of emergency – stored confidentially for security reasons
- health questionnaires
- accident, injury or illness forms
- copies of any quality check questionnaires given to the athlete to assess the quality of service.

Remember!

Record training sessions in terms of times, distances, frequency, type, equipment used and competition results.

■ Date and details of sessions

The dates and details of training sessions should be recorded in the training diary.

■ Competition results

It is important to log competition results on a regular basis so that you can match it up with your training programme. If you are aware that you have just started to train at a lower intensity level, such as after returning from injury, then you can justify competition results that are below your usual standard. When logging competition results, consider the following (where applicable):

- points scored
- final match score
- half-time score
- distance covered
- time taken
- ranking.

■ Fitness test results

When reporting the tests you carried out, it is important to record the following information:

- the name of the test
- the component of fitness tested, e.g. body composition
- units of measurement, e.g. metres or kilograms
- normative data rating, e.g. very good.

For more information on fitness testing, see Unit 6: Fitness Testing for Sport and Exercise.

▲ It is vital for a fitness trainer to review the athlete's progress on a regular basis to discuss the effectiveness of the training programme

Coach/trainer feedback and reviews

Feedback and reviews should take place on regular basis so that any issues with the training programme can be rectified as soon as possible.

Evaluate

An athlete's training programme should be evaluated regularly to gauge its success and effectiveness. Through appropriate fitness tests, the programme should be evaluated to assess whether personal goals and objectives have been met.

Remember!

Evaluation allows a judgement to be made as to the health or fitness status of the athlete before, during and after the implementation of a training programme.

The evaluation should come from both the trainer and the athlete. The following areas should be brought into focus:

- the overall suitability of the programme in terms of structure, goals, time and equipment
- achievements: physical, psychological, social and health-related
- negative aspects: issues such as boredom and lack of motivation
- future needs: new or modified goals
- whether the athlete has received value for money.

Extent to which programme is achieving goals set

To discover how the training programme is working, it is suggested that you fitness test the athlete halfway through the programme. To read more about the fitness tests you could use with the athlete, see Unit 6: Fitness Testing for Sport and Exercise. If things are going well, you should maintain the programme or even increase the intensity/frequency of exercise. However, if the athlete is unlikely to achieve the goals set you should adapt the training programme and/or goals.

Remember!

A review halfway through a programme can help to pinpoint any problems and indicate where valuable changes could be made.

Modification of programme to achieve planned goals

It may be necessary to change the training programme due to a variety of reasons:

- injury to athlete
- change in facilities or equipment
- change in motivation level
- lack of progress
- boredom.

In these cases, it is important that we consider changing the:

- frequency of sessions or exercises
- intensity of exercises
- type of exercises being performed
- location of training
- overload and progression within the programme.

Grading tips

Grading Tip P5

In the description you could say how they tackled the sessions in terms of their effort and motivation (you can do this for all of the sessions). Describe where you feel they have improved, for example they can run for longer on the treadmill. You could also describe areas for improvement, such as they were weak on their stretching programme and only covered stretches for two muscle groups.

Assessment practice

1 Continue with the work you completed for the last assessment practice on page 124. Describe the strengths and areas for improvement after the six-week training programme has been completed. You could include performance results, trainer witness statements and fitness test results. **P5**

2 Explain the strengths and areas for improvement you identified above. You will need to link back to the initial goals of the athlete and state why there are strengths and areas for improvement. To do this you could:

- consider motivation levels
- talk about the attitude towards training
- mention any injuries
- add any other factors that you feel are relevant. **M3**

3 a Evaluate the effectiveness of the training programme. You should consider:

- the suitability of the exercises
- the number of training sessions

- the intensity of the exercises
- the duration of the exercises
- the change in the athlete's fitness levels
- whether the goals of the athlete were met
- the athlete's own evaluation
- any changes you would make in the future, such as including a swimming session to avoid boredom.

b Evaluate the achievements, successes and future needs of the athlete on this programme. Think about:

- the suitability of the exercises for the athlete
- the number of training sessions
- the intensity of the exercises
- the duration of the exercises
- the change in fitness levels (if available)
- whether the goals of the athlete were met
- the athlete's own evaluation (if available)
- any changes you would make and future activities you would suggest. **D2**

Knowledge check

1 Describe the differences between muscular endurance and muscular strength using sporting examples.

2 Identify ways in which an athlete can change a training programme to allow for overload.

3 As a fitness trainer, what factors connected with specificity would you need to consider when designing a training programme?

4 Describe the key components of fitness you would need to play a racket sport.

5 Describe the similarities and differences between interval, continuous and Fartlek training.

6 Detail the differences between static and ballistic stretching.

7 Describe the advantages of using resistance machines in a training session.

8 List the seven key principles of training.

9 Name three pieces of information you would expect to see in a training diary.

10 What does FITT stand for? Define each aspect.

11 Why is evaluation an important stage in relation to a training programme?

12 Describe how the fitness requirements would differ between a goalkeeper and a midfielder in football.

Preparation for assessment

Imagine you are working as a lead fitness trainer at your local fitness centre, which has just opened in your area. As part of the job specification you need to provide information to other fitness trainers, athletes and the wider community on the role of fitness for sport.

1 Your first task is to go onto the local radio station and have a chat on air with the DJ about the importance of fitness for three contrasting sports, which you can choose.

Produce a radio script that includes dialogue from you and the DJ. The role of the DJ is to ask relevant questions, to which you must provide appropriate answers on the three different sports. Within the script you need to describe the physical and skill-related fitness requirements for each sport. Here is an example of how you should lay out your script.

> *DJ:* You have mentioned that netball players require good levels of aerobic endurance to last the full match, but what else do they need?
>
> *Fitness trainer:* They also need speed to run up and down the court during the match.

P1

To meet the M1 and D1 criteria please refer to the following grading tips.

Grading tips

Grading Tip **M1**

You need to add more depth to your radio interview by explaining the requirements. To do this, you need to make the points in relation to the following.

- Why it is important to the individual or team.
- What would happen in the game situation if they lacked that component of fitness.
- Why you do not need a component of fitness for that sport. For example, shot putters do not need aerobic endurance because the activity only lasts a couple of seconds.

Grading Tip **D1**

You need to compare and contrast the three sports. To do this, consider:

- fitness requirements
- movement patterns
- length and intensity of play
- importance of the components of fitness
- joint and muscle involvement
- any other factors you have discovered.

2 Part of your job relates to the training of new fitness trainers at the centre as they spend time at the centre completing work experience. You have noticed that the trainee trainers need extra support on the different methods of training.

To aid their understanding, you are going to produce an A3 poster. This will be displayed in the centre to help the athletes understand the methods of training for the following fitness components:

- aerobic endurance
- muscular endurance
- flexibility
- speed
- strength
- power
- body composition.

On the poster you need to describe one method of fitness training for each of these components, for example ballistic stretching for flexibility. You should also include diagrams and illustrations to aid your description.

To meet the M2 criteria please refer to the following grading M2 tip.

Grading tips

Grading Tip **M2**

On your poster you need to fully explain what an athlete needs to do to carry out the methods of training, for example the intensity or time required. You should also include how the athlete can adapt the training to make it harder and show progression.

3 One of the fitness trainers has shown a personal interest in fitness programme design and has asked you for some advice and guidance. To aid this you

have said that he can go through the full process with you because you are working with a number of personal clients at the moment. You need to choose who you are producing the programme for, for example:

- a student who plays for a school/college team
- a family member who has not exercised for a couple of years
- a part-time work colleague who wants to improve their physique.

These are just examples – you could use an athlete of your own choice.

You are going to produce a written report, which includes a six-week fitness training programme and training diary.

a The training programme should include:

- short-term, medium-term and long-term goals of the athlete
- lifestyle information
- medical history (possibly through a questionnaire)
- information on physical activity history.

You can use the following session plan to detail the individual sessions over the six weeks, but over this period the sessions should incorporate the principles of training.

The report should also include a representation of a microcycle, mesocycle and macrocycle.

b For the training diary, which can be in the form of a table, you need to include information on:

- progression
- attitude to training
- motivation to training
- links to goals set
- any other relevant information.

c As a follow-on to the report, you have been asked to produce a presentation to the other fitness trainers on the strengths and areas for

Training session planner

Date: _____ Individual/group name: _____ Time of session: _____

Aims: _____ Session location: _____

Equipment required: _____

	Time	Content
Warm-up		
Main session		
Cool-down		

improvement you discovered when working with the athlete. In your presentation you need to describe the strengths (for example, improved flexibility by 6 cm on the sit-and-reach test) and the areas for improvement (for example, poor commitment to aerobic work, which resulted in no improvement in sporting performance). **P5**

To meet the M3 and D2 criteria please refer to the following grading tips.

Grading tips

Grading Tip **M3**

You need to explain these strengths and areas for improvement. You need to link back to the initial goals of the athlete and state why there are strengths and areas for improvement. To do this, you may:

- consider motivation levels
- talk about attitude towards training
- mention any injuries
- include any other factors that you feel are relevant

Grading Tip **D2**

You should consider:

- the suitability of the exercises
- the number of training sessions
- the intensity of the exercises

- the duration of the exercises
- the change in the athlete's fitness levels
- whether the goals of the athlete were met
- the athlete's own evaluation
- any changes you would make in the future, such as including a swimming session to avoid boredom.

Think about:

- the suitability of the exercises for the athlete
- the number of training sessions
- the intensity of the exercises
- the duration of the exercises
- the change in fitness levels (if available)
- whether the goals of the athlete were met
- the athlete's own evaluation (if available)
- any changes you would make and future activities you would suggest.

To achieve a pass grade the evidence must show that the learner is able to:	To achieve a merit grade the evidence must show that, in addition to the pass criteria, the learner is able to:	To achieve a distinction grade the evidence must show that, in addition to the pass and merit criteria, the learner is able to:
P1 Describe the physical fitness requirements and skill-related fitness requirements of three different sporting activities **Assessment practice Page 101**	**M1** Explain the physical fitness requirements and skill-related fitness requirements of three different sporting activities **Assessment practice Page 101**	**D1** Compare and contrast the physical fitness requirements and skill-related fitness requirements of three different sporting activities **Assessment practice Page 101**
P2 Describe one method of fitness training for six different components of physical fitness **Assessment practice Page 111**	**M2** Explain one method of fitness training for six different components of physical fitness **Assessment practice Page 111**	
P3 Produce a safe and effective six-week fitness training programme for a selected individual that incorporates the principles of training and periodisation **Assessment practice Page 124**		
P4 Produce a training diary for a selected individual **Assessment practice Page 124**		
P5 Describe the strengths and areas for improvement following completion of a selected six-week fitness training programme **Assessment practice Page 127**	**M3** Explain the strengths and areas for improvement following completion of a selected six-week fitness training programme **Assessment practice Page 127**	**D2** Evaluate a selected six-week fitness training programme providing recommendations for improvement and future activities **Assessment practice Page 127**

4 Sports coaching

Introduction

This unit discusses how a sports coach can work with a participant to help them develop their sports-specific skills and to develop themselves as sports participants.

The unit explores the roles, responsibilities and qualities of a successful sports coach and identifies the skills and knowledge that are required to effectively coach an individual or team of participants. A good coach will not only know about these things but will also be able to adapt their coaching to meet the needs of their participants, the situation and the coaching environment.

As you begin to understand what is needed to be a good sports coach, you will be able to identify the basic techniques used by coaches to develop performance and develop an appreciation of the coaching process. You will be given the opportunity to put these principles into practice by planning, delivering and evaluating your own coaching sessions.

After completing this unit you should be able to achieve the following outcomes:

- Understand the roles, responsibilities and skills of sports coaches.

- Understand the techniques used by coaches to improve the performance of athletes.

- Be able to plan a sports coaching session.

- Be able to deliver a sports coaching session.

Think it over

Imagine it is your first year as a coach of a team and you reach the biggest cup final possible in your sport. It falls to you to select the team and the tactics that you will play. You do your planning, analyse the opposition and pick your starting line-up. You make a controversial decision about including a player who is not fully fit but you think it is worth the gamble.

The match starts and within minutes you are behind, then your 'gamble' goes horribly wrong as the player's injury reoccurs and he has to come off. Your greatest dream becomes a nightmare as you fall further behind and at the halfway point are facing a mountain to climb and likely humiliation. What do you do at the break? What do you say? What changes do you make? Your knowledge of your players and what they are able to do comes to the fore and you make some changes including a substitution that allows your star player to play their usual role. Will the changes reverse the score or at best save you from embarrassment? You watch anxiously as your team scores, then again and then... dramatically the scores are level – unbelievable! Your team goes on to win in a dramatic shoot-out and the greatest moment of your career sees your team finish as the Champions!

The highs and lows of coaching are reflected in this simple summary of one of the greatest football matches of all time. A coach has a variety of roles to play and decisions to make, some lead to success, some lead to defeat but a sound knowledge of the coaching process and of the performers you are working with will help convince you that anything is possible with good coaching. If you don't believe me, then ask Rafa Benitez and his Liverpool team that won the Champions League in 2005!

It is often said that behind every good sports performer is a good coach. This is undoubtedly true with many great teams and individuals openly admitting that they would not have been successful if they had not had a good coach to help guide and prepare them. In some sports the coach plays a very high profile role and is clearly an obvious part of the team. In other sports the coach's profile is considerably lower. Regardless of the profile that their sport gives them, the coach is very influential and will play a major part in any success.

Coaches at all levels can develop the characteristics, knowledge and skills of top coaches. Many good coaches are quite content to operate with lower level performers and still get the same rewards. The rewards that you get from coaching are dependent on your reasons for coaching – seeing a young tennis player successfully play a backhand shot for the first time can be as equally rewarding as seeing your team lift a trophy. Most coaches never reach the heights of working with elite performers but get as much out of coaching as the top names do. Coaches of all levels make an equally significant contribution to sport and the development of participants. Each year some of these coaches are recognised for their contributions to sport at a prestigious event in London in the presence of the Princess Royal, Princess Anne to celebrate the Coach of the Year Awards.

The terms 'coach' and 'coaching' are used in many different contexts and you may have heard them being used among business people in the phrases 'executive coaching', 'business coaching' or 'life coaching'. They are, of course, also used in a sports context to describe a person or a process associated with sport performance. But what do the terms mean?

▲ A sports coach is someone who assists the learning and development of another person or team of people in order to improve their performance in a sport, and who supports the personal development of individuals using sport as a vehicle for change and development

Activity

Access the **sports coach UK** website and the pages relating to the Coaching Awards at www.sportscoachuk.org/Events+and+Courses/Coaching+Awards.

1 How many different awards does **sports coach UK** present each year?

2 Two of the awards are named after famous people in coaching. Who are they named after and what did these people achieve in coaching?

3 Who won these awards last year?

Whichever context the terms are used in they mean much the same thing. A coach is someone who is involved in the development of other people through helping them learn and change the way they do things in order to improve themselves or their performance. Whether this is in a business, sporting or general 'life' sense the concept is the same. Coaching, therefore, describes the complex processes and interactions through which this learning and development takes place.

Activity

Make a list of the reasons that you think people might have for wanting to participate in sport. This list should include both sport-related rewards (e.g. winning medals) and other physical or emotional benefits (e.g. feeling more self-confident).

Taking it further

There are many reasons why society, local authorities and the government may wish people to become involved in sport.

Make a list of some of these reasons and see if you can find local examples of initiatives or programmes that have been developed to facilitate these different reasons for sport participation.

Sport is just another context in which an individual can learn and develop to improve themselves or their performance. Typically, we see a sports coach as someone who operates within a particular sport and who helps participants develop and practise sports-specific skills so that they can perform better in that sport. However, increasingly within society people are turning to sport and sports coaching not just as a way to get better at a particular sport but also to develop a range of other personal skills and to improve their general health and way of life. A sports coach, therefore, has to be able, not only to provide learning opportunities in a specific sport, but also to help individuals develop as people. To achieve this, the sports coach needs to be able to fulfil a number of different roles.

Think it over

Consider the different roles of a coach and try to identify examples of things that a coach might do when fulfilling each of these different roles.

Roles

In order for you as a coach to effectively develop a sports performer both as a participant in a sport and as a person, you will need to adopt a variety of different roles when coaching. These roles can be categorised as innovator, friend, manager, trainer, role model and educator.

Innovator

Many people see the coach as the 'font of all knowledge' but this is not necessarily the case. A coach is not expected to know everything but there is an expectation that a good coach will have the skills to be able to find solutions to problems. They should be able to think through problems and use their knowledge and experience to come up with new ideas and approaches to make training more fun and effective or to maintain a participant's interest and involvement.

A former Olympic champion once used this motto:

> 'If you always do what you have always done,
> You will always get what you always got.'

This suggests that doing the same thing all the time will always produce the same results. If, as we have already seen, coaching is about development and improvement, there is a need for sports coaches to be brave enough to try new things in order to get different, and hopefully better, results. This is why you, as a coach, need to access and use the latest scientific and technical knowledge to help inform your coaching practice. New and innovative

The Fosbury Flop – an example of coaching innovation ▶

approaches to coaching can help gain the extra advantages necessary for success.

Coaching sessions which are repetitive and which contain the same activities week after week will become boring and participants will soon lose interest and become frustrated. A good coach will be able to maintain performers' interest in training by devising new ideas and practices that encourage continued development. This may simply be about finding new ways to do things, so that sessions do not become boring, or it may be that the coach comes up with new ideas for practices, match tactics and training methods to solve problems and make improvements.

Effective coaches should also find time to reflect on their own coaching and, where necessary, return to the role of student and further develop their own understanding and professional development by learning from other coaches and other sports.

Activity

One function of the coach is to motivate participants.

1 Think about a coach you have either been coached by or worked with, and describe an example of how he or she motivated you to train.

2 What sort of things did the coach do to make the sessions fun?

3 Now think of a top coach who has been successful. Can you think of any examples of how he or she motivates performers to achieve?

4 What types of things might you wish to do as a coach to motivate people attending your coaching sessions?

Case study: Sam Allardyce

Sam Allardyce managed Bolton for five seasons after they were promoted to the Premiership. The Englishman introduced advanced scientific principles into his coaching. Bolton was one of the first Premiership teams to utilise the motion analysis software – ProZone® – to identify player workloads during a match, and players are subject to strict nutritional analysis and dietary controls on match day. Allardyce consulted with business guru Humphrey Walters – one of Clive Woodward's backroom staff when England won the 2003 rugby union World Cup – and players had access to a range of support services including massages, t'ai chi, yoga and Pilates to help them prepare and recover.

Had this type of approach belonged to foreign managers such as Arsène Wenger and José Mourinho it would have been branded as innovative and forward-thinking, but Allardyce struggles to shake off the old-school English manager tag and some people think his approach is gimmicky and question why he had such a large backroom staff (17 at the last count).

1 **What new technological developments did Sam Allardyce bring into play at Bolton?**

2 **Use the Internet to find out what ProZone® does and how it can help footballers.**

3 **Can you identify any other sport science developments that are now commonplace among Premiership football teams?**

Friend

Coaches and their performers spend a lot of time together. They will share positive experiences as well as negative ones, and they need to be able to do this in a friendly and respectful environment. The performance environment can be tough at times and performers will need someone to talk to in order to help them cope with the demands of training and competing. The 'friend' coach may need to be there to pick up the pieces if things go wrong and to be an outlet for emotions. The coach may also need to be there to help performers keep their feet on the ground if they are successful.

The coach who acts as a friend may also be able to motivate the performer. In most instances the performers you will work with will be highly self-motivated. They will come to you for coaching because they enjoy the sport and the coaching experiences they get. It is up to you to ensure that you manage the coaching environment in a way that enables them to maintain this self-motivation.

To achieve this, you should think about what motivates your performers to participate and what drives them to perform. If you understand why a person takes part in a sport, you will be better able to create a coaching environment that allows him or her to remain motivated.

There are numerous factors that may motivate people to take part in sports. These include enjoyment, to meet other people, to improve fitness, to give themselves a challenge, to be in a competitive environment, to gain some form of reward, or in some cases, to please others.

Manager

The role of manager can relate to the management of a number of different aspects of coaching. The manager may be expected to not only manage people, but also coaching sessions and training programmes, as well as a variety of administrative tasks.

Principally though, the manager should be able to demonstrate good leadership skills and be able to manage and direct other people effectively. The success or otherwise of a coach will depend largely on his or her ability to manage the other people in the coaching environment in an authoritative and respectful manner. Some people suggest that there are distinct styles of coaching and all coaches fall into one of several clearly defined categories. It is perhaps too simplistic to categorise coaching styles in this way. It is more appropriate to suggest that the styles used when coaching and managing the coaching environment exist as a pool of approaches with coaches selecting different styles to fit the context in which they are operating. Typical coaching styles range from the autocratic coach – someone who is the only decision-maker and who tells performers what to do – through to the more laissez-faire style of coaching which sees a more flexible and relaxed approach. These two styles are extremes and modern coaching now advocates a participant-centred style of coaching which falls between these two and creates a more democratic style of coaching in which participants are given the opportunity to inform the decision-making process. No single style is necessarily right or wrong and each of the styles mentioned here can have a place in a particular situation. For example, in situations where safety is important the autocratic approach may be necessary to ensure adherence to safety procedures. Similarly, young participants may not be able to contribute to decision-making processes and thus too much of a democratic or laissez-faire approach will not be effective.

The management of people is about trying to ensure that they perform to the best of their ability. In individual sports, the coach is aiming to manage the development of the performer effectively and to ensure that an appropriate relationship exists between coach and performer, so that optimal performance can be achieved. In team sports, the management role of the coach involves selecting teams, and in this context the 'manager' coach not only has to select the best players but also has to ensure that the players fit together and the team is able to perform to the best of its ability.

In some sports and at high levels of coaching, the coach may not be the only person involved in the coaching process. There may be assistant coaches, specialist coaches or support staff working alongside the coach. In these instances the coach has to manage the contribution of other coaching staff while maintaining the development of the performer as the focus for coaching activities.

Case study: Gary Lough

The following is an extract from a *Sunday Times* interview with Paula Radcliffe published on the morning of her world record performance in the London Marathon in April 2003. Paula's coach, Gary Lough, is also her husband and fulfils a number of different roles.

We are sitting in an apartment above Gerard Hartmann's clinic on Limerick's O'Connell Street. Radcliffe and Lough have been here in this room so many times that they see the sprawling Kenyan flag on the wall as part of the wallpaper. It is eight o'clock on a midweek evening, 12 days before the London Marathon, and they are half-watching 'EastEnders'.

'Gary is more into it than I am,' she says.

'That's not true,' he responds. 'You watch it more than I do.'

So they continue back and forth, neither prepared to back down. Spiky defiance is their way. 'We're both strong characters,' she says. 'We're also very secure with each other. We don't think, "Oh well, if I tell him what I really think, he might go off and leave me." That security probably comes from spending a lot of time together and being good friends even before we got together as a couple. We can say exactly what we think, and it will be taken like that.'

They disagree, too, on who's got the harder part. She says it is he. He has to be there all the time – training partner, facilitator, manager, personal assistant, media director and husband. 'You can't have the same motivation as I have, you don't get the end result,' and when she tells him that, he realises she struggles to understand that his motivation is seeing her do it.

Lough may also be her greatest fan. He tells a story of what could easily have been a calamitous accident towards the end of their time in Albuquerque. Twenty minutes into a 24-mile training run, Radcliffe was overtaking a young cyclist when the girl unwittingly turned her bike and clipped Radcliffe's trailing leg.

Lough was right behind, and watched as she flew through the air and crash-landed on the cycle path. Bending over her, he was horrified by the extent of the damage. Her elbows and knees were cut and burned, her shoulders were bruised, her face was a mess. There was a gash on her chin and blood everywhere. Suspecting that she might be seriously injured, she cried.

He saw her now only as his wife and soul mate. 'Your face,' he said. 'Your face is ruined.'

'I don't care about my face,' she cried.

'What do you mean, you don't care about your face?'

▲ **Gary Lough and Paula Radcliffe**

'I don't run with my bloody face.'

Why should we be surprised that alongside the ladylike calmness, there is a fiercely competitive athlete? How else could she have endured the years of near-misses and come through to enjoy the season she had last year?

Maybe we forget that this woman sat in the stadium at the 2001 world championships in Edmonton, held up a sign saying 'EPO Cheats Out', and wanted one of her fellow athletes to take the taunt personally. We talk about decision-making and how she likes to have control over her running. 'Well, I do, because it's my life. It's my career. I don't want Gary to have complete control.

'In a week before a big race, he will keep things from me so I am not distracted or bothered, but generally I like to know what's going on. Sometimes he might think he knows, and then he might get a shock when we discuss it, because I want to do it differently. He's very good about it, because he knows that at the end of the day, it's me going out and racing.

'We discuss things, I will say, "What do you think I should do?" but it's me that has to make the decision. On the business and commercial side I bow to his greater expertise, but on the side of running, the decision must be mine. After winning the 10,000 metres in the European championships at Munich last year, I thought of running in the 5,000 metres. We discussed it a lot, but he wouldn't tell me what he thought, because he knew it had to come from me.'

1 **Identify the different roles that Gary Lough plays.**

2 a **What are the disadvantages of having to play so many different roles?**

b **What are the advantages?**

Activity

Increasingly, certainly in elite sport, the sports coach no longer operates in isolation. Make a list of the other people who you think may work alongside a coach.

Taking it further

1 Select an elite sports team or performer – it could be a Premiership soccer team, a national rugby team or an Olympic athlete – and try to find out using their website or related Internet material who their head coach/manager is.

2 Try to identify all the different people who work alongside the head coach/manager and what functions they fulfil.

Depending on the structure of the sport or club within which the coach works, a coach may also have to adopt a number of administrative roles. These may include organising venues for practice and competition, registering and entering performers for competitions, coordinating the activities of other coaches and support staff, and dealing with parents and officials.

Trainer

The coach's role as a trainer is very much related to ensuring that their participants are able to meet the physical demands of the sport they are training to be involved in. In addition, there may also be a need to help participants meet the psychological demands of their sport. The coach is therefore expected, as a trainer, to devise and run training programmes to help develop the physical and psychological abilities of performers so that they are able to perform the technical skills appropriately.

The perception of the role of the trainer is probably most commonly associated with the physical development of performers. Virtually all sports place a physical demand on participants, and there is plenty of evidence that suggests participants can not only improve their performance in a sport by developing their general and sport-specific fitness levels, but also improve their general health and well-being through well-planned and well-structured training. The 'trainer' coach, armed with a good understanding of the different components of fitness (see Unit 3), should be able to devise a training programme that enables performers to develop and maintain good all-round health and be able to implement appropriate fitness training routines to enable participants to improve their fitness levels in order to be able to cope with the physical demands of their sport.

With careful planning a coach should also be able to include in the training programme clear progressions in technical development, and also routines and practices that help the performer to develop the psychological skills needed to meet the challenges of the sport.

Role model

As we have discussed already, sports coaching is no longer just about becoming better at a sport. Participants have a variety of different reasons for taking part in a coaching session and typically they will watch and copy the actions and behaviours of the person coaching them. This is particularly true of younger participants who will look to the coach for guidance and, therefore, a coach can be a very influential person. It is therefore important that the coach models good practice in all that they say and do and that they behave in a way that earns and maintains trust and respect. You need to ensure that the influence you exert as a coach is positive. There are recognised standards and practices that a coach should adhere to, and some issues related to these are covered in more detail on pages 143–150.

Educator

The educational role of the coach can take a number of different forms. The role may be sport specific and be related to the teaching and learning of sport skills and techniques, or it may be related to the more generic development of life and social skills. Whichever it is, the coach needs to be aware that there is a variety of different teaching methods and styles, and they need to be able to match the appropriate teaching methods to the stage, experience and motives of the people they are working with. A coach working with a young beginner would be expected to use different teaching methods from those used when working with an expert performer.

Young athletes and beginners who are not familiar with the skills of a sport will need to learn them and be given the opportunity to practise them. When educating, the coach should be able to understand how people learn new skills, and be able to devise practices and drills that will allow skills to be developed so that they can be performed correctly. Correct performance of a skill is important to ensure that a participant does not injure themselves or others when performing it and can also make a difference between winning and losing in a competitive situation. Similarly, developing performers or established competitors will require appropriate instruction to allow them to refine their skills. They may also need to be taught more advanced skills, which will make them more effective.

When teaching a skill, a coach will need to draw on his or her own experience and knowledge of sports skills and be able to demonstrate and explain how they are performed. In addition, the coach will need to educate performers about how the skills fit together and contribute to the overall performance of the sport. This will involve introducing performers to tactics, and patterns and styles of play.

An effective coach will not only teach somebody a new skill but also how and when to use it safely and effectively. A knowledgeable coach will be able to develop tactical awareness and strategy in performers in a way that is appropriate to their level of performance. Teaching detailed tactical manoeuvres and set plays in rugby to a group of young performers relatively new to the game would be inappropriate, yet a team which is looking for performance enhancement may benefit from new tactical inputs in training so that they can progress to a higher level of performance.

As well as the technical and tactical skills of a sport, a participant may also need to learn more general skills associated with sports participation. A coach needs to educate performers by teaching them how to control their emotions and develop their self-esteem through sport, and also by helping them to develop social skills such as teamwork, cooperation, citizenship, fair play and being able to compete with, and lose to, others. Through sport, young people can also develop personally by being encouraged to consider their own health and welfare and by being empowered to learn life skills and develop their own values and attitudes. Also, more senior participants may need to use the physical aspects of training to maintain a healthy lifestyle. Thus, the coach should be aware of the different implications and effects of the coaching sessions that they organise and seek to meet the variety of needs that different participants have.

Introduce and explain → Demonstrate → Practise → Analyse and correct

▲ Developing skills

Taking it further

1 Use a dictionary to define the following words:

   - coach
   - manager
   - teacher
   - trainer
   - educator
   - role model
   - innovator
   - friend.

2 Discuss with a partner how these words and their meanings might apply in a sports coaching context.

Coaching is a complex process in which a coach seeks to create a suitable environment in which they can facilitate and support participants to learn, develop and improve either their sports performance or their general character. To achieve this successfully the coach needs to be able to fulfil a variety of roles. How and when the coach has to play all of these different roles will depend on many factors, such as the aims, ability, experience and age of participants. Coaches who work with young beginner athletes will be required to fulfil different roles from coaches working with elite adult athletes.

Primarily, coaches working with young people will have a trainer or educator role to play because the emphasis may be on learning and developing new skills. They may also need to adopt a more personal, friendly and role-model type approach. However, an elite adult athlete will probably have mastered the skills of his or her sport and require the coach to play the roles of manager and innovator rather more than those of educator and role model.

Remember!

- A sports coach is somebody who works with people to develop their understanding and ability in a sport and to help develop them as people.
- A coach has many roles to play: educator, trainer, manager, role model, innovator and friend.
- These roles can vary according to who the coach is working with and what the aims, ability, experience and age of the participants are.

Responsibilities

Whatever role you undertake as a coach, you have a responsibility to ensure that sport is safe, inclusive, and ethically sound and meets the needs of those participating. Given the influential position of the coach and the important role that sport can play in the development of individuals, coaches have a duty to ensure that a person's experiences of sport are positive and long lasting.

To fulfil this duty coaches face a number of responsibilities towards the participants, their sport, the coaching profession and themselves. These responsibilities fall into three main categories.

- Professional responsibilities: the demonstration of proper personal and professional behaviour and conduct in light of legal and ethical duties.
- Health and safety responsibilities: the creation and maintenance of a safe environment for participants to receive sports coaching.
- Coaching responsibilities: the delivery of appropriate coaching sessions to facilitate the development and enjoyment of participants.

A good coach will always seek to meet these responsibilities and try to set a good example through modelling good practice.

Legal obligations

When coaching, coaches need to be fully aware of their legal responsibilities. We are all governed by the rules of the society we live in (common law), and these laws apply regardless of whether we are on the playing field or in the local shopping centre. In addition, in order to maintain fair play in competitive sport, coaches and performers are subject to the rules and laws of their sport.

As well as being aware of what is and what is not allowed in their sport, coaches must also be aware of how the law can affect coaching. Coaches should make every effort to ensure that they and their performers do not do anything that may be considered illegal or unethical.

■ Child protection

Common law also applies to matters relating to equal opportunities (see page 148), race relations, disability discrimination, child protection and age discrimination, all of which could affect a coach in some way or other. Of obvious implication is the Protection of Children Act (1999) as many coaches will undoubtedly spend a large proportion of their time working with and coaching children and young performers. This means that coaches will inevitably develop close relationships with their young participants and in some instances fulfil some of the more intimate roles of coaching – being a friend, 'parent', consoler or disciplinarian. In these instances, and throughout all coaching activities with children and young people, coaches must avoid engaging in any form of inappropriate contact or behaviour that may breach child protection guidelines.

Taking it further

Using the Internet, undertake a search to find details of the following laws.

- The Disability Discrimination Act (1995).
- The Race Relations (Amendment) Act (2000).
- The Children Act (1989).
- Protection of Children Act (1999).
- The Sex Discrimination Act 1975 (Amendment) Regulations 2003.

Write a short summary of how you think each of these Acts may impact on your future work as a coach.

Recent additions to the Protection of Children Act (1999) introduced a requirement that all people working with children should be checked for any previous offences related to children. Employers of coaches are now required to request a police check of the coaches' previous history via the Criminal Records Bureau. Full details of the legal implications of this Act and coaches' responsibilities under all related Acts is beyond the scope of this text but you should be aware of the need to be familiar with aspects of common law which may impact on your coaching.

■ Insurance

Many different sources of liability may affect a coach. The most directly relevant areas include common law and negligence.

Common law relates to the fundamental laws of the society that we live in. Sport does not exist outside of real life. And thus real life laws still apply. The most obvious examples of this can be seen by considering the laws of common assault. There have been numerous examples, mainly from soccer and rugby, whereby players involved in incidents during play have been subsequently arrested and charged with assault. In 1995 Manchester United footballer Eric Cantona was arrested for assault after he 'kung-fu' kicked a fan in the crowd after being sent-off during a match, while an incident in 2006 where Manchester City footballer Ben Thatcher struck an opponent across the face leaving him unconscious resulted in a police enquiry

Case study: Beyond the law?

In the early stages of the 2006/2007 FA Premiership season, Manchester City were at home to Portsmouth. During the match an incident occurred in which, according to the *Sun* newspaper, the Portsmouth midfielder [Pedro] Mendes chased the ball as it ran towards the sidelines – but as he kicked it up field [Ben] Thatcher came across him and whacked his jaw with a forearm smash.

The incident led to Mendes being left unconscious and he was given oxygen after fitting while unconscious.

Thatcher was booked by the referee and subsequently investigated by the police and the FA resulting in a ban and a club fine of £120,000.

Amidst the subsequent press coverage, the Manchester City manager was quoted as saying:

'From my point of view, once the players cross the white line they are under the authority of the referee, they are the ones who should deal with things that happen during matches. Police forces in this country are overburdened as it is.'

1 **What do you think about the reaction of the Manchester City manager?**

2 **Was his comment in line with good practice regarding professional conduct and the ethical and legal obligations of coaches?**

into assault. Unfortunately, some incidents which appear unsavoury on the field of play do seem to go unpunished by society, although sport governing bodies do act with fines and bans. Soccer's most glamorous showpiece, the World Cup Final was marred in 2006 when Zinedine Zidane of France head butted an opponent in the chest after alleged racist remarks. The Frenchman was sent off and subsequently banned by football's governing body, but his actions on the field of play did not set a good example. Coaches should ensure that their participants, and indeed their own conduct, do not encroach beyond the boundaries of acceptable behaviour.

Negligence is another important area for coaches to be aware of. Coaches must understand that should a participant suffer an injury, loss or damage to their property as a result of the coach's negligence, the coach may be deemed liable. Negligence can be a result of both actions and omissions – what you do and what you don't do. As a coach you will have a 'duty of care' towards participants. A coach has a duty to be:

- safe: in relation to coaching this means the equipment you are using, the environment you are coaching in, the size of the group you are coaching and the nature of the activities you choose to use

- qualified: coaches should hold relevant, current qualifications which are at the appropriate level for the group they are coaching

- insured: coaches should hold insurance cover appropriate for the sport they are involved with and the status of their employment. In most instances a national governing body qualification is linked to insurance cover. It is your responsibility to check whether you are insured.

- competent: to select appropriate activities to match the age and ability range of the participants.

As is the case with most things in coaching, good planning and adherence to the principles of good practice can help you to avoid falling foul of the law both in terms of common law issues and negligence.

▲ Coaches often spend much time working with children

Taking it further

1 Access the **sports coach UK** website at www.sportscoachuk.org and download or note down any information you can find about codes of conduct and child protection.

2 Prepare a short summary document for your classmates, highlighting the key messages.

3 What educational workshops or resources does **sports coach UK** offer relating to:

   a disability sport

   b child protection

   c equity issues

   d gender-related issues?

4 Access the website for the governing body of your sport. Does the governing body have a Child Protection Policy?

5 Access the Child Protection in Sport Unit website (www.thecpsu.org.uk). Use the information available on this site to produce a single A4 sheet of information that you could give to parents of children you coach.

An NSPCC report, 'Child Maltreatment in the United Kingdom', was published in November 2000. This major research report included the following statistics:

- 43 per cent of the young people surveyed identified bullying or being discriminated against as the most common source of distress or upset.
- Bullying occurred as a result of some personal feature (e.g. size, race, speech or dress).
- 14–15 per cent of the young people said they had been physically attacked while being bullied, and many reported that they had had possessions stolen.
- 6 per cent of boys under 18 and 4 per cent of girls under 18 reported a serious lack of supervision.
- 6 per cent of boys under 18 and 8 per cent of girls under 18 reported serious physical abuse.

1 **What would you do as a coach to prevent bullying and physical abuse from taking place in your coaching sessions?**

2 **With a partner, design a poster or leaflet that you would give to your performers to warn of the dangers of bullying.**

Professional conduct

A coach is often viewed as a person of authority who has a certain amount of power. It is important that a coach knows how to use this authority and power appropriately and not to abuse it. Unfortunately, there are some coaches who have used their position to achieve inappropriate gains and it is a coach's responsibility to ensure that they know how to behave and that they know what constitutes good and acceptable practice and what does not. Keeping your coaching practice within the boundaries of acceptability is an important aspect of good coaching.

Coaches should always ensure that what they do is in line with acceptable standards and good practice. All coaches should demonstrate a professional approach to their participants and ensure that they are fair, honest and considerate of participants' needs. As with many professions, coaching promotes its own code of conduct. This ensures that coaches practice in the most ethical and professional manner. Across all levels of coaching it is stressed that coaches 'must demonstrate… a high degree of honesty, integrity and competence'. **sports coach UK**, the lead body for coaching and coach education in the UK, has produced a code of conduct for sports coaches, and this forms the basis for good coaching practice. It is underpinned by the following key principles, with which all coaches should familiarise themselves.

- Rights: to respect and champion the rights of every participant in sport.
- Relationships: to develop open and honest relationships with participants.
- Responsibilities: to demonstrate appropriate personal behaviour and conduct and achieve a high level of competence through qualifications and continued professional development.

An integral part of coaching is the responsibility of a coach to keep his or her coaching knowledge up to date. This will ensure that what coaches are doing is accurate and has not been superseded by new information, and will help coaches to continue to provide a safe coaching environment and retain the respect of colleagues and participants.

Most national governing bodies of sport provide courses for coaches to update and develop their coaching knowledge, and gain professional recognition for their knowledge and expertise. Recent developments have identified a vision for coaching up to and beyond 2012. As part of this vision, coach education standards have been addressed and the standardisation of coaching qualifications through the implementation of the UK Coaching Certificate will ensure that all coaches will receive high-quality coach education delivered by qualified tutors in flexible and accessible formats. Coaches will have no excuse not to be appropriately trained and qualified and, with the imminent implementation of licensing and registering schemes for coaches, continuing professional development for coaches is very much a feature of modern coaching.

Health and safety

All coaching sessions should take place with a consideration being given to health and safety issues. They should take place in a safe environment that allows the benefits to be maximised and the risks to be minimised. The health and safety responsibilities of a coach can be split into three essential components (see also pages 166–67).

- The safety of the facilities: when you are preparing a coaching session you must consider the facilities in which the session is to take place. You must ensure that the activities you are planning can be done safely with the space and equipment you have available. You must also make sure that you are aware of any emergency procedures that may need to be followed and what should be done in the event of an emergency. In short, a coach must undertake a full risk assessment of the venue and make sure that he or she knows how to deal with any incidents that may arise.

- The safety of the activities: a good coach will select practices and activities that are safe and technically correct. They should pose no risk to the performer. In selecting activities the coach needs to consider the following points:
  o Performers should always undertake an appropriate warm-up before attempting any demanding activities.
  o Performers should not be required to perform activities of which they are not physically or technically capable.
  o Performers should always undertake activities that remain within the rules of the sport.
  o Coaches should not allow activities that are unsafe, technically incorrect or against the rules of a sport.

- The safety of the participant: if a coach appropriately addresses the safety issues related to the coaching venue, the equipment and the selected activities as suggested above, the safety of the participant will have been addressed. Coaches should remain aware of potential risks to ensure that there are no instances where the safety of the participant is compromised.

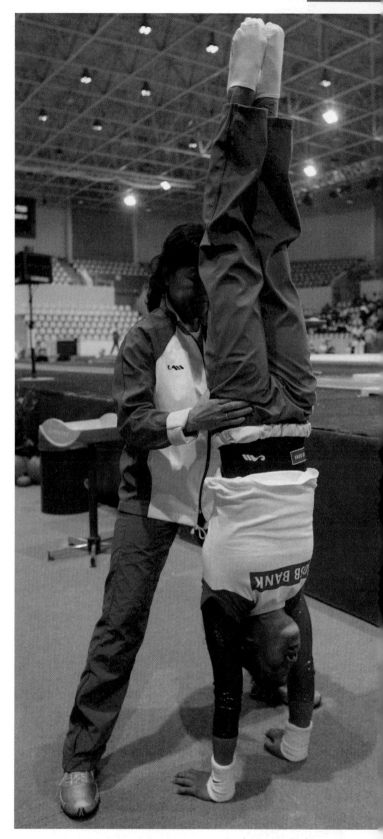

▲ Good practice makes the safety of the performers paramount

Equal opportunities

While sport is often seen as a physically competitive activity, this should not be seen as a reason for excluding certain groups of people from gaining the benefits of sport and sports coaching. Sport should be equitable in nature and all individuals within society should be given an equal opportunity to take part in sport. Making sure that your coaching is consistent with equal opportunities legislation and good practice is an important responsibility.

On their coaching website **sports coach UK** states Sport England's definition of equal opportunities as 'treating people as individuals and providing them with opportunities on the basis of their skills, talents and qualifications so that they are neither disadvantaged nor denied access on the grounds of their age, disability, ethnicity, race, sex or sexual orientation'. The focus of this definition is that people should not be disadvantaged or denied access to sport and it is the responsibility of the coach to ensure that coaching sessions are adaptable in terms of their content, timing and structure to allow anybody who wants to, to take part. Nobody is suggesting, for example, that a visually-impaired person should train in a full contact situation with a rugby team – health and safety and common sense would suggest otherwise – but there is no reason why, for example, a tennis session cannot be adapted to include a wheelchair user. The London Marathon is a great example of an event which fully embraces the diversity of the population and is one of the few major events that allow people of all abilities and disabilities to compete on the same stage.

With increasing job opportunities in sports coaching there is also a need for the coaching profession to ensure that jobs in coaching are also subject to equal opportunities. Most local authorities, national governing bodies and other sports clubs and organisations would now consider themselves equal opportunities employers. Thus, the barriers that have previously prevented minority groups from moving into coaching are being removed and, therefore, the time is right for the coaching population to better reflect the population at large.

Knowledge of the coaching environment

Coaching is about developing people and their understanding and abilities in particular areas. It is not simply about a specific sport. You will have almost certainly heard people saying that they coach football or that they coach athletics, the reality is that they actually coach people! Your responsibilities as a coach are to the people who you are coaching and as such you should have a good knowledge of the coaching environment that you are working in.

A key responsibility that you have as a coach is to provide coaching sessions that meet the individual needs of the participants. Whether you are working with beginner tennis players or elite-standard high jumpers, you have the responsibility to plan and design training programmes and coaching sessions that will help them develop and learn and improve their performances. Coaching sessions should provide participants with the opportunity to develop and maximise their potential. Each session should be well organised and planned and offer participants the opportunity to develop an appropriate range of skills.

Coaching sessions should be constructed so that they meet the demands of the participants, and if they form part of an ongoing programme, they should show progression and variation from one session to the next. To help you meet this responsibility you might wish to discuss with the participants what their desired goals and outcomes might be and then you will be able to plan your coaching to help achieve the identified outcomes.

In some instances the performance levels and demands of the participants might be beyond what you are capable of dealing with as a coach. In such cases it is your responsibility to acknowledge your own shortcomings and work with the participants to access other coaching opportunities.

In order for participants to gain the most out of being coached, coaches should always try to ensure that the coaching sessions they deliver are enjoyable and rewarding. A participant who has had a positive and enjoyable experience is more likely to be motivated to keep attending sessions and will be well placed to develop their skills and performance levels. It is a coach's responsibility to engage with and motivate their participants so that their continued involvement is maintained.

Coaching sessions should always be accessible, equitable and free from fear and harassment. A coach has the responsibility to ensure that the coaching sessions they deliver are accessible to all those who wish to be involved and they should take place in a non-threatening environment. Relationships between the coach and the participants and between each of the participants should be built on trust and respect. There should not be any barriers to prevent people from taking part in, or benefiting from, coaching.

Activity

Many coaching sessions will include participants who have different levels of skills in a particular area. Assume you are planning a coaching activity for a group of children aged 7 to 8. The aim of the activity is to teach the children how to hit a tennis ball with a racket. You have been informed that out of the group of 12 children, 6 of them can already hit the ball with a racket. How will you run your activity knowing that there are different levels of ability in the group?

Case study: Moving on?

▲ A coach has the duty to encourage performers to progress and develop

Claire is a level 2 tennis coach who enjoys coaching young beginner tennis players and teaching them the fundamental skills of the game. She has never played top-level tennis himself and recognises that she does not know enough about some of the advanced skills, tactics and drills needed to coach at a higher level. She is content to work on introducing and developing young players to gain enjoyment from the game, and she does not have the time to advance her coaching skills to allow her to coach young players to a high level.

One of Claire's young players, Craig, has just won a regional under-14s tournament – her first major success. After the match Craig's opponent's coach, Simon, approaches Claire. Simon is more qualified than Claire and has experience of coaching junior players to national level. The conversation ends with an invitation for Craig to join Simon's coaching group. Claire is not sure whether Craig should join Simon's group. She decides to draw up a list of positives and negatives to help her decide.

1 **What might be some of the things Claire includes on her 'positives' list?**

2 **What might be on her list of 'negatives'?**

3 **Should these issues be considered in relation to Claire or to Craig?**

4 **What would be your advice to Claire?**

Taking it further

Assume that the night before you deliver the activity above you are informed that one member of the group is a wheelchair user. How will you run your activity now?

Remember!

- Coaches have a responsibility to ensure that their coaching is safe and ethical and meets the needs of their participants.
- Coaching sessions should be organised, planned, progressive, enjoyable, and accessible to all, and should offer participants the opportunity to develop their skills.
- Coaches should undertake a full risk assessment of the coaching environment to minimise the risk to participants.
- Coaches should be familiar with the required standards of good coaching practice and adhere to them at all times when coaching.

Assessment practice

Design a poster to use in a presentation to your group about the roles and responsibilities of sports coaches.

1 Describe and explain four roles and four responsibilities of sports coaches. Include in your talk some examples of real coaches and how they demonstrate these roles and responsibilities. **P1 M1**

2 Provide a handout that compares and contrasts the roles and responsibilities of successful coaches from different sports. **D1**

Grading tips

Grading Tip P1 M1

Describe and explain four roles and four responsibilities using examples of coaches from different sports.

Grading Tip D1

Make sure you compare and contrast the roles and responsibilities of successful coaches who are from different sports.

Skills

As you should by now be aware, the roles of the coach are extremely diverse. As a result, the range of necessary skills that you will need to have to function effectively as a coach is broad. You have, hopefully, recognised that being a coach is not just about teaching somebody how to play a sport. The roles encompass very much more than that, with the coach also having to be able to establish good relationships with their participants, be able to manage themselves, their training programmes and the participants effectively as well as be able to plan, organise, deliver and analyse coaching sessions.

This section will now address the main skills required to be an effective coach, giving you an opportunity to appreciate the significance of these required skills and also begin to assess how well you as a coach are able to perform selected skills.

Communication

Some coaches feel that effective communication is all about talking and telling participants what to do. But communication is a two-way process, with the sending of a signal (verbal or non-verbal communication) being as important as the receiving of a signal (listening and understanding). Coaches should think carefully about their ways of communicating – there is a saying that a coach has one mouth and two ears and should use them in the same proportions! How a coach sends a signal to a participant can have a huge impact on the effectiveness and interpretation of that signal. Communication is of two types: verbal and non-verbal.

Verbal communication is characterised by use of the spoken word, and most coaches are certainly able to talk! Varying the tone, pace and volume of the spoken word is an important means of conveying specific messages. A coach needs to remember that constant shouting does not make communication more effective – in fact it may become less effective as a participant may begin to ignore the shouting.

Activity

Non-verbal communication is a powerful way of conveying messages. Try the following tasks and see how much you can learn about the use of body language and non-verbal communication. Use a dictionary, encyclopaedia or the Internet to help if necessary.

1 What is semaphore? Who might use it?

2 Obtain a copy of the semaphore alphabet. Make two flags and practise sending a message to a partner.

3 What is British Sign Language (BSL)? Who might use it?

4 Obtain some examples of the signs used in BSL, and practise signing.

5 Watch a video clip of a sporting activity with the sound turned down. Observe who uses body language and try to work out what message people are trying to convey.

6 How might a referee or umpire use body language?

7 Can you give some common examples of body language or signs that are used in sport? What do they mean?

Non-verbal communication involves alternative methods of sending signals, which might include body language, facial expressions and gestures. In general, coaches are less adept at using non-verbal communication. Remember, a well-timed facial expression can say more than a thousand words. In

competitive situations, non-verbal communication may be the only way to communicate with your performers.

An important element of communication is the use of correct and understandable language and of utmost importance in coaching is the ability to 'talk the talk' and 'walk the walk' in the context of your sport. Coaches will command respect from their participants if they have a good understanding of the sport they are coaching. Part of this is about using the right language, for example basketball players 'shoot baskets' rather than 'score goals', and archers 'loose the arrow at the gold' rather than 'fire arrows at the bulls-eye'. A simple appreciation of the terminology will help the coach establish a relationship with their participants. Of course, in most instances coaches will tend to coach sports that they know about and have either participated in themselves or seen close family members participate in. Some people argue that in order to coach a sport effectively you have to have played that sport to a high level in order to fully understand the demands of the sport. This is not necessarily the case, although the ex-participant almost certainly has an advantage in that they go into

▼ Manchester United's coach uses verbal and non-verbal communication

their coaching knowing all the terminology and rules, etc. of their chosen sport. Just because you have not participated in a sport should not exclude you from coaching that sport, it might just mean you have to work a little bit harder to get to know the sport.

Theory into practice

Different sports use different language and it is important for a coach to be able to understand the different terminology used in his or her sport. Try the following task to see how much you know about the different terms that are often used in sport.

Below is a description of a passage of play in cricket. Read through it and rewrite it using non-cricket terminology to describe how the ball was bowled, how exactly the batsman hit it and where the ball ended up.

> It was Wahid's last delivery of the over. He used his usual bowling approach – left-arm over the wicket. This time he bowled a 'reverse swing' that was somewhere between middle and leg and just short of a length. Jackson came down to meet it and hit a wonderful drive through the leg side just missing the square-leg umpire. Smith, fielding at deep square leg, made a brilliant stop and returned the ball underarm missing the leg stump by inches. Unfortunately, the wicketkeeper missed it and Jenkins had to run round from silly mid-off to field the overthrow. The running between the wickets was slow and Jackson only took a single – enough to prevent Wahid from getting a maiden.

Communication is not just about sending signals; it is also about receiving and interpreting them as well. As such, listening is an important feature of good communication. Effective listening can serve two main functions. First, it is a good way to check understanding; it is important for a coach to be sure that performers have understood the information they have been given. By questioning performers and listening to their responses, a coach can assess whether or not a message has been received correctly.

Second, listening can be a good source of useful information. Listening to a participant's opinions and how he or she feels during a practice or a drill may help the coach identify errors that are not immediately obvious through watching the participant.

Think it over

What is the difference between hearing and listening? What are the important characteristics of listening? How can you tell whether somebody has been listening?

Organisation

If a coaching session or a training programme is to be effective, it has to be organised well. This requires a range of skills that may include organisation, analysing and problem-solving skills, evaluation, time management, and health, safety and security skills. How and when a coach requires these skills is related to the different stages of the coaching procedure.

Even before the coaching session begins, a coach has to be well organised. He or she will need a clear idea of the equipment and facilities required and available for use, the activities to be undertaken, and who is to be coached. Good organisational skills prior to a coaching session will ensure that during the session the participants are doing the right thing, in the right place, at the right time.

Most coaches find the administrative aspects of their role the least enjoyable part of their work. However, these are of equal importance to the other aspects of coaching. Obviously, a coaching session cannot take place if the facilities have not been booked; similarly, participants cannot use their newly-developed skills in a competitive environment if they have not been entered for a competition. Some coaches will seek to involve other club members or parents in these organisational aspects associated with coaching. This is a good idea as it will reduce the amount of time that a coach has to allocate to basic administrative duties, and it also involves other people who may be better at this work than the coach!

Activity

You have been asked by your head coach to organise the next coaching session. Working in pairs, write a list of all the things that you need to do before the next session starts to ensure that it is effectively organised.

Analysing

Coaching is as much about analysing people's actions as it is about instructing them what to do. A lot of useful information about the participant can be gained through careful observation of a participant while they are practising a skill, undergoing a training session or competing. The ability to observe participants and then to compare the observed performance with the desired performance is the basis of good analysis. The ability to develop appropriate coaching practices to address any differences is a key aspect of the coaching process.

A coach, therefore, has to have a good knowledge of a sport and its demands in order to effectively analyse their participants. A coach needs to know what the correct technique looks like in order to teach a beginner how to perform it. As you will have read previously, most coaches operate within a sport they are very familiar with. Many are former performers or have been coaching in that sport for many years. As a result, they will be familiar with the specific techniques, skills and tactics of their chosen sport. The good coach will be able to observe and analyse a performance and compare it to a desired ideal performance. A key to effective coaching is being able to analyse a participant carrying out a skill or technique and then being able to identify any errors in its execution.

Problem solving

Coaching will not always go smoothly – things will go wrong and problems will arise. A coach must be able to identify when things have gone wrong and be able

to determine the exact nature of the problem. He or she should then be able to assess the situation and try to identify appropriate solutions to the problem. This requires logical thinking and reasoning, and being prepared to rethink an approach to a particular coaching situation.

Problem solving can be the most challenging part of coaching but it can also be the most rewarding. The problems a coach faces may take a variety of different forms.

- The problem may lie with the participant: they may be unable to carry out the particular skill that is being taught. In this case the coach will need to try to identify why the participant is being unsuccessful and then try a different set of practices to help them grasp the skill.
- The problem may be associated with the coaching environment: a particular pitch or court may not be available and the coach will need to plan alternative arrangements to solve the problem.
- There may be a problem with the competitive arena: a team may have difficulty dealing with a particular opponent or with a tactic used by opponents. The coach will have to use tactical knowledge to find a strategy for overcoming the problem.
- The coach may struggle to grasp a scientific concept or some aspect of the planning process: they may need to seek advice from others or attend a coaching course to gain the required information.

Evaluating

Coaches are always keen to assess and pass comment on their participants' abilities and performances. However, they are rarely prepared to reflect on their own performances and, if they are, they will tend to focus on what worked well. Effective evaluation of a coaching session should be impartial and identify not only what went well but also what worked less well. The key to good evaluation is honesty, and this will allow the coach to learn from mistakes and improve coaching skills.

Time management

Coaches often complain that they do not have enough time with their participants to achieve the desired outcome. This can sometimes be a poor excuse for bad time management. Coaches must try to use the time they have available effectively. Careful planning of a session should minimise the time wasted and maximise the learning opportunities. Coaches must try to strike an appropriate balance between providing enough time on a practice or a drill for the participants to learn and improve, and spending too much time on activities which do not provide new learning opportunities.

Assessment practice

1 Add to your poster presentation by describing and explaining three skills common to successful sports coaches. Include in your talk some examples of real coaches and how they display these skills. **P2 M2**

2 Create a handout that compares and contrasts the skills of successful coaches from different sports. **D1**

Grading tips

Grading Tip P2 M2

Describe three skills using examples of coaches from different sports.

Grading Tip D1

Make sure you compare and contrast the skills of successful coaches from different sports.

4.2 Understand the techniques used by coaches to improve the performance of athletes

You will have learnt from the previous sections that the job of the coach involves a variety of different roles that have to be fulfilled. When you choose to take on the job of a coach you are taking on these different roles and with them a host of responsibilities. It is a daunting task but you can help yourself by learning to utilise some of the key techniques that coaches use to improve the performance of their participants.

The various techniques adopted by coaches fall into two different categories. First, techniques which can inform the planning process by helping the coach assess the current status of the participants (e.g. performance profiling, fitness assessment and goal-setting). Second, techniques which, if utilised before and during coaching sessions, can make the delivery of a coaching session more effective (e.g. simulation, modelling and effective demonstrations).

The following section outlines some of these techniques that will aid you in the identification of your participants' current performance levels and how you can go about developing these levels effectively.

Techniques

The starting point for any planning is always a comprehensive overview of where things currently stand. In a coaching context this means an assessment of the current status of the participant(s) in terms of their ability, their fitness and their motives for participating in sport. At the outset of your coaching you may have a limited understanding of the ability, motives and aspirations of your participants and as such will need to collate this information. The degree to which you need to undertake this 'fact-finding' process largely depends on your relationship with the participants you are coaching. If you are coaching a group of participants for the first time, then your knowledge of them will be limited and you will need to make sure that you 'do your homework' on them before setting out to coach them. Your approach and philosophy of coaching might be totally opposite to theirs and, therefore, it is important that you take time to find out what motivates them, what they want to achieve and how well they are currently able to perform. If you are coaching the same people, perhaps after a close-season break, you will already have gleaned useful information from your previous

Case study: What have I let myself in for?

▲ Roy Keane upon taking over as Sunderland manager

Over the Summer Bank Holiday weekend in August 2006 the former Manchester United footballer, Roy Keane, was appointed as the new manager of Sunderland. The following summary of events is an example of how observation by a new coach can be effective.

Sunday 27 August. p.m.: Keane was introduced to the players and spent time talking with some of the players and club officials. Afterwards, the club chairman, Niall Quinn said, 'When Roy met the players, you could almost see them standing an inch or two taller thinking "We are going to be working with that man, that is incredible".'

Monday 28 August. p.m.: Keane arrives at the Stadium of Light with Leicester City youth coach Tony Loughlan for Sunderland's home game against West Bromwich Albion. He is mobbed by fans asking for his autograph.

Sunderland goes on to win 2-0. After losing their first five matches of the season this is Sunderland's first win of the new season. The club chairman said afterwards, 'He brought a buzz to the place. They showed they wanted to play for the manager, they were playing for their futures... Possibly the players are a bit scared. I hope they are, not in the sense they will under perform but that they will give their all when they go training.'

Tuesday 29 August. 1.00 p.m.: Roy Keane is officially named as the new Sunderland manager at a press conference and Tony Loughlan is named as head coach.

The team go on to win their first two matches under Keane.

This highlights the fact that the new manager met the players prior to a match and then attended a match with his soon-to-be assistant in order to see for himself the current status of the players he was about to take charge of. This is a good example of the need for coaches to assess their participants before beginning to coach them.

1 If you were Roy Keane in this situation, what would you be looking for?

2 What sort of questions would you have asked the players when you met with them?

experiences of working with them. However, it may still be necessary to assess their pre-season fitness and their readiness for training in order to identify an appropriate starting point for any new training programme you might wish to implement. Assessing the starting point for your coaching is, therefore, of vital importance in all contexts. There are a number of techniques which you can apply to help with this.

Observation analysis

Coaches should observe their participants both in a training environment and, if appropriate, in a competitive context. Watching how participants behave and respond in training and competition will give the new coach a meaningful insight into why the participants are involved in the sport, what they wish to get out of it and how they respond to the demands placed upon them. Observation is one of the key techniques that all coaches should adopt, both as part of the planning process and also during coaching sessions when participants are in action. In addition to watching participants, coaches should also take the time to talk to their participants to identify vital information about, among other things, their attitude, motivations, fears and aspirations.

Performance profiling

Aside from watching and talking to the participants, there are a number of more sophisticated techniques that can be used to develop a profile of participants' current status. Many coaches adopt a process known as performance profiling to gain a detailed picture of their participants' current skill levels. The process was originally established within the field of sports psychology and was aimed at identifying a performer's strengths and weaknesses in a range of mental skills. However, the principles can be applied to all aspects of performance and the performance profile can allow a coach and their participants to identify their strengths and weaknesses in different aspects of performance.

The initial stage of the process involves the coach and their participant identifying a number of characteristics which they feel to be important in their sport. The original model for performance profiling suggested that these should be the characteristics expected of an elite performer, but the characteristics you identify can be relative to your participants. Ideally, the participants would come up with the list of things that they think are important for them to be able to achieve their goals. Having agreed upon this list, participants should then give each characteristic a score of between 0 and 10 in terms of how important they feel that characteristic is to them (0 is not important and 10 is extremely important). Next, the participants should use the same 0 to 10 scale to rate their current perception of themselves in relation to an ideal state of 10. Those characteristics which have the greatest discrepancy between the perceived importance and the self-assessment rating are the ones that may need to be the focus of future training and planning.

The process of performance profiling is seen as an effective technique for the identification of strengths and weaknesses and, because the evaluation is done by the participant on themselves, it helps the coach understand the participant's perspective and enhances a coach's understanding of how their athlete sees themselves. The process also allows the athlete to focus on a range of skills, not just physical and technical skills.

Fitness assessment

Another important technique that coaches adopt to inform the planning process is an assessment of how well participants are able to meet the physical demands of the sport. This usually involves a form of fitness assessment whereby a number of appropriate fitness parameters are identified and tested to see how well the participant matches up to the demands of their sport. It is important that the coach recognises the relative importance of each of the different elements of physical fitness and is also aware of 'benchmark' data with which to compare their participants. Some aspects of fitness assessment may require specialist input but many aspects can be simply adapted by coaches based on their knowledge of their sport and its demands.

For example, a sport such as netball has a variety of different physical demands on the players. There is a need for players to be aerobically fit as they are likely to be in action for at least an hour and, depending on their position, may cover a considerable distance during a match. Also, they need to have the ability to move fast and recover quickly between sprints as the nature of the game is very high intensity and intermittent. Similarly, the stop-start and twist-turn nature of the game means that players need to be flexible and agile, as well as have good leg power to allow them to jump efficiently.

This simple analysis of the physical demands placed on a netball player suggests that to see how well players meet the demands of the sport a coach might wish to conduct a basic aerobic running test, a sprint/agility test, a jumping test and a flexibility test. Performing such tests at regular intervals throughout a season will help the coach see how their participants have developed in terms of their physical fitness. Further details on issues related to fitness assessment can be found in Unit 6.

Goal setting

Coaches who adopt the above two techniques will be well informed about their participants and should have a good picture of where they are at the outset of a coaching programme. Using the information collected from these different techniques will provide a useful starting point for the planning process. Knowing, for example, that after a performance profiling exercise a player rates their physical fitness levels as poor, and that the results of a fitness assessment suggest that their basic underpinning aerobic fitness is poor, should lead the coach towards establishing the development of basic fitness as a priority target for the first phase of a coaching programme. The creation of a set of goals as a result of this information gathering will aid participants to address their weaknesses and build on their strengths.

Regardless of whether you are planning a single session or a whole series of sessions, you will need to set goals both for the sessions you are delivering and for your participants to work towards. You and your participants must have something that you are aiming to achieve. You may hear established coaches refer to the concept of SMART goal-setting. This is a clever way of remembering the key features of the goals that you should set for your participants. According to the acronym, SMART, goals should always be Specific, Measurable, Acceptable, Realistic and Time-bound. Table 4.1 summarises what these terms mean and gives examples of goals you might set for a coaching session

Feature	Coaching session goal	Participant goal
Specific: what precisely are you aiming to achieve? What do your participants want to achieve?	By the end of this coaching session the participants will be able to successfully perform an overhead tennis serve.	To complete the London Marathon.
Measurable: goals should have some measurable outcome so that you and your participants know whether or not they have achieved them.	Participants will be able to land 10 serves in the correct service box.	Successful completion of the marathon distance.
Acceptable: participants must be willing and prepared to work towards the goals. They should have an input to what the goals are.	Participants have expressed a desire to be able to serve properly so that they can begin a game effectively and put their opponent under pressure at the start of a service game.	It is a lifelong ambition and I really want to do it.
Realistic: the goals you set must be within the scope of the ability and resources available to the participant. Not all athletes can become Olympic champions.	All participants can already successfully serve underhand and are able to hit the ball from an overhead position.	I have run previously and have completed a 10 km road race this year.
Time-bound: goals have to have a phased approach and be achieved within a realistic timescale.	An hour's coaching session with instruction and practice drills should allow them sufficient time to develop this skill.	It is May now and that gives me 11 months before the next London Marathon and I can build up my training mileage gradually.

Table 4.1 Features and examples of SMART goals

and also for a participant who is looking to develop their performance levels.

It is important to remember that you should involve your participants when setting goals for them as they are more likely to want to achieve them if they are involved in the process.

Having identified the current status of participants the coach must now set about designing and delivering effective coaching sessions that help participants achieve their goals and improve their performance. There are a number of techniques with which a coach should be familiar that can aid this process.

Simulation

One good way to ensure that participants are prepared to meet the demands of their sport is to simulate the competitive environment in training. This does not mean that they should always be playing competitive matches in training but it is a useful way to try out new tactics and set plays and to see how well participants can meet the demands that would be placed on them in a competitive environment. One example of simulating competition in team sports is to play conditioned games in which players are only allowed to do certain things. For example, to simulate the high speed of match play, players may only be allowed to touch the ball once and then they must pass it to a team-mate. Alternatively, the participants could be split into attackers and defenders and practise corners, line-outs, short corners, free kicks/hits, etc. In non-team sports simulation of competition demands may take the form of time trials in which runners or swimmers, for example, do repetitions at race pace or 'handicapped' events in which tennis or squash players start a set behind an opponent and have to work to catch up.

Simulation can also be used to prepare for an event. Many athletes, for example, will train at the same time of day that they expect to race at. In major championships many of the qualifying rounds take place in the morning so athletes will, in training, simulate getting up at the appropriate time, warming-up and racing in the morning. Effective use of simulation as a training tool can help the coach check to see if participants are ready and able to cope with the demands that they will face in competition.

Modelling and effective demonstration

When learning new skills participants have to be able to see what it is they are trying to achieve and when it comes to learning a new skill there is no substitute for seeing it being performed correctly. This allows the learner to have a model to which they can refer. An effective demonstration of a skill should create a technically correct visual image for the participants to copy. It is important, however, that the demonstration is completely correct. If you as the coach are to perform the demonstration, you have to be confident of being able to recreate the desired image, otherwise participants may imitate a technically incorrect model.

Some coaches who may not feel technically able to demonstrate a skill may choose to use video images instead, or may ask experienced performers who are technically competent to perform the demonstration on their behalf.

Whoever performs it, a demonstration will be most effective if it follows these simple guidelines:

- Make sure the participants are paying attention and that all are able to see the demonstration.
- Ensure that the demonstration emphasises the key coaching points you are trying to get across.
- Ensure skills are demonstrated at the appropriate level for the participants.
- Repeat the demonstration enough times for participants to understand what is required.

Technical instruction

Previously, it has been suggested that coaching is about coaching participants not about coaching a sport and some people would argue that a good 'generalist' coach can apply the principles of coaching to a number of sports. This does not mean that an understanding and knowledge of your chosen sport is not important: it is your ability to coach the technical elements of your sport which will set you aside from the 'generalist' coach. A good coach will have a good appreciation of the technical elements of their sport and, importantly, they will also be able to instruct their participants how to perform the skills and techniques associated with their sport.

When giving technical instruction a coach should ensure that they begin with a good introduction to the skill or technique that is being taught. This introduction should inform the performers what they will be learning, why it is important, when it will be useful and how it fits in with other skills and techniques they have already learnt. Some important points to note when instructing participants about skills and techniques include the following.

- Ensure that you have planned what you are going to say and make sure that what you do say is clear and logical.
- Remember not to give too much information and to keep the explanations brief.
- Relate what you say to what the participants have already been taught and can already do.
- Where possible use visual examples, for example demonstrations or video clips.
- Ensure that the explanation/demonstration is accurate. Participants need to see the correct skill or technique being performed.
- If the skill or technique is complex, try to break it down into component parts (see Unit 26: Technical and Tactical Skills in Sport).

Judging when, how and at what rate to teach a skill or technique is an important decision to make. A coach needs to know what techniques and skills are most appropriate for different situations and at what stage they should be introduced. Techniques need to be coached in the correct sequence. For example, when coaching a young swimmer it is important to secure the basic technique of effective stroke execution before the swimmer is taught the complexities of the tumble turn. As the abilities and experience of the participants improve, the range of options can be increased. Coaches must be able to help their participants develop techniques at an appropriate rate of progression and the timing of technical instruction is therefore important.

Developing performer coaching diaries

Coaches should always keep a record of the sessions they have delivered so that they know what their participants have been taught and so they can reflect on the coaching that they have done. Many coaches also encourage their performers to keep a diary which records not only what they have done in a session but also how they felt about the session and what developments they think they have made.

Developing performer coaching diaries can have a number of advantages. First, it gives the participants a permanent record of what they have done so that if they forget something they can check back in the diary to refresh their memory. This can be developed further if the coach gives a supporting handout to go with a session. This might contain illustrations of the techniques being taught or some examples of exercises that can be used in a warm-up or cool-down. Second, a diary can provide a record of the things that the participant might do in between coaching sessions. This feature of a diary is very popular in endurance sports where coaches might set their runners or cyclist sessions to do on the days when they do not attend coaching sessions. Athletes might be asked to record the number of miles run in a session, the time taken to run the distance along with some indication of how they felt while running. The coach can then view the diary on regular occasions to check that the athlete has been doing the required sessions and also how hard or easy they found them. Finally, a diary is a good way of recording participants' thoughts and feelings about the training they are doing. Asking them to record simple phrases which reflect how they felt might be useful in gauging the intensity of the training programme you are providing. For example, a participant might record that they 'felt generally tired tonight and struggled with some of the practices due to being tired'. This would tell the coach quite a lot about how well the participant is responding to the training.

At higher levels of performance performer diaries can become more detailed and performers might record their heart rate at rest, what they eat, how long they sleep for each night as well as how much training they have done. This helps the coach gauge the overall impact of training and how well the performer is responding to training.

Adapting practices to meet individual needs

As has been emphasised earlier, coaching is about developing people and each participant that you coach will be different and will have different aspirations, different experiences and different reasons for coming to your coaching sessions. As such, it is one of your responsibilities as a coach to ensure that you try to meet the individual needs and requirements of your participants. Nobody is suggesting that you should have a separate coaching session for each participant. Instead, you should have the ability and understanding to be flexible enough to adapt your coaching practice to meet individual needs. The sample coaching session in Table 4.2 on pages 162–63 gives some examples of how the coach can be flexible to meet individual needs.

To effectively meet the needs of participants, coaches should seek to adhere to the following tips.

- Coaches should avoid spending too much time on the same activity and should be prepared to change the practices and drills they are using. This does not mean introducing lots of new ideas: coaches should provide a range of different tasks that enable individuals to practise the same skills but in different ways.
- Individuals learn from doing things rather than being told about them. Explanations should be simple and instructions for drills and practices should be easy to understand. A good coach will make sure that the participants spend a large amount of time actually doing something. Meeting individual needs can be further enhanced by ensuring that participants of similar ability work together. That way those who are struggling are not put off by watching others performing the skill well.
- Success is a major factor in sport and coaches should structure sessions in a way that allows participants to experience some form of success and thus gain satisfaction from their achievement.
- It is important to realise that each participant will learn at a different rate and a coaching session must take this into account. Coaches should avoid progressing too quickly as some of the group might not have learned a skill properly, yet if progress is too slow some participants might get bored. The coach has to achieve a good balance and progress at a rate that is appropriate for the participants.

Designing effective practice sessions

In order for participants to gain the maximum benefit from a coaching session, the learning environment has to be right. Coaches have a responsibility to help their participants develop and this should include ensuring that they create and maintain an effective learning environment. To achieve this, coaches should understand the type of environment in which people learn best. It is generally accepted that people learn best when they are:

- interested and motivated
- actively involved in their own learning
- able to build on their own previous experiences
- able to see how things fit together
- able to see improvements in their performance.

Coaches should ensure, therefore, that their coaching sessions encompass these points and allow the participants to remain interested and involved in the process and able to see progression in their performance.

Assessment practice

You have been asked by the coach of a local health club to put together a report about different techniques that are used by coaches so she can use the report when training new coaches.

1 Describe and explain three different techniques that are used by coaches to improve the performance of athletes. **P3 M3**

2 Evaluate the three different techniques, giving your recommendations of how the techniques can be used successfully to improve an athlete's performance. **D2**

Grading Tip M3 D2

You could use a coaching logbook to keep a record of when you use these techniques or observe another coach using these techniques to help you achieve M3 or D2.

The coaching process

In previous sections you will have learned the roles and responsibilities that you as a coach are expected to fulfil and how you should go about fulfilling them. This section will round-off the principles of coaching by exploring the coaching process and what it actually involves. The actual process of coaching is complex and is often dynamic in nature. It is forever changing and no single coaching session is like any previous or subsequent one. To try and simplify coaching, many people view it as a cyclical process consisting of three distinct phases.

First, there is a planning phase in which the coach identifies what it is they are aiming to achieve in a session and how they intend achieving it. This will include planning and identifying the practices and activities that will be used within a session to help participants develop new skills, practise existing skills or develop physical fitness. Second, there is the session itself in which the practices and activities are conducted and the coaching points delivered. Finally, the coach must review how effective they think the session has been and evaluate the session in light of the original aims that they set out to achieve.

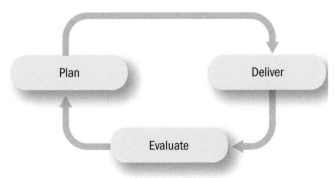

▲ The coaching process

This process is a cyclical one because it does not simply stop after a session has been completed. A good coach will perform a coaching session and then evaluate it and use the observations and information gleaned from the evaluation to inform the planning for the next coaching session. If a coach is working with the same group of participants week after week, then the evaluation of one session should take into account the progress of the participants and form the basis of the planning for the next session the following week. Participants would expect to see progression in the sessions so that they feel they are improving or learning new skills. If, however, a coach only works with a group for a single session then they should still use the information from their evaluation to help them plan how they might deliver that session better the next time. The whole cycle is often termed the 'plan-do-review' process because the coach is planning what they are going to do, then doing it and finally reviewing how well it went. Good coaches will continually go through this process as they plan their coaching sessions, deliver them and then evaluate how well they went.

Activity

1 a For a sport of your choice, identify what you think are the main demands of that sport. Give consideration to the physical, mental and technical demands.
   b Select a partner, ideally someone who has chosen a different sport. Interview your partner about how well they think they meet the demands that they have identified for their sport.
   c Identify where they think they are the weakest in terms of these demands and decide on an action plan that they might follow to help them improve in that aspect of their performance. Try and make a goal that is SMART.
2 You have been asked by the England women's football coach to produce a plan of a practice session that you might use to help her players prepare for a forthcoming tournament. Specifically, she wants you to simulate a penalty shoot-out so that her players get some practice of what it might be like. How might you go about this?

The planning stage usually represents the starting point of the process and is arguably the most important part of the process. A coach needs to plan well otherwise all other aspects of the coaching process will be ineffective.

Most coaches plan each coaching session in advance. This is easier when you have been working with participants for some time and the sessions follow on from each other. You will already know a little about the participants and their aims, abilities and behaviours, and be able to build on your existing knowledge and experience of the group.

On some occasions coaches may be working with a group for the first time and know very little about them. In this case coaches should take some time to collect relevant information about the participants and try to build up a picture of what their aims and abilities might be. When planning to coach a group for the first time, it is advisable to use the first part of the session to get to know the participants and their current levels of ability.

Date: Monday 30 November	Age group: 11/12	Number in group: 15 to 16

Session aims:
i) To introduce players to the principles of passing the ball backwards.
ii) To introduce players to the principles of passing for distance.
iii) To give players an opportunity to practise passing in a controlled game situation.

Resources available: 12 rugby balls, cones, bibs, 1 rugby pitch (outdoors)

Duration	Outcome	Organisation	Activity	Points to remember
15 mins	Introduction/ Warm-up – Introduce session aims – ball handling. – Warm-up with focus on skills related to ball handling.	– Grid work (10m × 10m) – half the number of balls than players. – Grid work (20m × 20m) – Grid work (30m × 30m) – 'Passing game' (40m × 40m grid) – '**Plan B**' – Be prepared to change grid sizes if space is restricted or if the group is bigger and needs more space.	– Participants to move around the grid passing the ball to each other. Start with pop pass, and then low to high, high to low, one handed. – Players make passes longer than 5m, first off right hand then off left hand. – Start with passes longer than 10m, first off right hand then off left hand. – Two teams, players are not allowed to run with ball. Score by placing ball in circle at end of grid. Defence not allowed stripping of the ball. Turnovers for ball going to ground.	– Set up grids – care with positioning of cones. – Ensure 10m × 10m is not too crowded. – Be prescriptive about what you want each skill to look like. – Encourage highly skilled players to help less skilled players. – Increase grid size to 40m × 40m to allow movement of the ball.

Duration	Outcome	Organisation	Activity	Points to remember
15 mins	Principles of passing backwards	– Relays – 2–3 equal sized groups. – Players stand in lateral lines. – Progressions: i) Arm's distance. ii) 2m apart. iii) 5m apart. iv) Run forward. v) Run length of pitch. – '**Plan B**' – Be prepared to omit or extend i) or v) if group is particularly poor at passing tasks.	– Players stand arm's distance apart. The ball should move from one end to the other of the line, with the ball not leaving any players' hands. After two practice attempts, have a relay race. – Players now stand 2m apart and repeat process. – Players now stand 5m apart and repeat process. – Players now run forward and pass the ball up and back along the line, ensuring that they always pass the ball backwards. – After two practice attempts, line the groups up along the try line and get them to run and pass up and back the length of the field.	Focus on accuracy of passing technique. Correct errors. Ensure safety for running activity. Balls may be dropped at this stage and players may stop to collect balls while next group is running.
15 mins	Principles of passing in relation to distance	– Tutor-led – last man standing (groups of four). – '**Plan B**' – If group is good at above task and can achieve good distance then omit this activity and progress straight to game. – If poor on the above task, extend.	– Players stand on four corners in a 3m × 3m grid, passing off right hand. After each rotation, each person takes one pace out. If the ball is dropped or a poor pass is made, the guilty player sits down and is out of the game. Team that is still passing last wins. – Repeat above but challenge group to see how far apart they can get and still be successful.	– Mix groups by ability. Have a highly skilled player next to a less skilled player. Get highly skilled players to coach less skilled. – Focus on accuracy of passing technique. Correct errors.
10 mins	Implement passing skills in game.	– Utilising width of pitch from 5m line to ½ way, split group into two teams and play a conditioned game of tag rugby.	– Tag rugby but the non-ball holding team must allow ball holders three passes before being tagged.	– Emphasis on passing – backwards and for distance. – Mix groups by ability. Get highly skilled players to give feedback to less skilled players.
5 mins	Cool–down and summary	– Tutor-led cool-down	– While stretching, summarise key points.	

Table 4.2 An example of a coaching session plan

Whether you are coaching your usual group or working with participants for the first time, there are a number of things you need to take into consideration when planning a session. Table 4.2 gives an example of a coaching session plan that will be referred to throughout the following sections. This table outlines some of the key features of the planning process.

Plan

Aims and objectives

The first thing a coach needs to think about when planning a session is the desired outcomes of the session. Knowing what it is that you are aiming to achieve in a session will make planning the practices within the session easier.

When trying to identify the desired outcomes of a coaching session, coaches should consider:

- the specific needs of the participants and what their goals may be
- the ability level of the participants and whether they can realistically achieve the desired goal
- their own goals for the session
- whether their own goals match the participants' goals and abilities
- whether the session builds on a previous session and/or prepares participants for the next session.

Targets

When deciding the aims of a single session it is likely that the coach will set short-term goals – things to be achieved by the end of the session. Coaches planning for a series of sessions may also set medium- or long-term goals, which may be things they want participants to be able to do by the end of the series of coaching sessions. Progress towards these long-term goals may be measurable by the achievement of short-term goals along the way.

In the example coaching session plan (Table 4.2) the coach has already worked with the group before and, therefore, has some idea of their ability. The session is clearly part of an introductory programme as it focuses on a basic skill which you would expect to learn reasonably early on in a rugby coaching programme. The aims of the session are identified and the session plan is structured in a way that allows these aims to be met.

■ SMART targets

Any targets that you set should follow the SMART principle set out in Table 4.1 on page 157:

- **S** – **s**pecific
- **M** – **m**easurable
- **A** – **a**chievable
- **R** – **r**ealistic
- **T** – **t**ime-bound

By following this principle, you and the group you are coaching can conduct a continuous review of performance and ensure that identified goals are realistic and achievable. This will also allow you to make any modifications as necessary.

Roles

When planning a session you will need to consider exactly what role you need to fulfil. If the session is about the development of fitness and is based around fitness and conditioning activities, then you may fulfil predominantly a trainer role, although, if the session is about the introduction of a new skill, then you are more likely to be wearing your 'educator' hat.

It is very difficult to plan to play different roles within a coaching session although it is important for coaches to recognise the different roles they may need to play and adapt their behaviour and practices accordingly.

Responsibilities

A coach must act responsibly at all times when coaching and it is very difficult to plan to be responsible or to fulfil certain responsibilities. A good coach will be aware of their responsibilities and their plans will be informed by their need to remain responsible.

Participants

Modern coaching is now all about providing positive experiences for participants. To support this approach the coach should always plan their sessions with the participants in mind. You should always make sure that you give consideration to the following when planning a coaching session:

■ Number

If you have lots of participants you will need to consider whether the activities you have planned will be safe and also whether everyone is going to get a chance to be involved. Participants will not get a lot out of the session if they are not involved and are left to watch others performing. If you only have a small number, or an odd number, of participants, are you going to be able to do some of the things you had planned? For example, how might your tennis match simulation turn out if three people turn up?

■ Ability

Most instances that you will experience will probably involve performers of similar levels, but you must consider how you will address situations where some participants pick up the skills you are coaching them quicker than others and become better quicker.

■ Needs

The example presented in Table 4.2 shows how the coach has given consideration to the needs of the participants. Reference is made to the group sizes and the activities are designed to include all participants. Can you see how, in his coaching notes, the coach has reminded himself to draw on the better players to work with the less-able players to help them develop the skills? Note also the comments highlighted as 'Plan B': they refer to the need to be flexible with group and pitch sizes to accommodate the number of participants who turn up and also the relative speed at which the players develop appropriate skills.

■ Age and gender

Coaches must consider the age and gender of their participants and ensure that activities within a session are inclusive and do not exclude certain groups of people.

Activity

Many coaching sessions will include participants who have different levels of skills in a particular area. Assume you are planning a coaching activity for a group of children aged 7 to 8. The aim of the activity is to teach the children how to hit a tennis ball with a racket. You have been informed that of the group of 12 children, 6 of them can already hit the ball with a racket. How will you run your activity knowing that there are different levels of ability in the group?

Taking it further

Assume that the night before you deliver the activity above you are informed that one member of the group is a wheelchair user. How will you run your activity now?

Resources

In our example session plan (Table 4.2) the coach has identified the resources that he has available. He has also clearly allocated time slots to each activity and is aware of how long each activity might take. He also identifies within his 'Plan B' notes which activities could be omitted or extended depending on the rate of progress.

■ Human

Sometimes when you are coaching you may need, or have available, the help of other coaches. This can be very useful, especially if you have a large number of participants involved in the session. Knowing whether you have help can assist you with your planning and may allow you to include different activities than you would otherwise include. With more coaches to help out the participants can be spread out amongst the coaches making for safer activities and allowing participants more attention from coaches.

You will need to give consideration to the age and qualifications of any assistant coaches remembering that they may not be as knowledgeable and experienced as you are and that they may not be able to do the same things as you. Careful planning of how you intend to use any assistance is vital in order for them to be effective.

■ Physical

When planning a session, the coach needs to know what facilities are available and what equipment is on hand. For example, if you are coaching basketball and are planning to teach shooting skills, you will need to know if an appropriate facility is available allowing you to access the required number of baskets so that your participants can practise effectively.

If you are planning a regular session, you will already have a good idea of what is available and whether other people use adjacent space or have particular requirements that might impact on your coaching. If you are coaching somewhere for the first time, visit the venue and get an idea of the size of the space and the resources available. If you do not have your own equipment, you will need to make sure you know where you can access it, where it is kept and how much of it is available when you need it. Imagine planning a basketball shooting session for 15 people and arriving to realise that there is only one basket available and only one ball!

You will also need to ensure that you take into account the amount of time available and make sure that you allocate enough time to each activity. Try not to spend too much time on any one activity, as participants may become bored. Also, do not rush through practices without giving participants enough time to practise. A session plan that contains this information will reflect a good level of planning and you should be able to deliver an effective coaching session.

■ Fiscal

In most of the instances that you will find yourself the facilities will have been organised by your employer or the club you are coaching for and, therefore, you should not have to worry about payment. However, if you are planning your own independent coaching sessions then you need to think about how much the facilities and equipment might cost to hire. If this is the case, then you need to consider these costs in your planning

because you do not want to waste money. Imagine hiring 30 tennis balls and planning an activity where young players end up hitting them all over the place and losing some – you will have to pay to replace the lost ones. Also, you should ensure that you only hire the equipment that you will use. Don't plan a session that requires you to pay to borrow 10 basketballs and then spend the whole session playing a match and only using 1 ball.

Health and safety

The equipment and facilities, as well as the numbers and ability of participants, need to be considered with respect to health and safety. Coaches will need to ask themselves some important questions about whether the practices they are planning are safe. A checklist of health and safety questions might include the following.

- Can the participants perform the required practices in the space available?
- Is there enough room for a large group to practise all at the same time?
- Is there a risk of injury from using the equipment in a limited space?
- Are the participants able to perform the skill safely, or are they not ready yet?
- What are the emergency procedures that need to be followed if something goes wrong?

Coaches should make sure that they consider all the different aspects of safety when they are planning their sessions. The session in Table 4.2 identifies a number of safety issues with the coach highlighting to himself in his notes to consider safety issues related to the placing of the cones, the size of the area being used for the activity, and also the activities which have the potential to cause problems, i.e. passing and running may lead to dropped rugby balls and players stopping while others are moving.

■ Risk assessment

Risk assessments are used to evaluate the chances of an accident occurring during an exercise or training session. A risk assessment will identify the factors that are likely to cause an injury or illness and the likelihood of this happening. Therefore, any exercise practitioner should conduct a risk assessment before any session. This will include:

- venue: correct size, heating and ventilation, floor free from obstructions
- equipment: sufficient and suitable, free from damage
- clients: appropriate clothing, no jewellery, correct footwear, illness or injury.

A record form should be used to record all conducted risk assessments and these can be referred to if necessary.

■ Emergency procedures

Prior to carrying out your coaching session, you will need to make any last-minute safety checks and, if using the venue for the first time, familiarise yourself with the emergency procedures.

■ Contingencies

One of the most important requirements for your coaching plan is to have alternative ideas available ('Plan B' notes in Table 4.2). Coaches who are good planners will plan for every eventuality and will be able to resort to alternatives if problems arise with their original plan. This is particularly important when coaching outdoors: what happens if it rains? You should have contingency plans for an alternative session indoors. What would the coach planning to deliver our example session plan do if the weather is too cold for the participants to be able to handle the ball effectively?

Check also whether there are any contingency measures that you may need to take. Once you have made the final preparations, you can put your coaching plan into operation.

Components of session

Different coaches will undertake planning in different ways but it is always advisable to write down your plan. Various planning sheets or session plan formats exist for coaches to use – some of them are now even available in electronic form. But some coaches find it difficult to fit their planning into someone else's format and, therefore, develop their own versions – the session planner used in Table 4.2 may be useful for one coach but may not have sufficient detail for another.

Experiment with different versions of planning sheets and perhaps develop your own. It does not really matter what your planning sheet looks like as long as it contains the key 'signposts' to help you remember what you need to cover in your session. The following gives you an idea of the important things you will need to note down on your planning sheet.

- Session goals: what are you aiming to achieve in the session?
- Coaching styles and techniques: how are you going to deliver the session? Does the session require you to adopt an autocratic approach or is it more appropriate for you to adopt a different approach?
- Warm-up/cool-down: what warm-up activities will you include? How will you allow the participants to cool-down at the end?
- Theme: what skill, tactic or fitness aspect will you be working on in the session? How will you introduce the session?
- Practices and drills: what practices will you use? How long will participants be given to practise? Will practice be massed or distributed?
- Monitoring and feedback: how will you monitor progress? When and how are you going to offer feedback?
- Teaching points: what are the important teaching points for the skill?

■ Warm-up

It is well established that any period of physical activity needs to be preceded by a warm-up. The body is not able to go straight from rest to high intensity exercises so there needs to be a gradual increase in the exercise intensity. You will have been introduced elsewhere in this text to the physiological rationale for a warm-up but you need to ensure when you are planning a coaching session that you allow time for participants to prepare for the activity both mentally and physically. It is one of your responsibilities as a coach to ensure that adequate time is allocated to the warm-up.

Many coaches have set routines for their warm-ups, some leave the participants to warm-up themselves prior to the coach starting the session, others may ask one of the participants to plan and lead the warm-up. Whichever approach you use you need to plan what you are going to do and ensure that the basic principles of the warm-up are adhered to. Primarily, a warm-up should start off as a period of low intensity aerobic activity (e.g. gentle jogging) followed by a period of dynamic and static stretching. This should then be followed by some sport-specific activities done at low to moderate intensity and gradually building up to higher intensity activities. Table 4.3 gives an example of a warm-up session that a middle-distance runner might do prior to a track session.

Warm-up phase	Low intensity aerobic activity	Stretching	Bounding and sprinting
Duration	10 mins	8 mins	7 mins
Activity	Jog for 4 laps of the track	Combination of dynamic and static stretching working through every major joint and muscle group starting with the neck, shoulders, trunk, etc.	3 ×20m high knee lifts 3 × 20m 'kick-backs' 3 × 20m 'point the toes' 3 × 20m bounding 3 × 20m 'wind-up sprint'

Table 4.3 Typical warm-up plan for a middle-distance runner prior to track session

■ Main body

The main body of the session is where the session outcomes will be achieved so your planning of this element is essential. As we have seen before, the coach really needs to make sure that they have given an appropriate amount of thought to this aspect of the session. What drills and practices will be used? How long needs to be spent on each task? How quick can the participants move on to the next task? All these are questions that need to be addressed at the planning stage. Making these decisions as the session continues without having given prior thought to them can be disastrous. Good coaches will have an exact plan of what they are going to do and in this plan there will be alternatives depending on how well the participants are progressing and also there will probably be a number of additional activities that can be included should the

need arise. Most good coaches will include too many activities in their plan but will be able to gauge how well the session is going and select the appropriate ones to use. Only poor coaches run out of things to do early and struggle to find things to occupy the participants right through to the end.

■ Cool-down

In the same way as coaches need to allow adequate time for participants to warm-up at the start of a session, so too must they plan for a cool-down. Again, the exact activities that you choose to use do not really matter as long as you apply the basic principles and include in your plan sufficient time to allow participants to cool-down.

■ Feedback

Coaches need to be aware of the need to offer their participants feedback during sessions. As such it is important to build in time within the session to allow participants to practice and for the coach to offer feedback. A good coaching plan will include sufficient time to allow the coach to observe all performers and ideally offer each of them some individual feedback about their progress.

Sequencing

The coaching of new techniques and skills requires a systematic approach so that they are taught in a way that can be easily understood and learnt by the performer. As part of the planning process the coach will need to consider the following questions.

- In what order will you introduce skills and techniques?
- Does the skill need to be taught as a whole skill, or might a whole-part-whole approach be more effective?
- How will you allow the participants to practice?
- Will there be an opportunity at the end of the session for a match which allows the skill or technique to be practised in the right context?

Coaching skills and techniques

There are a number of stages that are often adopted to coach new skills and techniques and some coaches remember these stages by referring to the word IDEA as the following list illustrates. The stages of this process are as follows.

- **I**ntroduction and explanation.
- **D**emonstration.
- **E**xecution of the skill or technique.
- **A**nalysing and correcting errors.

As we have seen earlier, the introduction to a new skill or technique should explain to the participants what they are about to learn, why it is important, how it fits with what they have already learnt and when they might need to use it. Clear and concise explanations need to be offered to ensure that the participants understand what it is they are about to learn.

Once you have introduced the skill or technique that is to be the focus of the session participants will want to see what it looks like. This is the time for an effective demonstration.

No amount of introduction or demonstration can replace the need for the participants to have a go at the skill for themselves. The repeated execution of a skill by a learner is the only way of effectively learning that skill. Your session planning should include appropriate drills and practices to allow the participants plenty of opportunities to execute the skill or technique for themselves.

As participants practice a new skill it is important that you watch them and offer them guidance and comment as to how well they are performing the skill. This means close observation of them performing the skill and a thorough analysis on your part of how they perform. This requires a good understanding of the different techniques and skills required in your sport and an ability to recognise the correct technical aspects – to have a clear picture of the right way to perform a skill. This is one of the reasons why a coach must have a good technical knowledge of the sport they are coaching. Once a coach has a clear picture of the correct way to execute a skill, they need to be able to contrast the actual execution by the participant with the ideal execution. This is one of the keys to good coaching – being able to identify the differences between how a performer executes a skill or technique and how that skill or technique should be performed.

Assessment practice

1 Imagine you have been invited by your local sports centre to run a guest coaching session. The coaching session is a prize in a local charity fund raising event and the sports centre are offering 15 children the opportunity to be coached by you. You are able to choose the sport that you want to coach but have no idea yet who will be in the group of children so you don't know their age, gender or ability.

Compile a comprehensive list of all the things you need to consider as you plan for your coaching session.   **P4**

2 The big day is getting nearer and you have received two letters in the post. One is a letter from the sports centre detailing the winners. They were unable to narrow it down to 15 so are asking you to take 20. They are all aged between 13 and 15. 12 of them are girls, 8 of them are boys. One of them is a wheelchair user. None of the 20 has ever played your sport before so are totally new to the sport. All are really looking forward to the day and are keen to take part and learn something new from you. The other letter is from the local newspaper who has asked you to give them details of what you will be doing so that they can run a feature in the week before the event. The editor wants to know what you aim to achieve in the session and what type of activities you will be doing. In his letter he also informs you that the Council's Health and Safety Officer will be attending to watch as his son is the wheelchair user. Draft a letter responding to the newspaper's editor with a detailed outline of what your session will include and how you will run the session.   **P4**

Grading tips

Grading Tip   **P4**

To plan your sports coaching session, you can use your own coaching session plan or a suitable sport-specific template. You could incorporate this plan into your logbook or diary with your evidence for other criteria.

For many coaches this is the fun part of coaching: standing in front of a group of participants and teaching a skill or leading a training session. There are, however, still a lot of things to do and delivering a session requires more than simply reading out your session plan.

Deliver

While delivering a session, a coach should be putting together all the aspects of coaching that have been addressed in this unit. A range of different coaching roles may be required, and varied skills and techniques are necessary to ensure that they fulfil the appropriate roles, the session runs smoothly, and that the session achieves the desired outcomes. Coaches will need to identify appropriate techniques to enable their participants to learn, and may have to adopt different coaching styles to achieve this. The coach is doing a lot of different things at the same time and is trying to perform a complex juggling act.

The coach has to be able to organise the group to ensure that they are doing the right thing, at the right time, in the right way. This will require the coach to use communication skills to make sure that he or she is delivering messages correctly and that the participants understand the information being given to them and learn from it.

Throughout the delivery of a session, coaches should be watching what is going on and observing how participants are undertaking the required tasks. They should be checking progress against the identified teaching points and analysing performance to identify any errors that may be occurring. The effective coach will be able to observe, analyse and correct errors as a session continues, as well as begin to think about future activities and future developments.

The foundations of effective delivery of coaching sessions are laid in the planning stage. We have seen in the planning sections above the sort of things that coaches need to be aware of when planning for a session.

Appropriate role

At the start of this unit we explored the different roles that a coach might need to play during their time as a coach. When considering these roles we need to recognise that it is unlikely that all of these roles will be fulfilled at the same time or in the same coaching session. Clearly some of them will overlap: we would expect the coach to always be a role model and a friend and not suddenly stop being these things for one session. There may, however, be a need for the coach to 'change hats' at certain points during a session. If something suddenly goes wrong and the participants are at risk, there may be a need for the coach to adopt an authoritarian role and instruct participants exactly what to do to avoid the dangers. Also, if during a fitness session the coach has adopted a trainer role and she notices that one of the participants is performing a skill incorrectly, she may need to step in and revert to the teacher role and identify the error and seek to correct it.

As coaches become more experienced they will find themselves adopting the different roles 'automatically' and without necessarily planning or thinking about it. Shifting from one role to another as the situation demands is a skill that good coaches have mastered.

Responsibilities

It is expected that the coach will fulfil their professional coaching responsibilities throughout their time as a coach and experienced coaches will do so automatically and not have to think about behaving in a certain way – it becomes their natural coaching behaviour. The coach is expected to be aware of their professional responsibilities at all times.

It is the coach's responsibility to ensure that coaching sessions are safe, fun and rewarding for the participants. As a coach you are expected to deliver sessions that allow people to learn and develop skills safely, in an enjoyable and non-threatening manner. It is all about giving participants a positive experience so that they enjoy their involvement in sport and come back again for more. This is a heavy burden of responsibility which coaches need to consider and in the early stages of their career will have to make conscious efforts to fulfil. However, like most skills, you will soon master it and be able to deliver enjoyable and safe coaching sessions in a responsible way.

Demonstration of skills and techniques

The characteristics of a good demonstration have been presented previously but by way of a reminder you need to ensure that a demonstration:

- is a technically-correct visual image for the participants to copy (get somebody else to demonstrate or use a video clip if you don't feel you can accurately represent the desired skill or technique)
- is seen clearly by all participants
- emphasises the key coaching points you are trying to get across
- is at the appropriate level for the participants
- is repeated enough times for participants to understand what is required.

Consideration of health and safety

Coaches must ensure that they have undertaken a full risk assessment of the coaching environment. Look again at the activity that you undertook on page 148. Use this task as the model for all future coaching sessions ensuring that you undertake a thorough risk assessment and satisfy all your health and safety responsibilities before starting a session.

■ Emergency procedures

When delivering a session you will need to be aware of the emergency procedures that are in place at the venue you are using. Your planning and any previous visit to the venue should have informed you of the necessary information.

■ Contingencies

A good coach will be able to judge how well a session is going by the way the participants are responding and progressing. Having your pre-planned contingencies – your 'Plan B' – will help you adjust your session to meet the needs of the participants. If they are progressing well, then move on to new activities and skills, if they are struggling, then utilise additional activities to reinforce the points you are trying to make and give participants more chance to practice the new skills.

Use of resources

To present a professional image any session should be planned in advance and should outline all the key objectives. You must identify the venue, time of session and the equipment needed. In advance of the session, you should set up the equipment to be used so that it is ready when the client(s) arrive. The equipment should be checked for damage and not used if you are unsure.

■ Equipment

When delivering a session it is important to remember that the equipment you use can cause a safety hazard and you need to make sure that it is used properly and put away safely after use. When using equipment, always make sure that it is stored away safely when not in use.

■ Facilities

Facilities too can pose a hazard if not used correctly. Good planning and good management of a coaching session will ensure that you get the best out of the facilities available.

Components of session

■ Warm-up

The actual amount of time spent on a warm-up may depend on a number of things. If the weather is particularly cold, you might need to spend more time warming the participants up and might even consider the intensity of the practices you expect them to do – choosing to have moderate intensity drills early on so that participants are not expected to work flat out when their muscles may not be warmed-up. If, however, it is a hot day or you are coaching indoors, the amount of warm-up may be reduced. If the session that you have planned is very technical in nature and requires participants to repeat activities a number of times or to watch demonstrations, you will need to ensure that they are fully warmed-up from the start to reduce the risk of injuries and also to ensure that they do not get too cool in between activities. If the session involves a lot of standing around watching things, then a good warm-up is vital. If, however, you have a session planned that is very active and requires the participants to be on the move a lot, then less time needs to be dedicated to the warm-up.

■ Main body

It is this element of the coaching session which should include all the practices and drills that are necessary to convey the learning points that you wish to get across. This is where your skill as a coach really comes into play. Your ability to design informative, interesting and fun sessions that allow participants to learn and practise new skills, techniques or tactics is really tested in this part of the session.

■ Cool-down

After a period of exercise the body does not return to normal straight away. There is a need to gradually allow time for the body to recover and to allow any waste products produced during exercise to be removed.

After the main body of the session is over there needs to be time to allow participants to cool-down. Many coaches adopt the approach that the cool-down is the reverse of the warm-up and they may often use the same activities as in the warm-up but in reverse – namely the sport-specific activities of moderate intensity first followed by some stretching and then concluding with gentle aerobic exercise.

Feedback

When instructing participants it is important to provide them with feedback on how well they are progressing. Feedback should be constructive and helpful and delivered in a supportive way not full of criticism and

delivered in an aggressive and threatening manner. The different forms of feedback that a learner receives have been discussed in Unit 6, but as far as the coach is concerned there is a need to provide participants with positive and corrective feedback which contributes to the learning process. The coach should find an appropriate form of words to signal that something is being performed incorrectly without being too critical. Which would you rather hear as a beginner golfer?

> 'You're holding the club all wrong and the ball is going all over the place!'

or

> 'If you hold the shaft a little tighter the club face will not open out when you hit the ball and the ball will go straighter.'

The last comment offers some constructive advice as to how to correct the fault.

You should look to offer feedback as soon as possible, but not before participants have had time to process their own internal feedback. In most cases, coaches watching a participant in practice will be able to give their feedback concurrent with the participant's own internal feedback.

Sometimes, however, it can be useful to supplement this with delayed feedback. The use of video to show performers how they have performed a skill can be an effective form of feedback. This allows performers to watch themselves in action. It is particularly useful in sports where actions are performed very quickly and it is difficult to see or feel the skill at normal speed. Visual feedback from a video allows performers to see for themselves where the errors are occurring and what may be causing them.

Whether the feedback comes from themselves, the coach or a video, it is important that performers receive it clearly and are able to learn from it.

Sequencing

Did the order you used work well? Does the skill need to be taught as a whole skill, or might a whole-part-whole approach be more effective? If you ended the session with a game, how well did this work?

Review

The coaching process does not stop when the session stops. Coaches must take time after a session to evaluate it and decide what worked well and what worked less well.

The evaluation process is best done immediately after the session, when it is still clear in the memory and the coach can recall incidents and issues more readily. The accuracy of recall can be enhanced if the session is video taped, as events can be reviewed again later.

In the same way as coaches identify errors in participants' actions, so they must also identify errors in their coaching and try to find out the cause of the problem in order to rectify it for next time. Most coaches find evaluating the progress of the participant and the effectiveness of the session fairly easy, but when asked to evaluate themselves they struggle. It is always difficult to be honest about your own performance: it is human nature to maximise the positives and minimise the negatives, and to make excuses. Trying to identify things you can improve in your own coaching is difficult, but good coaches learn to be reflective about their performance and recognise some of their faults and errors. Once you are able to identify what you are less effective in, you are a long way towards becoming more effective.

Against aims, objectives and targets

When evaluating the effectiveness of the session a coach needs to evaluate against the aims, objectives and targets of the session. If they were not met, the coach needs to try to find out why. It may be due to bad planning, inappropriate amounts of time allocated to key practices, tasks being too demanding for the participants, poor coaching technique, lack of attention and effort by the participants, or a variety of other reasons.

A coach may also wish to consider whether any aspects of the coaching session worked particularly well or particularly poorly. Was there one specific practice that participants enjoyed? What was it about that practice that made it enjoyable? Was there a particular drill that did not work well? Why did it not work so well?

Was it explained clearly? Did participants understand what was required? These are the kinds of questions a coach should ask about a coaching session and use the information gained to benefit future coaching.

Formative and summative

Adopting an honest self-review after each session will also contribute to future improvements. Therefore, you should always ask yourself some questions after each session and you must answer these honestly, even if the answers are likely to identify weaknesses in your performance. Self-evaluation is an important tool as it means future sessions will be safe, effective and the client will remain motivated and make targeted progression. Self-evaluation will also help you to identify any future training needs you may have and allow you to update your skills. SMART goals will be beneficial in improving your performance.

- Fit for purpose: by reviewing performance you can identify whether your selected activities are fit for purpose. This means making sure that the exercises used are actually addressing the long-term and short-term goals of the client. Ask yourself 'Are these goals being achieved and, if not, why not?'

- Track progression: using clear targets that are measurable means that any changes can be tracked throughout the lifetime of the session. If a specific aspect of the programme is not effective, then changes can be made and the session adapted.

- Adapt session: by performing regular session reviews you are able to identify how effective the programme is and whether the client's identified goals are being achieved. If they are not being met, then it is important that the session is amended or adapted. Such adaptations should take into account the client's needs and may even address whether a client has become demotivated. Adaptations will also allow variety which can further enhance enjoyment.

- Modify activities: by modifying a session you are able to enhance a client's motivation through variety of training and further target their long-term goals. Activities may be modified to take into account factors such as injury, illness or unexpected changes to length of sessions. It is important that any modifications are fully discussed with the client so that they are fully aware of what to expect in the future.

- Improve own performance: by conducting a full personal performance review you are able to identify areas of strength and weakness in your own performance. This may include whether you can improve your clients' motivation and the way in which you instruct them. Remember each client is different and you may have to adapt your approach and instructor skills for each individual – what works for one client may not work for another.

Feedback

■ Participants

Evaluating the participant is best done by measuring the progress he or she has made during the session. If a participant was able to meet the desired outcome of the coaching session, the session could be considered a success. If a participant can perform a skill at the end of the session that he or she could not do at the beginning, the session has been effective in developing performance.

Evaluation should not be done solely by the coach; the participants will have a different view of the coaching session and the coach, and they should be invited to comment on how well they feel the session went and how much they think they learnt or progressed during the session.

■ Observers and peers

It can also be useful for another coach or an observer to comment on the session. They too will have a different viewpoint and may well have noticed things that neither the coach nor the participants noticed.

■ Assessors

It may not be practical to invite the comments of participants or observers after every coaching session, but it can be useful occasionally to gain a different view. How you do this is up to you. Some coaches ask participants to complete short questionnaires after a session. These may contain simple questions about the session, about the coach or about the practices and drills

being used. Observers could be asked to complete a checklist while they are watching a session. This may be a list of different coaching behaviours and the observer is required to tick a box each time a particular behaviour is shown. Some coaches use this to try to identify their dominant coaching behaviours, and use the findings to modify undesirable behaviour.

On a larger scale and over a longer term, if the competitive performance of an individual or a team has improved and there has been an obvious benefit to performance, a coach can be said to be successful. In professional sports the success of a team is the measure of the success of the coach. Conversely, the failure of a team usually reflects failure by the coach. How many professional soccer managers or international rugby coaches lose their jobs after a run of poor results?

Strengths

Many coaches when evaluating their performance or reviewing a coaching session will tend to focus on the negatives – what went wrong? It is, of course, equally important to address the good things about your session and your coaching by looking at your strengths. Knowing what you do well will help you to develop and enable you to plan your future sessions around your strengths. This is not to say that you should not seek to address the negatives but knowing what you do well will help you focus on what needs your attention.

Areas for improvement

Because the coaching process is a cyclical one, the final phase will always lead you back to the first phase. The results of the evaluation phase should inform the next cycle of planning. If your evaluation of a coaching session reveals that a participant has been unable to learn a particular skill, the planning of the next session should begin by identifying the problems the participant faced and planning a new approach.

Development

If, however, a participant has mastered a technique, in the next phase of planning the coach can build on this newly learnt technique and develop the participant even further. In applying the coaching process, the effective sports coach will be able to plan appropriate sessions for participants, deliver effective sessions, evaluate the progress made in the sessions and then use the information to plan further sessions to build on the progress made.

■ Opportunities

Videoing yourself coaching may not always be practical and some coaches find it uncomfortable to watch themselves on video. It can, however, be an effective way of evaluating how well a coaching session went, and also how well a coach performed.

■ Potential barriers

Traditionally coaches are left to their own devices to overcome potential barriers to their development, location being one of them. However, projects such as Developing Female Coaches in Rural and Remote Areas have established a joint initiative to develop female coaches in rural and remote communities of North Yorkshire. This scheme was set up by the Women's Sport

Foundation (WSF), North Yorkshire Sport (NYS) and **sports coach UK**. The scheme aims to develop women as individuals and role models, inspiring other women and girls to step up to the mark and realise their potential.

A project of this nature ensures that individual coaches who, without targeted assistance, might find it difficult to progress up the coaching ladder are supported and encouraged to develop to their full potential.

Assessment practice

1 Now that you have been introduced to the coaching process and had the opportunity to observe some practical coaching, you should be in a position to lead a coaching session yourself.

   With your tutor's support, plan, deliver and evaluate a coaching session for a group of your peers. Remember all the different features that have been discussed in this unit and ensure that you undertake all the important stages of effective coaching. Consider the following points.

   - What issues do you need to consider when planning a session?
   - What are the potential risks?
   - What should a session contain?
   - What practices are you going to include?
   - How will you know if you have been successful? **P5 M4**

2 Once you have completed your sports coaching session you need to review your planning and delivery of the session. Consider the following points.

   - How well did you plan your session?
   - Did you achieve your aims and objectives?
   - Did you successfully identify the potential risk?
   - What were the strengths of the session?
   - Were there any areas for improvement?
   - Why do you need to make these improvements?
   - How might you make these improvements?
   - What feedback do you have from the participants? **P6 M5 D3**

Remember!

- The coaching process is a cyclical process of planning, delivering and evaluating coaching sessions.
- When planning a session, the coach should take into account a number of factors including the needs of the participant and the resources available.
- Coaches should have a well-organised lesson plan to help them deliver the session. This should include all necessary details required to deliver the session effectively.
- When delivering a coaching session, coaches should strike an appropriate balance between all the different roles required.
- All sessions should be evaluated and positive and negative factors should be noted and used in the planning of future sessions.

Grading tips

Grading Tip P5 M4

Your tutor will assess your delivery of the session, probably using an observation checklist that you can include in your logbook or diary. To achieve M4 you need to deliver your coaching session without any support.

Grading Tip P6 M5

To achieve P6 you can do a straightforward review of your sports coaching session in your logbook or diary. To aim for M5 you must also include an action plan to target your areas for improvement.

Grading Tip D3

You must review your own coaching performance and the feedback of your performance from other sources, such as the participants. You must say why you think your suggestions for how to improve your coaching performance will be successful.

Knowledge check

1 What are the main roles of a coach?

2 For each of the main roles, give an example of a situation when a coach may be required to fulfil that role.

3 What are the main responsibilities facing a coach?

4 What are the three main categories of health and safety considerations for a coach?

5 Where can a coach go to get information about codes of conduct for coaching?

6 Name three laws that coaches must be aware of when they are coaching.

7 What are the main components of communication used by sports coaches?

8 Under what conditions do individuals learn best?

9 Draw a diagram that represents the key stages of the coaching process.

10 What questions should you ask yourself when evaluating a coaching session?

Preparation for assessment

1 Imagine you have been given an interview for a coaching position that is open to you on a local coaching scheme. As part of the interview, you will need to show that you have a solid understanding of the sports coaching process. You are to plan and present a ten-minute presentation on the roles, responsibilities, techniques and skills of successful sports coaches.

  a You need to cover four roles and four responsibilities of sports coaches and use examples from different sports. **P1 M1**

  b Describe and explain three skills common to successful sports coaches. Use examples from different sports to help you with your explanations. **P2 M2**

  c Compare and contrast the roles, responsibilities and skills of successful coaches from different sports. **D1**

  d You need to describe and explain techniques used by coaches to improve the performance of athletes. Use at least three techniques. **P3 M3**

  e Evaluate these three techniques. **D2**

2 The interview went well and you have been given a coaching role within the scheme. Your boss wants you to plan a sports coaching session. Choose a team from the coaching scheme and devise your first sports coaching session for them. **P4**

3 Now is the time to deliver your sports coaching session! Are you prepared? Have you thought about the potential risks and planned in contingencies if anything goes wrong? How will you know if the session has gone well? Check back through this unit to make sure you have covered everything. **P5 M4**

4 You think your sports coaching session went well but your boss wants you to review and evaluate the session.

  a You need to identify strengths and areas for improvement. **P6**

  b Suggest how improvements could be made in the areas you have identified. **M5**

  c Justify how these suggestions for improvement will help you develop as a sports coach. **D3**

Grading tips

Grading Tip P1 P2 M1 M2 D1

To achieve P1 and P2 you need to describe four roles and four responsibilities and three common skills of sports coaches. Select examples of successful coaches from different sports to support your answers. To provide evidence for M1, M2 and D1 you need to extend these answers with further explanations and compare and contrast the attributes and skills for successful coaches.

Grading Tip M4 M5

For M4 you need to deliver your coaching session without any support. To provide evidence for M5 you need to include an action plan of how you will develop those areas that you need to improve in.

Grading Tip D3

You must review your own coaching performance and review the feedback of your performance from a variety of other sources. You must say why you think your suggestions for how to improve your coaching performance will be successful to your development.

To achieve a pass grade the evidence must show that the learner is able to:	To achieve a merit grade the evidence must show that, in addition to the pass criteria, the learner is able to:	To achieve a distinction grade the evidence must show that, in addition to the pass and merit criteria, the learner is able to:
P1 Describe four roles and four responsibilities of sports coaches, using examples of coaches from different sports **Assessment practice Page 150**	**M1** Explain four roles and four responsibilities of sports coaches, using examples of coaches from different sports **Assessment practice Page 150**	**D1** Compare and contrast the roles, responsibilities and skills of successful coaches from different sports **Assessment practice Page 150 and 154**
P2 Describe three skills common to successful sports coaches, using examples from coaches from different sports **Assessment practice Page 154**	**M2** Explain three skills common to successful sports coaches, using examples from coaches from different sports **Assessment practice Page 154**	
P3 Describe three different techniques that are used, by coaches, to improve the performance of athletes **Assessment practice Page 160**	**M3** Explain three different techniques that are used, by coaches, to improve the performance of athletes **Assessment practice Page 160**	**D2** Evaluate three different techniques that are used, by coaches, to improve the performance of athletes **Assessment practice Page 160**
P4 Plan a sports coaching session **Assessment practice Page 169**		
P5 Deliver a sports coaching session, with support **Assessment practice Page 175**	**M4** Deliver a sports coaching session **Assessment practice Page 175**	
P6 Review the planning and delivery of a sports coaching session, identifying strengths and areas for improvement **Assessment practice Page 175**	**M5** Evaluate the planning and delivery of a sports coaching session, suggesting how improvements could be reached in the identified areas **Assessment practice Page 175**	**D3** Justify suggestions made in relation to development in identified areas for improvement **Assessment practice Page 175**

Sports development

Introduction

This unit introduces the key concepts that underpin sports development and give you an understanding of the work that goes on in this important area of the sports industry.

Sports development might be a career you would like to consider. However, such a route requires a good understanding of the diverse aims and purposes that need to be met by sports development programmes and activities. These purposes are called cross-cutting agendas as modern sports development encompasses both social and political agendas.

Many different types of people are sports developers and many types of organisations have sports development schemes. This unit explores a range of these so that you can appreciate the scope.

It is important when professional sports developers are setting up their schemes that they have agreed targets and ways of ensuring that the programme delivered is of good quality. It is also important that the standards and achievements can be measured against the objectives set (usually called evaluation criteria). This unit will help your awareness of these aspects of managing a sports development programme.

After completing this unit you should be able to achieve the following outcomes:

- Understand key concepts in sports development.

- Know about key providers of sports development.

- Understand how quality is measured in sports development.

- Know about sports development in practice.

Think it over

Not everybody can take part in sport. Why do you think this might be the case, based on your experience?

Use the following headings to help you think of some answers why this might be the case: social reasons, cultural reasons, economic reasons. You might be able to base some of your answers on your own experiences or ask your classmates for their views.

Once you have created a list for each reason, think about how you would try to overcome difficulties if you worked in the sports development sector or were a politician responsible for sport.

What do you think are the key ingredients for a successful sports programme?

Sports development has evolved over the last 30 years, but it is a flexible concept that can be interpreted in many ways to bring a variety of benefits to different areas, people and sports.

If we compare three adjacent local authorities in the North of England, Scarborough Borough Council has only one person dealing with a few schemes, while neighbouring East Riding based in Beverley has five teams of sports development staff involved in varying schemes. Kingston-upon-Hull City Council, on the other hand, has a whole department based at the K.C. stadium, which links what the team does in sports development with the city's overall strategy.

Theory into practice

Find out how your local authority tackles its sports development programme.

Remember!

You may find that there are many 'partners' involved in sports development schemes today.

The sports development continuum

Key term

Sports development continuum A model that shows the different levels at which people can develop their sporting skills.

There are four levels in the sports development continuum: foundation, participation, performance and excellence.

■ Foundation

Sports development programmes at the foundation level are mainly aimed at young participants such as primary school children or complete beginners in an activity. They tend to provide basic skills education such as catching or

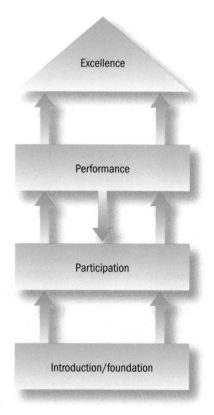

▲ A simple sports development continuum

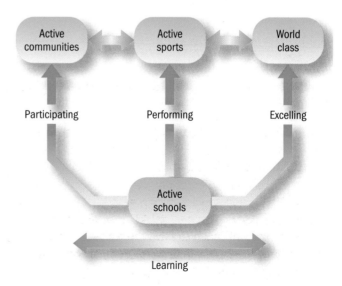

▲ Sport England's sports development model

throwing and simple rules, but there is much emphasis on 'fun' so that youngsters enjoy their sessions and continue the activity. Sport England's strategy includes an Active Schools scheme, which focuses on this level.

Remember!

The foundation level focuses on young people gaining key movement and coordination skills, learning the basics of the game safely, making friends and having fun. It is mainly found in school-age sports schemes, teams and clubs.

Taking it further

Many sports clubs run similar schemes for children, perhaps on a weekly basis such as mini-rugby or tennis training during the school holidays. Information on these types of schemes should be available locally.

■ Participation

This level is less easy to define, with many different participants of all ages and types, and with many different schemes too. However, the schemes tend to focus on community participation by trying to get people to take part more regularly, especially those who do not take regular exercise or play sport at all.

This level is illustrated by the Active Communities scheme in Sport England's model. These schemes tend to be delivered by local authorities.

Case study: Reading Borough Council

In Reading, the Sport England Active Communities scheme is about ensuring that everyone has access to sporting opportunities that suit their needs and choices. The sports development projects focus mainly on groups such as ethnic minority community groups, women and girls, people with disabilities and those hard-to-reach groups, predominantly of young people. There is an Active Communities manager who offers support with funding bids, planning and running a club.

Identify an Active Communities programme in your area. Which groups of people make up the participants?

■ Performance

This level in the continuum emphasises improvement through regular practice, competition or skills training. A feature of this level would be the selection of

Case study: Stirling Triathlon Club and Stirling University

Stirling Triathlon Club is a relatively new club that has grown to 135 members in ten years. It now provides an extensive programme of training sessions in swimming, fitness, running and cycling, seven days a week. It also organises a popular programme of training camps and competitive events. With the appointment of a professional coach to drive the training and race programme, the club now provides competitive squad facilities and is now at full capacity.

Stirling University is committed to providing the opportunity for all students to fulfil their potential in sport and to enhance its reputation as a centre for sporting excellence. The university focuses on the management, administration and delivery of participation and higher-level performance by students in competitive sport at university club level.

Describe possible barriers to participation for some students at Stirling University.

participants to go on a course, take up a place at an academy or perhaps obtain sponsorship to practise. Attendance usually helps with skills and the athlete's knowledge of their sport, as well as nurturing talented players. An example would be a county scheme that helps to identify players who can gain representative honours and possibly move on to the excellence level.

Think it over

Sports development at performance level clearly involves many things other than simply participating. What do you think these are?

■ Excellence

This is national and on to international level, which might involve preparation for competition at championship levels around the world. From April 2006, UK Sport took over the running of this for a range of sports at least through to the Olympics to be held in London in 2012. UK Sport has set out three new aspects of the world-class programme (WCP), the excellence

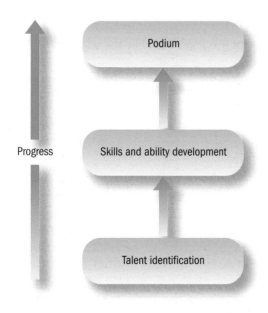

▲ The world-class programme model

level of the continuum that supports top athletes in their training and funding.

- WCP Talent, which supports athletes who have the potential to progress through to the next two stages.
- WCP Development, which supports athletes building up to Podium level.
- WCP Podium, which supports athletes with realistic medal potential.

Purpose

■ Show progression

Most sports development schemes focus on helping participants to progress with their skills, tactics and training. These are programmes that show progression, either through the levels of the continuum or higher up in a level itself, such as when a regular participant becomes good enough to be picked for a club team. Those programmes have sport at their heart but do not focus entirely on it. They tend to have social and confidence-building purposes too and may have more of a participation focus with less emphasis on progression.

Appropriateness

Some sports development schemes are more specific in their approach. They are designed around other factors so that their content and delivery are just right for the participants. This is called appropriateness.

■ Target groups

Some schemes are tailor-made for youngsters wishing to learn football skills or targeted at overweight adults who have a low-activity lifestyle.

■ Communities

Some schemes are based around events for the whole community, such as a fun run for charity.

Cross-cutting agendas

Some complex schemes focus on more than just sports development. They incorporate a range of areas such as health, social, cultural and economic benefits. These diverse aims and purposes are called cross-cutting agendas.

Key term

Cross-cutting agendas The various purposes of a sports development scheme. They cover more than just sport and may involve things such as helping people to integrate more readily or meeting the needs of people in lower-income areas.

■ Pro-health

This area has a health bias, such as guiding youngsters into taking part in an activity, and promoting healthy eating and regular exercise.

■ Pro-education

This agenda might be based on helping people to understand fair play and follow the rules, or it might try to show how to work together in multicultural teams.

Key term

Multicultural A society that has many different nationalities and cultures in it.

■ Anti-drug

This area might be aimed at highlighting the dangers of drug taking or helping those with a drug problem to find a way back into normal activities, such as playing sport.

■ Anti-crime

This aspect is staged to encourage young people to avoid criminal activity and to take part in sports and activities.

■ Regeneration

These schemes have been put in place in cities such as Sheffield and Manchester, where the regeneration of previously rundown areas of the city help to attract

▼ Regeneration creates new sports venues, often on old derelict factory areas

A scheme called Football in the Community has been established at Bolton Wanderers for 18 years. The range of activities offered has grown to include in-term coaching, after-school and holiday courses, match-day experiences and sponsored events, and fun events. The scheme tries to reach as wide a range of people in the community as possible. Here are the aims of the scheme:

- to bring families together
- to offer sports opportunities to children

- to build awareness of healthy activity, good eating and drug abuse.

Club players are nearly always involved, as well as qualified coaches.

1 **Which cross-cutting agendas can you identify here?**

2 **What weaknesses are there in this approach?**

major games. Areas of East London are currently undergoing regeneration in order to host the Olympic Games there in 2012.

Taking it further

Identify a sports development scheme, large or small, that has contributed to regeneration in your area.

Grading tips

Grading Tip M1

To gain a merit grade, make sure you identify strengths and weaknesses of the sports development continuum.

Assessment practice

Imagine you are preparing for an interview for a sports development job. The organisation has set the following tasks to go into a short Microsoft PowerPoint® presentation for the interview panel.

1 Using diagrams and different sports at each level, describe the levels in the sports development continuum. **P1**

2 Using at least three examples of real sports development schemes, compare and contrast what goes on at different levels in the sports development continuum. **M1**

Barriers to participation

Not everyone can take up a sport or get to where an activity is taking place. There are many reasons why this is the case, which are called barriers to participation.

Key term

Barriers to participation The factors that prevent people from taking part, such as lack of time, money or skills.

Barriers are classified under five main headings: cultural, social, economic, historical and educational.

Cultural

These barriers to participation stem from differences in culture. The UK is a multicultural society, which means it has people from many different nationalities and cultures living here. Some cultures have value systems that have rules or traditions about the right of women to participate in sport, or they have rules about playing sport in the same place or way as men. Some cultures will not be familiar with British sports at all or may have different games that have evolved in their culture e.g. netball or korfball.

Taking it further

Use a dictionary to look up 'culture'. Give two further examples of cultural differences that could affect sports participation.

Social

Social barriers might be based on what your peers think and do, and taking part in sport might not be considered 'cool'. People might feel they are a bit inept and are perhaps too embarrassed to try a sport in front of others. There might also be social barriers created by a range of circumstances, such as age differences, parental pressure and an overly competitive coach.

In recent years, a great deal of the gender imbalance has been redressed, and women are finding more opportunities to participate.

Think it over

Think about other social barriers to participation, which are caused by other people, yourself or prejudice.

Economic

These are usually created by an individual's lack of ability to pay to participate, such as match or entry fees, or club membership. Economic barriers could also apply to everyone in an area, if it is rundown it has little to offer in the way of sports or places to play. Some inner-city areas or residential estates in the suburbs might be like this. Similarly, wealthier areas may have had good facilities for many years that are now in need of renewal.

Taking it further

As a class, debate what you think should be done to help economically rundown areas develop sport.

Historical

In the UK, historical traditions in sporting terms have meant that men were dominant in most sports while women were limited to playing games such as hockey, tennis and netball. These traditions may have limited involvement by certain groups, such as Asian footballers and female boxers. Although struggles still persist – for example, women's sports still have to combat stereotypes and the old-boys' network – equality and stability no longer seem unattainable goals.

Other barriers to participation have also existed in the past, such as class, religion and race.

Activity

It is normal to break these traditions and today different games can be played by women. List three or four sports for which this is the case.

Educational

Through sport, young people often first encounter their own weaknesses in performance and become less confident and more self-conscious about their body shape and size. This leads to poor attitudes to PE and even poorer skills (both mental and physical) to help progress. PE teachers should either rebuild that confidence or find a sport that the individual can enjoy. Other educational factors that might cause barriers include:

- lack of facilities or choice of sports
- no after-school clubs or teams
- lack of funding to pay for extra sessions, such as courses or trips.

Activity

List two more reasons for education barriers, based on your own experiences or those of friends.

Think it over

What issues can arise if pupils do not get enough exercise or if they do not have positive self-esteem?

Taking it further

Carry out some research to find out what barriers to participation in sport disabled people might face.

Target groups

Target groups include overweight children, young players, women and the elderly. These target groups

Key term

Target groups Groups of people that organisations carrying out sports development judge would benefit the most from a scheme or programme.

may also have other characteristics, such as low income or a disability, which increase the barriers to participation.

Targeted schemes have long been a tradition in sports development. They are aimed at reaching the neediest or those who can benefit the most. Targeted approaches help to give value for money.

Women

Women have traditionally participated less in sport than men. Sports development schemes aimed specifically at women, such as single-sex classes, help to overcome inhibitions. Through female-orientated activities and sports such as aerobics, dance and other fitness classes, there should have been an upsurge in female participation.

However, statistics gathered for the *Sport and Leisure General Household Survey 2002* (www.statistics.gov.uk) show a drop in overall participation rates. Among both men and women, overall sports participation decreased between 1996 and 2002 (see Table 5.1).

	1996 (%)	2002 (%)
Men	54	51
Women	38	36

Table 5.1 Participation in at least one activity in the four weeks before the interview

Taking it further

Analyse the statistics in the table and say why you think the sports participation has fallen despite all the efforts to develop women's participation and equality?

In recent years some traditional male barriers have been broken with schemes to attract women to sports such as rugby, football, cricket and rowing. However, the imbalance still exists in certain areas so women will remain a target group for some time to come.

◀ Women have pushed their playing boundaries into many traditionally male-dominated sports

provide a sporting pathway for all young people from 18 months to 18 years, providing the tools required for the delivery of high-quality PE and school sport. They encourage all young people, including those with disabilities, teenage girls and gifted and talented athletes to thrive, as well as providing ongoing support to teachers and others working with young children.

The YST has a range of other initiatives including helping with the following.

- Zoneparc/sporting playgrounds: a playground improvement project that aims to tackle social exclusion and increase the activity levels of young people.
- Specialist sports colleges: position PE at the centre of the school curriculum, using it to develop and improve learning opportunities for all.
- School sport partnerships: groups of schools working together to develop and improve learning opportunities for all.

Web links

Visit the Women's Sports Foundation website to assess current developments at www.womenssportfoundation.org.

Think it over

Better facilities and funding have also had their part to play in development. How have these helped to develop women's participation?

Young people

This is a key target group. If good sporting habits can be introduced to young people, they are more likely to continue through life and up through the sports development continuum stages. This can lead to them gaining fitness, fun, a healthy lifestyle and socialisation skills too. Many schemes are targeted at this age group through the Active Schools programme (see pages 182–83).

Among the best known are the TOP programmes implemented by the Youth Sports Trust (YST). They

Web links

Go to the Youth Sports Trust website at www.youthsporttrust.org to find out more about the organisation's work.

50+

There are more elderly people in the UK than ever before, so this age group is a key target area. People are living longer lives, so there is also a need for them to live healthier lives too.

Schemes aimed at this group are mainly focused at the participation level of the sports development continuum and mostly run by local authorities. A key element in all programmes is the social factor. Here are some examples.

- The Brighton and Hove area offers Age Concern t'ai chi, 50+ exercise and Pilates classes, over-60s gentle exercise classes and a short mat bowls club.
- Manchester City Council has its own over-50s development officer, who coordinates programmes such as aerobics, tennis, aqua fitness, tea dances and indoor curling.

Theory into practice

Assess what your local authority offers for the over-50 age group.

Web links

Look at the Sport England website for more up-to-date data on the Active People programme at www.sportengland.org. This covers many of these target groups.

Disabled people

Since the early 1990s and the Disability Discrimination Act 1996, progress has been made for disabled people in terms of acceptance, funding, sports development schemes and equality of access to sports facilities.

The English Federation of Disability Sport is the official national organisation responsible for the development of sport for disabled people in England. There has been progress on several fronts in 2006.

- As part of a 46-strong team, Britain's top disability athletes competed at the IPC World Athletics Championships in Assen, Holland.
- At the IPC World Cycling Championships in Switzerland, Britain won seven golds and two bronze medals from the track events.

Web links

Take a look at the English Federation of Disability Sport's website for more details at www.efds.net.

At grass-roots level, disability sports development schemes are being set up regularly. Here are some examples.

- On the Isle of Man, the role of disability sports development officer has been created. The job involves providing services and opportunities for disabled people, allowing them to take on a more active role in sport.
- In Kent, as part of the Sportslink development scheme, there is a learning disabilities netball team and coach in Shepway.
- In Warwickshire, a Sport England lottery-funded project called the Inclusive Fitness Initiative helps fitness facilities to become accessible to disabled and non-disabled people.

Activity

What further examples of grass-roots disability sports development schemes are you aware of?

Think it over

What issues do you feel disabled athletes have to overcome, other than their disability?

Black and minority ethnic groups (BMEs)

Black athletes and players are well known in sport, but other ethnic groups in the UK's multicultural society do less well in terms of sports participation. This is due to a range of factors such as poverty, lack of facilities, coaching or lack of knowledge about UK sports. Extra support helps them to break through barriers of ethnicity and lack of opportunity.

Sports development schemes are often used as a way of bringing ethnic minorities together, helping to create understanding in an effort to relieve racial tensions. The Commission for Racial Equality works with Sport England and other providers to support schemes like this. However, this target group would still benefit from more input and development.

Case study: Sport Hampshire and Isle of Wight

Sport Hampshire and Isle of Wight is the county sports partnership for Hampshire and the Isle of Wight. It is committed to addressing the barriers for people from black and minority ethnic backgrounds. It promotes Sporting Equals, a national initiative working to promote racial equality in sport in England. Sporting Equals is a partnership between Sport England and the Commission for Racial Equality.

Why is it important to have racial harmony?

Web links

Visit the Commission for Racial Equality's website at www.cre.gov.uk for further information about Sporting Equals.

Another local programme is the Nottinghamshire Black and Ethnic Minorities Sports Project. This was developed as a result of a partnership working between Nottingham City Council, Active Sports Nottinghamshire, Sport England and Voice East Midlands. The project works with all age groups and across all sports. It aims to:

- increase participation of black and ethnic minorities in sport and physical activity as players, coaches and officials
- develop stronger links between black and ethnic minority communities and mainstream sports providers
- build the capacity of black and ethnic minority community organisations and sports clubs to deliver sport and physical activity.

Activity

Which cross-cutting agendas are involved in the Nottinghamshire Black and Ethnic Minorities Sports Project?

Projects and campaigns run in Nottingham are typical of those around the UK. Here are some examples.

- A Let's Kick Racism Out of Football 5-a-side tournament: this involved 19 teams with players from the Pakistani, African Caribbean, Indian, Angolan and Vietnamese communities in Nottingham.

▼ Many teams around the UK play in the true multicultural sense

- The Ashiana Asian Elders' Exercise Project: through funding from Nottingham City Council, the project bought gym equipment for residents. A qualified fitness instructor came to the centre and advised people on how to use the equipment in a way that would most benefit their health.

Activity

1 a   Give a clear definition of what a target group is in sports development terms.

   b   Give three examples of a target group.

2 a   Sum up the benefits of the types of campaigns like the Football tournament and the Asian Elders' Exercise Project.

   b   Explain what difficulties might arise.

   c   What improvements could you suggest?

Think it over

Think about why there do not appear to be many programmes for black and ethnic minority women.

Assessment practice

Imagine you are a local sports development officer researching the barriers that exist to participation for target groups in your local community. You have been asked to write a short report to present to your department head.

1   Describe two barriers to participation at each level of the sports development continuum, using different examples drawn from at least three target groups. **P2**

2   Explain why barriers to participation occur for at least three different target groups using different sports. Show how these can occur at different levels of the sports development continuum. **M2**

3   Analyse why the barriers to participation occur for varying target groups at all levels of the sports development continuum and provide realistic recommendations for how these might be overcome. **D1**

Grading tips

Grading Tip P2

You must be able to show a basic understanding in describing the barriers you select for each stage of the continuum and each target group. If you can provide real working examples, that will help to show this. Ensure you choose different sports as that will determine your grade as well.

Grading Tip M2

The merit criteria demands a bit more from you in terms of the quality of what you produce as evidence and in terms of complexity, so pay attention to detail in your responses. Explaining means showing that you know why something happens and can give that explanation clearly.

Grading Tip D1

To be graded at distinction level means you can show an in-depth understanding, use appropriate terminology well and have a really thorough approach. Above all, you must analyse, which means showing you can break up the components of the question and respond to them with critical insight. In other words, you have the ability to see important points that others miss, as well as identifying faults and making realistic suggestions as to how something could have been done better.

Providers

There are various types and levels of providers:

- national organisations
- local authorities
- governing bodies
- voluntary organisations
- private sector providers
- professional providers.

National organisations

■ Sport England

Look again at Sport England's sports development model on page 182 and you will see that this organisation has a full range of sports development aims. It is the lead body in the UK, and is 'committed to creating opportunities for people to start in sport, stay in sport and succeed in sport'. Sport England's business objectives are to get people to:

- start in sport: to improve the health of the nation, particularly for disadvantaged groups
- stay in sport: through a thriving network of clubs, coaches and volunteers, and a commitment to equity
- succeed in sport: via an infrastructure capable of developing world-class performers.

Think it over

Sport England is 'committed to creating opportunities for people to start in sport, stay in sport and succeed in sport'. How does this statement reflect the levels in the sports development continuum?

The organisation works through nine regional offices and sports boards (who help sports organisations in each major area of England). They share best practice,

set standards, build area sports partnerships and networks and promote the benefits of sport, such as healthier living, social inclusion and crime prevention.

Case study: Tameside Sports Development

Working with Sport England, Tameside Sports Development in the North West has been singled out as an example of good practice. The main objectives are to boost social inclusion, community development and promote the link between health and activity.

To do this it created strong relationships between schools, voluntary clubs and local communities and set up networks to work with local people and to allow them to establish their own activities. Achievements include increasing access to physical activity to local people, increasing participation in the under 10s winter league cricket, indoor athletics competitions and coaching centres for girls' football.

1 **Which target groups are mentioned in this example?**

2 **Which cross-cutting agendas are highlighted?**

Think it over

Why do you think the case study on Tameside Sports Development represents best practice?

■ sports coach UK

This is a charitable organisation dedicated to the development and implementation of coaches and coaching throughout the UK.

It provides a central resource of expertise, advice and support for its sports development partners and helps to coach the coaches. It works with funding agencies and sports governing bodies, local authorities and other sports agencies that have an interest in coaching and its development.

Activity

In small groups, identify the key elements in sports coach UK's strategy then try to explain them.

Website: www.sportscoachuk.co.uk

■ Youth Sports Trust

This organisation was established in 1984 to support the education and development of all young children through sport and physical education. As well as setting up the TOP programmes, the organisation has many more aspects to its sports development strategy. The Youth Sports Trust has developed a number of creative and innovative projects for young people aged 18 months to 18 years, which focus on specific issues including:

- social inclusion
- encouraging more teenage girls to take part in PE and sport
- playground development in primary schools to tackle social exclusion issues
- supporting gifted and talented children and young people.

Think it over

In relation to the Youth Sports Trust, which cross-cutting agendas and targeting can you identify?

The Youth Sports Trust has formed partnerships with sponsors to help sports development, such as the one with Sainsbury's and its Active Kids campaign.

Local authorities

Local authorities (LAs) are councils or metropolitan boroughs. They play a really important role in sports development because they are usually close to all types of target groups in the community. LAs can help sport because their other objectives, such as making the community healthier and more inclusive, can be achieved by providing sporting and leisure facilities.

Some local authorities take this on board in a big way and have teams of sports development officers running a range of programmes to meet the community's needs. Other LAs have programmes such as GP referral schemes (for those needing exercise to get them back to health) or disability sport (for those with some kind of similar disability, for example football for those who have lost a limb).

LAs also have many facilities at their disposal to run sports development schemes, such as leisure centres, parks and swimming pools.

Another feature of the way they work in sports development is through partnership schemes. LAs often join up with other social service providers and organisations, such as:

- health authorities to run health schemes
- voluntary clubs and groups to aid their sports development

- police and other welfare agencies to help reduce crime and exclusion
- charities and neighbourhood groups who work in poor areas.

Think it over

Why is it important that organisations form partnerships and networks? What could go wrong with these sorts of arrangements?

Activity

In small groups, discuss what sports development might add to the quality of life in an area and how it might help with equal opportunities.

Taking it further

How could you go about finding out what your local authority does?

Case study: West Lancashire District Council

West Lancashire District Council has several schemes in place, including the following.

- Summer Activities 06: their sports development team runs numerous 'informal sporting activities on the kick-about areas in Skelmersdale. These are for children aged between 8 and 13 years and are free of charge.
- Aqua Fun is a three-year initiative led by the council to provide a comprehensive activity programme for children living in Skelmersdale. It offers inflatable, sub aqua, snorkelling and lifesaving sessions.

Identify:

a **the purposes of the programmes**

b **cross-cutting agendas**

c **target groups**

d **levels covered**

e **possible barriers to participation.**

Case study: Colchester Borough Council

Colchester Borough Council recognises three key target groups in Colchester: young people, people with disabilities and people who live in rural parts of the borough. It promotes the following initiatives.

- The Free Access for National Sportspeople (FANS) scheme helps to support local people who are performing at an elite level in their chosen sport. By signing up to the scheme, residents can gain free access to a network of sports facilities throughout the borough to help them with their training programme. This initiative is aimed at athletes who are in the national squad or the top ten in their age group.
- Active Sports is a five-year development programme that aims to help young people get more from

their participation in sport, from grass-roots level to elite young performers. The programme is based around targeted sports including basketball, cricket, women's football, hockey, netball and rugby union.

Identify:

a **the purposes of the programmes**

b **cross-cutting agendas**

c **target groups**

d **levels covered**

e **possible barriers to participation.**

Governing bodies of sport (GBSs) are organisations that oversee a particular sport in terms of its management, rules, structure and development. They operate at four different levels: locally, regionally, nationally and internationally.

Using football as our example, we can illustrate these levels and strategies as follows.

■ International

Football is governed by FIFA, which is the International Football Federation. Football in Europe is governed by EUFA, which is the European Union Football Association. Both organisations have similar aims for the sport in terms of its development, which can be summarised as promoting, protecting and developing the game of football.

Web links

Look at the following websites for more information on FIFA and EUFA: www.fifa.com and www.uefa.com.

■ National

The governing bodies' mission statements give their aims and objectives. For example, here is the Football Association's mission statement:

> To increase the participation, quality, and enjoyment of football through four key strategies:
> - football for life: providing everyone with a clear lifelong journey in the participation of football
> - opportunities for all: everybody having the opportunity to participate in football
> - football in education: providing children with a quality introduction to football
> - club development: having the best football club structures in the world providing high-quality coaching and development opportunities for all.

■ Regional

The North Riding County Football Association's development plan has many features that reflect these principles, values and aims:
- mini-soccer
- girls' and women's football development
- applying a charter standard
- equity and inclusion
- ethnicity and disability partnership
- volunteer development.

■ Local

The Scarborough Junior Football Association reflects these development aims as well, with themes of
- equality of access
- support for player development
- caring coaches.

As you can see, GBSs operate at different levels and geographical locations (locally, regionally, nationally and internationally). The diagram shows the inverted pyramid this structure creates, together with the role at each level.

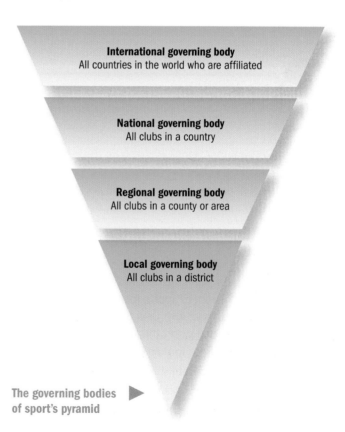

International governing body
All countries in the world who are affiliated

National governing body
All clubs in a country

Regional governing body
All clubs in a county or area

Local governing body
All clubs in a district

The governing bodies of sport's pyramid ▶

Think it over

Look at the diagram showing the GBS structure. What similarities can you identify with the sports development continuum?

Taking it further

In the governing bodies of sport diagram, which type of sports development do you think each level might undertake?

Activity

Look at the diagram of the GBSs hierarchy. Using football as an example, place the following organisations alongside their correct levels.

- The Premiership.
- North Riding County Football Association (NRCFA).
- European Football Association (EUFA).
- The Football Association (FA).
- The International Football Federation (FIFA).
- Scarborough Junior Football Association (SJFA).
- Holt Football Club (HFC).

Voluntary organisations

These types of sports organisations are often known as the 'grass roots of sport' as they represent the wide variety of sport that goes on at a recreational and basic competitive level in the UK. This is achieved through low-cost participation supported by voluntary (not paid) people giving their time freely.

This network of small clubs around the UK lays on a range of sports development opportunities such as practice sessions, coaching and skills development, competitive matches and awards. Many clubs belong to a district sports association, which helps to give them a structure, sources of funding and new ideas. Volunteers often join to take part in refereeing, administration, coaching and running club committees. Sports club volunteers may be eligible for awards for their performance, commitment, help, dedication or other involvement in sport.

One of the key issues for small clubs is funding. In recent years, schemes have been set up to help with this problem, such as Sport England's Community Sports Club Initiative. This scheme has over 1,000 clubs benefiting as it hits the £60 million mark. Examples of this programme in action include the following.

- Westway in London: a large strip of derelict land under the A40 in West London was transformed into a multi-sports hub that offers affordable, high-quality and accessible facilities for local people to get involved in sport without travelling great distances.
- Ledbury Rugby Club, Herefordshire: a massive increase in the number of hours of junior and adult coaching carried out each week is just one of the results of Sport England's investment in the upgrading of Ledbury Rugby Club's facilities.

Other examples of the work in developing sport come from volunteers such as the following.

ALAN WATSON: CHAMPION VOLUNTEER

Seeing his son enjoy playing football for a club inspired Alan Watson to become a volunteer. Now Alan, who also works full time, fulfils a range of roles at Sandy Colts FC in Bedfordshire, from coach to organiser, driver, fund-raiser and schools liaison manager.

Hayley Williams: sports buddy

Hayley Williams, from Arnold, Nottingham, is a sports buddy. Hayley volunteers her time to support young people with learning difficulties to achieve the goal of becoming involved in sports coaching.

David Russell: swimming pioneer

Sports volunteer David Russell has played a significant role in the development of swimming in his native Bristol and nationally. David, who is in his 70s, recently gained a certificate of higher education in sports development from Liverpool John Moores University.

Web links

Visit the Sport England website at www.sportengland.org to research your own examples of volunteer work.

Think it over

Are there any weaknesses in relying on volunteers and sports grants?

Private sector providers

The private sector includes companies that normally operate commercially to make a profit. Private sector businesses normally get involved in sports development to further their business interests, but they often give

Case study: Matched funding

In 2001, the Children's Kayak Charitable Trust, a charity set up by a Worcester policeman, obtained £1,180 in sponsorship from Aztec Watersports, a local watersports retailer. They matched this with a Sportsmatch award and ran a three-year project offering free kayak coaching to children from 12 local schools.

Doncaster Rovers Belles Ladies FC has, like most other large clubs, a set of teams at many age ranges for girls. Most of these teams have local businesses as sponsors, such as Pentagon Toyota. Businesses are offered the chance to sponsor the teams, the club provides the pitches and kit, and players pay their membership fees.

1 **How important do you think image is for these companies?**

2 **How important is marketing for these commercial providers?**

benefits to local communities. Sports and participants can still gain from these types of businesses as they might provide new venues, sponsorship and administer leagues.

Some businesses get involved with sport as sponsors. For example, the Institute of Sports Sponsorship – on behalf of the government and Sport England – manages Sportsmatch, a business sponsorship incentive scheme for grass-roots sport. The institute does this by matching new sponsorship money from businesses with funding on a pound-for-pound basis.

Web links

Visit the Institute of Sports Sponsorship website to assess its role in connecting sports to sponsors at www.sports-sponsorship.co.uk.

Professional providers

These are individuals and organisations that operate in the area of sports development. Some are specialists in one sport and travel from location to location, while others stay at one centre or venue. Examples of professional providers include:

- independent coaches who work for several clubs, such as a gymnastics or swimming coach
- self-employed developers or coaches who are employed by local centres for mini-soccer, netball or tennis coaching.

Professional providers often need to be licensed or approved by a sports governing body. They must have insurance and a criminal record bureau (CRB) check if they want to work with children or young people. Some professional providers work on a franchise basis.

Key term

Franchise A business arrangement where one organisation makes a contract with another to deliver a service within its own premises, such as coaching services franchised within a sports centre or stadium.

Case study: i9 Sports®

One of the best known franchises in the USA is i9 Sports®. This organisation is marketed as the world's first complete amateur sports franchise for the 100 million youth and adult athletes nationwide. i9 Sports® offers franchise opportunities for people to own and operate local amateur sports leagues, tournaments, camps, clinics, special events and child development programmes in over a dozen sports for people of all ages.

1 **Describe an equivalent organisation in the UK.**

2 **Compare two similar organisations in the UK.**

Associated benefits

■ Cross-cutting agendas

Many sports development providers work in partnership with other agencies, each trying to achieve something on their own agenda. A scheme might be run in a poor area, which helps local people and welfare services. It might also bring down crime rates (and help police) as young people are kept busy while participating. The scheme might bring a sense of pride back to the area or a new image if it is sponsored by a private company. The private company can advertise its product, which improves the company's image by helping the local community.

■ Improving performance

Improvement in performance is always desirable, regardless of the level of the sports development continuum at which the scheme is operating. For example: beginners could advance to novice, intermediate to accomplished, recreationalist to competitor, competitor to champion. Performance might be improved in terms of speed, agility, strength, dexterity and teamwork.

■ Opportunity

This benefit most often applies to areas where there is low provision in terms of teams, activities, facilities or coaching. Once an opportunity is provided for people to participate, it is hoped they will be motivated to continue. Many stories exist of young players emerging from poor areas through sports development schemes. Such schemes allow them to show their talents, which means they can be identified and offered further opportunities.

Think it over

Can you name any sports stars who have come from poor areas?

■ Healthy lifestyles

Sports development programmes should contribute to healthy lifestyles as they involve activity. Many schemes might spark people's desire to exercise more often through a sport. Some programmes also include diet and nutrition guidance, especially at elite level. The theme that generally runs through sports development schemes is often aimed at lifelong learning or activity, hence Sport England's Active Lifestyle scheme.

Case study: Celtic FC

Celtic FC, in partnership with the Big Lottery, NHS, Glasgow Big Breakfast and Glasgow City Council, are providing primary school children with a unique opportunity to 'start their day with Celtic'.

Youngsters get the opportunity to take part in a physical activity programme and are provided with a healthy breakfast before they start school. Research suggests that taking part in physical activity and eating a healthy breakfast is the perfect way to start your day.

What issues can you identify that might occur with schemes such as these?

Structure

It is important to understand how sports development providers organise themselves to help them function effectively. All organisations have a structure or set up that staff should follow to help deliver their programmes. This gives lines of communication, authority, roles and links to outside organisations.

Four main types of organisational style are explored in this section: committees, working groups, forums and consultation groups. Each style has its own merits and features, but they all need to work democratically for them to be successful.

Committees

These are most common in the voluntary sector. For a small club offering sports development, committees would be made up of three people: a chairperson or captain having overall leadership, a treasurer looking after financial affairs, and a secretary doing the

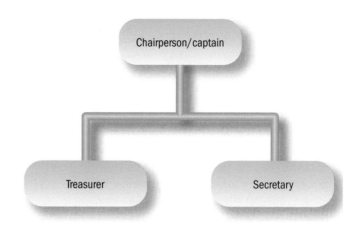

▲ The structure of a simple committee

administration and communications work.

Note that the lines represent lines of authority and communication, which help to keep the post holders focused on their roles, but in touch with others. This is sometimes called a functional approach.

Working groups

Working groups are a looser arrangement than a committee and often found where many organisations work in partnership. They function by each partner sending a representative to work with the others in the group. This ensures every interested party is kept informed and able to achieve the aims they have set out for the scheme.

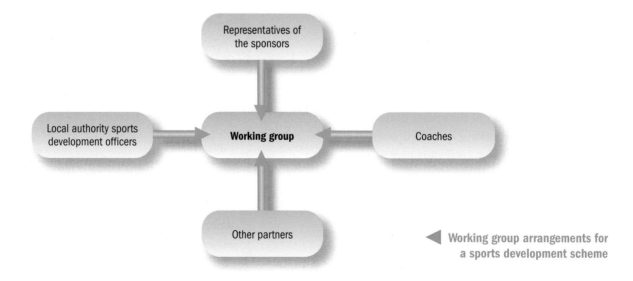

◀ Working group arrangements for a sports development scheme

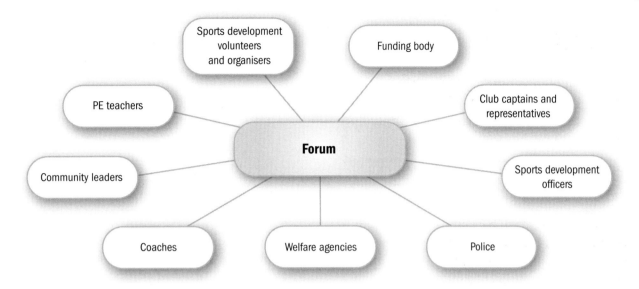

▲ Those who might attend a forum meeting

Forums

These are sets of people who tend to be experts on the issues involved with sports development. Forums meet to discuss issues or problems and to put forward ideas for sports development. They are not the organisation that will implement the changes, but more like the 'think tank' that gives ideas for others to follow.

Consultation groups

These can be large groups as they tend to be used for consulting a range of people who might be involved in a scheme for sports development. This allows a really well informed set of decisions to be made, but it may act slowly.

The sorts of participants that might be consulted include local politicians, Sport England, community representatives (reps), club reps, social services, the police, sports governing bodies, experts in planning events or disability sports, sports scientists, tutors, volunteers, safety experts, sports centre managers, health authority reps and professional bodies in sport.

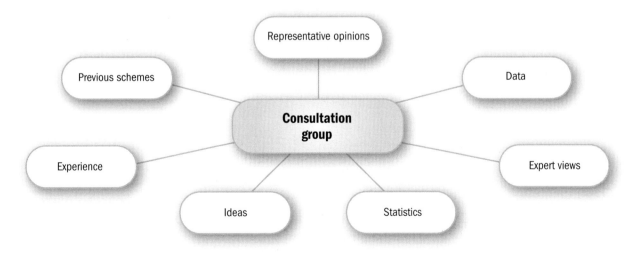

▲ The role of consultation groups in a sports development scheme

Think it over

In small groups, discuss what problems each of the types of organisational style could bring, such as its aims and purposes, how it gathers data and what sorts of schemes can be initiated.

Theory into practice

Which organisations or individuals would you consult if you decided to offer a sports development programme that involved orienteering in the countryside?

Roles

Providers

Sports development has many partners, aims, dimensions, individuals and organisations, each playing a role. This leads to a range of different schemes and approaches. Here are a number for you to familiarise yourself with.

■ Enabling and facilitating

The first style of delivery is called enabling. This means the provider responds to the needs of participants' by providing facilities or resources to give people the opportunities they need to take part.

Key term

Enabling The enabling type of programme provides facilities or resources to enable participants to play, start up a club or improve their skills.

Another type of delivery is known as facilitating. This might involve motivating and helping people, so that by the end of the facilitation period they are able to look after themselves and keep the scheme going without the help of others.

Both enabling and facilitating focus on the participants running the club or team by themselves in the long run.

Key terms

Facilitating Helping a sport or target group by providing coaches or administration and refereeing courses.

Direct delivery This means the programme is delivered directly by professional sports development people.

Strategic This type of programme links in to other, large-scale plans and are sometimes called an integrated approach.

Operational These programmes tend to be done at club level and are tailored and delivered to the clubs.

Advisory Helping an organisation that has never run a sports development scheme for a certain target group before and needs some advice.

■ Direct delivery

This means sports development schemes that are carried out directly by professional sports development people, such as those done by local authority officers or coaches employed by large clubs.

■ Strategic

Strategic delivery links into other, large-scale plans and is sometimes called an integrated approach. An example of this would be Sport England's Active Communities strategy, which links to healthy living and lifelong learning aims of the government. Local authorities might also use this style to meet objectives in their local plans.

Operational

Operational level programmes deal with the people concerned directly, such as disaffected youngsters or Asian women. Such a scheme would be tailored and delivered locally, but it might be put into action in several areas at once. Operational schemes tend to be delivered by professionals.

Advisory

Sports development people can be asked to act in an advisory role. For example, a sports centre might wish to run a disability basketball team, but has no one on the staff who could do this. They might need guidance on safety factors and requirements for disabled athletes.

Participation

Sports development organisations may fulfil a role that focuses on the participation level of the continuum by helping to increase the numbers of people who actually take part. These can be across age ranges, ability levels, gender and sports.

Think it over

All these types of provision tend to be decided by professional sports development staff who supply the programme in line with development plans laid down by the organisation. Is this the best way?

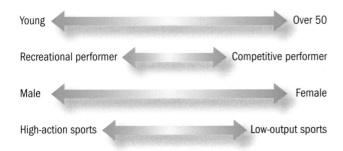

Young		Over 50
Recreational performer		Competitive performer
Male		Female
High-action sports		Low-output sports

▲ Some spectrums of participation

Activity

What other spectrums of participation can you think of? What are the common factors?

Participation programmes can have several aims, such as to keep people playing, attracting old players back or lifting the level of participation from novice to intermediate level. Motivations are also varied and include enjoyment, fitness, new skills and social contact, so schemes have to match these in their content.

North Tyneside Council has a strategy to increase participation through several dimensions such as education, learning and better communication. These are combined with sports development schemes.

Case study: North Tyneside Council

The first ever North Tyneside 10 km run attracted 800 people in total. The sports development team bid for funds and managed to secure enough for a full-time multi-skills coach, a part-time club development coach and nine part-time coaches for various sports. They also launched a user's card to help improve participation by giving discounts at swimming pools.

Give three benefits that this type of direct and indirect sports development could provide.

In 2004, Sport England published a report called *Driving Up Participation: Challenge for Sport*, which criticised sporting organisations. Despite many years of promoting 'sport for all' and extending participation within a range of targeted social groups, there is apparently no evidence to suggest that sport has widened its participation base to include more people from low incomes, ethnic minority groups or those with a disability.

Think it over

Do you agree that participation in sport has not increased in recent years?

Case study: London 2012

It is clear from the forthcoming London Olympics in 2012 that organisers are committed to increasing sports participation at community and grass-roots levels.

'Winning the Olympic Games and Paralympic Games represents the single biggest opportunity in our lifetime to transform sport and participation in sport in the UK forever,' says Sebastian Coe, chairman of the London Olympic Games and Paralympic Games Organising Committee.

'We have a unique opportunity that we must not squander to increase participation in sport, at community and grass-roots levels as well as elite levels; from the school playground to the winner's podium.'

Imagine you are part of the Olympic planning team and you need to decide how you will evaluate the success of the games in developing sport in the UK. What criteria will you set and what funding issues might there be?

Think it over

Do you think the Olympics will be a success story for the whole of the UK?

■ Performance

For organisations dealing more with the performance end of the sports development continuum, a more targeted or sports-specific approach is followed. These are sometimes known as methods aimed at excellence, the highest level of the continuum, and something that will receive a lot of focus in the period running up to the London Olympics.

Key organisations at this level try to work in harmony to develop talent. They are UK Sport, the English Institute of Sport (EIS), Sport England and **sports coach UK**. These organisations support the sports governing bodies to develop world-class performers.

Case study: UK Sport

UK Sport has taken over high-performance development in the run-up to the London Olympics. However, generally its mission is to try to lead sport into world-class levels in the UK. It has set two key challenges: to foster world-class performance through developing world-class personnel and to develop home-grown expertise to support athletes before the Beijing Olympiad in 2008.

1 **What barriers do you think might exist for elite athletes and how might they differ from those of average performers or participants?**

2 **What possible solutions do you think are realistic to overcome the barriers?**

Web link

Visit UK Sport's website at www.uksport.gov.uk to see how it links to other worldwide organisations in the development of sports globally.

Think it over

How closely do you think UK Sport and the English Institute of Sport have to work, and in what ways? What might they disagree about?

Case study: The English Institute of Sport

The English Institute of Sport is a nationwide network of world-class support services designed to foster the talents of elite athletes. Services are offered from nine regional multi-sport hub sites and an evolving network of satellite centres, which represent a range of high-performance training venues. The depth of the EIS's support for high performers stretches to the following dimensions:

- performance lifestyle and sports massage
- bio-mechanics, strength and conditioning
- physiology and performance analysis
- psychology and nutrition
- sport medicine and physiotherapy.

1 **As the areas in which the EIS works seem to be spread around the UK, how are they structured? Carry out some further research to investigate how the EIS is structured and funded, and how it carries out its role.**

2 **Make a list of weaknesses in the organisation.**

Taking it further

Investigate what your nearest football academy does for younger players to improve their performance.

The Lawn Tennis Association (LTA) has a number of dimensions to its performance development schemes.

- The Talent ID programme includes county talent days and performance roadshows for players from the age of 8 upwards.
- The LTA runs talent camps for players from 8 to 14, under-14s camps at the National Junior Tennis Centres and junior camps at the National Tennis Centre.
- National coaches make visits to high-performance centres and club-based performance programmes.
- Representatives from the LTA also attend many domestic tournaments.
- They are in regular contact with coaches, tennis managers and club development officers to identify talent throughout Britain.

Web links

To learn more about these aspects of performance development, visit the LTA's website at www.lta.org.uk.

The All England Netball Association focuses on a ten-year development programme for athletes. It is committed to achieving standards rather than an age-related development framework. The organisation operates a national squad structure, as shown in the diagram.

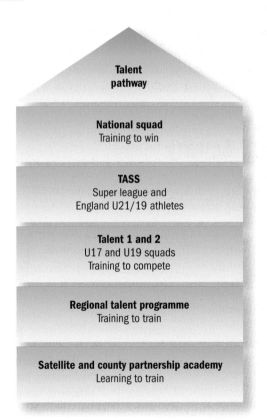

 The All England Netball Association's performance athlete development model

Sports development officers

A sports development officer is someone who is employed by a local authority or large club. There are three main types of sports development officers: sports specific, non-sports specific and community.

■ Sports specific

Sports-specific development officers are employed to cover the development of one sport such as rugby, football or tennis.

■ Non-sports specific

Non-sports specific development officers are employed to cover a range of different sporting activities.

■ Community

Community development officers are employed to cover all types of sports in the local community.

Volunteers

Volunteers are the backbone of British sports organisations. The role of volunteers is vital across many sports for their development. They give their time, effort, expertise and resources free of charge to help people to play their sports. Volunteers are often parents of young players, ex-players or sports enthusiasts who want to give something back to their game or community. They take on the role of coaches, administrators, secretaries and general helpers for their local clubs.

Web link

If you are interested in volunteering, visit Time Bank at www.timebank.org.uk to sign up!

Volunteering to help run sports events can have personal benefits too: it builds confidence, makes a real difference for some people, introduces you to new friends and keeps you active. Volunteering also means you have that bit of extra experience to include on a CV.

Research carried out by the Leisure Industries Research Council in Sheffield in 2003 showed that:

- there are 5.8 million sports volunteers giving 1.2 billion hours to sport each year
- this contribution to sport is valued at over £14 billion.

Think it over

What are the problems of sports development relying on volunteers?

Activity

In small groups, discuss what pressures volunteers face in today's hectic lifestyles.

Assessment practice

Imagine you are a senior sports development officer for a city council. Your job is to assess the set-up and role of three providers in your area before deciding what funding you will give them for the following year. Choose one of the following tasks, which you think you can complete well.

1 Select three different types of sports development providers and describe their structure. Give a description of their role in sports development. **P3**

2 Select three different sports development organisations and evaluate why they have structured themselves in their own way. Evaluate what functions they have and how they carry out their role in sports development. **M4**

3 For three different sports development providers, evaluate their role and structure. Analyse how you think they could improve their set up and purpose. **D2**

Grading tips

Grading Tip P3

Choose some providers and sports with which you are familiar or have easy access to, and ensure you cover structure, roles and functions or purpose with good, clear descriptions.

Grading Tip M4

Ensure you identify some effective criteria for evaluation, such as numbers on programmes, use of resources or gaps in provision.

Grading Tip D2

An analysis should consider strengths and weaknesses. If you give recommendations, ensure these could actually be carried out. Set out clear areas for your analysis at the start.

It is important to measure performance. Organisations do this in a number of ways, such as assessing staff, facilities, participants and spending. This means they can evaluate things that gave value for money, provided satisfaction or were just plain bad. Standards of performance are usually laid down by national organisations or independent bodies so that comparisons can be made. Most schemes try to measure quality in the hope that this can be continuously improved upon.

Key term

Quality This refers to the good features of something. In terms of sports development, providers try to have excellent features for their sports development programmes so that they score highly, are ranked highly and get a good reputation.

Methods

A range of measures is available for sports development providers to assess themselves or be assessed by independent inspectors. This allows them to get a measure of the quality and effectiveness of their provision. It is important that whatever method is applied, it is as objective as possible and gives a true picture of the organisation's position and delivery.

Some quality systems are local and perhaps offered in-house (run by the centre). Other systems are national and well accepted.

Key term

Quality systems Systems of management and evaluation that help organisations to cover every detail needed to give good customer service.

Benchmarks

A quality system encourages organisations to benchmark themselves. This means making comparisons with other similar organisations in order to compare standards and processes of delivery, for example.

Quality schemes

■ Quest

This is a national quality system that can be used for assessing the management of sports development schemes. Quest is an industry standard developed by Sport England and measures specific elements of sports development work including research, management, customer service and partnership working.

Quest is aimed at sports development units in local authorities, governing bodies and voluntary organisations. Sports development organisations can use either a self-assessment/improvement programme or submit themselves for an independent external assessment in their pursuit of an award.

The administration of the scheme is overseen by an independent consultancy to ensure it is fair. There are currently 38 sports development units registered for awards.

Quest operates a grading system based on the following scores:

- to be registered, a score of above 60% is needed
- to achieve highly commended, the score needs to be between 75% and 84%
- an excellent score is 85% and above.

The assessment criteria are based on the following categories:

- objectives and the actions targeted at achieving these
- timekeeping, workmanship and coaching
- quality of equipment
- problem-solving techniques
- organisational culture – elements of pride, professionalism and standards.

Think it over

Are there any areas that you feel should be assessed but which are not mentioned?

Case study: Barking and Dagenham

One example of improvement comes from the London Borough of Barking and Dagenham. The sports development team was assessed in 2003. It scored 72%, which was the top score of all the London boroughs that achieved Quest accreditation.

In January 2005, the team's second assessment involved a two-day visit from an assessor, who spoke to staff members, volunteers, partners and users of the sports development service. This time the team earned 78%, which has promoted the unit to the highly commended category.

Do you think this is a good way to evaluate the quality of the organisation? Explain why.

Web link

You can find out more information about the Quest scheme from its website at www.quest-uk.org.

■ IiP

The Investors in People (IiP) award follows many of the same principles as Quest. It focuses on organisations attaining standards for training and development of their staff, which in turn help in achieving the objectives of the sports development unit. During the process, you would expect participants to benefit too.

Think it over

What benefits for sports development officers are there likely to be in training and development?

The IiP standard provides a national framework for improving performance and competitiveness. It involves a planned approach to setting and communicating objectives, and developing people to meet these objectives.

The scheme provides three things:

- the opportunity to review current policies and practices against a recognised benchmark
- a framework for planning future strategy and action
- a structured way to improve the effectiveness of training and development activities.

It is based on these main principles:

- a commitment to invest in people, such as by providing training
- effective planning to set down how skills, individuals and teams are to be developed to achieve these goals
- effective action being taken to develop and use necessary skills
- evaluating the outcomes of training and development for individuals' progress towards goals, such as checking that what was planned has been achieved.

Taking it further

Use a dictionary to look up a definition of 'performance' that would suit this context. Use this definition to write a short paragraph describing how performance criteria are used to measure quality of service delivery in sports development.

Organisations that feel they are ready to be assessed can contact their local quality centre to arrange the process (there are nine in England). The quality centre is responsible for allocating an assessor to individual organisations and quality assuring the assessment process.

The assessors would be looking for indicators and evidence under the four principles outlined above.

Activity

In pairs, discuss what you think sports development teams would need to prepare for an inspection by IiP.

Web link

You can check out a range of further examples on the IiP website at www.investorsinpeople.co.uk.

Case study: Bath University

In December 2003, the IiP award was presented to the sports development department at Bath University. Over the past few years the department, which promotes many of its elite and community sports facilities and activities under the university's TeamBath brand, has been working with IiP to improve management and staff development practices.

The department was assessed by IiP in the South West and, as a result, was put forward for the award.

Director of Sport, Ged Roddy, was delighted with news of the award. 'We are very proud to have received this award,' he said. 'We are constantly looking at ways of improving what we do.'

The department has grown from 6 staff to over 100 in the past ten years and has attracted upwards of £25 million in investment.

In small groups, discuss how valuable you feel this type of award would be to a sports development unit.

■ Charter Mark

Charter Mark is an award that can be attained by any public-sector organisation or department, such as a museum, art gallery or even refuse collection. It is an easy-to-use quality system designed to help everyone in the organisation focus on and improve customer service. Achievement of the standard is recognised by awarding the right to display the prestigious Charter Mark logo, which is much sought-after by sports development units in the public sector.

The publicity material about the award says that Charter Mark is more about achieving a change of culture (to help target groups) than winning a trophy, but change and improvement must be ongoing. Those seeking a Charter Mark have to demonstrate that:

- they offer choice to their customers so that a wide range of needs are catered for
- participants and staff are consulted on where choices can be made, and communities have a say in the design and delivery of local sports development programmes
- continuous improvement is sought, which means new targets are set every year at a slightly higher level or lower cost.

To achieve the award, sports development units have to show that staff are involved in planning services and are encouraged and given the power to put things right wherever possible.

Case study Stockton-on-Tees sports development team

A recent example is Stockton-on-Tees sports development unit, which achieved continuing Charter Mark status. The assessor identified the five areas where the team had clearly established good practice. It:

- set standards and targets, which were met well
- worked with the local tax office to get a discretionary rate for sports clubs
- developed high standards of benchmarking (comparisons)
- worked well with other partners

- provided good value for money and used resources well.

If you were responsible for setting the next set of targets for the Stockton team, what would you have them aiming for? Consider the following points:

- **choice for participants**
- **new types of programme**
- **new benchmarks**
- **continuous improvement.**

- active – getting the best out of young people
- accessible – giving everyone a sporting chance
- accredited – the Sport England mark of high quality.

The aim of Clubmark is to provide more and better opportunities for children and young people to participate in sport in their local communities. The award shows that a sports development scheme at a club is a safe, effective, child-friendly scheme. It gives a new nationally adopted set of standards for national governing bodies (NGBs) of sport. The sports clubs have to set and meet standards that will lead to better-quality sports club provision for children and young people.

The scheme applies across a wide range of sports. It is promoted nationally to enable parents, carers and young people to quickly recognise a club that is committed to providing a quality experience.

Clubmark sets out standards for:

- duty of care and child protection
- coaching and competition
- sports equity and ethics
- club management.

▲ Sport governing bodies make many awards available for young players

Think it over

What benefits are there for clubs achieving the Clubmark award?

Think it over

Why would a sports development unit strive to achieve a Charter Mark?

Taking it further

Use a dictionary to find out what the terms 'duty of care', 'equality' and 'ethics' mean. Why are these terms important in sports development?

■ Clubmark

Clubmark was introduced in 2002 by Sport England. It is a cross-sport quality award for clubs with junior sections. The scheme demonstrates to partners, parents and young people that Clubmark accredited clubs are:

To apply for a Clubmark, clubs need to contact the relevant national governing body for further information. Sport England produces a resources pack for clubs trying to get accredited. The award can be renewed annually through a simple self-certification scheme, showing that standards and processes remain at the same level.

Less than two weeks after England won the Ashes at The Brit Oval in 2006, Lingfield Cricket Club was at the ground to celebrate yet another cricketing success – receiving the prestigious Clubmark award. Lingfield was presented with their Clubmark award by Surrey's Mark Ramprakash.

In association with Surrey Cricket, Lingfield has developed codes of conduct, child protection policies and coaching plans. Session attendance has soared since the introduction of the new systems, with word getting around Lingfield and the surrounding area about the positive vibe throughout the club.

The number of volunteers has also grown, with parents giving unprompted offers of help in a number of different activities from coaching to running social events.

What do you think Lingfield could do to improve their standards now?

Activity

Identify the similarities and differences between the schemes involved in Quest, IiP, Charter Mark and Clubmark.

Theory into practice

What difficulties might there be for small clubs in attaining the Clubmark award?

Internal or self-assessment

It is possible to achieve all of the quality scheme awards described above through internal audits or inspections, which can be set up in-house. For example, Quest can be tackled this way through self-assessment evidence. Sports development units assess their delivery in comparison to industry standards and best-practice information provided in the Quest guidance pack. This enables managers and their teams to:

- make informed judgements about how they are performing against recognised industry standards
- identify strengths and areas for improvement
- draw up their own plans of action to raise standards of service delivery to participants.

Remember!

Internal audits differ from the external audits. They are less objective (less independent) and more open to bias.

Think it over

What things do you think should be assessed during self-assessment and how would you go about it?

External audits

These are audits that take place under inspection from independent outsiders to an organisation (hence external). External audits help to ensure objectivity and consistency in assessment. Quest, IiP, Charter Mark and Clubmark are all based on external audits.

National governing body schemes (Swim 21)

Swim 21 links with Sport England's Clubmark scheme and is the Amateur Swimming Association's (ASA) quality mark. By October 2006, more than 270 clubs have achieved the ASA's Swim 21 accreditation. This is based on long-term athletic development with clubs working towards accreditation in teaching, skills, competition and performance. Clubs that achieve the award are nationally recognised as having provided safe, effective services for their members. They also try to ensure that coaches, teachers, officials and volunteers can reach their potential. The ASA aims to have 800 clubs accredited by 2009.

Recent award winners include:

- Walsall Swimming and Water Polo Club, which has been awarded Swim 21 accreditation for swimming at skill development level
- Teddington Swimming Club, with a silver award for skill development
- Harrogate District Swimming Club, which is the first club in Yorkshire to do so.

Taking it further

Find out if there is a swimming club near you that takes part in this scheme.

Purpose

■ Measure improvement

The main purpose of all these accreditation schemes is to help sports development organisations to see some improvement in their delivery in order to achieve high standards.

■ Continuous improvement

Continuous improvement is always desirable. Improvements may only be possible in small steps but they should still be rewarded. Some of the awards have scales and percentages at each stage so that even small improvements can be identified.

■ Standardisation

Standards ensure that sports development units have something to aim for or refer to if they are not sure how to deliver an aspect of sports development. Standards might involve the quality of child protection offered, level of coaching or types of resources required.

Advantages

■ Benchmarking

The first advantage of quality schemes is that sports development units can compare how they work and what they achieve with others around the UK. This is called benchmarking.

■ Accessing funds

A quality award helps to obtain funding for sports development as it assures the awarding body that the club or team that has been given the funding has achieved certain standards, it is reputable and that it is likely to use the funding well.

■ Quality delivery

Quality systems delivery should benefit participants, the organisation, staff and any other stakeholders or partners such as members of the community.

■ Recognition

Recognition of having a quality award will result in good press reports and a good reputation among colleagues and with the public. This is called a virtuous spiral.

Key terms

Improvement Can be measured by setting targets and goals and then evaluating what has actually been achieved against these targets.

Standardisation Standards are usually set by leading bodies and they refer to the levels that organisations need to aim for.

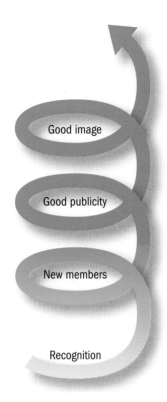

Good image

Good publicity

New members

Recognition

▲ Quality recognition may result in positive publicity and a good reputation among colleagues and with the public. This is known as a virtuous spiral

A quality system does not solve all working practice problems and there may be a number of disadvantages in getting a system up and running. Here are a few examples.

- The overall costs of putting a system in place may be too high.
- There may be problems with getting staff to become fully involved. They may feel they have to work harder or differently without a pay rise or bonus.
- It may be too tough for some staff members who are trying to make fewer mistakes and their motivation may suffer.
- Officers are expected to be creative and flexible, and to stick to a system for delivery. This might prove difficult for some.
- New ideas and improvements are expected without any additional reward.
- Confidence needs to be built so that staff are not afraid to speak up.
- The sports development unit's culture may have to change and move away from comfortable old working practices.
- Everyone in the team needs to be involved, including councillors and committee members.

■ Cost

The overall costs of putting a system in place, which can range from the paperwork involved to computer software or new resources.

■ Time

It takes time to train staff, plan systems and resolve any problems.

■ Expertise

Another hurdle may be in creating expertise where none existed before, such as customer or disability care.

Activity

1 Write down how you think a quality scheme could benefit each of the following groups:

- participants
- organisations
- staff
- members of the community.

Can you add any other stakeholders?

2 Draw a table to sum up the disadvantages of a quality scheme to each of the interested parties.

Taking it further

What other disadvantages of such schemes can you think of?

Activity

Sum up the disadvantages of quality systems using key points.

Think it over

Why are objective assessments important for any accreditation scheme?

Assessment practice

Imagine you are the duty manager at a sports centre. You are about to brief the staff on ways of measuring quality as part of the centre's preparation for delivering sports development programmes and signing up for an award scheme. Choose one of the following tasks, which you feel you can achieve best. Your task is to prepare a short Microsoft PowerPoint® presentation as follows.

1   Describe two ways of measuring quality in the provision of a sports development programme, giving some examples.   **P4**

2   Evaluate two methods of measuring quality in the provision of sports development schemes using real examples.   **M3**

Grading tips

Grading Tip **P4**

Remember that quality is measured by 'valuable features' that make the scheme better. It would be good if your examples are drawn from real schemes to show you really understand what you are describing.

Grading Tip **M3**

It is important that you say why the methods of evaluating quality that you have chosen are effective. Try to choose several methods and back them up with good examples.

Sports development is a dynamic sector with local initiatives, regional schemes and national campaigns. It is important for you to know about a selection of current initiatives as well as the practical dimensions of running programmes and the skills staff need.

Current initiatives

2012

Working towards London's Olympics and Paralympics in 2012 has given great impetus and focus to many sports, facilities and individuals in the UK. Some argue it is the greatest boost to British sport possible. Preparation through sports development means finding talent and making sure coaching, facilities and finance are in place. Here are a few examples.

- Buckinghamshire local authority has set up a scheme called BuckSport, which has begun developing proposals for a talent development programme for Buckinghamshire athletes leading towards London 2012.

- The five London boroughs linked to the 2012 Olympic Games have teamed up to submit a 10-year, £70 million funding bid to support sport and businesses in the area. Greenwich, Hackney, Newham, Tower Hamlets and Waltham Forest plan to use the Games as a catalyst to secure training and employment opportunities for local people, as well as long-term sport and business growth.

However, the Newham sports development plan has identified the following issues that need to be tackled with this ambitious sports development scheme:

- poverty and deprivation
- unemployment
- poor health
- low participation rates
- low volunteer rates
- a wide ethnic mix.

Activity

1 What benefits could the area around the Olympic Park receive?

2 What issues and problems might arise?

3 What barriers will need to be overcome to achieve sports development targets?

▶ Elation that London's Olympic bid pipped Paris at the post

Theory into practice

What possible difficulties can you see in putting theory into practice here?

Awards for All

This is a funding scheme for many things, including sports development. It is supported by the Arts Council of England, the Big Lottery Fund, the Heritage Lottery Fund and Sport England. Grants are awarded of between £300 and £10,000 for people to take part in art, sport, heritage and community activities, and projects that promote education, the environment and health in the local community. Support for sport-related activities may be given for the following:

- promoting healthy eating and more exercise
- involving more people in a community event.

Case study: Awards for All

The Awards for All website (www.awardsforall.org.uk) reports Cleveland groups did well, with £4,980 going to Whinney Banks Sports Section Football, Middlesbrough, towards its work in providing actual or potential young offenders with physical activities and encouraging feelings of self-worth; £10,000 will enable Brambles Primary School, also in Middlesbrough, to improve its playground and open it up to the wider community; and £2,032 for Billingham Synthonia Hockey Club, Stockton-on-Tees, to run league matches, including for under 13s.

1 What is the role of the funding organisation and what evidence is there of cross-cutting agendas?

2 What criteria do you think should be in place in order for funding to be awarded?

Case study: Big Lottery Fund

The Big Lottery Fund announced grants totalling £987,457 to get young people active in the East Midlands. The funding will help 12 school partnerships provide out-of-hours sporting activities, particularly targeting young people needing encouragement to participate in sports, including those with special needs.

Funding comes from the Big Lottery Fund's £54 million School Sports Coordinators' programme, which is establishing partnerships to provide sport and physical activities for young people. These activities not only improve health, they also motivate, build self-esteem and increase social skills.

A £94,950 grant will provide sporting opportunities for pupils with weight issues, special needs and low self-esteem at South Wigston High School in Leicestershire. Activities such as dance, aerobics, cheerleading, huff and puff, golf and a walking kite club will be used to improve fitness, attainment and attitude.

1 Which level of the sports development continuum are these grants targeted at?

2 Who do think would need to be involved to initiate and see this scheme through?

3 What problems do you think might be encountered?

4 How would you apportion the amounts and evaluate the success of the scheme?

Theory into practice

If the Awards for All funding stopped, what issues might arise for those schemes relying on grants?

Activity

In small groups, discuss what the underlying reasons might be for the private sector getting involved in sports development.

Big Lottery

The Big Lottery Fund, launched on 1 June 2004, is distributing half of all National Lottery good-cause funding across the UK. It is building on the experience and best practice of the merged bodies to simplify funding in those areas where they overlap and to ensure lottery funding provides the best possible value for money. The Big Lottery Fund has committed more than £5 billion to initiatives with national, regional and local partners from the public, voluntary, charity and private sectors, with a particular focus on disadvantage.

Private sector programmes

These are more likely to focus on regeneration and facility-building schemes because this is where the private sector is most likely to get a good return on any investment. This idea was at the heart of the Manchester Commonwealth Games and is also driving the 2012 strategy for London. Private-sector involvement usually increases jobs and training, which helps to develop local skills in such areas as coaching, volunteering and sports administration. Local people can also set up sports-related businesses such as sports shops.

Local programmes

There are many local programmes available, a small selection of which have been identified in this unit.

Other examples include sports development for students at Loughborough University whose sports development centre offers performance sport coaching and support programmes:

- The sports development centre employs a number of highly qualified coaches and supports Loughborough's sports teams and individual athletes performing at national- and international-level competitions in the British Universities Championships (BUSA) and other competitions. The scheme benefits both local students and the local community.
- Community programme activities are operated specifically to provide access by members of the

▶ Many ex-players set up their own sports shops as a small business in their local towns

STOP PRESS

CRICKET FACTORY 2007

Next year's Cricket Factory will be held at the same time on
SATURDAY SEPTEMBER 1 2007
Tell your friends…..

Filey Road, Scarborough YO11 3BA   Tel: 01723 360620   www.scarboroughcollege.co.uk

SCARBOROUGH COLLEGE

 Many sports organisations offer activities and coaching during the school holidays

public to Loughborough's extensive range of sports facilities, classes and courses in sport, events on campus, and to help qualified students coaching in local community clubs.

- Programmes include sports camps for children in soccer, rugby and badminton, as well as community 5-a-side leagues, youth games and a wide range of other sporting activities and events.

Think it over

What practical issues do you think need to be solved in order to support top athletes as well as accommodate the local community?

■ Local authority sports development

These are the most common types of programmes and providers of sports development.

Local authority sports development programmes are often linked to local community plans and are therefore of strategic importance for local councils. They get best support where a council or trust created by a council to run its leisure and sport has the will, skills and resources given to them.

Case study: Wigan Leisure and Culture Trust

Wigan Leisure and Culture Trust employs a dedicated team of sports development professionals. The team of eight, managed by the senior sports development officer, works across the whole borough through targeted generic and sports-specific programmes. The sports development unit seeks to work in partnership with all individuals and agencies that have an interest in sport and young people.

The unit has established 11 sports-specific development groups, each created in order to allow local people the opportunity to influence the work of the sports development unit. Development groups exist for the following sports: athletics, basketball, cricket, girls' football, gymnastics, hockey, netball, rugby league, rugby union, swimming and tennis.

What issues do you think such a large local team would have to face while running such a diverse set of schemes?

Taking it further

Make a list of skills you think sports development officers need to have to be able to run sports development teams.

Governing body sports development

We have already looked at the Amateur Swimming Association's Swim 21 scheme on page 213, so how do other sports governing bodies structure their schemes?

Web links

Visit the FA's website at www.thefa.com and assess what it plans for football development at other levels in the sports development continuum.

Voluntary clubs

Voluntary clubs are supported by many agencies such as funding bodies to help them to develop and become sustainable. Here are two examples.

- Harrogate Borough Council's leisure development team provides a range of support and advice to voluntary-sector groups, sports clubs, village halls and parish councils on potential funding and project planning schemes.
- Forest Green District Council offers financial assistance to support local community organisations in its efforts to provide facilities, equipment and services for sport and recreation. Grants are also available to individuals who have achieved or seek to develop a standard of excellence in sport.

Voluntary clubs can find funding, guidance and support for almost anything they want to do. Whether it is player development, coach improvement, new buildings, umpiring and refereeing courses or setting up a new club, professional support is there. Voluntary clubs work mostly with those groups low on the sports development continuum, leaving the elite and performers to governing bodies, UK Sport and the EIS.

Taking it further

Voluntary groups work with target groups such as the disabled, people on low incomes, children, ethnic minorities and the elderly. Carry out your own research to identify examples for your own case studies.

Partnerships

These are common today as organisations seek to share scarce resources and the need to achieve cross-cutting agendas (see page 184). Local authorities and metropolitan boroughs often collaborate with national organisations to get large areas covered more effectively.

One example is Nottingham City Council. Its sports development team works in partnership with a wide

Case study: The FA's Elite Player Development scheme

As well as maximising footballing opportunities for all, the Football Association plays a lead role in encouraging, promoting and nurturing the talented players of tomorrow.

The game's future, from a domestic point of view as well as from the perspective of a successful England senior side, depends upon ensuring that the best young players are given every opportunity to fulfil their talent and potential.

At the heart of the FA's commitment to sports development is the Charter for Quality, which ensures

best practice in terms of the coaching and education received by young players. All premier league clubs must have academies and all football league clubs must have Centres of Excellence to help encourage and nurture young talent.

What issues are there in developing elite-level youngsters under the following headings?

- **welfare**
- **social**
- **educational and protection**

Case study: Edwards Lane Sports Project

This project aimed to encourage more participation from people within Sherwood and Mapperley areas, and particularly from an estate called Edwards Lane. The joint aims of the partnership were to:

- employ a sports development worker
- encourage more participation from young people, those over 50, families on low income and other under-represented groups including people from ethnic minorities, women and girls and people with disabilities
- improve the health of local people, learning and job prospects
- provide support for local clubs and organisations

Do you think these outcomes are ambitious? If so, explain why.

range of organisations including the Primary Care Trust, Connexions, voluntary clubs, Sure Start, the Youth Offending Team, healthy living centres and the police. One of its best partnership projects is the Edwards Lane Sports Project.

Areas of work

By now you should have a good idea of the three key areas that sports development workers focus on, as they are explained in detail in this unit. The case studies in this section also help to illustrate them. However, here is a brief summary to remind you.

■ Target groups

These are specific groups of people who will benefit most from an initiative.

■ Sport specific

Individual sports that would benefit from a boost through an initiative.

■ Location

The location of the initiative may involve deprived areas with few facilities.

Activity

Using the case studies in this section, draw a table like the one below to summarise each project's typical areas of work, if a specific sport is identified, and the location. One example has been done for you to show you how to work.

Project	Area of work	Specific sport	Location
Edwards Lane Sports Project	Young people, elderly people, low-income families, ethnic minorities, women and girls, disability groups		Nottingham (inner-city poor area)

Effectiveness

All areas of sports development work and investment should be evaluated. With increasing accountability for spending, sports developers must show they are value for money and make good use of resources, as well as accounting for all monies spent and showing the real benefits for participants.

Activity

Analyse the flow chart to identify problems that could occur at each stage.

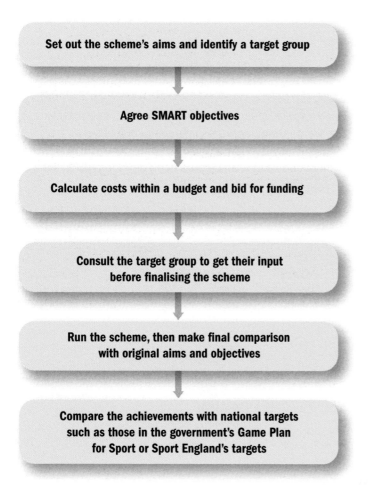

Set out the scheme's aims and identify a target group

Agree SMART objectives

Calculate costs within a budget and bid for funding

Consult the target group to get their input before finalising the scheme

Run the scheme, then make final comparison with original aims and objectives

Compare the achievements with national targets such as those in the government's Game Plan for Sport or Sport England's targets

Measuring effectiveness

Assessment practice

Imagine you work for Sport England and are responsible for advising on sports development schemes for a region of England.

You have been invited by local college to give a talk on the range of sports development initiatives in your area. Choose one of the following tasks, which you feel you can achieve well. You will prepare a short Microsoft PowerPoint® presentation outlining the key points as follows.

1 Describe two different sports development initiatives from any sector but at different levels of the sports development continuum and for different sports. **P5**

2 Compare and contrast two different sports development initiatives from two differing providers, giving strengths and weaknesses and possible problems areas. **M4**

3 Use two contrasting sports development initiatives from different sectors in different sports and at different levels of the continuum. Analyse these using quality-related criteria and the grading tips below and make realistic recommendations for improvement. **D2**

Grading tips

Grading Tip **D2**

Simply describing the sports development scheme will not be good enough: you must go on to evaluate or analyse specific factors such as purpose, agendas, level, the organising body, type of scheme and quality levels. This means reviewing a scheme or information and making your own conclusions about effectiveness based on factors such as numbers, costs, advantages or problems.

Grading Tip **D2**

Offering effective examples and reasons for your judgements or comments will help you to gain a higher grade. The highest level of skill for you to aim for is analysis. This means more than just an explanation: you need to pick out relevant factors and issues, and say what effects these might have.

Knowledge check

1 How many levels does the sports development continuum have and what are they?

2 Name three long-standing target groups.

3 Give four barriers to participation.

4 Chose one barrier for a particular target group and make recommendations on how it could be overcome.

5 Devise a classification system for providers to help you to clarify who they are. Give some examples.

6 Describe four different ways of structuring a sports development initiative.

7 Select three roles of providers and compare and contrast them.

8 What are audits, quality awards and benchmarking?

9 Give three advantages of quality awards and three difficulties that might be encountered.

10 How might you assess the effectiveness and funding of a scheme?

11 What are the key differences between a local scheme and national one?

12 Describe three key differences between public, private and voluntary schemes of sports development.

13 What issues might emerge if funding were to be scarce for elite or grass-roots participants?

14 How important is quality for the success of a scheme?

End of unit assessment

Preparation for assessment

Imagine you are a newly appointed sports development officer working for a local borough council, where there are six other colleagues you will work with. To assess whether your knowledge is up to date, your department head has asked you to do the following.

1 Give a brief summary of the sports development continuum. Then write three paragraphs describing three different sports development initiatives from any sector, but at different levels of the continuum and for different sports. **M1**

Grading tips

Grading Tip M1

You might want to use a diagram to show the continuum. For M1 criteria, you need to prepare material that compares and contrasts the schemes and gives some strengths and weaknesses of their content and aims. Thinking about how successful the schemes were, if they were well resourced and how many participants were attracted. You need to have fairly comprehensive amounts of information about the schemes to hand.

2 In preparation for your next team meeting, everyone has been asked to prepare a list of barriers to participation for discussion, for at least three target groups that your authority deals with. You need to make your contribution a good one to try to show you have good working knowledge of these factors. **P2 M2 D2**

Grading tips

Grading Tip P2

Use at least three different target groups at different levels of the continuum.

Grading Tip M2

You have to explain these barriers really clearly at the meeting, so additional notes would be a good idea explaining why they occurred. This means reviewing each scheme and making your own conclusions about problems.

Grading Tip D2

You need to provide an analysis of your selected barriers, which shows how you would propose to overcome these barriers with effective and realistic solutions. This might be shown best on a handout for your colleagues, which includes a diagram giving an analysis of each barrier, how it affected potential participants and in what ways, and appropriate solutions alongside. Effective examples and reasons for your judgements or comments will help the process of getting a higher grade and impressing your colleagues.

3 You contribution at the meeting went down well and, as a result, your boss has decided you are the right person to carry out a small review for him. You have half an hour to brief him and three days to prepare a short Microsoft PowerPoint® presentation as follows.

a Slides 1–3 should cover the structure of three different sports development providers in the UK.

b Slides 4–6 should show the roles of three different providers in the UK. **P3**

Grading tips

Grading Tip **P3**

'Structure' means how they are organised – charts would help here. 'Roles' show what purpose(s) they have – this might be quite diverse. Make sure you provide good descriptions to accompany each slide.

You could include one extra slide showing the functions of the three different providers. You need to be able to explain clearly the three areas of structure, function and roles, probably with some accompanying explanations for your boss, in the form of slide handout notes. Some comparative points would be an effective additional slide to summarise such things as similarities and differences.

4   Your first task outside the office has arrived on your desk. You are to visit a new sports centre in the town to give a talk to the staff there on how they might achieve a quality award for sports development. You have to prepare a briefing sheet to leave after your visit showing two methods of measuring quality. The briefing sheet should show:

- two contrasting awards the sports centre could go for
- the stages the centre might go through
- how the centre might be inspected
- the types of improvement the centre might need to show
- examples of two successful centres who have gained the awards. **P4**

To meet grading criteria M4, you would also have to include:

- the benefits of a quality award
- the relative merits of each award, together with a recommendation as to which would suit the sports centre best. **M4**

Your briefing sheet would need to use terminology clearly to help the members of staff understand what the key terms are. Your material also needs to be current.

5   You have been in the post for more than six months and have worked on a number of schemes with your colleagues. You have created a really good reputation for yourself now both within and outside the office of sports development. It is time for the annual report to be written up for the councillors at the town hall so that they can assess your effectiveness and progress. Everyone on the team contributes to this in some way. Your contribution is to update the sports development portfolio with two of the best schemes in the past year 'on your patch'. The following brief has been given to you by your section head.

Remember!

You should include the following elements in your portfolio:

- a list of references from where you found your schemes
- appendixes, which could include statistics, raw data or scheme details not needed in the main body of the report.

Current initiatives in sports development for the Borough of Hazleton, 2007

Year-end assessment summary

Introduction and background to the two schemes, types of providers and areas of work.

The portfolio can have sections on:

- schemes linking to the 2012 Olympics
- an Awards for All scheme
- a Big Lottery-funded scheme
- a private-sector scheme
- a scheme focusing on specific local needs.

Types of providers with sub-sections on:

- local authority work
- sports governing body work
- voluntary club work.

Partnership schemes showing areas of work with sub-sections on:

- target groups
- sports-specific schemes
- schemes in specific locations (e.g. urban/rural, deprived/regenerated)

a Write about two appropriate schemes, following the above guidelines. **P5**

b Compare and contrast the two selected schemes. You could do this using qualitative reports on the two programmes, or quantitative data. **M5**

c Write an evaluation of the effectiveness of both schemes, together with recommendations and conclusions. **D2**

To achieve a pass grade the evidence must show that the learner is able to:	To achieve a merit grade the evidence must show that, in addition to the pass criteria, the learner is able to:	To achieve a distinction grade the evidence must show that, in addition to the pass and merit criteria, the learner is able to:
P1 Describe three examples of the sports development continuum, from three different sports **Assessment practice Page 186**	**M1** Compare and contrast three examples of the sports development continuum, from three different sports, identifying strengths and weaknesses **Assessment practice Page 186**	
P2 Describe barriers to participation for individuals from three different target groups at different levels of the sports development continuum **Assessment practice Page 192**	**M2** Explain barriers to participation for individuals from three different target groups at different levels of the sports development continuum **Assessment practice Page 192**	**D1** Analyse the barriers to participation for individuals from three different target groups at different levels of the sports development continuum, providing effective and realistic solutions **Assessment practice Page 192**
P3 Describe the structures and roles of three sports development providers in the UK **Assessment practice Page 207**		
P4 Describe two methods of measuring quality in sports development **Assessment practice Page 215**	**M3** Evaluate two methods of measuring quality in sports development **Assessment practice Page 215**	
P5 Describe two different sports development initiatives **Assessment practice Page 222**	**M4** Compare and contrast two different sports development initiatives, identifying strengths and weaknesses **Assessment practice Pages 207 and 222**	**D2** Analyse two different sports development initiatives, offering realistic recommendations for improvement **Assessment practice Pages 207 and 222**

Fitness testing for sport and exercise

Introduction

This unit introduces you to the concepts of fitness testing and health screening. The aim of the unit is to give you the skills, knowledge and experience to allow you to carry out fitness tests on an individual, for example a client from your local sports club. You will look at the different fitness tests, such as the multi-stage fitness test and the sit-and-reach test.

In addition to practical fitness testing, you will also develop the skills and knowledge that will allow you to analyse fitness test results. You will be expected to give feedback to clients based on their results, concentrating on their strengths and areas for improvement, such as a poor level of flexibility.

You will also explore health screening and how it relates to fitness testing. Through medical screening you will consider such topics as questionnaires and blood pressure measurement.

After completing this unit you should be able to achieve the following outcomes:

- Understand a range of laboratory-based and field-based tests.
- Understand the practice of health screening.
- Be able to prepare for, and conduct, appropriate fitness tests.
- Be able to analyse the results of fitness tests.

Think it over

There are many definitions and explanations of fitness – it is a complex subject. Fitness relates to those components of fitness that make up our health and skill status: strength, muscular endurance, aerobic endurance, flexibility, body composition, speed and power.

A fitness trainer, personal trainer or coach assesses a client's fitness through the use of fitness tests such as the multi-stage (or bleep) test, which you might have performed at school or college.

Imagine you are a personal fitness instructor working in your local fitness centre. You work with a variety of people who require testing for their health and fitness. What types of client could you work with at the fitness centre? What health and fitness tests could you perform with your clients?

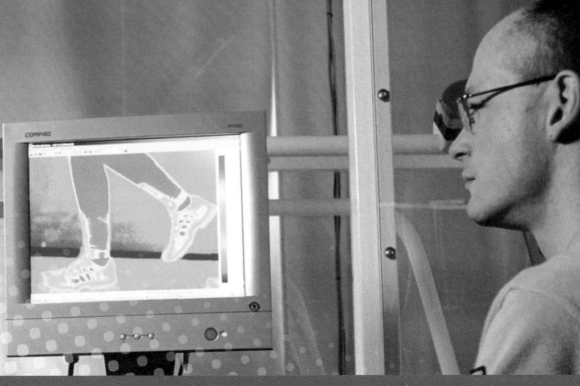

In this section you will consider a range of fitness tests that you can use with a client or athlete. You will also look at the protocol (method) and equipment required. A fitness test is used to measure a client's fitness level for a specific component of fitness, for example strength. Each test measures a specific component ranging from aerobic endurance to flexibility. You will also look at the practicality of the tests in conjunction with the advantages and disadvantages of using a specific one.

All fitness tests are classed as either laboratory-based or field-based. Laboratory tests are performed in sports and exercise laboratories and generally use specialist equipment with fairly complex protocols. In the laboratory, a scientist takes measurements of the athlete's body, such as blood lactate levels. These measurements are highly accurate and are used with athletes who have the access and funding for this type of scientific support. In comparison, field-based tests – which include tests in the sports field or sports hall – tend to be more basic in nature and do not need specialist equipment. These tests are fairly simple to use and are used with school children, beginner athletes and local sports clubs.

Fitness tests

There is increasing use of fitness testing in professional sports clubs, especially in football, rugby, athletics and hockey. County-level clubs now use fitness testing as many tests are inexpensive and require only a limited level of experience to carry out effectively. Professional sports clubs use the tests to measure an athlete's fitness levels after injury or during pre-season training. These clubs, sometimes in conjunction with universities, have access to the specialist equipment required for more complex fitness tests. Your local sports or fitness centre will use some fitness tests on a daily basis with their clients. These tests will probably be more basic in nature, although they still require some level of expertise and equipment.

Flexibility

Good flexibility allows you to pick up shopping bags from the floor or to reach for something. Flexibility is defined as the ability of a specific joint, such as the knee, to move through a full range of movement. A flexible joint has a greater range of motion, which aids the performance of skills.

Flexibility is often undervalued and under-trained. Sports performers tend to perform stretches for a couple of minutes at the start and end of their sessions within the warm-up and cool-down. However, flexibility is as important as aerobic endurance and should be trained for some sports. The sport, health and lifestyle benefits associated with a good level of flexibility are:

- improvement of posture
- prevention of lower back pain
- maintenance of healthy joints
- reduction in the risk of injury
- better dynamic balance (balance while moving)
- reduction in muscle soreness after exercise
- increased blood flow and nutrients to the joints.

Activity

In pairs, choose one sport and identify which techniques (e.g. the tennis serve) or skills require a high level of flexibility. Then state the joints where the flexibility is important.

■ Sit and reach

The most common test for measuring flexibility is the sit-and-reach test, which is designed to assess the flexibility of the hamstrings and lower back.

Key term

Fitness testing The process of evaluating an individual's fitness through a fitness test.

The sit-and-reach test

Activity

When performing flexibility tests, it is important that the client has performed a suitable warm-up to avoid injuries. As the tester, it is always good practice to have a warm-up and cool-down available to use. In small groups, produce a double-sided summary sheet that gives details of a suitable warm-up and cool-down.

The equipment required for this test is minimal – a yardstick and a bench. It is recommended that the client's legs should be 12 inches (30.5 cm) apart with the heels touching the bench. The client should reach forward slowly and as far as possible without causing injury, keeping the hands parallel. The knee joint should not flex. The score is obtained by recording the furthest point obtained by the fingertips against the yardstick.

The test should be done three times with the best score recorded. Evaluate the score against the data in Table 6.1.

Strength

Strength is also known as muscular strength. It is important for everyone, and not only clients. Strength can be defined as the ability of a specific muscle or muscle group to exert a force in a single maximal contraction to overcome some form of resistance. A good level of strength allows the individual to perform daily tasks involving strength without feeling fatigue or tiredness. As well as this, a good level of strength:

- helps maintain good posture in old age
- helps maintain an independent lifestyle, e.g. being able to climb the stairs at home
- helps avoid certain types of injures, e.g. back injuries
- helps with coordination while moving, e.g. for walking and running.

Key term

Strength The ability of a specific muscle or muscle group to exert a force in a single maximal contraction to overcome some form of resistance.

Rating	Males (cm)	Females (cm)
Excellent	>17.9	>17.9
Good	17.0–17.9	16.7–17.9
Average	15.8–16.9	16.2–16.6
Fair	15.0–15.7	15.8–16.1
Poor	<15.0	<15.7

Table 6.1 Sit-and-reach test scores

In relation to sport, strength is vital for a number of activities, such as:

- weightlifting – to lift a heavy weight
- boxing – to produce a powerful punch
- gymnastics – upper body strength is important to maintain a handstand.

■ 1RM

The one-repetition maximum strength test (1RM) is often used to measure dynamic strength in a specific muscle group. The test measures the maximum mass in kilograms that the client can lift in one single movement and is normally performed on a fixed resistance machine.

The machine selected for the test should reflect the specific muscle groups used by the client in his or her sport. For example, a rugby league player who requires a good level of lower body strength should use a machine such as a leg press. However, these pieces can be expensive and need to be used in a room that has a supportive floor.

After a suitable warm-up to avoid injury, the client attempts a mass, which is well within his or her capability. After each attempt, the client should increase the mass by no more than 5 kg. Between trials there should be a rest period of three minutes. The client continues to add mass until the one-repetition maximum is achieved. The score can be converted into a percentage of the client's body mass.

Example: a rugby league player who has a body mass of 100 kg and a one-repetition maximum of 110 kg would have a 1RM percentage of 110 per cent.

■ Grip dynamometer

The basic concept behind dynamometers is that the client has to squeeze, push or pull to measure isometric strength, which is measured in kilograms. The dynamometer is a mechanical device to measure the force generated in a specific muscle group. There are a number of different types of dynamometers that test strength in the handgrip, back and leg.

The grip dynamometer takes a direct measure of peak force generated by the client. The result obtained from the handgrip test should not be used to assess the muscular strength in other muscle groups. In addition, this test is not specific to any sport in particular, although it may be of interest to a racket sport player in terms of holding the racket.

Once the results have been obtained, they can be compared against a table similar to the one shown in Table 6.2. Dynamometers are relatively cheap to buy and maintain, and easy to use for the client and tester. One disadvantage is that they may lead to strained muscles if poor technique is used. From a health and safety perspective, individuals who have high blood pressure should avoid these isometric exercises as they increase blood pressure and may lead to medical complications.

▲ A grip dynamometer

Rating	Grip (kg)
Super	65.5–73.0
Excellent	60.0–65.4
Good	55.0–59.9
Average	48.5–54.9
Fair	44.0–48.4
Poor	38.0–43.9
Very poor	29.0–37.9

Table 6.2 Norms for the 16–19-year-old age group

Taking it further

By using another type of dynamometer, you can measure strength in the back. Using your research skills:

1 Find a picture of a back dynamometer.

2 Make a note of the protocol for measuring strength when using a back dynamometer.

3 Describe the health and safety issues you would need to address when using this piece of equipment.

4 Explain in your own words which sports need a good level of back strength.

Aerobic endurance

Aerobic endurance is also known as stamina or aerobic fitness. It is defined as the ability of the cardio-respiratory system to supply the exercising muscles with oxygen to maintain aerobic exercise for a long period of time. Another common term related to the concept of aerobic endurance is Vo_2 maximum, which is the maximal amount of oxygen uptake that can be used by the client during aerobic exercise, such as long-distance swimming, running or cycling.

Key terms

Aerobic endurance The ability of the cardio-respiratory system to supply the exercising muscles with oxygen to maintain the aerobic exercise for a long period of time.

Vo₂ maximum The highest rate at which oxygen can be taken up and utilised during exercise by a person.

It is important to understand that Vo_2 maximum is not the amount of oxygen inhaled by the client; it is the amount extracted and used by the working muscles. Vo_2 maximum can be measured using the following units:

- $l.min^{-1}$ (litres per minute)

- $ml.kg^{-1}min^{-1}$ (millilitres per kilogram of body mass per minute).

Aerobic endurance is important for most sporting activity because good levels of aerobic fitness will supply the muscles with the oxygen required for exercise. As well as helping to decrease body fat, a good level of aerobic fitness can lead to improved confidence and psychological well-being There are a number of key fitness tests that you could use to measure a client's aerobic endurance.

■ Multi-stage fitness test

This test is ideal for testing in sports based on multi-sprint activities, such as football and rugby. The test is progressive in terms of intensity (speed) and is used to predict a client's Vo_2 maximum based on how far the client progresses during the test. The equipment required for the test is minimal, consisting of the multi-stage fitness test tape, audio cassette player, cones and a space in excess of 20 metres. Once the tester is clear about the protocol, the test normally takes around 20 minutes.

Before starting the test the client is advised to do a warm-up, which should include a stretching programme. The client is asked to run between cones placed 20 metres apart and keep in time with the bleeps emitted from the tape. The aim is to reach the cone when the tape bleeps, not before or after. After every minute the bleeps become progressively faster, which has the effect of increasing the speed at which the client must run. The goal is to run for as long as possible while keeping up with the bleeps, until fatigue makes it impossible to keep pace. If the client misses three consecutive bleeps, he or she is asked to stop the test. While the client is running the tester should be monitoring the level and shuttle number the client has reached. The Vo_2 maximum score is converted from the last shuttle number completed.

From a health and safety perspective, the following considerations should be taken into account:

- ensure there is a non-slippery surface
- ensure the room is well ventilated
- check that running footwear is suitable, with adequate grip

Rating	Males (age in years)					Females (age in years)				
	14–16	17–20	21–30	31–40	41–50	14–16	17–20	21–30	31–40	41–50
Excellent	12/7	12/12	12/12	11/7	10/4	10/9	10/11	10/8	10/4	9/9
Good	11/2	11/6	11/7	10/4	9/4	9/1	9/3	9/2	8/7	7/2
Average	8/9	9/2	9/3	6/10	6/9	6/7	6/8	6/6	6/3	5/7
Fair	7/1	7/6	7/8	6/7	5/9	5/1	5/2	5/1	4/6	4/2
Poor	<6/6	<7/3	<7/5	<6/4	<5/2	<4/7	<4/9	<4/9	<4/5	<4/1

Table 6.3 Each score gives the test level and the number of shuttles completed successfully (e.g. 4/6 = level four and six shuttles completed)

- ensure the client has not eaten for two to three hours before the test
- avoid dehydration by ensuring a high fluid intake has been achieved over the previous day.

The test is ideal for testing a large number of people (for example, a class of schoolchildren) and produces results within a matter of minutes. However, there is a possibility of inaccurate measurements if the tester miscounts the finishing level, and the audio tape requires calibration (one minute on the tape should be one minute in reality). Table 6.3 gives indicators for aerobic fitness.

■ Step test

The step test, also known as the Harvard step test, is a sub-maximal test, which means it uses the client's recovery heart rate to estimate the V_{O_2} maximum score. As this test is not too physically demanding, it can be used with special populations such as over 55s. The client is asked to step up and down on a bench approximately 41.3 cm high to a specific beat (normally generated by a metronome) for a period of five minutes.

Males taking the test should step at 24 steps per minute, and females should step at 22 steps per minute. The heart rate is recorded for a 15-second period, between

Case study: Components of fitness

Tariq, a footballer aged 21, plays for the local team. Compared to the other players he has always had a high level of all the components of fitness. However, over the past six months the coach has not been training flexibility, so Tariq's flexibility has become poor. Lack of flexibility in the hamstrings leads to constant muscle tightness and to strains and tears, which means he has missed a number of key matches.

Sheila, a woman aged 50, has a good level of fitness for all components except strength in her triceps and biceps. This lack of strength influences her ability to perform basic activities such as opening a jar.

1 Explain why it is important for a footballer to have good flexibility.

2 Will missing a number of key games through injury have an effect on Tariq's other components of fitness?

3 What other daily activities will Sheila struggle with if she lacks strength in the biceps and triceps?

4 Explain why having good flexibility and aerobic fitness are important for someone of Sheila's age.

5 and 20 seconds after finishing the exercise. The 15-second heart rate count should then be multiplied by 4 to calculate the heart beats per minute (b.min^{-1}). For example, 15 b.min^{-1} $\times$ 4 = 60 b.min^{-1}. The respective heart rate for males and females should then be put into the following formulae to calculate the Vo_2 maximum:

- Male: Vo_2 maximum (ml.kg^{-1}min^{-1})
  = 111.33 − (0.42 × heart rate)
- Female: Vo_2 maximum (ml.kg^{-1}min^{-1})
  = 65.81 − (0.1847 × heart rate).

It is strongly recommended that this test is not used with elite clients, who require precise results, because the validity of the Vo_2 maximum score is questionable. The test is sub-maximal in nature and predicts the score, so there are possible errors. It has been reported that there may be variability in scores of ± 16 per cent, which is considerable.

Taking it further

There are a number of different protocols for the step test. Carry out some research into the different types and compare and contrast three of them. Within your research, explain the advantages and disadvantages of using the step test.

■ Maximal treadmill protocol

There are a number of treadmill protocols you may use, but here we will look at the Bruce test. For this aerobic endurance test you will need a treadmill where speed and grade of slope can be adjusted, together with a stopwatch and a helper to administer the test. There are some important health and safety points to consider prior to testing.

- The client must not eat or drink for three hours before the procedure. This reduces the likelihood of nausea that may accompany strenuous exercise after a heavy meal.
- Diabetics, particularly those who use insulin, will need special instructions from their doctor before attempting this test.
- The client should wear comfortable clothing and shoes that are suitable for exercise.

The athlete runs on the treadmill until he or she is fully fatigued. At timed stages during the test, the speed and grade of slope of the treadmill are increased, as in Table 6.4.

Stage	Time (minutes)	Speed (km/hr)	Slope (%)
1	0	2.74	10
2	3	4.02	12
3	6	5.47	14
4	9	6.76	16
5	12	8.05	18
6	15	8.85	20
7	18	9.65	22
8	21	10.46	24
9	24	11.26	26
10	27	12.07	28

Table 6.4 The speed and grade of the treadmill slope are increased during the Bruce test

The assistant starts the stopwatch at the start of the test and stops it when the athlete can no longer carry on. Most tests should be around 12 minutes long. To analyse the performance, the results can be compared with the results of previous testing sessions. You can estimate the Vo_2 maximum using the following formulae:

- Male: Vo_2 maximum (ml.kg^{-1}min^{-1})
  = 14.8 − (1.379 × T) + (0.451 × T^2) − (0.012 × T^3)
- Female: Vo_2 maximum (ml.kg^{-1}min^{-1})
  = 4.38 × T − 3.9.

where T represents the total time of the test expressed in minutes and fractions of a minute.

Speed

Speed is the ability to cover a set distance quickly, and is explosive in nature. Speed is vital for a number of

Key term

Speed The ability to move a short distance in the quickest time possible.

activities in sport and exercise, especially sprinting and jumping activities. It is also important for certain positions in team-based sports, such as a winger in rugby.

■ Sprint tests

A client can be tested for speed over various distances, depending on the demands of his or her sport. For example, a long jumper may wish to test his or her speed over 15 metres, which is a relevant distance for long-jump technique.

On response to a stimulus such as a whistle, the client should sprint as quickly as possible over the prescribed distance. The time is measured in seconds. It is common practice to give the client a one-metre flying start regardless of the test distance. This is because you want to measure the athlete's true speed and not their ability to react to a stimulus (e.g. a whistle).

This test requires only a suitable surface, a timing device, cones and a measuring instrument. In the past, the timing device was always a traditional stopwatch, but with that method the tester's reaction speed influences the result, so it is now common to use electronic timing gates.

Table 6.5 gives the rating system for a 35m sprint test.

Rating	Males (seconds)	Females (seconds)
Excellent	>4.80	>5.30
Good	4.80–5.09	5.30–5.59
Average	5.10–5.29	5.60–5.89
Fair	5.30–5.60	5.90–6.20
Poor	<5.60	<6.20

Table 6.5 Rating system for a 35m sprint test

Power

Power is strongly related to strength in conjunction with the speed of movement. It is the ability to generate and use muscular strength quickly. Clients who are stronger tend to be able to produce a greater amount of power during the action. This can be seen with a boxer who is able to produce a fast punch, which shows good strength as well as power.

Key term

Power The ability to generate and use muscular strength quickly.

■ Vertical jump

The vertical jump is a measure of anaerobic power and is specifically related to the leg muscles. The client reaches up against the wall and makes a clear mark (perhaps with chalk), which signifies his or her standing reach. The client then jumps as high as possible in order to make a second mark on the wall. The result is calculated by subtracting the lowest mark from the highest, and is known as the jump distance, measured in centimetres. It is simple to use and requires little equipment.

The client should make up to three attempts, and the highest jump should be recorded. A break of 30 seconds between jumps is advisable. The following formula is applied to calculate power:

$$\text{power (watts)} = 21.67 \times \text{mass (kg)} \times \text{vertical displacement (m)}^{0.5}$$

Activity

1 In groups, test six group members who are each to perform a 20m sprint test. You need three testers who will record the times of each sprinter separately.

2 Once you have the results, plot line graphs of the results, with three lines to represent each tester.

3 Discuss any differences you may have found between the sprinters' times and between the testers' scores.

4 Identify ways in which you could improve the consistency of the scores between testers.

You can also compare the results against a table like the one shown in Table 6.6. However, one drawback is that there are a number of techniques used, which makes comparing against the table rather difficult.

Rating	Males (cm)	Females (cm)
Excellent	>65	>55
Good	60	50
Average	55	45
Fair	50	40
Poor	<46	<36

Table 6.6 Normative data for the vertical jump test

■ Wingate test

The Wingate test uses a stationary exercise bicycle to measure anaerobic capacity. It is conducted in a laboratory and requires the following specialist equipment:

- computer with printer
- Wingate software
- motion sensor (to measure the frequency of the cycle wheel)
- power supply and adaptor
- Monark cycle: a special exercise cycle that can be adapted for this test.

The Wingate test calculates the client's mean power in watts (averaged over a five-second period), therefore measuring anaerobic fitness capacity. It can also measure the peak power (in watts), which is the highest power output during the test (normally after a couple of seconds).

A warm-up on the cycle of three to five minutes is advised so that the heart rate rises above 130 beats per minute, usually with only a small load. The client's mass determines the load applied for the test: 0.075 kg per kilogram of body mass. For example, a 70 kg client would have a resistance or load of 5.25 kg.

After the warm-up, the client pedals as fast as possible without any resistance in order to get a flying start. This normally takes three seconds. On command a helper applies the mass and the computer starts collecting the data. The client cycles as fast as possible for a period of 30 seconds (although this can be changed). The client should then perform a cool-down. The computer will calculate the mean power, peak power and fatigue index. A graph can be produced to show the results. The peak power usually comes after approximately two to three seconds.

The Wingate test is often reported as being the toughest, both physically and psychologically. Some subjects feel dizzy, vomit or even faint after the test, so caution is required to maintain the client's well-being. However, because it is a laboratory-based test, it does produce accurate results, which can be stored and produced in graphical form.

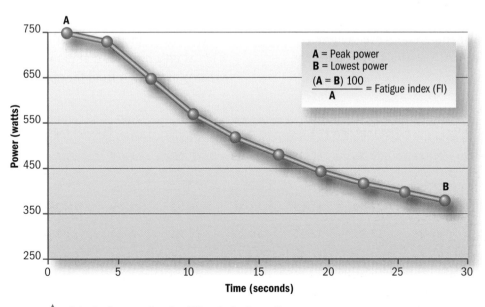

A = Peak power
B = Lowest power
$$\frac{(A = B)\ 100}{A} = \text{Fatigue index (FI)}$$

▲ **A typical curve showing Wingate test results**

Muscular endurance

Unlike strength, which involves the muscle performing one action, muscular endurance involves the muscle making a number of continuous movements. Muscular endurance can be defined as a specific muscle or muscle group, such as the biceps, making repeated contractions over a significant period of time (possibly over a number of minutes). There are a number of sporting activities that require good muscular endurance, such as:

- a hockey midfield player would need to make numerous sprints over 10 to 20 metres during the game at high speed
- a boxer would need a high level in their arms when trying to punch their opponent repeatedly
- a rower would need muscular endurance in their arms to make repeated strokes.

Key term

Muscular endurance A specific muscle or muscle group, such as the biceps, making repeated contractions over a significant period of time (possibly over a number of minutes).

All these activities would be classed as requiring a good level of muscular endurance because they require a number of muscular contractions over a number of minutes. The following tests will help you test for muscular endurance.

■ One-minute press up

The press-up test, also known as the push-up test, is used to assess muscular endurance in the upper body. To improve the validity of the results and avoid injury, it is important that the client uses the correct technique for the test. The hands should be shoulder-width apart and the back straight. The tester should place a fist below the client's chest on the mat or floor. For the press-up to be counted as one repetition, the client's chest should touch the fist on the floor. The client is required to do as many press-ups as possible within one minute, based on the correct technique.

For some individuals who have less upper body strength, the technique can be modified. The client can flex his or her knees to 90° in a kneeling position, with the ankles crossed. However, this method cannot be used to compare against the data in Table 6.7.

The main advantages of this test is that it is quick to run and requires little equipment. However, it is hard to make sure the correct technique is being used, which can make cross-group comparisons difficult.

■ One-minute sit up

The one-minute sit-up test is similar to the press-up test in nature, as it measures local muscular endurance. It is also known as the curl-up or abdominal curl test. It is important that there is a helper for this test to hold the feet in a stationary position. The client is positioned on the mat with the hips flexed and knees flexed to 90°, with the feet flat on the mat. The normative data in Table 6.8 is based on a protocol that requires the client to perform as many as possible until there is total fatigue. A full

Rating	Males (age in years)					Females (age in years)				
	15–19	20–29	30–39	40–49	50–59	15–19	20–29	30–39	40–49	50–59
Excellent	>39	>36	>30	>22	>21	>33	>30	>27	>24	>21
Good	29–38	29–35	22–29	17–21	13–20	25–32	21–29	20–26	15–23	11–20
Average	23–28	22–28	17–21	13–16	10–12	18–24	15–20	13–19	11–14	7–10
Fair	18–22	17–21	12–16	10–12	7–9	12–17	10–14	8–12	5–10	2–6
Poor	<17	<16	<11	<9	<6	<11	<9	<7	<4	<1

Table 6.7 Norms for the press-up test

Rating	Males (age in years)					Females (age in years)				
	18–25	26–35	36–45	46–55	56–65	18–25	26–35	36–45	46–55	56–65
Excellent	60–50	55–46	50–42	50–36	42–32	55–44	54–40	50–34	42–28	38–25
Good	48–45	45–41	40–36	33–29	29–26	41–37	37–33	30–27	25–22	21–18
Above average	42–40	38–36	34–30	28–25	24–21	36–33	32–29	26–24	21–18	17–13
Average	38–36	34–32	29–28	24–22	20–17	32–29	28–25	22–20	17–14	12–10
Fair	34–32	30–29	26–24	21–18	16–13	28–25	24–21	18–16	13–10	9–7
Poor	30–26	28–24	22–18	17–13	12–9	24–20	20–16	14–10	9–6	6–4
Very poor	24–12	21–6	16–4	12–4	8–2	17–4	12–1	6–1	4–0	2–0

Table 6.8 Norms for the sit-up test

movement requires the elbows to touch the knees, and the shoulders must touch the mat after the downward movement. Clients with neck or back pain should not try this test. It should be preceded by a suitable warm-up of neck and leg muscles.

Body composition

Body composition is the amount (normally expressed as a percentage) of body fat and lean body tissue the athlete possesses. Lean body tissue is water, blood, skin, muscle and bone. From a health point of view, it is important to have low levels of body fat. Increased levels of fat can usually happen through injury or during the off-season period and can lead to a decrease in performance. You can see this when footballers return to pre-season training in July and are carrying extra weight, which has to be lost. The increase in body fat can reduce the fitness of the player by making them slower. You can use the following tests for body composition.

Key term

Body composition The amount (normally expressed as a percentage) of body fat and lean body tissue the individual possesses.

■ Skinfold callipers

Skinfold measurement requires a trained and competent tester who can make reliable measurements over a period of time. Skinfold measurement is a reliable test because it has a correlation of 0.70 to 0.90 (see page 244). The following procedure is used to complete the test.

- Measurements are taken from the right side of the client (for consistency).
- Use the thumb and finger to pinch the client's skin.
- The callipers are applied 1 cm below and at right angles to the pinch.
- A reading should be taken from the gauge after one or two seconds.
- Two measurements should be taken and the mean used.
- Measurements within one to two millimetres of the previous reading indicate the results are reliable.

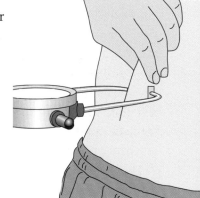

▲ Skinfold callipers measure the amount of subcutaneous fat (fat immediately below the skin) in millimetres

Numerous sites can be measured: abdomen, triceps, biceps, chest, calf, subscapular, suprailiac and thigh muscle. Most protocols use three sites, such as:

- male – chest, thigh and abdomen
- female – triceps, suprailiac and thigh.

The measurements for the three sites are added together to produce a total in millimetres, which can be evaluated in terms of a percentage of body fat using conversion tables that take into account the client's age. A body fat percentage of 15–25 per cent is considered optimal for women, and 10–20 per cent for men.

However, there is no distinction between fat and fat-free mass. This method cannot be used with pregnant women or with clients who are very muscular.

■ Bioelectrical impedance analysis

This method requires little in the way of tester skill and experience. The machine passes a harmless electronic current through the client's body and records the impedance (opposition) to the current. The current will flow through tissues with a high water content faster than through tissue with less water, such as fat. A client who has more fat will record a slower speed for the current. The speed at which the current moves is measured and used to determine body composition.

One type of impedance machine requires the client to remove footwear including socks and stand on a plate. It produces a computer printout detailing the parameters of body composition, such as fat-free mass. Research has shown that this method has a good level of accuracy with only ± 4 per cent error.

The following are the requirements for a bioelectrical impedance procedure.

- The client should not drink for three to four hours prior to the test.
- The client should not undertake physical activity of moderate or high intensity for 12 hours prior to the testing session.
- The client should not consume alcohol for two days prior to testing, and should avoid caffeinated drinks such as coffee.

■ Hydrodensitometry

Hydrodensitometry is also known as hydrostatic weighing, or weighing underwater. It is fairly common in the research field and is the method often found in universities and specialist sports science facilities.

Research has proven that this method produces the most accurate results in terms of determining body composition. Other methods such as skinfold measurements can be assessed against it to determine the reliability of their results.

The dry weight of the client is recorded. Then, wearing a swimsuit, the client is lowered into a tank of water, after exhaling the air from the lungs. All parts of the body must be underwater. Fat is less dense than water and acts as a buoyancy force, causing the individual to rise. However, bone and muscle tissue are more dense than water, causing the client to sink. Therefore, a client who has a greater amount of muscle mass and bone will weigh more underwater in relation to his or her dry weight.

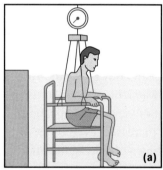

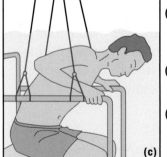

(a) The client sits in a special chair with his chin above the warm water.

(b) He blows all the air from his lungs and holds his breath.

(c) He completely submerges his head underwater while holding his breath. The test takes about five seconds to complete.

▲ Because of cost and space requirements, hydrodensitometry is unlikely to be found in the local fitness centre

Assessment practice

Produce and prepare a presentation which explores a range of fitness tests that you might use with a client. You need to describe one fitness test for each of the following components of fitness:

- flexibility
- strength
- aerobic endurance
- speed
- power
- muscular endurance
- body composition.

Describe and explain the advantages and disadvantages of the tests you use. **P1 M1**

Advantages and disadvantages of different tests

Regardless of whether you are using a laboratory- or a field-based test, there are certain advantages and disadvantages of each test. It is important to recognise these because you need to be able to select the test that is right for each client. Poor test selection may lead to results that are invalid or have no meaning to the athlete. Specific advantages and disadvantages for each test are given on pages 230–240. This section highlights the general issues you need to consider.

Cost

Some of the fitness tests we have looked at require little financial investment to set up. For example, the step test can be run just using a stop-watch and a step at the bottom of a flight of stairs. On the other hand, some tests such as the Wingate cost a great deal of money because it needs specialist:

- computer software (Wingate package)
- computer hardware (printers, cables, etc.)

- bicycle equipment
- scientific knowledge and support.

Most schools are able to afford only basic equipment and technical knowledge, whereas top universities and sports clubs are usually able to purchase all the equipment they need as they have access to more funding. This funding pays for sports and exercise scientists and specialist lab technicians. However, it is important to note that they may not use all the methods because they can afford the more accurate ones, which are normally laboratory-based.

Think it over

Which of the following tests do you think would be available at your local school and which would be used at a top university? Your decisions should be based not only on cost but also on the practicality and validity of each test. Discuss your views with the rest of your group.

- Step test.
- Bruce test.
- One-minute press-up test.
- Sprint test.
- Hydrodensitometry.
- Sit-and-reach test.
- Multi-stage fitness test.
- Wingate test.

Time

When considering time in relation to selecting a test, there are two key aspects:

- time taken to test the client
- time taken to analyse the results and produce feedback.

For example, you can test up to 20 clients at once using the multi-stage fitness test and get almost immediate results (within 20 minutes). However, it can take more than 20 minutes to test one client during a treadmill protocol, with over an hour for the results to be

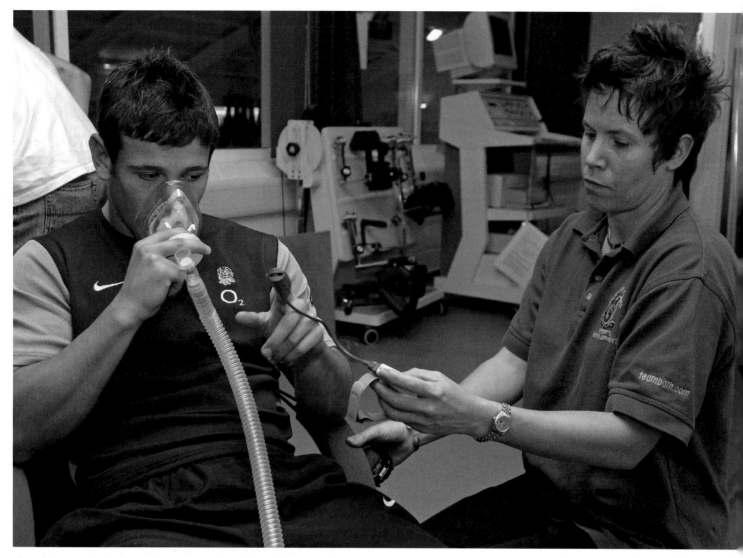

▲ A laboratory contains a wide range of scientific equipment, which can measure a client's athletic capability

generated. So if you were testing a full rugby squad in a laboratory, you can see the cost in terms of time.

Equipment requirement

Certain fitness tests require specialist equipment, which will have cost implications. However, all fitness tests require some form of equipment – even the one-minute press-up test needs a stopwatch and an exercise mat.

Facility requirements

In a sports or leisure centre, you will have basic equipment such as a grip dynamometer and height

Activity

In pairs, produce an equipment list that can be stored on a database. Each pair should look at three different fitness tests and add the equipment required to the database. Therefore, when all the pairs have added their information, the group can access the database to find out what equipment is required for each type of test.

charts, etc. On the other hand, a sports science laboratory will have specialist equipment that requires specialist technical knowledge to use it.

Taking it further

One of the pieces of equipment that a sports science laboratory will have is a Douglas Bag system. Through your research, answer the following questions.

1 What component of fitness does the Douglas Bag system measure?

2 Explain briefly how the Douglas Bag system works.

3 Detail a treadmill protocol that could be used with the Douglas Bag system.

4 Explain the advantages of using this piece of equipment over a field-based method.

Skill level of person carrying out test

Through your training within the sports centre or within this course, you will be able to perform basic tests such as one-minute press ups or the multi-stage fitness test with your clients. However, when you are working with elite-level athletes, you will need to use specialist equipment and protocols, which require more training. Part of this extra training can come through working with the British Association of Sport and Exercise Sciences (BASES).

In the UK, BASES works in the field of sport and exercise science, and its members include academics and fitness practitioners. Its aims include promoting the relevance of sport and exercise to society. When you are working with elite-level athletes, you need to become BASES accredited. This means you have a professional status and the experience to work with the best athletes.

Web links

Visit the BASES website at www.bases.org.uk to find out more about the association and the accreditation process.

■ Issues with test validity

When choosing a fitness test, the tester must consider its validity. Only a test that has reliable results and is valid will provide useful information. When assessing for validity, the tester should try to answer the following question: Does the fitness test or piece of equipment (for example, heart rate monitor) measure what it is supposed to measure?

Key term

Validity A concept relating to truth or worth in relation to a fitness test.

The component of fitness to be tested should always be matched with an appropriate test.

Activity

The new coach of a local rugby team needs to test the players' fitness levels. He decides to test the players' speed, as this is important for rugby. After some thought, the coach decides to time the athletes in a step test.

1 Is the step test a valid test in this context? Explain your views.

2 Suggest other aerobic endurance tests the coach could use.

3 Discuss the implications of this test for the players, the coach and the possible team selection.

■ Issues with test reliability

A major part of whether a test and its results are valid is its reliability.

Key term

Reliability The consistency of the scores obtained while testing on different occasions.

We can see from Table 6.9 that the results of the second client's tests were highly variable, and we would class these scores as unreliable. Poor reliability means that the test is not valid and does not produce any meaningful or useful information. There may be a number of reasons for poor reliability, such as poor testing technique or a different tester being used. The first client's scores do seem consistent and valid, so the results could be used in relation to a baseline score.

When you assess a test's reliability, you should consider the *r* value that is given to the test. For example, the multi-stage fitness test has a value ranging from 0.87 to 0.93. This test looks at the relationship between the score obtained on the test (in levels and shuttles) and the actual Vo_2 maximum score. The closer the score is to 1 the better, because this means there is a perfect correlation, but remember that not all tests have an *r* value. Table 6.10 will help you assess a test's reliability (r) value.

Client 1	Client 2
32	25
32	34
31	36
33	21
32	23
34	29

Table 6.9 Two client's fitness test scores obtained from the vertical jump

Rating	Correlation value
Excellent	0.90–1
Very good	0.70–0.89
Good	0.50–0.69
Moderate	0.30–0.49
Weak	0.10–0.29
None	0–0.09

Table 6.10 Correlation data

6.2 Understand the practice of health screening

Health screening is an important component of any exercise programme, and should be carried out with all individuals who are contemplating starting an exercise or fitness testing programme. It should be taken seriously by testers in the health and fitness industry, because its aim is to ensure the health and well-being of clients.

The aims of the health screening process are to identify individuals who:

- have a medical condition (e.g. angina), which should exclude them from a testing or exercise session

Key term

Health screening This aims to detect any diseases, illnesses or injuries before starting an exercise programme. It also provides the individual with a number of baseline scores (for example, body fat percentage) so that any changes to health status can be monitored.

- require supervision or assistance while involved in a structured exercise programme
- because of their background and history, should have a medical check with their GP before having a fitness test or starting an exercise programme
- possess other special needs, e.g. Braille testing instructions for the visually impaired.

In this section you will look at all aspects of health screening, such as questionnaires and client consultation. In addition, you will be able to gain practical experience in assessing an individual's health by measuring heart rate, blood pressure and other health-related tests.

Health screening procedures

Health screening must take place before any exercise or testing is performed by the client, and it must be administered by the tester. It usually takes the form of a questionnaire and its aim is to identify any medical condition that may prevent the client from exercising safely. Its aim is to ensure the health and safety of the client.

A high-quality health screening programme should involve a number of health checks, which might include the following components:

- taking the client's past medical history
- taking the client's family's medical history
- recording blood pressure
- measuring lung function
- checking cholesterol levels
- measuring body composition
- using an electrocardiograph (ECG) for monitoring heart conditions (used only in specialist facilities).

Remember!

Health screening aims to identify any medical condition and takes place before any form of exercise.

Taking it further

Carry out some research into the practice of health screening at your local gym or fitness centre. Try to discover what health tests might be performed on you before starting an exercise programme.

It is important to understand that a number of organisations offer exercise facilities and programmes and are therefore involved in the practice of health screening and fitness testing. These organisations include:

- local authority-owned leisure centres
- health clubs
- fitness facilities
- primary care settings that offer facilities for target groups, such as the elderly.

Health screening questionnaires

The health or fitness instructor/tester should use a questionnaire on health and physical activity. These questionnaires ask specific questions relating to past or current illnesses. The instructor should use the information to select the correct level and types of exercises for the client. The aim of the health screening questionnaire is to identify any conditions that might worsen with exercise. It is important that the completed questionnaires are kept in a secure place for reasons of confidentiality, and that they can be accessed only by authorised people looking to find details about the client's medical history.

Client consultation

The client consultation stage is important for the tester and the client as it builds the relationship between them. The initial consultation may take up to an hour and involves a number of factors, such as:

- taking a record of personal details, e.g. name, contact number, GP's name
- identifying and setting out the client's goals, e.g. assessing and improving aerobic fitness
- lifestyle evaluation (cont. on page 248)

Medical history questionnaire

General information

Surname _____ First name _____ Middle initial _____

Date of birth _____ Sex _____

Home phone _____ Mobile phone _____

Work phone _____ Doctor/GP _____

Address _____

_____ Post code _____

Section A

1 When was the last time you had a physical examination?

_____

2 If you are allergic to any medications, foods or other substances, please name them.

_____

3 If you have been told that you have any chronic or serious illnesses, please list them.

_____

4 Give the following information on the last 3 times you have been hospitalised. *Note:* Women, do not list normal pregnancies.

	Hospitalisation 1	*Hospitalisation 2*	*Hospitalisation 3*
Type of operation	_____	_____	_____
Month and year	_____	_____	_____
Hospital	_____	_____	_____

Section B

During the past 12 months:

1	Has a doctor prescribed any form of medication for you?	Yes	No
2	Has your weight fluctuated by more than a few pounds?	Yes	No
	If yes, did you attempt to bring about this weight change through diet or exercise?	Yes	No
3	Have you experienced any faintness, light-headedness or blackouts?	Yes	No
4	Have you had any trouble sleeping?	Yes	No
5	Have you experienced any blurred vision?	Yes	No
6	Have you had any severe headaches?	Yes	No
7	Have you experienced chronic morning cough?	Yes	No
8	Have you experienced any temporary change in your speech pattern, such as slurring or loss of speech?	Yes	No
9	Have you felt unusually nervous or anxious for no apparent reason?	Yes	No
10	Have you experienced unusual heartbeats such as skipped beats or palpitations?	Yes	No
11	Have you experienced periods in which your heart felt as though it were racing for no apparent reason?	Yes	No

Section C

At present:

1 Do you experience shortness or loss of breath while walking with others your own age?   Yes   No

2 Do you experience sudden tingling, numbness, or loss of feeling in your arms, hands, legs, feet or face?   Yes   No

3 Have you ever noticed that your hands or feet sometimes feel cooler than other parts of your body?   Yes   No

4 Do you experience swelling of your feet and ankles?   Yes   No

5 Do you get pains or cramps in your legs?   Yes   No

6 Do you experience any pain or discomfort in your chest?   Yes   No

7 Do you experience any pressure or heaviness in your chest?   Yes   No

8 Have you ever been told that your blood pressure was abnormal?   Yes   No

9 Have you ever been told that your serum cholesterol or triglyceride level was high?   Yes   No

10 Do you have diabetes?   Yes   No

If yes, how is it controlled?

☐ Dietary means   ☐ Insulin injection   ☐ Oral medication   ☐ Uncontrolled

11 How often would you characterise your stress levels as being high?

☐ Occasionally   ☐ Frequently   ☐ Constantly

12 Have you ever been told that you have any of the following illnesses?

☐ Myocardial infarction   ☐ Arteriosclerosis   ☐ Heart disease   ☐ Coronary thrombosis

☐ Rheumatic heart   ☐ Heart attack   ☐ Coronary occlusion   ☐ Heart failure

☐ Heart murmur   ☐ Heart block   ☐ Aneurysm   ☐ Angina

Section D

Has any member of your immediate family been treated for or suspected to have any of these conditions? Please identify their relationship to you (e.g. father, mother, sister, brother).

Diabetes _____   Stroke _____

Heart disease _____   High blood pressure _____

It is important that the trainer uses appropriate questions and listens for any possible issues that may warrant further discussion with the client

- health evaluation
- listing any medications taken
- obtaining informed consent for fitness tests and programmes
- health-related fitness tests, e.g. blood pressure and body composition
- setting out your aims as a tester: what you will do, how you will approach the issue, etc.

Activity

Many clients do not enjoy the initial consultation stage for a variety of reasons. This means that some people are deterred from returning to the fitness or leisure centre. In small groups, draw up a list of the possible reasons why people could regard the initial consultation as an unpleasant experience. In your discussions, include possible communication issues between the client and the tester.

■ Questioning

With some clients, it may be necessary to hold a further one-to-one session where you question them further to gather more information. You may need clarification on some of the details obtained from the health screening questionnaire. In addition, the health-based tests (e.g. blood pressure) or fitness tests (e.g. treadmill) might have alerted you to certain issues, such as shortness of breath, that need to be explored with the client. When questioning, ensure it is a quiet environment with no distractions, as some information may be confidential and personal. It is important not to baffle the client with science or technical jargon unless he or she understands these terms. For example, say 'stamina' rather than 'aerobic endurance'.

■ Listening

Although questioning the client is important, the key to a good consultation is to listen to the client. If you are a good listener, which will come from experience, you should be able to identify any issues that are not obvious at first. You will also be able to discuss in more depth any issues that come to light.

Non-verbal communication

It is estimated that 93 per cent of all communication is based on non-verbal communication. This type of communication is information we take from others, but it does not involve any words. Non-verbal communication is based on body language and includes things like how we sit and our hand actions when we talk. When having a consultation with a client, it is important that we try to recognise non-verbal communication, as this may bring up some key issues that need to be addressed.

Case study: Data Protection Act

Under the Data Protection Act, clients have the right to have inaccurate data corrected, destroyed, blocked or erased. They may seek compensation for any damage or distress caused by you by such inaccuracy. Inaccurate data means information that is incorrect or misleading about any matter of fact. The Act also governs the way in which you may use the personal information given to you, and clients have the right to require you to stop, or not to begin, using their personal information for direct marketing purposes.

1 As a fitness tester, you will hold a great deal of personal information that must be kept safe and confidential. Draw up a list of the types of information you must keep confidential.

2 As a fitness tester, explain why you need to abide by the Data Protection Act.

3 If clients discover that you have passed on their personal information to a third party, outline the implications for yourself and the fitness centre that employs you.

Activity

In small groups, produce a short information booklet that shows some different forms of non-verbal communication and their possible meanings. Include drawings and photos of body language to help the reader's understanding.

Client confidentiality

Anyone involved in health screening and fitness testing has a duty of confidentiality regarding their clients. They should ensure that personal information such as medical history is stored in a secure place. The details should remain confidential and should not be discussed with other instructors or clients. It is also recommended that, when working in exercise referral schemes, exercise testers have a policy on confidentiality included in their contract of employment.

Informed consent

The client must complete an informed consent form before testing begins. The form should explain the purpose and nature of the physical fitness tests the client is about to undertake. It should also detail any potential risks that may be present, and explain the benefits of the tests to the client. If you are testing anyone under the age of 18, the consent form must be signed by a parent or carer before testing.

A number of designs for informed consent forms are available. An example is given on page 250.

Key term

Confidentiality This means that you will not pass on any personal information to anyone else without that person's permission.

Consent form

Informed consent for physical fitness test

In order to more safely carry on an exercise programme, I hereby consent, voluntarily, to exercise tests. I shall perform a graded exercise test by riding a cycle ergometer or walking/running on a treadmill. Exercise will begin at a low level and be advanced in stages. The test may be stopped at any time because of signs of fatigue. I understand that I may stop the test at any time because of my feelings of fatigue or discomfort or for any other personal reason.

I understand that the risks of this testing procedure may include disorders of heart beats, abnormal blood pressure response, and, very rarely, a heart attack. I further understand that selection and supervision of my test is a matter of personal judgement.

I also understand that skinfold measurements will be taken at a number of sites to determine percentage body fat and that I will complete a sit-and-reach test and a one-minute sit-up test to evaluate factors related to lower back function.

I desire such testing so that better advice regarding my proposed exercise programme may be given to me, but I understand that the testing does not entirely eliminate risk in the proposed exercise programme.

I understand that information from my tests may be used for reports and research publications. I understand that my identity will not be revealed.

I understand that I can withdraw my consent or discontinue participation in any aspect of the fitness testing or programme at any time without penalty or prejudice towards me.

I have read the statements above and have had all of my questions answered to my satisfaction.

Signed _____

Witness _____

Date _____

(Copy for participant and for programme records)

Case study: Coronary heart disease

Coronary heart disease (CHD) is a preventable disease that kills more than 110,000 people in England every year. More than 1.4 million people suffer from angina and 275,000 people have a heart attack annually. CHD is the biggest killer in the country. The government is committed to reducing the death rate from coronary heart disease and stroke and related diseases in people under 75 by at least 40 per cent (to 83.8 deaths per 100,000 population) by 2010.

1 If someone has a heart attack, what are the possible lifestyle implications for that person and their family?

2 How can people reduce their chances of getting a CHD?

3 What are the costs for the National Health Service in treating CHD?

4 What initiatives can the government bring in to meet its 2010 target?

Remember!

The aim of the form opposite is to explain the purpose and nature of the physical fitness tests that the client is about to undertake.

Coronary heart disease risk factors

Coronary heart disease (CHD) can be classified into two types: angina and heart attacks (myocardial infarction). Both occur because the arteries carrying blood to the heart become blocked or narrowed, usually by a deposit of fatty substances. Angina is a severe pain in the chest brought on by exertion such as exercise and relieved by rest and medication. A heart attack is due to obstruction of a coronary artery either as a result of fatty substances or a blood clot. There is a variety of causes of CHD:

- cigarette smoking
- increased blood pressure over a long period of time
- high cholesterol levels
- a diet high in saturated fats
- lack of exercise
- increased weight over a long period of time
- high levels of stress
- lack of sleep over a long period of time.

Medical referral

Since the early 1990s, many areas of the UK have introduced medical referral schemes, also known as exercise-on-prescription schemes, with the aim of promoting a healthier lifestyle for individuals with certain medical conditions. The medical referral scheme works through a partnership of medical testers – GPs, practice nurses and other healthcare professionals – with local authority leisure centres. There are a number of specific conditions that may benefit from regular exercise, including:

- hypertension (raised blood pressure)
- obesity
- depression.

The referral process involved is shown in the following flowchart.

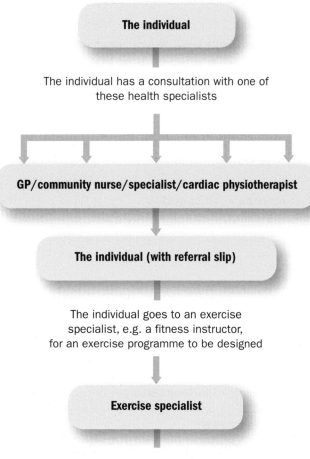

The individual has a consultation with one of these health specialists

The individual goes to an exercise specialist, e.g. a fitness instructor, for an exercise programme to be designed

The individual is then prescribed an exercise programme, with consideration of the level of supervision required

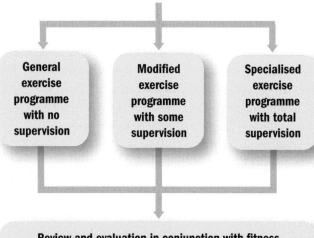

▲ The referral process

An individual can be given a recommended exercise programme on the initiative of a variety of health specialists, for example the GP. The individual is then directed to a facility or professional who can design a specific fitness programme based on the individual's background. If the health specialist deems the individual low risk, the programmes reflect this, with a reduction in the supervision required. A high-risk individual requires more supervision while working on the specific programme.

High-risk clients may have angina, established CHD or high blood pressure, for example. As shown in the flowchart, the referral may come from a cardiac physiotherapist or specialist at the local hospital. For low-risk referrals, it is the GP's role to ensure the patient is medically fit to start the exercise programme, but in high-risk cases the specialist (e.g. the cardiologist) takes clinical responsibility.

Assessment practice

1 Design a short health screening questionnaire that you could use with one of your fellow students and a member of your family. The questionnaire should have around ten questions and should focus on items such as diet, smoking, exercise, etc. **P2 P3**

2 After your classmate and family member have completed the questionnaire, describe each participant's strengths (e.g. non-smoker) and areas for improvement (e.g. too many fatty foods). Do this by providing them each with verbal feedback. **P3 M2**

3 As part of your verbal feedback, evaluate the health screening questionnaire. To aid your evaluation, support your findings with appropriate literature. For example, explore the possible health implications of smoking and eating too many fatty foods. You also need to offer lifestyle recommendations, such as changes to their daily diet. To record the verbal feedback, record the consultation on tape or ask your tutor to write you a witness statement. **D1**

Health monitoring tests

As the fitness tester within the health screening process and during the initial consultation, you will need to perform health monitoring tests. These tests include assessing heart rate, blood pressure, lung function and body composition. They are vital as they may help you to highlight a possible health issue with a client. However, it is not your job to diagnose a health condition. Your role is to send a client to a GP for an exercise referral if you have any concerns.

Remember!

If any doubts are raised during health screening over a client's suitability for exercise, ask them to visit their GP immediately prior to any exercise.

Heart rate

To test heart rate, you may take a number of measurements with the aim of identifying any possible health issues. It is likely that you will have access to a heart rate monitor, which can produce more reliable results than counting the pulse under normal conditions.

It is important that you place a small amount of water on the electrodes (inside the band) before fitting and place it below the sternum (breast bone). As part of the screening, you need to monitor both resting and exercising heart rate.

Heart rate varies depending on the client's age ▶

Resting heart rate should be between 60 and 80 beats per minute, although it may be higher due to anxiety. In terms of exercising heart rate, you need to consider the intensity of exercise being performed and the age of the client. The graph below should be used to assess heart rate.

Activity

Briefly describe any factors that might raise heart rate but which are not exercise-related.

Blood pressure

Measuring blood pressure is an important part of any test and it should be done with all individuals. Hypertension (high blood pressure) is a widespread health problem. It affects 20 per cent of the world's adult population according to the World Health Organization. If blood pressure remains high over a long period, there is an increased risk of heart attacks, strokes and kidney failure.

There is an increase in blood pressure as we age. A number of factors cause hypertension, including:

- excessive amounts of body fat
- low levels of physical activity

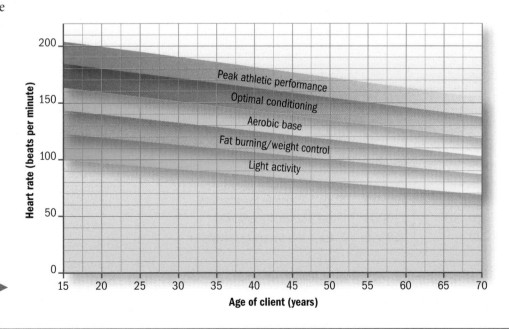

- excessive intakes of salt
- excessive consumption of alcohol.

Blood pressure is normally measured using a mercury or digital sphygmomanometer. This measures systolic and diastolic blood pressure. The average adult reading for blood pressure is 120 (systolic) over 80 (diastolic). Blood pressure is measured in millimetres of mercury, which is written down as mmHg. Everyone has a different blood pressure and it can change in the same person during the day and night. The lowest blood pressures occur when you are asleep or if you relax all your muscles. Standing up, exercising or anxiety all cause an increase in blood pressure. In a single day, your blood pressure may vary by 30–40 mmHg systolic, with similar proportionate changes in diastolic pressure. This is why it is important to measure blood pressure under the same conditions every time.

Key terms

Systolic The pressure in the arteries when the heart contracts and forces blood through them.

Diastolic The pressure in the arteries when the heart relaxes.

The following table shows what different readings indicate.

Blood pressure Average adult reading 120 over 80 Values:		
Systolic:	Diastolic	Rating
130–139	85–89	High Normal BP
140–159	90–99	Stage 1 Mild Hypertension
160–179	100–109	Stage 2 Moderate Hypertension
180_209	110–119	Stage 3 Severe Hypertension
210 or >	120 or >	Stage 4 Very Severe Hypertension

Case study: Blood pressure

Martin, the local butcher aged 40, has been referred to your fitness centre in order to start a training programme. He was told by his local GP that his blood pressure was 165 over 100, and that he should start to exercise.

1 Comment on the blood pressure reading given to Martin, in terms of the possible health risks.

2 Which components of health-related fitness should you train, with the aim of reducing blood pressure? Explain why.

3 Are there any forms of exercise that Martin should not do for health reasons?

A number of sources of inaccuracies can influence the reading given. Poor technique by an inexperienced tester can invalidate the reading. The presence of a doctor, nurse or tester can cause an increase in blood pressure because the client feels anxious, so an incorrect diagnosis of hypertension can be made. The protocol for measuring blood pressure is as follows.

- The client should be in a resting state, normally seated, for five minutes before measurement.
- The client should avoid intake of nicotine and caffeine for 30 minutes before measurement.
- The arm should be relaxed and at heart level.
- Place the rubber cuff around the upper arm so it covers the brachial artery (see the diagram below).
- Inflate the cuff, using the pump, above 170 mmHG – this stops the blood flow.
- Place a stethoscope over the brachial artery – there should be no sound because there is no blood flow.
- Release the pressure slowly by using the valve. At the systolic pressure the blood comes through the artery and a tapping sound is heard.
- Continue to reduce the pressure. When the sounds disappear this represents the diastolic blood pressure.
- Measure blood pressure twice within a three-minute period and record a mean average reading.

Taking it further

Carry out some research to investigate 'white coat syndrome' and explain why you would need to consider its effects when measuring blood pressure.

If you are using a digital blood pressure machine, follow these guidelines.

- The client should be in a resting state, normally seated, for five minutes before measurement.
- The client should avoid intake of nicotine and caffeine for 30 minutes before measurement.
- The arm should be relaxed and at heart level.
- Place the rubber cuff around the upper arm so it covers the brachial artery (see the diagram below).

- Inflate the cuff, using the pump, above 170 mmHG – this stops the blood flow.
- When you hear a double beep, stop inflating.
- The pressure will gradually decrease, as will the monitor value.
- The final value will be displayed on the monitor with a signal beep.

Lung function

The tester should assess the client's lung function during the health screening process. Assessing lung function may identify conditions such as:

- asthma – lung disease that reduces the amount of air inhaled
- dyspnea – shortness of breath or laboured breathing, possibly due to various types of lung or heart diseases.

The normal measurement used when assessing lung function is known as peak flow. This is a measurement of how much a person can exhale. Peak flow is measured by using a simple device known as a peak flow meter.

As with other tests, it is important that you use the correct procedures for measuring peak flow.

- Ensure the meter is set to zero or base level.
- Ask the client to stand, unless disabled.
- Ask the client to take a deep breath.
- Place the meter in the client's mouth, ensuring the lips are placed around the mouthpiece.
- Instruct the client to blow out as hard as possible, which normally takes one to two seconds.
- Repeat this process so you have three readings. Take the highest value.
- Make sure you record the score on the evaluation sheet for the client.

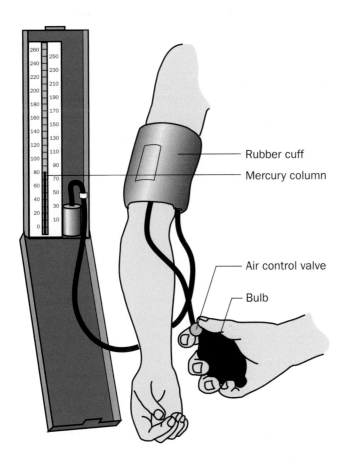

▲ Preparing to measure blood pressure with a sphygmomanometer

Rubber cuff
Mercury column
Air control valve
Bulb

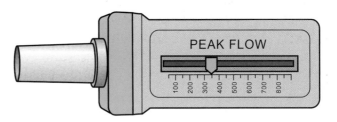

▲ Peak flow meter used to measure lung function

PEAK FLOW

Peak flow depends on age, height and sex. For example, a young boy who is 4 feet 10 inches tall should have a peak flow of approximately 350 litres per minute. A 50-year-old man of 5 feet 9 inches should have a peak flow of approximately 600 litres per minute. It is also important that you evaluate peak flow readings based on the client's previous scores, looking for any deterioration that might indicate a problem.

Waist to hip ratio

Waist to hip ratio is a measure of the body's fat distribution. The ratio is used to predict the possible health risks associated with obesity. An increased amount of fat around the abdominal area is associated with an increased risk of conditions such as hypertension and type 2 diabetes. The following equation is used to calculate the ratio:

$$\frac{waist\ circumference}{hips\ circumference}$$

The measurements should be taken at the narrowest part of the waist and the widest part of the hips.

For men, a ratio above 0.85 to 0.90 would be deemed unsafe; for women a ratio above 0.75 to 0.80 is a cause for concern.

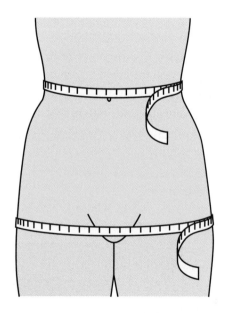

▲ Measure the waist at the narrowest point and the hips at the widest point

Body mass index

Another method of evaluating body composition is to use the body mass index (BMI) method, which evaluates weight in relation to height using the following equation:

$$\frac{body\ weight\ in\ kilograms}{height\ in\ metres\ squared\ (m^2)}$$

This method assesses the appropriateness of an individual's weight in comparison to height. For example, if a client's height is 1.70m and weight is 70 kg, then:

$$1.70 \times 1.70 = 2.89$$

$$\frac{70}{2.89} = 24.22\ \text{BMI}$$

This can be evaluated using Table 6.11.

Classification	BMI score
Underweight	<20
Normal weight	20–24.9
Overweight	25–29.9
Very overweight	30–40
Seriously overweight	>40

Table 6.11 BMI classification table

Case study: BMI

The Health Services Authority's community dietitian, Bethany Smith, along with many other health experts, dietitians and nutritionalists, recently advised using the BMI to help determine someone's appropriate weight.

'A person's weight is considered healthy if their BMI is between 18.5 and 24.9,' she said in a recent article. However, recent research from the USA suggests that this popular way of assessing health and body fat may be flawed and a more accurate gauge should be developed, according to doctors. Writing in the *Lancet* medical journal, the researchers from the Mayo Clinic College of Medicine, Rochester, Minnesota, found that patients with a low BMI had a higher risk of death from heart disease than those with normal BMI. Overweight patients had better survival rates and fewer heart problems than those with a normal BMI.

This apparently perverse result, drawn from data from 40 studies covering 250,000 people with heart disease, did not suggest that obesity was not a health threat but rather that the 100-year-old BMI test was too blunt an instrument to be trusted.

'Rather than proving that obesity is harmless, our data suggests that alternative methods might be needed to better characterise individuals who truly have excess body fat compared with those in whom BMI is raised because of preserved muscle mass,' said lead researcher Francisco Lopez-Jiminez.

1 **What do you think about the range given above for a 'healthy' BMI?**

2 **Explain the main weakness of using BMI as a method for measuring body composition.**

3 **What are the possible implications for you as a fitness tester when using the BMI?**

4 **What do you think of the validity of the findings based on the data sample size (number of people studied)?**

Assessment practice

1 Measure two members of your group's resting heart rate, blood pressure, peak flow and BMI. Then ask them to complete a health-screening questionnaire. In this way, the group members are acting as your clients. **P4**

2 Record your results on a table because you will need to report your findings back to your clients. The feedback should be in the form of a two-page typed summary document. In the document, you should describe the strengths and areas for improvement of the clients in relation to accepted health ranges. **M2**

3 Evaluate the health screening tests you have carried out. To aid your evaluation, support your findings with appropriate literature. For example, explore the possible health implications for someone with high blood pressure. You also need to offer lifestyle recommendations, such as increasing certain types of exercise. **D1**

In this section, you will be expected to carry out fitness tests with your clients to gain practical experience and awareness. There are a number of activities within this section that you could use with your fellow students to improve your practical skills. It will be important to use the correct protocol (method) and equipment while maintaining a high level of health and safety so that you provide a professional service to the client.

Fitness tests

See pages 232–240 for details on the correct procedures to use for the following fitness tests.

Multi-stage fitness test

In groups, test each other using the multi-stage fitness test and record your results in a table. During the following week and at the same time of day to avoid biological fluctuations, test for aerobic fitness using the step test, and again record your results.

1 Calculate the differences between the two sets of raw data from the different protocols.

2 Compare and contrast any differences and offer any possible reasons.

3 Based on the reliability and validity of results, decide which protocol would be most suitable for use with an elite-level athlete. Explain your opinions.

Step test

There are a number of protocols for the step test. In groups, perform two tests using two different protocols to increase your understanding of the influence on results. Once you have your results, draw a scattergraph to look at the correlation between the two sets of data.

Maximal treadmill protocol

One of the main factors that can explain an athlete's fitness level is age. As a general rule, as we become older we tend to lose some of our aerobic endurance.

Theory into practice

In groups, draw up a list of the possible reasons for a decrease in aerobic endurance as people age. Discuss the key points.

Activity

Carry out the Bruce test with the following people and compare the results:

- a fellow group member aged 16–18
- a 30-year-old (possibly a teacher in your school or college)
- a 50–60-year-old from your family or local community.

1RM

Depending on the sport you play, you may require strength in different parts of your body. For example, shot putters need strength in their upper body whereas sprinters need it in their lower body.

Activity

In small groups, test for a group member's upper and lower body strength and then convert the data into a percentage of the person's body mass. Once you have your results, test your results using Microsoft® Excel to test for a correlation. Remember that your value should be between –1 and 1 (see page 244 for more details about correlations).

Grip dynamometer

In some sports such as tennis and cricket, you need grip strength in both your dominant and non-dominant hand.

Activity

In small groups, test for any differences between your dominant and non-dominant hand and look for any significant individual differences. Then draw a correlation graph using appropriate software if available.

Vertical jump

Due to the similarity of muscle groups used, there should be some correlation between vertical and horizontal jump performance.

Taking it further

Research the protocol for the standing broad jump (horizontal jump) including a normative data table. Then test members of your group for both vertical and horizontal performance. Using your raw data, run a Pearson's correlation test (see page 244) through Microsoft® Excel to assess the correlation. Once you have your r value, write a brief report on your findings and suggest possible reasons for your results.

Wingate test

If you have the equipment within your school or college, you will be able to administer this test. However, if you do not you can work through the following activity, which will aid your understanding of the test.

Activity

Using the graph on page 237, answer the following questions.

1 At what point has fatigue set in for the athlete?
2 What is the peak force (in watts) recorded by the athlete?
3 Write a brief summary of the profile by explaining the results.
4 Why is it important to have a rolling start on the Wingate test?

Sprint tests

Test members of your group for their speed over the following distances: 15m, 25m and 40m. Once you have collected your results, rank them in order for each of the three distances. Try to answer the following questions.

1 Are there any differences in the order of group members for the different times? If so, why do you think this is?
2 How reliable do you think the timings are, and how could the timing be improved in terms of reliability?
3 Which sporting activities require a high level of speed?

One-minute press up and one-minute sit up

Muscular endurance is the capacity of a specific muscle or muscle group to make repeated contractions over a period of time. The two main tests for muscular endurance are the one-minute press-up and the one-minute sit-up tests. Muscular endurance is very specific to a particular muscle group. To demonstrate this, test your group using the press up and sit up test and look for any similarities and differences on an individual basis.

Skinfold callipers

To due the technical nature of this test, make sure you understand the correct protocol (see page 239). Remember most protocols use three sites, such as:

- male: chest, thigh and abdomen
- female: triceps, suprailiac and thigh.

As this test requires practice to perfect your technique, use your fellow students as clients.

When using skinfold callipers, make sure you use a private room to maintain the dignity of the client.

Bioelectrical impedance analysis

Look at the reading shown below, which was taken using a bioelectrical impedance machine, and answer the following questions.

Bioelectrical impedance read-out	
Name	Joe
Age	30
Height	1.70m
Weight	87 kg
Fat	34%

1 Consider the percentage body fat and the age of the client. Is the percentage too high for an individual of this age and gender?
2 Using the height and weight chart on page 267, comment on the client's weight.
3 Identify possible health issues that may arise from an excessive amount of body fat.

Hydrodensitometry

It is unlikely that your school or college will have the facilities to measure you using hydrodensitometry, but if you continue your studies you should have the opportunity at university.

Web links

Use the following website to identify the strengths and weaknesses of hydrodensitometry as a technique for measuring fitness: www.topendsports.com/testing/tests/underwater.htm.

Preparation for tests

When you are prepare for a test there are a number of key jobs you must do before the testing starts. You can use the following checklist to help you.

Preparation for tests checklist

☐ Complete a risk assessment.
☐ Ask the client to complete a consent form.
☐ Ensure the client has completed a pre-testing health questionnaire.
☐ Check the equipment works.
☐ Familiarise yourself with the protocol.
☐ Make sure you are comfortable with any calculations you will need to do.
☐ Produce a raw data recording sheet.
☐ Book the facility, e.g. sports hall.
☐ Inform the client of any appropriate clothing to be worn.
☐ Ensure the client has observed pre-test routines, e.g. no eating and drinking before.
☐ Make sure you have an assistant if required, who is comfortable with the testing procedure and their role.

■ Selection of tests

A number of tests are available for you to use, so it is important that you select the appropriate test for your client.

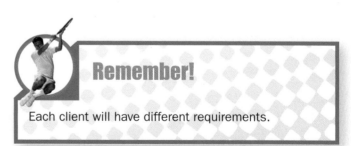

Remember!

Each client will have different requirements.

When choosing a test, consider the medical and lifestyle history of the client. For example, a patient who suffers from angina should not be given a maximal test for aerobic endurance as this may cause severe injury or illness. It would be advisable to select a low-intensity exercise test for this type of client, such as the step test.

You also need to consider the main sport of your client. For example, if the local rugby team wants you to test a player for aerobic endurance, this should be a test based on running and not swimming.

■ Reliability

For more information on reliability and validity, see pages 241–244. In addition, have a look through the different tests at the start of the unit on pages 230–240 as this contains important information on reliability and validity.

■ Validity and practicality of tests

When you are choosing a test to use with a client, it is important to consider the practicality of the tests. Consider:

- the time available to you and the client
- the equipment and facilities you have access to
- the understanding and experience you have
- the level of the athlete, e.g. it is not practical to use the step test with an elite-level athlete
- the speed at which the results are needed.

■ Pre-test procedures

Use the following points as a pre-test procedure checklist.

Pre-test procedures checklist

☐ Ensure that all tests are suitable for the client.
☐ Check that all the resources needed for the test are available.
☐ Check whether the cost of the equipment is within your budget.
☐ Use a health and safety checklist to ensure client safety at all times.
☐ Put tests in the correct sequence to avoid fatigue and false results.
☐ Check the relevance of tests – are they appropriate for the sport in question?
☐ Ensure a risk assessment, health screening questionnaire and informed consent form have been completed.

Fitness testing has become more popular with the widespread recognition of the importance of fitness to physical performance and health. Fitness testing is used to measure and evaluate a component of fitness for a variety of reasons.

■ Identify components of fitness which need to be improved

Fitness tests are used for identifying the strengths and areas for improvement of a performer. For example, a speed test may find that a goalkeeper has poor speed, which influences his or her ability to clear a through ball.

Tests are also used as part of the health screening process. They identify issues that require further discussion with the sports practitioner or medical staff.

■ Give a benchmark from which to measure improvement

Fitness tests provide information on the level of the client's fitness before a training programme. These are known as benchmark scores. Retesting the client after a significant number of training weeks makes it possible to evaluate whether the programme has been a success.

Key term

Benchmark scores Give a current fitness status (baseline score) prior to starting a training programme.

■ Allow a more specific programme to be written

Using fitness tests allows for a specific programme to be devised, according to the needs of the client. In the case of rehabilitation after injury or illness, for example, the fitness test informs the client about his or her recovery. Before injury, a runner could run one mile in five minutes. After months of rehabilitation, the runner records a time of 5 minutes 20 seconds. The test has highlighted the fact that the runner is still not at the level of fitness achieved before the injury and requires further aerobic training.

■ Play a role in educating individuals about health and fitness

When testing a group of individuals such as schoolchildren, it may be possible to identify talent in relation to a specific sport. If a child performs well in a test of upper body strength, he or she may be suited to the shot put, for example.

Conduct

When conducting fitness tests with your client, it is important to implement a number of key factors such as test sequence and health and safety.

Test sequence

When you administer a number of tests, it is important that you test in the correct sequence with adequate rest periods in between. If you do not test in a logical order, the results are likely to be invalid. For example, if you test for aerobic endurance, which is physically demanding, this will lead to an increase in heart rate. If you then test for resting heart rate, your results will be distorted. Follow these guidelines for test sequence.

1 Resting blood pressure and heart rate.
2 Body composition.
3 Aerobic endurance.
4 Strength/muscular endurance.
5 Flexibility.

Test protocols

Each fitness test has a specific protocol. A test protocol is a list of rules that sets out the correct way of using the test. If the tester does not follow the correct protocol, the results will not be valid and will not show a true picture of the client's fitness.

Key term

Test protocol A list of rules that sets out the correct way of using the test.

The protocol for each test should state the following:
- the equipment to be used, e.g. treadmill
- the duration of the test, e.g. three minutes
- the correct technique for the test
- the type of facilities required, e.g. a gym
- who the test is suitable for, e.g. schoolchildren
- the sequence of activities, e.g. run for three minutes and then take the pulse rate for 15 seconds
- the data required, e.g. pulse rate or distance covered in metres

Case study: Test sequence

Paulo, 17, is a new employee at the Sunshine Gym. He has recently performed his first set of fitness tests on a client, John. He performed the tests in the following order.

1 Flexibility.
2 Aerobic endurance.
3 Resting blood pressure and heart rate.
4 Strength/muscular endurance.
5 Body composition.

1 Why did John suffer a pulled abdominal muscle while performing the flexibility test?

2 Why were his resting blood pressure and heart rate readings higher than his normal values?

3 Why did John feel uncomfortable and self-conscious about having his skinfold measurements taken after an aerobic fitness test?

- how to calculate the results: some fitness tests require a specific formula to be used.

Remember!

As all fitness tests have different protocols, they require different equipment to be used. This equipment can range from a simple tape measure to a complex machine that measures body composition.

Health and safety

As a tester, you have three main duties regarding the equipment.

- Ensure on a regular basis that the equipment works as described by the manufacturer and that it is calibrated correctly (one kilogram on the scales should really be one kilogram).

- Through practice and guidance, you should be capable of using the equipment in a professional manner, for example taking blood pressure readings requires a level of experience and expertise. If you do not possess this level of expertise, your results are likely to be invalid and unreliable, giving the client the impression that you are unprofessional.

- Maintain the health and safety of the client. As a tester, you should have a good understanding and awareness of health and safety when testing a client. Maintaining good practice is paramount to ensure the health and safety of yourself, the client and others.

It is important to consider health and safety issues before, during and after the testing session. Throughout this unit we have identified a number of factors that must be considered in relation to health and safety. To remove these factors prior to testing, it is advisable to carry out a risk assessment similar to the one below.

Risk assessment

Name _____

Date _____   Signature of assessor _____

Hazard	Those involved	Outcome	Severity (1–5)	Probability (1–5)	Ways to reduce risk
Slipping on floor while running during the multi-stage fitness test	Athlete	Possible bruising, broken bones	2	2–3	Check floor surface before testing sessions

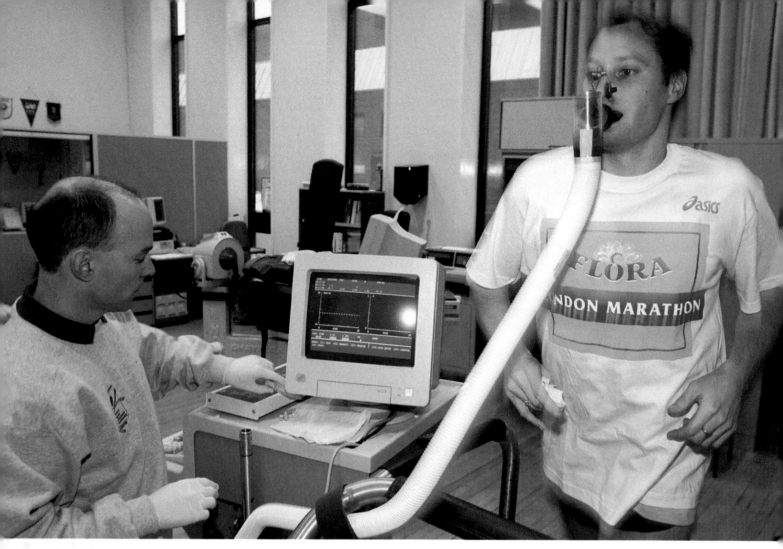

▲ Clients can stop the test at any point during the test, as their welfare is your top priority as the tester

You may decide to stop testing due to the following reasons:

- equipment failure
- a radical change in environment, e.g. the weather (if you are testing outside)
- fire alarm
- the athlete seems to be in distress, e.g. feeling faint or becoming uncoordinated
- the tester has to leave the testing environment for any reason.

Recording test results

When recording results, it is important to store them in an appropriate place for future reference. You will need to access them in the future to look for changes in fitness levels. The results can be stored using the following formats:

- spreadsheets
- databases
- tables
- graphs
- charts
- log books
- training diaries.

Always keep your raw data results in case you need to recheck anything later.

Assessment practice

1 Carry out six fitness tests on a member of your group and write a report covering the following points.

  a Decide on the components of fitness that are important for your client. These may come from the sport they play.

  b Identify the fitness tests you are going to use with your client.

  c Complete a risk assessment and health screening questionnaire for the tests prior to testing.

  d Ask the client to read and sign an informed consent form.

  e Administer the fitness tests, making safety a priority. Record the results on a raw data sheet. **P5**

2 Justify why you have used the six fitness tests with your client. Add notes to your report on the following topics:

  a suitability

  b reliability

  c validity

  d practicality. **M3**

6.4 Be able to analyse the results of fitness tests

In this section you will consider the important aspects of results analysis and feedback. As a tester, it is important to evaluate fitness tests because you need to provide valid feedback that identifies strengths and areas for improvement. Based on this feedback, you need to provide recommendations for future training to improve fitness. You will explore how to give feedback to a client, including assessment of normative data, as well as offering recommendations for future activities or training.

Normative data

You can use normative data tables to analyse your fitness testing results. Researchers who have studied hundreds of people to generate normal values produce these normative data tables. When using normative data tables, there are some important factors to consider:

- they can be gender-based
- most are based on specific age ranges

- some specify the level of performance, e.g. county standard
- they can have different values based on the source of information
- some tests do not have normative data tables.

Population norms

Normative data tables are based on different populations (e.g. gender, age, sporting background). Make sure you use the correct normative data table in relation to your client.

Norms for sports performers

Although it may be difficult to locate, you should be able to compare some of your results to data generated by sports performers. This is useful because you can compare a client's results with data from sports they play.

Norms for elite athletes

Unlike other clients elite-level clients or athletes will be tested for their fitness on a regular basis to maximise their training and performance potential.

The testing procedure is designed to:

- assess fitness levels against previous levels
- monitor progress towards a major competition
- assess fitness after or during injury/illness
- identify strengths and areas for improvement.

This information is kept confidential so that fellow athletes do not gain a competitive advantage.

▼ Elite-level athletes will compare their fitness test results with their previous tests or performance

Accepted health ranges

On page 256 we looked at some accepted health ranges for health variables such as BMI.

In addition, you need to assess a client's height and weight. This is the most widely used method of assessing an individual's body composition. It offers a judgement about the client's weight in relation to his or her height, although it makes no attempt to assess the percentage of body fat. It is common to see a graph like the one on page 267 displayed on posters in local fitness centres and GPs' surgeries, suggesting acceptable weight ranges for each height.

Knowledge check

1 Outline the protocol for the multi-stage fitness test.

2 Why is it important to consider flexibility in relation to sporting performance?

3 State the advantages and disadvantages of the step test.

4 Explain why it is important to maintain client confidentiality.

5 Use an example to explain how to calculate BMI.

6 Why is it important to screen a client's health prior to starting a fitness test or training programme?

7 What is the difference between the reliability and validity of a test?

8 Outline the factors that may cause coronary heart disease in the long term.

9 Identify three tests that can assess a client's aerobic endurance.

10 Identify three reasons why you would terminate a fitness test.

11 Describe two methods of measuring body composition.

12 Why is it important to evaluate test scores against normative data?

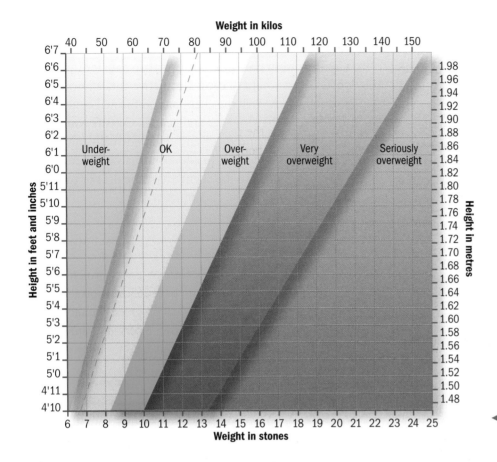

Weight in kilos

Height in feet and inches / **Height in metres**

Under-weight | OK | Over-weight | Very overweight | Seriously overweight

Weight in stones

There are many height and weight charts available

Feedback

The feedback you give to the athlete can take many forms, including:

- verbal
- written
- text-based
- numerical
- tables
- graphs or charts.

Some feedback may be presented immediately after the performance and some at the next training session.

Verbal

The information you have gained from the fitness test should be given to the client as verbal or written feedback. There are a few basic rules to follow when giving verbal feedback.

- Ensure the feedback is given in a quiet environment with no distractions, as some information may be confidential and personal.
- Don't baffle the client with science or technical jargon unless he or she understands these terms.
- Remember to link the results to the targets or goals set.
- If the client has made only small improvements below target, remain positive and stress that the results are going in the right direction.
- If the results are poor, be ready to suggest other ways of improving fitness. For example, what about changing from running to swimming, if this is more suitable for the individual?
- It may be appropriate to reset goals or targets based on the results. For example, someone who now has good aerobic endurance may want to concentrate more on speed or flexibility.

Written

Written feedback to clients can be produced in a number of formats. However, as with verbal feedback, it should be clear and easy to understand, and applicable to the client. You can show a comparison of the client's data against normative data using graphs or table. These can be generated using a computer programme, which then provides a fitness profile for the client to show strengths and weaknesses.

Tests carried out

When reporting the tests you carried out, remember to include the following information:

- name of test
- component of fitness tested, e.g. body composition
- units of measurement, e.g. metres or kilograms
- normative data rating, e.g. very good or poor
- reference for normative data: author, year of book or full website address.

Test results

It is vital that you record all the results from all your testing sessions as these form the basis of your analysis and interpretation. Remember that these results must remain confidential.

For recording your results, you may wish to use a simple paper-based method using a table designed by you. However, it is a good idea to transfer these results to a computer programme, which will help you generate graphs and tables for analysis. You must keep your records in a safe place (asking the client to retest because you have mislaid the results would be very unprofessional). The results should be filed with the health and medical questionnaires in the client's own file.

Some of the tests you do will require a number of practitioners or helpers. It would be advisable for someone else to write down the results while you are involved in the testing to avoid confusion.

You need to analyse and interpret the data you have gathered, with the aim of making an assessment of the client's fitness in terms of either a baseline score or progress in a training programme.

Compare your data against normative data for the specific test you have used. Normative data allows you to analyse how well the client has performed compared to others of the same age and gender. Classify your data according to the rating given, which normally ranges from poor to excellent. In addition, analyse the results in comparison with the client's baseline data or previous scores for that test.

Levels of fitness

We have discussed the importance of using normative data for assessing levels of fitness on page 265, but you also need to consider each client's individual progress. You should look at the profile of the results over a period of time to make a judgement on strengths and areas for improvement.

Case study: Test results

Brian, a 35-year-old truck driver who suffered an arm injury, has been trying to build up his strength in his arm because driving requires upper body strength. To assess his progress, Brian has completed a number of 1RM tests, which measure strength by looking at how much weight can be lifted in kilograms. The results are shown in the table below.

Schedule	Result (kg)
Before training programme	35
Four weeks into training programme	40
Eight weeks into training programme	50
End of programme (12 weeks)	55

1 Using normative data, report on Brian's test results.

2 Describe the progress made by Brian based on his test results.

3 Explain the strengths and weaknesses of a 1RM test.

Strengths and areas for improvement

In any feedback you need to identify the strengths and areas for improvement (also known as weaknesses). This will allow you to suggest possible recommendations for future training and activities. It is probable that you will have a combination of strengths and areas for improvement.

Strengths

- High levels of hamstring flexibility.
- Excellent levels of aerobic endurance.
- Good levels of muscular endurance.

Areas for improvement

- Overweight on BMI classification (Baxter and Smith, 2005).
- Poor flexibility at the shoulder joint.
- Very poor strength using the leg press.

As good practice you should also provide the normative data reference where possible, as in the example above.

Recommendations

To complete the evaluation process, you need to offer recommendations to the client to either improve or maintain their fitness. You may have to design a training programme, although, for high-level athletes, this is usually done by a fitness coach. For example, if you need to improve a client's aerobic endurance, you could use the following training methods:

- continuous/steady state exercise
- interval training
- Fartlek training.

When looking to improve fitness, you should also consider more contemporary approaches such as spinning or Pilates.

Activity

In pairs, produce an A3 poster that explores the different training methods you can offer a client. You should describe the different training methods. In your group, you should cover all physical and skill-related components.

Assessment practice

1 As a follow-on from the Assessment practice on page 265 where you performed six fitness tests on a group member (client), you are to give feedback to the client. Add a new section called Feedback at the end of your report and write notes on the following points.
   a A description of the results.
   b Data representation (e.g. graphs and tables where appropriate).
   c An interpretation of the results against normative data.   **P6**

2 Identify the strengths and areas for improvement for the client, which could be in the form of a bullet-point list. Compare the results with normative data.   **M4**

3 Provide future training or activities to improve your client's fitness. You need to explore the different training methods such as Interval training, as well as carry out a results analysis. This analysis needs to be backed up by supporting literature. The analysis could concentrate issues such as:

   • What do the results mean in relation to your client's sports?
   • How will this level of fitness influence your client's performance?   **D2**

Preparation for assessment

1 Imagine you have decided to work at a local fitness centre to gain work experience during your course. As part of the work placement, you have been asked by your supervisor to perform some extra tasks to expand your knowledge of fitness testing and health screening.

You are to produce and prepare a PowerPoint® presentation which explores a range of fitness tests that you may use with a client. In the presentation you should describe one fitness test for each of the following components of fitness:

- flexibility
- strength
- aerobic endurance
- speed
- power
- muscular endurance
- body composition.

In the descriptions, you should include:

- protocols
- equipment required
- equations/calculations
- units of measurement.

Printouts from the presentation will be displayed in the consultation room to increase awareness for clients, so make sure you describe the advantages and disadvantages of each test. **P1**

Grading tips

Grading Tip **M1**

Try to explain the advantages and disadvantages of the tests you use. For example, you could say that the step test is fairly unreliable because it uses a predictive heart rate and therefore is open to variability.

2 There have been some concerns about the quality of the health screening questionnaire used by the fitness centre. Based on these concerns, you have been asked to produce a new health-screening questionnaire.

To help you generate some suitable questions, research some examples on the Internet or look again at the one on pages 246–247. Your questionnaire should have about 15 questions and focus on issues such as diet, smoking, exercise and alcohol intake. You should use:

- closed questions, e.g. 'Do you smoke?'
- open questions, e.g. 'What causes you stress in your life?'
- scaled questions, e.g. 1 = poor; 5 = excellent. **P2**

3 To test the new questionnaire, you have been asked to use it on 20 clients within the fitness centre (you can use the tutors at your college or school). **P3**

Grading tips

Grading Tip **M2**

Once you have the completed questionnaire, describe the strengths and areas for improvement for two clients by providing them with verbal feedback through a consultation. It is important you go through all the questions step by step with the client, so you should write down some notes before the consultation so that you are clear.

Grading Tip **D1**

As part of the verbal feedback, you need to evaluate the health screening questionnaires. To aid your evaluation, support your findings with appropriate literature, such as exploring the possible health implications of not eating enough vegetables. You also need to offer lifestyle recommendations such as changes to their daily diet.

4 One of the key objectives for your work placement is to improve your practical skills for health assessment. Using two clients, administer four health monitoring tests, for example peak flow. Record your results in a table. **P4**

Grading tips

Grading Tip **M2**

Produce a written report that describes the strengths and areas for improvement of the clients in relation to accepted health ranges such as blood pressure data.

Grading Tip **D1**

As part of the written report, evaluate the health monitoring tests. To aid your evaluation, support your findings with appropriate literature, for example explore the possible health implications of having a BMI above 25. You also need to offer lifestyle recommendations such as changes to their daily diet to reduce their intake of fatty foods.

5 Your supervisor has suggested that you should add to your health-based testing with physical fitness testing and suggests you test a client. You need to administer six fitness tests, such as the vertical jump test, on one individual, who could be:

- a member of your family
- a member of your class
- a school or college sports person
- a tutor or teacher
- a local athlete.

You should produce a report that includes the following parts.

a Decide on the components of fitness that are important for your client. These may come from the sport they play.

b Identify the fitness tests you are going to use with your client.

c Complete a risk assessment and health screening questionnaire for the tests prior to testing.

d Ask the client to read and sign an informed consent form

e Administer the fitness tests, making safety a priority. Record the results on a raw data sheet. **P5**

Grading tips

Grading Tip **M3**

Justify why you have used the six fitness tests with your client. Add notes to your report on the following topics:

- suitability
- reliability
- validity
- practicality.

6 It is has come to the attention of your work placement supervisor that you have little knowledge and experience of providing feedback to clients. Therefore, he has suggested that you provide feedback to the client whom you performed six fitness tests on.

In the consultation room, provide verbal and written feedback to the client on their test results and interpretation of their fitness levels. The feedback should include:

- a description of the results.
- data representation (e.g. graphs and tables where appropriate)
- an interpretation of the results against normative data. **P6**

Grading tips

Grading Tip M4

Identify the strengths and areas for improvement for the client, and compare the results with normative data by showing them normative data tables.

Grading Tip D2

Provide future training or activities to improve your client's fitness. You need to explore the different training methods such as Interval training, as well as carry out a results analysis. This analysis needs to be backed up by supporting literature. The analysis could concentrate on issues such as:

- What do the results mean in relation to your client's sports?
- How will this level of fitness influence your client's performance?
- What effects might your client's fitness have on their lifestyle?

To record the verbal feedback, record the consultation on tape or ask your tutor to write you a witness statement.

To achieve a pass grade the evidence must show that the learner is able to:	To achieve a merit grade the evidence must show that, in addition to the pass criteria, the learner is able to:	To achieve a distinction grade the evidence must show that, in addition to the pass and merit criteria, the learner is able to:
P1 Describe the test for each component of physical fitness, including advantages and disadvantages **Assessment practice Page 241**	**M1** Explain the advantages and disadvantages of one fitness test for each component of physical fitness **Assessment practice Page 241**	
P2 Prepare an appropriate health screening questionnaire **Assessment practice Page 252**		
P3 Devise and use appropriate health screening procedures for two contrasting individuals **Assessment practice Page 252**	**M2** Describe the strengths and areas for improvement for two contrasting individuals using information from health screening questionnaires and health monitoring tests **Assessment practice Pages 252, 257**	**D1** Evaluate the health screening questionnaires and health monitoring test results and provide recommendations for lifestyle improvement **Assessment practice Pages 252, 257**
P4 Safely administer and interpret the results of four health monitoring tests for two contrasting individuals **Assessment practice Page 257**		
P5 Select and safely administer six different fitness tests for a selected individual recording the findings **Assessment practice Page 265**	**M3** Justify the selection of fitness tests commenting on suitability, reliability, validity and practicality **Assessment practice Page 265**	
P6 Give feedback to a selected individual following fitness testing, describing the test results and interpreting their levels of fitness against normative data **Assessment practice Page 269**	**M4** Compare the fitness test results to normative data and identify strengths and areas for improvement **Assessment practice Page 269**	**D2** Analyse the fitness test results and provide recommendations for appropriate future activities or training **Assessment practice Page 269**

Sports nutrition

Introduction

This unit introduces you to the links between nutrition, health and performance in sport and exercise. You will learn about the fundamentals of a healthy diet and develop an understanding of the influence of nutrition on exercise performance, along with a solid foundation of knowledge on which to develop good eating practices for yourself. You will also consider factors that affect food intake and choice, and methods of collecting and analysing dietary information to assess nutritional needs. By the end of this unit you should be able to demonstrate the application of nutrition strategies in a variety of sports contexts through examination of the diets of a range of sports from the amateur athlete to the Olympic elite performer.

It is important to emphasise that you will not develop the breadth of knowledge and skills of a sports dietitian or nutritionist upon completion of this unit. What you will develop is an appreciation of how diet affects sporting performance before, during and after training and competition. You should be able to recognise the limitations in your own knowledge and know how and when to refer to a more suitably qualified professional.

It is also important to remember that where sport is concerned there should be no conflict between eating for health and eating for performance. The sound foundations of the sports performer's diet lie in the pursuit of healthy eating through a balanced and varied diet.

After completing this unit you should be able to achieve the following outcomes:

- Understand the concepts of nutrition and digestion.
- Understand energy intake and energy expenditure in sports performance.
- Understand the relationship between hydration and sports performance.
- Be able to plan a diet appropriate for a selected sports activity.

Think it over

Take a few minutes to think about all the factors that might influence your food intake and choice. If you can think of 10 factors, this is good going, and a list in excess of 20 factors is excellent. Awareness of these factors will assist you in formulating realistic and achievable dietary goals and plans when meeting some of the assessment requirements of this unit.

The list you have devised may include simple factors such as likes and dislikes, time, money, taste, accessibility, religion, culture and convenience, as well as also others such as fashions and trends promoted by celebrities and sports personalities in the media, and food packaging and advertising, which can have a huge influence on our choice of food.

Now consider the range of nutrition-related topics that have featured in the news in the past two weeks or take a look at a range of health, fitness and sport-related magazines. Scan them for nutrition-related features and advertisements. How many are there? What kinds of topics do they focus on?

Finally, consider ways in which nutrition and eating habits might influence performance in sport and exercise.

All activity stimulates your body's need for fuel and fluid and as such, good nutrition is seen as important to performance in sport and exercise. Knowledge of the nutrients that your body requires, along with their different functions, provides the basis for the science of nutrition, the study of which is a relatively new area of scientific investigation and one in which new discoveries are constantly being made.

Good nutrition, and in particular healthy eating, sounds simple in theory but is often difficult to achieve in practice, particularly for those with busy lifestyles or intense training programmes. Nutritional topics now appear regularly in the media and in advertising, often presenting us with contradictory information on what is good for our health and/or performance.

Remember!

There should be no conflict between eating for health and eating for performance.

Theory into practice

Take a few minutes to write down everything you had to eat and drink yesterday. Ensure you record sufficient information on the different types of food, their portion size and the cooking methods used, and don't forget any snacks and drinks as well as meals. You will use this information in future exercises throughout this unit. This will be known as your '24-hour diet recall'.

Key terms

Sports nutrition The influence of nutritional strategies on sports performance during the preparation for, participation in and recovery from training and competition.

Nutrition The means by which the energy and nutrients in food are taken in by your body to sustain growth and development and keep it alive and healthy.

Healthy eating The pursuit of a balanced diet to support health and reduce the risks of chronic disease.

Balanced diet A diet that provides the correct amount of all the nutrients required by your body without excess or deficiency.

Food Any substance derived from plants or animals containing a combination of the nutrients carbohydrates, fats, proteins, vitamins, minerals, fibre, water and alcohol, the amounts of which will vary from food to food.

Diet Usual eating habits and food consumption.

Nutrition

The foods you consume contain the nutrients carbohydrate, protein, fat, vitamins, minerals, fibre and water. The amounts of these nutrients vary from food to food. Most foods you eat are categorised based on their macronutrient (carbohydrate, protein and fat) content, but they usually consist of more than one of these nutrients. For example, bread is classed as a carbohydrate food because it contains more carbohydrate than protein or fat, but it is also a source of these nutrients and others such as vitamins, minerals and fibre.

Key term

Macronutrients Nutrients that are required by your body in daily amounts greater than a few grams such as carbohydrate, fat and protein.

■ Carbohydrates

Carbohydrates consumed in your diet are made of the chemical elements carbon, hydrogen and oxygen. The main role of carbohydrates is energy production. They form your body's most readily available source of energy and can be accessed rapidly. One gram of carbohydrate, whether this is derived from sugar or starch, will provide you with approximately 4 kilocalories of energy. The carbohydrate foods you eat are divided into two basic types and are generally referred to as either simple or complex.

▲ It is important to have a balanced diet in order to stay healthy

Remember!

Macronutrients are the energy-providing nutrients of your diet.

Macronutrients

The nutrients found in your food are also categorised according to the relative amounts required by your body. Carbohydrate, protein and fat are termed macronutrients, as they are required in relatively large amounts on a daily basis. These nutrients are also the energy-providing nutrients of your diet.

▲ Good sources of carbohydrate in the diet include bread, rice, pasta, potatoes and cereals

Simple carbohydrates are essentially sugars and are formed from single and double sugar units. They are easily digested and absorbed to provide your body with a quick energy source. The simplest unit of carbohydrates is the monosaccharide, the most common of which in your diet is glucose. Saccharide means sugar, mono means one; therefore a monosaccharide is a single sugar unit. Glucose is used to produce adenosine triphosphate (ATP), the compound required for muscle contraction (see page 42).

Other monosaccharides in your diet include fructose, also known as fruit sugar as it is found in fruits and vegetables, and galactose found in milk. Monosaccharides mostly occur combined together in carbohydrate foods. When two monosaccharides are found together they form a disaccharide or what is known as a double sugar. The most common disaccharide in your diet is sucrose or table sugar. Other disaccharides include lactose (found in milk) and maltose (found in beer and cereals).

Longer chains of these simple sugar units are known as polysaccharides or complex carbohydrates. These allow large quantities of glucose to be stored in the cells of plants as starch or in animals as glycogen in the muscles and liver. All carbohydrate consumed in your diet ends up as glucose to provide energy.

Complex carbohydrates are commonly known as starches and make up an important source of energy in most diets. They are composed of many sugar units so they are also called polysaccharides. These are broken down more slowly in your body and provide a sustained release of energy over longer periods. Complex carbohydrates should form the largest percentage of your total carbohydrate intake. Unrefined sources such as wholemeal bread, wholegrain rice and pasta are preferable as they also contain a higher nutritional value by way of micronutrients and fibre.

After you eat foods containing carbohydrate your blood sugar level rises, which stimulates the pancreas to secrete the hormone insulin. The role of insulin is to normalise blood sugar levels and aid the transport of glucose from the blood into the cells. Glucose is then used directly by the cells for energy or stored as glycogen in your liver and muscles if it is not required immediately to provide energy. Glycogen is a crucial source of glucose for fuelling activity.

Table 10.1 gives some examples of simple and complex carbohydrates.

Simple	Complex
Sugar, syrup, jam, honey, marmalade, sugary fizzy drinks, boiled sweets, fudge, fruit juice, sports drinks	Bread, bagels, crispbread, crackers, rice, pasta, noodles, couscous, potatoes, breakfast cereals, pulses, root vegetables

Table 10.1 Simple and complex carbohydrates

Any excess carbohydrate not required to replenish your body's glycogen stores is converted to fat and stored in your body's adipose tissue. Around 80 per cent is stored in your muscles while the rest is stored in your liver, with a small amount of circulating blood glucose (see Table 10.2).

Source	Glycogen stores (g)
Muscle	325
Liver	100
Blood glucose	15–20

Table 10.2 Approximate adult glycogen stores

Carbohydrate can only be stored in your body as glycogen in limited amounts – approximately 375–475

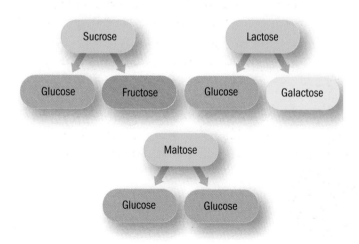

Double sugars or disaccharides and their monosaccharides

grams in the average adult, which is equivalent to approximately 1,500–2,000 kilocalories. Your day-to-day stores of glycogen are influenced by your dietary carbohydrate intake and levels of physical activity or training. Regular exercise can encourage your muscles to adapt to store more glycogen. This is an important training adaptation for the elite sportsperson, particularly those involved in endurance-type sports.

Remember!

The intensity and duration of exercise influences the rate and amount of glycogen usage. The harder the exercise and the longer its duration, the greater the depletion of glycogen.

■ Proteins

Proteins have a variety of functions that are essential to maintaining optimal health and physical performance. They contain the chemical elements carbon, hydrogen and oxygen, but are more complex in structure than carbohydrates and also contain nitrogen. Some proteins may also contain other elements such as sulphur or iron.

At this point in your study it is not necessary for you to be familiar with the names and functions of the individual amino acids. You should note that the body needs all 20 amino acids to be present simultaneously for protein synthesis to occur, in order to sustain optimal growth and functioning. Different proteins contain different numbers and combinations of these amino acids. Of the 20, there are eight that your body is unable to make for itself and as a result these are called essential amino acids (EAAs) – they are a necessary part of your diet. The remaining amino acids are called non-essential – your body is able to synthesise these if all the essential amino acids are present.

The chief role of protein in your body is to build and repair tissue. However, proteins may also be used as a secondary source of energy when carbohydrate and fat are limited, such as towards the end of prolonged endurance events or during the severe energy restriction that may accompany dieting.

Proteins, like carbohydrates, have an energy value of approximately 4 kilocalories per gram. Unlike carbohydrate and fat, your body is unable to store excess protein. All proteins carry out functional roles in your body, so daily protein ingestion is required. If your protein intake exceeds requirements to support growth and repair, the excess amino acids are broken down, the nitrogen component is excreted and the rest of the molecule is used to provide energy immediately or converted to fat or carbohydrate and stored for later use.

◀ The typical UK diet contains adequate amounts of protein

Protein foods in your diet are classified into two groups (see Table 10.3). The value of foods for meeting your body's protein needs is determined by their composition of amino acids. Foods that contain all of the eight essential amino acids are known as first-class or complete proteins. These are mainly foods of animal origin such as eggs, meat, fish, milk and other dairy products, and soya. Foods that are lacking in one or more of the essential amino acids are called second-class or incomplete proteins. These are foods from plant sources such as cereals, bread, rice, pasta, pulses, nuts and seeds. Vegetarians and vegans must make sure that they eat a wide variety of these foods in careful combinations to ensure that adequate intakes of all essential amino acids are achieved; for example, beans and wheat complement each other well.

Complete	Incomplete
Meat, poultry, offal, fish, eggs, milk, cheese, yoghurt, soya	Cereals, bread, rice, pasta, noodles, pulses, peas, beans, lentils, nuts, seeds

Table 10.3 Protein foods

Remember!

There are eight amino acids which your body is unable to make for itself. These are known as essential amino acids (EAAs).

■ Fats

It is important to note that fat is an essential nutrient for your body. Fats, or lipids, are composed of the chemical elements carbon, hydrogen and oxygen, but in different ratios to carbohydrates. The ratio of hydrogen to oxygen is much higher, which explains why fat is a more concentrated source of energy than carbohydrate.

Triglycerides form the basic component of fats. Each triglyceride is made up of a glycerol molecule with three fatty acids attached. It is to these two substances that triglycerides are broken down when digested and absorbed by your body. Fats consumed in your diet are obtained from both animal and vegetable sources and are of two main types: saturated and unsaturated.

Fatty acids contain chains of carbon atoms to which hydrogen atoms attach. The number of hydrogen atoms relative to the number of carbon atoms determines if a fatty acid is classified as saturated or unsaturated. If all the carbons are associated with two hydrogens, the fat is saturated, but if one or more of the carbons is without hydrogen then the fat is unsaturated. Unsaturated fatty acids can be of two kinds: monounsaturated and polyunsaturated.

All fats consumed in your diet are a mixture of these three different fatty acid types (see Table 10.4). Dietary fats that contain mostly saturated fatty acids are generally solid at room temperature, like butter and ordinary margarine, and are usually found in foods of animal origin such as meat, eggs and dairy foods. The two exceptions are palm and coconut oil, which are plant sources. Fats that are composed mainly of unsaturated fatty acids are usually liquid at room temperature such as olive or sunflower oils.

Most dietary experts recommend that we should cut back on our fat intake for health. This is sound advice for athletes as it allows them to consume a greater proportion of energy intake from carbohydrates to maintain glycogen stores, to support training and competition.

Saturated	Monounsaturated	Polyunsaturated
Full-fat dairy products, butter, hard margarine, lard, dripping, suet, fatty meat, meat pies, paté, cream, cakes, biscuits, chocolate, coconut, coconut oil	Olive oil, olive oil spreads, rapeseed oil, corn oil, peanuts, peanut butter, peanut oil	Soft margarine, low-fat spreads labelled high in polyunsaturated fats, sunflower oil, safflower oil, soya oil, oily fish, nuts

Table 10.4 Sources and types of fat in the diet

There are two essential fatty acids that must be provided by the diet: linolenic and linoleic acid.

Fats have many and varied functions within your body, but the primary function is to provide a concentrated source of energy, forming your body's largest potential energy store. Even the leanest of individuals will have large amounts of energy stored as fat. Fat is more than twice as energy dense as the other macronutrients, yielding 9 kilocalories per gram.

Fats also have many other functions. They protect and cushion your vital organs, provide a structural material for cells and act as an insulator preventing heat loss. Animal fats are a source of the fat-soluble vitamins A, D, E and K. Fats also provide flavour and texture to foods, features that often lead to over-consumption.

Theory into practice

Take a look at your 24-hour diet recall. What types of fat do you normally eat? Do you think you eat too much fat? What might you need to do to reduce your intake of fat?

Micronutrients

Vitamins and minerals are termed or referred to as micronutrients as they are required in much smaller amounts – in some cases in minute quantities. Despite your relatively small requirements for these nutrients, many play a critical role in regulating chemical reactions in your body.

■ Vitamins

Vitamins are vital, non-caloric nutrients required in very small amounts by your body. They perform specific metabolic functions and prevent particular deficiency diseases. Unlike macronutrients, they do not have a common chemical structure.

Most vitamins required to maintain health cannot be produced by your body and must be supplied by your diet. The exceptions are vitamin D, which your body is able to synthesise by the action of sunlight on the skin, and vitamin K, which can be produced by the bacteria of your large intestine. Vitamins play essential roles in regulating many metabolic processes in your body, particularly those that release energy. They are

also required to support growth, and the immune and nervous system functions, and some are involved in the production of hormones.

Vitamins are obtained from a wide variety of plant and animal sources and are grouped into two broad categories based on their solubility as either fat- or water-soluble. Vitamins A, D, E and K form the fat-soluble group, with the B vitamins and vitamin C making up the water-soluble group.

Your body requires differing amounts of each vitamin, with specific vitamins having specific functions. Individual vitamin requirements vary and are determined by age, sex, state of health and levels of physical activity. The Department of Health has set Dietary Reference Values (DRVs) (see page 286) for all nutrients for different groups of healthy people within the UK population. The Reference Nutrient Intake (RNI) value should meet the needs of almost all individuals in the population (97 per cent). A balanced and varied diet that provides an adequate energy content should supply sufficient intakes of all vitamins.

It is important to note that some vitamins can be harmful to health if they are consumed in large amounts above your body's requirements. This is particularly true for the fat-soluble vitamins as they have the potential to be stored in your body. The only situation in which large doses of any vitamin may be beneficial is when the body has a severe deficiency of a particular vitamin or when it is unable to absorb or metabolise vitamins efficiently. Supplementation with high doses of any vitamin should always be medically supervised and not self-prescribed.

Remember!

Individual vitamin requirements vary and are determined by age, sex, state of health and physical activity level.

- Fat-soluble vitamins: all fat-soluble vitamins have a number of common features. As the term suggests, they are found in the fatty or oily parts of foods. Once digested they are absorbed and transported in the lymph and ultimately reach the blood. As a result of their insolubility in water, they are not excreted in the urine and can accumulate in the liver and adipose tissue.

- Water-soluble vitamins: this group is formed from the B group of vitamins and vitamin C. Many of the B vitamins serve similar functions, facilitating the use of energy within your body. As a group the water-soluble vitamins have different characteristics from the fat-soluble group. Excesses are excreted via the urine and as a result your body has only limited stores, necessitating regular intakes. It should be noted that many of these vitamins are destroyed by food processing and preparation.

Antioxidant vitamins

Beta-carotene (a form of vitamin A) and vitamins C and E are probably the most well known antioxidant nutrients in our diet and are often referred to as the ACE vitamins. Research suggests that antioxidants can help to prevent damage to the body from the effects of free radicals. There has been a lot of interest in the role of antioxidants from both health and performance perspectives. Intense training may deplete your body's stores of these vitamins. It is thought that they could have an important role to play in the protection of muscle fibres from free-radical damage during exercise and in reducing post-exercise muscle soreness, but more research is required in this area.

■ Minerals

Minerals are vital, non-caloric nutrients that are essential to life, and like vitamins they are required in small or trace amounts. Minerals are classified in terms of the relative amounts required by your body and can be placed broadly into two categories.

- Macrominerals such as calcium are required in relatively large amounts, sometimes as much as several hundred milligrams.
- Trace elements such as copper and selenium are required in much smaller quantities (micrograms).

All minerals are essential to health and form important components of your body tissues such as bone, connective tissue, enzymes and hormones. Some have essential roles to play in nerve function and muscle contraction. Others regulate fluid balance in your body. Levels of minerals within your body are closely controlled by absorption and excretion to prevent excessive build up. Some minerals compete with each other for absorption, especially iron, zinc and copper.

Fibre is a complex carbohydrate. Non-starch polysaccharide (NSP) is the new scientific term for dietary fibre. NSP forms the main component of plant cell walls and these are the principal component of dietary fibre. They resist digestion by the stomach and small intestine and provide bulk in your diet, which aids the transit of food through your digestive system.

Fibre is obtained from wholegrain cereals, nuts, pulses, fruits and vegetables. It is thought to have a role in both preventing and treating certain diseases including cancer of the colon, diabetes, heart disease and irritable bowel syndrome. A high-fibre intake accompanied with a high-fluid intake also helps to keep your bowel functioning efficiently. Adequate amounts may also play a role in weight control by helping to achieve the feeling of fullness.

There are two types of fibre: soluble and insoluble. Soluble fibre can be found in oats, rye, barley, peas, beans, lentils, fruits and vegetables. This type of fibre is important in the control of blood glucose and cholesterol. Insoluble fibre is found in wholewheat bread, rice and pasta, wholegrain breakfast cereals, fruits and vegetables. It is thought to be important in the prevention of bowel disorders. A healthy diet requires a good mix of both types of fibre, with adults requiring around 18 g in total per day. As a population we have a long way to go to achieve adequate intakes of this nutrient, as current average intakes are around 12 g per day.

Remember!

Non-starch polysaccharide is the new scientific term for dietary fibre.

Nutritional requirements

You require many different nutrients if you are to remain in good health and reduce your risk of diet-related disorders. The amount of each nutrient you need is referred to as the nutritional requirement. The requirements differ depending on age, sex, levels of activity and state of health. Some nutrients are more essential during different stages of life such as calcium in childhood and iron during pregnancy.

■ Essential and non-essential

Carbohydrates

To support health and performance, it is recommended that around 50–60 per cent of your total daily calorie intake is derived from carbohydrates. Greater intakes may be required by sportspeople engaged in regular intense training. For example, a marathon runner or a triathlete may require up to 65–70 per cent of total energy to be provided by carbohydrates.

However, a sedentary individual will require around 50 per cent of total daily calorie intake to be supplied by carbohydrates, of which the majority should be from starchy sources. This would equate to around 250 g per day for the average female and 300 g per day for the average male. As a simple guide, Table 10.5 estimates the carbohydrate requirements that can be prescribed based on activity levels.

Level of daily activity	Carbohydrate per kilogram of body weight (g)
< 1 hour	4–5
1 hour	5–6
1–2 hours	6–7
2–3	7–8
> 3 hours	8–10

Table 10.5 Carbohydrate requirements based on daily activity levels

Theory into practice

Based on your current body weight and levels of physical activity, estimate your carbohydrate requirements in grams per day. Do you think your carbohydrate requirements are constant, or do they vary from day to day?

Whether eating for health or performance, the best approach to achieving an adequate carbohydrate intake is to eat at regular intervals and ensure that all your meals and snacks are centred around starchy carbohydrate foods. People with high carbohydrate requirements may need to eat more frequent meals and snacks or rely on a greater intake of simple carbohydrates to achieve their requirements.

Remember!

The best way to achieve an adequate carbohydrate intake is to ensure that all meals and snacks are based around starchy carbohydrate foods.

Theory into practice

Take a look at your 24-hour diet recall and, using Table 10.6, estimate your carbohydrate intake for the day. For foods not in the list refer to McCance and Widdowson's tables in the following publication: The Composition of Foods, 6th Edition (2002).

1   Did you meet your estimated carbohydrate requirements?

2   If you did not meet your estimated requirements, devise a day's menu to meet your carbohydrate needs.

Food	Approximate carbohydrate content per serving (g)	Food	Approximate carbohydrate content per serving (g)
1 large slice of bread	15	1 currant bun	30
1 pitta bread	45	1 wholemeal scone	20
1 large naan bread	80	1 cereal bar	20
1 bagel	50	1 bag of crisps	10
1 tortilla	20	1 pint of milk	30
1 chapatti	30	1 small pot of yoghurt	25
1 crispbread	10	1 small can of rice pudding	30
1 large jacket potato	45	1 banana	30
1 medium portion of chips	55	1 apple	10
1 medium portion of new potatoes	35	1 orange	10
1 medium portion of boiled potatoes	35	1 satsuma	5
1 large serving of rice	60	1 handful of raisins	15
1 large serving of pasta	90	5 dried apricots	15
1 medium serving of couscous	35	1 small carton of fruit juice	20
1 slice of pizza	35	1 can of Lucozade drink	60
1 Shredded Wheat	15	1 can of lemonade	20
1 Weetabix	15	1 can of cola	35
1 medium serving of muesli	50	1 Mars bar	40
1 large tin of baked beans	60	1 small bar of milk chocolate	30
3 tablespoons of sweetcorn	10	2 teaspoons of honey	15
3 tablespoons of peas	10	2 teaspoons of jam or marmalade	10
3 tablespoons of carrots	10	1 tube of fruit gums	20
1 digestive biscuit	10	2 teaspoons of sugar	10
1 Jaffa cake	10		

Table 10.6 Carbohydrate content of common foods

Protein

Active individuals require greater intakes of protein in order to promote tissue growth and repair following training and competition. Overall, protein intake should represent between 12 per cent and 15 per cent of your total daily energy intake.

In sports circles the misguided belief that additional dietary protein will automatically help to build muscle has been perpetuated since the times of the ancient Greeks. Regular exercise does increase protein needs but most people already eat enough protein in the typical diet, unless of course their diet is severely calorie restricted. The sports performer is also likely to be eating more food to meet increased calorie requirements, and therefore should automatically be eating more protein to meet any theoretical increase in requirements.

Table 10.7 gives the estimated daily protein requirements for an adult.

Type of activity	Protein per kilogram of body weight (g)
Mainly sedentary	1
Mainly endurance	1.2–1.4
Mainly strength	1.2–1.7

Table 10.7 Daily protein requirements based on type of activity

Theory into practice

1 Using the information outlined in Table 10.7, estimate your daily protein requirements.

2 Take a look at your 24-hour diet recall and, using Table 10.8, estimate your protein intake for the day. For foods not in the list refer to McCance and Widdowson's tables in the following publication: The Composition of Foods, 6th Edition (2002).

   a Did you meet your estimated protein requirements?

   b If you did not meet your estimated requirements, devise a day's menu to meet your protein needs.

Food	Approximate protein content per serving (g)
1 small lean steak	24
1 small chicken fillet	24
1 medium portion of fish	24
1 small portion of soya mince	10
1 pint of milk	18
1 small pot of yoghurt	6
1 small can of rice pudding	7
1 medium portion of Cheddar cheese	10
1 egg	6
1 large slice of pizza	12
1 thin slice of bread	1
1 Shredded Wheat	2
1 Weetabix	2
1 large portion of pasta	14
1 large portion of rice	8
1 large jacket potato	4
1 bag of crisps	2
1 cereal bar	3
1 small bar of milk chocolate	2
1 banana	1
1 small bag of peanuts	12
1 tablespoon of sesame seeds	2

Table 10.8 Protein content of common foods

Fat

National diet and nutrition surveys have shown that the average diet in the UK contains around 40 per cent of calories from fat, a level deemed by experts to be too high. It is recommended that fat intakes are reduced to 30–35 per cent of total calorie intake. This equates to around 70 g per day for the average female and 90 g per day for the average male. Of this, only

6–10 per cent should be derived from saturated fats. Sportspeople involved in regular intense activity may need to reduce their overall fat intake further to around 25–30 per cent of total energy consumed to achieve adequate carbohydrate intakes, but in absolute terms this may equate to the same quantity of intake as that of the sedentary individual, as sportspeople will be eating more calories to meet their increased energy requirements.

Food	Approximate fat content per serving (g)
1 medium portion of thin-cut chips	20.0
1 medium portion of thick-cut chips	10.0
1 medium portion of roast potatoes	10.0
1 medium baked potato	0.2
1 medium portion of new potatoes	0.2
1 medium portion of boiled potatoes	0.2
1 medium portion of cheddar cheese	15.0
½ pt of whole milk	5.0
½ pt of semi-skimmed milk	2.5
½ pt of skimmed milk	0.3
1 small lean steak, grilled	5.0
1 small chicken fillet, grilled	3.0
1 small cod fillet, grilled	1.0
1 large thin sausage, grilled	10.0
Butter spread on 1 slice of bread	10.0
Margarine spread on 1 slice of bread	10.0
Low-fat spread on 1 slice of bread	5.0
1 small bar of milk chocolate	15.0
1 packet of crisps	10.0

Table 10.9 Fat content of common foods

Remember!

Government guidelines recommend 70 g of fat per day for the average female and 90 g per day for the average male.

■ Recommended Daily Allowance (RDA)

Dietary standards have been used in the UK since the Second World War. The first set of standards focused on Recommended Daily Allowance (RDA), which aimed to prevent nutritional deficiency through the recommendation of one intake target per nutrient.

In the late 1980s, the government set up a panel of experts to review the RDAs of nutrients for the UK population, and new Dietary Reference Values (DRVs) were established. The phrase 'dietary reference value' is an umbrella term that can be applied to any of the following measures of nutrient intake values:

- Reference Nutrient Intake (RNI)
- Estimated Average Requirements (EAR)
- Lower Reference Nutrient Intake (LRNI)
- Safe Intake (SI).

Remember!

DRVs provide a yardstick against which the nutritional adequacy of your diet can be assessed.

■ Optimum level

It is thought that some recommended nutrient intakes may be set too high or too low. The theory of optimal levels of nutrient intake is grounded in nutritional therapy and attempts to take more account of individual requirements, lifestyle habits and circumstances such as smoking and stress. Defining optimal nutrient intakes has presented nutrition scientists with considerable challenges. To determine an individual's optimum nutrient intake level requires biochemical screening through the analysis of blood or urine and this is not routine practice.

Safe Intake (SI)

Safe Intake (SI) is a term used to indicate the intake of a nutrient where there is insufficient scientific information to estimate the distribution of requirements within a population. It represents an intake that is thought to be adequate for most people's needs but not so high as to cause undesirable effects on health.

Estimated Average Requirements (EAR)

Estimated Average Requirements (EAR) is an assessment of the average requirement for food energy or nutrients. Many individuals require more than the EAR and many require less. The EAR is the value most used when assessing energy requirements and intakes.

Taking it further

To find out more about Dietary Reference Values, take a look at the Department of Health's *Report on Health and Social Subjects 41: Dietary Reference Values for Food Energy and Nutrients for the United Kingdom*, HMSO, 1991.

Remember!

Dietary Reference Value is an umbrella term that can be applied to the other terms relating to nutrient intake such as RNI, EAR, LRNI and SI.

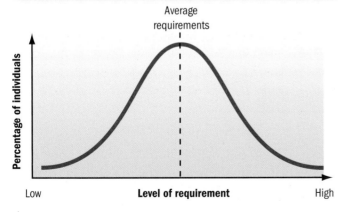

▲ The normal distribution curve of nutrient requirements in a population

Assessment practice

Produce a leaflet aimed at sports participants that describes the importance of good nutrition to health and performance and introduces them to common terminology associated with nutrition. **P1**

Grading tips

Grading Tip P1

You must be able to describe nutrition and the relevant components of a diet along with frequently used terminology.

Digestion

You have already seen that food provides the energy and nutrients you need to stay alive and in good health. Before your body can make use of this energy and nutrients, the food has to be broken down to release them through the process of digestion.

Structure of digestive system

Digestion starts in the mouth (**buccal cavity**). Your teeth and jaws crush and grind food to mix it with saliva, which contains the enzyme amylase that begins the breakdown of starch. You then swallow the food, which enters the **oesophagus**. This is the tube that connects your mouth to your **stomach**. The food bolus is squeezed along the oesophagus by the process of peristalsis. It takes around 3–6 seconds for food to travel from your mouth to your stomach. Your stomach acts as a large mixing bowl, churning the food into a liquid called chyme. Lining your stomach are cells that produce and release gastric juices containing enzymes and hydrochloric acid, which assist in the breakdown of the food and kill any bacteria present in it. Food normally remains in your stomach for 1–4 hours, but fluid may pass through much more rapidly.

From your stomach the chyme passes to your **duodenum** and then to your **small intestine**, a tube about six metres long. As the chyme enters your small intestine, it is mixed with more **digestive juices**, this time from the **pancreas**. Pancreatic juice contains bile made by the **liver** as well as enzymes to further assist the breakdown of carbohydrate, protein and fat. It is also alkaline to neutralise the acid from the stomach. Your **gall bladder**, a pear-shaped organ, stores and concentrates bile until it is required for digestion. Then it is released into your digestive tract to emulsify fats and neutralise the acids in partly digested food. The process of peristalsis continues to move the chyme through your digestive system to your **large intestine** (another long tube in your digestive system) and eventually the **rectum** and **anal canal**.

As the chyme moves through your small intestine, vitamins, minerals, amino acids, fatty acids and sugars are absorbed by your intestinal wall. Lining the wall of your small intestine are finger-like projections known as villi, which increase the surface area available for absorption and speed up the process.

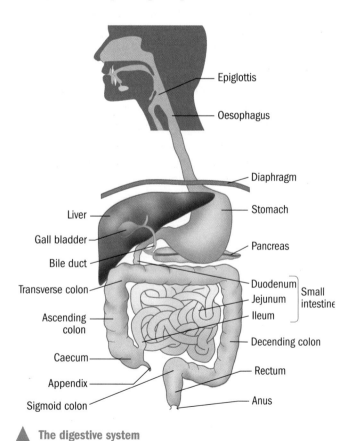

▲ The digestive system

By the time the chyme reaches your large intestine, it is less fluid and has been reduced to mainly indigestible matter. Your large intestine does not produce any digestive enzymes but continues to absorb mainly water. Bacteria in your large intestine produce vitamin K. The residue (faeces) left behind is eliminated (excreted) from your body through your anus.

Function of the digestive system

Digestion

Digestion can be considered a multi-stage process following the ingestion of raw materials (the food you eat). It involves mechanical and chemical elements in the process that ultimately leads to enzymes in the gut breaking down the larger chemical compounds in the foods you eat into smaller compounds so that they can be absorbed by your body.

Absorption

This is the movement of digested food from your stomach and small intestine into your body tissues and blood. The process of absorption happens in specialised structures called villi that line your small intestine. These finger-like projections provide a large surface area for absorption to take place. Each villus has a network of capillaries to quickly absorb nutrients. Amino acids (from the breakdown of proteins) and glucose (from the breakdown of carbohydrates) enter your bloodstream directly. Fatty acids and glycerol (from the breakdown of fats) are taken up by your lymphatic system.

Excretion

Excretion is the removal of potentially poisonous end-products from metabolism, normally in your urine and faeces. In humans the main organs of excretion are the kidneys, through which urine is eliminated, and the large intestine, through which solid or semi-solid waste is expelled.

Assessment practice

Create a short PowerPoint® presentation to describe the structure and function of the digestive system. **P2**

Grading tips

Grading Tip P2

You need to describe the digestive system and the enzymes that break down specific food types.

10.2 Understand energy intake and energy expenditure in sports performance

All activity stimulates your body's need for fuel, so understanding energy intake and expenditure is vital to successful sports performance.

Energy

Energy is essential to life. It is obtained from the foods you eat and used to support your basal metabolic rate (the minimum amount of energy required to sustain your body's vital functions in a waking state), and all activity carried out at work and leisure. At some stages in the life cycle extra energy is required, such as when pregnant or breast-feeding and during illness and growth spurts.

Measures

Energy is measured in calories or joules. As both of these units are very small they are multiplied by 1,000 and referred to as kilocalories (the UK system) or kilojoules (the metric or international system).

Key terms

Calorie The energy required to raise 1 g of water by 1°C.

Joule One joule of energy moves a mass of 1 g at a velocity of 1 metre per second. Approximately 4.2 joules = 1 calorie.

Kilocalorie The energy required to raise the temperature of 1 kg of water by 1°C. Equal to 1,000 calories and used to convey the energy value of food. Kilocalories are often simply referred to as calories.

Kilojoule A unit of measurement for energy but like the calorie the joule is not a large unit of energy; therefore kilojoules are more often used.

Remember!

- 1 calorie (cal) = 4.2 joules (J)
- 1 kilocalorie (kcal) = 4.2 kilojoules (kJ)
- 1 kilocalorie (kcal) = 1,000 calories (cal)
- 1 kilojoule (kJ) = 1,000 joules (J)

The various macronutrients supply different amounts of energy per unit of weight. The potential fuel sources available to your exercising muscles are listed below. However, their relative value as fuels for activity differs. Protein may be used during prolonged periods of exercise and towards the latter stages of endurance events like the marathon, particularly if fat and carbohydrate as sources of fuel within the working muscles have become limited.

■ Fats

1 g fat   = 9.0 kcal = 38 kJ

■ Carbohydrates

1 g carbohydrate = 4.0 kcal = 17 kJ

■ Proteins

1 g protein   = 4.0 kcal = 17 kJ

Fat and carbohydrate, which is stored in the muscles as glycogen, are the main energy fuels for your exercising muscles. Exercising muscles prefer glucose as a fuel, particularly as the intensity of the activity being undertaken increases. When you exercise, your muscles use energy at a rate that is directly proportional to the intensity of the activity you are undertaking. If this energy is not replaced as it is used up, your muscles will be unable to maintain their rate of work and the intensity of the activity will need to be reduced or stopped as fatigue sets in.

Measuring requirements

■ Body composition

Individuals come in all shapes and sizes. However, the most commonly used method of classification of body type is known as somatotyping. This classification method recognises three basic body types:

- ectomorph – a slim build, long limbs, delicate bone structure, a low body fat and muscle content, and usually finds weight gain difficult

- endomorph – a heavy build, rounded shape, a tendency to gain weight, and generally finds weight loss difficult
- mesomorph – a muscular build and large bone structure.

Very few individuals fit neatly into these extremes. Most of us have characteristics of each body type to a varying degree, and although it is fashionable for many women in particular to want to be slim and ectomorph-like, it is important to note that it is not possible to alter our basic body type. The body is composed of a perplexing number of cells, tissues, organs and systems but the components of most interest to exercise scientists and nutritionists are muscle, bone and fat.

■ Lean body mass

Body composition simply refers to the amount of lean body mass and body fat that makes up your total body weight. Lean body mass includes the bones, muscle, water, connective and organ tissues. Body fat includes both your essential and non-essential fat stores.

■ Percentage body fat

Sportspeople and those actively engaged in fitness regimes are often concerned about their weight, whether for performance or health reasons. Unlike your basic body type, it is possible to alter your body composition, with exercise generally having the effect of increasing lean body mass and decreasing body fat.

Methods of assessing percentage body fat include:
- skinfold analysis
- bioelectrical impedance analysis
- hydrodensitometry (underwater weighing).

All these methods have most merit in measuring changes in body composition over time rather than absolute values. A number of steps can be taken to minimise potential errors in measuring changes in body composition over time:
- always use the same method
- ensure the subject is assessed by the same person
- take repeat measurements at the same time of day.

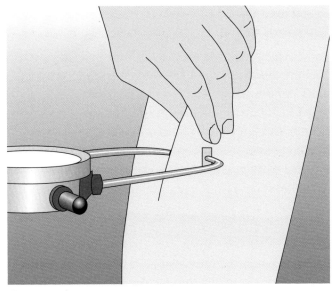

Skinfold callipers measure the amount of subcutaneous fat (fat immediately below the skin) in millimetres

Skinfold analysis

With this technique, callipers are used to measure the thickness of skinfolds at various sites, with the biceps, triceps, subscapula and suprailiac crest being the most common anatomical sites of measurement. The sum of these measurements is then used to calculate percentage body fat using a method that takes into account the age and gender of the subject using equations or tables. (This technique is covered in more detail in Unit 6, on pages 239–240.)

This is a relatively cheap and convenient method but it does require a high degree of skill. This method is thought to be generally reliable if performed correctly but it has been shown to have an error margin of ± 3–4 per cent and may not be effective for use on very fat or very thin subjects.

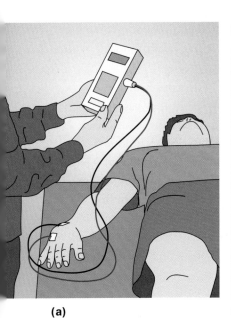

(a)

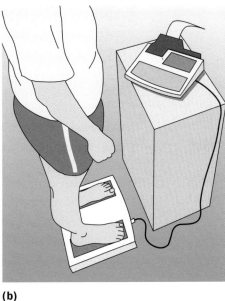

(b)

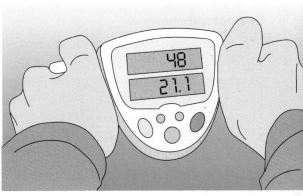

(c)

Bioelectrical impedance machines: (a) using electrodes, (b) foot-to-foot and (c) hand-to-hand

Bioelectrical impedance analysis

Bioelectrical impedance analysis (BIA) is fast becoming the standard technique for assessment of body composition, particularly in the health and fitness sector. Bioelectrical impedance machines have an advantage over callipers in providing a quick, easy and non-invasive method of estimating percentage body fat. There is now a range of equipment that uses BIA principles to assess body composition. Some require the attachment of electrodes to the hands and feet of the subject (Bodystat), others require the athlete to stand on specially designed scales (Tanita) or to grip handles (Omron). (This technique is covered in more detail in Unit 6, on page 240.)

BIA measures the resistance to the flow of an electrical current through the body, using the fact that different body tissues display different impedance to the flow of the current. Tissues that contain a large amount of water, such as lean tissue, provide a lower impedance than tissues such as bone and fat.

When using BIA techniques a number of assumptions have to be made, and equations applied, to obtain a body fat percentage figure. One potential drawback to this method is that impedance measurements are related to the water content of tissues. This means that for accurate results subjects must be fully hydrated, and they are required to abstain from exercise and substances which exert a diuretic effect – such as alcohol or caffeine – for a period of at least 24 hours before the test. Invalid results may also be obtained for women if they are measured immediately before or during a period, when the body water content may be higher than normal.

Hydrodensitometry

This is considered to be one of the most accurate methods of assessment of body composition. However, it is expensive and time consuming to perform and can be potentially stressful to the athlete as it requires him or her to be totally submerged in water. The technique measures body density that can be translated mathematically into percentage body fat. It relies on Archimedes' principle of water displacement to estimate body density. As a technique it is rarely used because it is expensive.

For more information on hydrodensitometry, see page 240.

Body weight

Body weight describes the mass of your body. In scientific terms it is more precisely referred to as body mass and is usually measured in kilograms. Some individuals have problems controlling their body weight, often resulting in obesity. In an athletic context some sports are categorised based on body weight. Energy and nutrient requirements may also be expressed relative to body mass.

Direct and indirect calorimetry

Energy expenditure can be assessed by direct or indirect calorimetry, essentially through the measurement of heat production.

- Direct calorimetry (DC) measures the actual amount of heat produced by the body. It requires the use of expensive and sophisticated equipment involving a sealed, airtight chamber where heat produced by the subject warms water surrounding it.
- Indirect calorimetry (IC) estimates heat production by measuring respiratory gases (oxygen consumption and carbon dioxide production). It can be undertaken using different techniques – the most common is via mouthpiece and Douglas bag collection or mouthpiece and gas analysis system, with energy consumption calculated from the amount of oxygen consumed. The consumption of 1 litre of oxygen equates to approximately 4.8 kcal of energy expended assuming a mixture of fats and carbohydrates are oxidised.

Taking it further

Using the Internet, undertake a search using the search term 'body composition assessment'. Evaluate the range of body composition assessment products available in terms of their affordability, ease of application and suitability for use with sports performers.

Taking it further

Undertake your own research using the Internet to investigate other measures of energy expenditure including doubly labelled water and motion analysers.

(a)

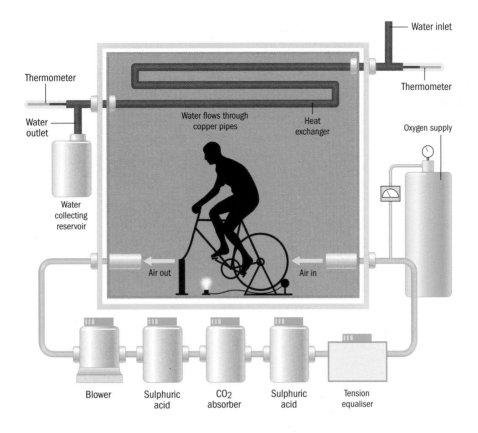

(b)

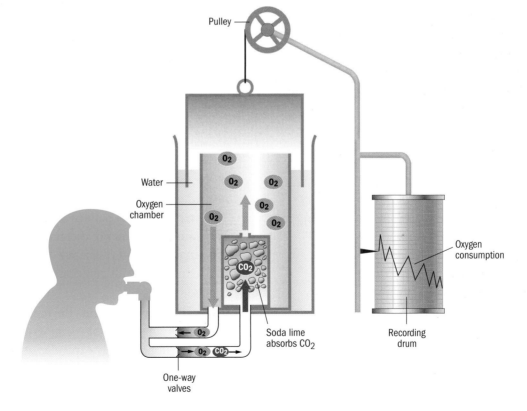

▲ **(a) Direct calorimetry and (b) indirect calorimetry**

Assessment practice

1 Hold a group discussion to identify the range of sports participation in your class.

2 Working in small groups, investigate the energy demands of some or all of these sports and then prepare a short presentation to describe energy intake and energy expenditure in sports performance. **P3**

3 Produce a fact sheet for a specific sport to explain energy intake and energy expenditure in sports performance. **M1**

Grading tips

Grading Tip P3

You need to consider the importance of energy balance in sports performance.

Grading Tip M1

Consider the role nutritional supplements such as sports drinks, and energy gels and bars might have on achieving and maintaining energy balance.

▲ Nutritional supplements are sometimes used to achieve and maintain energy balance

Energy balance

You are in energy balance when the amount of energy you take in (energy input) equals the amount of energy you expend (energy output). You will neither be losing nor gaining weight. Energy input comes from the food and drink you consume. There are four major components to energy output: resting metabolic rate (RMR), dietary thermogenesis (DT), physical activity (PA) and adaptive thermogenesis (AT).

- Resting metabolic rate can account for up to 60–75 per cent of total energy output and represents the largest component of your total daily energy expenditure. RMR is closely related to your lean body mass and so is influenced by your body composition. Muscle tissue is much more metabolically active than fat tissue. Gains in muscle mass will result in increases in RMR. RMR is also influenced by your age, sex and genetic background.

- Dietary thermogenesis refers to the energy expended above that of RMR for the processes of digestion, absorption, transport and storage of food. It is influenced by the calorie content and composition of the meals consumed in your diet along with your individual nutritional status. High energy intakes and a regular eating pattern are thought to help us maintain higher rates of dietary thermogenesis, while skipping meals and restrictive dietary practices lead to a reduction in this component of total energy expenditure.

- Physical activity represents the most variable component of your total energy expenditure. This is the additional energy expended above RMR and DT, and will obviously contribute more to total daily energy expenditure in active individuals. Exactly how much varies according to how active your general lifestyle is, how often, how energetically, and for how long you participate in sport and exercise, and what type of activity it is.

- Adaptive thermogenesis is energy expenditure that occurs as a result of environmental or physiological stresses placed on your body, such as a change in temperature that may require you to respond by shivering or stress that causes anxiety or fidgeting.

When energy intake exceeds expenditure, this is referred to as positive energy balance and weight is gained. If intake is less than requirements to meet energy expenditure, the additional energy required will be drawn from your body's fat reserves and weight will be lost. This is referred to as negative energy balance. Even small imbalances in energy intake and expenditure can produce profound effects on body composition and weight.

Remember!

Energy balance is achieved when energy input equals energy output.

Basal metabolism

To estimate energy requirements, you first need to calculate basal metabolic requirements (BMR) in kilocalories per day using the data in Table 10.10.

	Age (years)	Basal metabolic requirements in kilocalories per day (W = weight in kilograms)
Males	10–17	BMR = 17.7W + 657
	18–29	BMR = 15.1W + 692
	30–59	BMR = 11.5W + 873
	60–74	BMR = 11.9W + 700
Females	10–17	BMR = 13.4W + 692
	18–29	BMR = 14.8W + 487
	30–59	BMR = 8.3W + 846
	60–74	BMR = 9.2W + 687

(Schofield et al, 1985)

Table 10.10 Calculating basal metabolic requirements

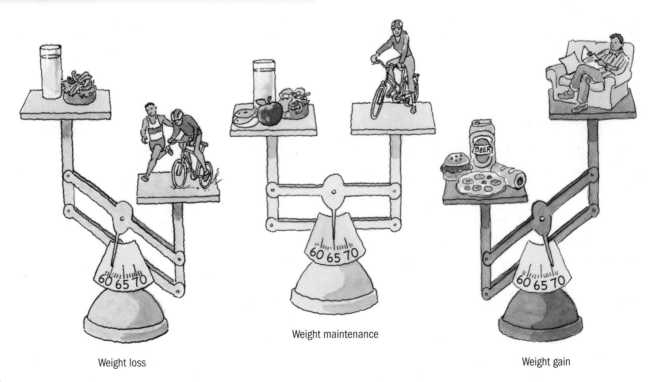

Weight loss

Weight maintenance

Weight gain

▲ Energy balance

■ Age

Your basal metabolism reduces with increasing age. After the age of 30 years, it falls by around 2 per cent per decade.

■ Gender

Males generally have greater muscle mass than females so they generally have a higher basal metabolic rate.

■ Climate

Exposure to hot or cold climates causes an increase in basal metabolism to maintain your body's internal temperature.

Taking it further

Using your own research, identify any other factors that affect basal metabolism.

■ Physical activity

To estimate your total energy requirements you also need to consider your level of physical activity and training. The simplest method of estimating your total energy requirement is by multiplying your BMR by your physical activity level (PAL). Calculating PALs requires you to make an assumption about the energy demands of both your occupational and non-occupational activity levels (see Table 10.11).

Non-occupational activity	Occupational activity					
	Light		Moderate		Heavy	
	Male	Female	Male	Female	Male	Female
Non-active	1.4	1.4	1.6	1.5	1.7	1.5
Moderately active	1.5	1.5	1.7	1.6	1.8	1.6
Very active	1.6	1.6	1.8	1.7	1.9	1.7

Table 10.11 Physical activity levels for three levels

Activity

1 a Imagine you are a sportsperson in regular training and calculate the calories required in your diet to be contributed by the three macronutrients. Record your answers in kilocalories.

b Once you know how many kilocalories are required from each of the three macronutrients, you can calculate the number of grams of each that you need, remembering that carbohydrate and protein provide 4 calories per gram and fat 9 calories per gram. Calculate the grams of carbohydrate, protein and fat required in your diet by dividing the kilocalories required by the appropriate energy value, and record your answers.

2 Plan a day's diet for a female endurance athlete who has an energy requirement of 2,500 kilocalories. In particular, pay attention to achieving an adequate carbohydrate intake and calculate the amount of energy to be contributed by carbohydrate, and the number of grams of carbohydrate this equates to.

Assessment practice

1 Is energy balance important in sport? Prepare a short PowerPoint® presentation to support your views. **P4**

2 Explain the role of body composition assessment in the achievement and maintenance of energy balance in the sports performer? **M2**

3 Analyse the effects of energy balance on sports performance. To do this you might use some of the information you have collected in the Theory into practice and Taking it further activities in this section. **D1**

Grading tips

Grading Tip P4

Describe energy balance and its importance to sports performance.

Grading Tip M2

Explain the importance of these measures in relation to the achievement and maintenance of energy balance in the sports performer.

Grading Tip D1

Consider examples from different sports and categories of sports performer.

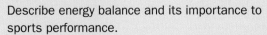

Water is often overlooked as a nutrient, but it is one of the most important nutrients in your diet. Your body can not survive more than a few days without water. It is essential to life and performs numerous functions. During exercise, fluid requirements increase according to the type, duration and intensity of the exercise and the environmental conditions under which it is taking place. Understanding the relationship between hydration and sports performance is vital for achieving optimal performance in both training and competition.

Hydration

Water acts as the main transport mechanism in your body, carrying nutrients, waste products and internal secretions. It also plays a vital role in temperature regulation, particularly during exercise, and aids the passage of food through your digestive system.

Water is the largest component of body mass, making up around 50–60 per cent of your total body weight. Actual amounts vary depending on age, sex and body composition. Muscle has a higher water content than fat tissue, so leaner individuals have a higher water content than fatter individuals of the same body mass.

Water is lost from your body though a number of routes including urine, faeces, evaporation from the skin and expired breath. If water loss is high, your body becomes dehydrated. Under normal circumstances your body maintains a balance between fluid input and output. Table 10.12 illustrates the balance between sources of water intake and routes of water loss.

Water is one of the most important nutrients required by your body. Water losses may be as high as a litre per hour during endurance-type exercise. This could be even higher if the exercise takes place in hot or humid conditions.

Fluid losses incurred by sportspeople during training and competition are linked to the body's need to maintain temperature within very narrow limits. During exercise, your body temperature rises and the extra heat this produces is lost through sweating – the process of evaporation of water from your skin's surface. If fluid lost through sweating is not replaced, there is a risk of dehydration and performance may suffer.

■ Dehydration

Dehydration can affect performance by reducing strength, power and aerobic capacity. Severe dehydration can cause heat stroke and has the potential to be fatal. A loss as small as 2 per cent of body mass can be enough to begin to affect your ability to perform muscular work. For a 75 kg male this would be equivalent to a fluid loss of only 1.5 litres from the body. It is therefore important to minimise the risks of dehydration, and very important to note that thirst is a poor indicator of your body's hydration status.

Daily water input		Daily water output	
Source	**ml**	**Source**	**ml**
Fluids	1,200	Urine	1,250
Food	1,000	Skin	850
Metabolism	350	Lungs	350
		Faeces	100
Total	2,550	Total	2,550

Table 10.12 Daily water balance for a sedentary 70 kg adult male

Remember!

Dehydration can hinder performance by affecting strength, power, coordination and aerobic capacity.

The warning signs for dehydration include:

- lack of energy and early fatigue during exercise
- feeling hot
- clammy or flushed skin
- not needing to go to the toilet
- nausea
- headache*
- disorientation*
- shortness of breath.*

* These are signs of advanced dehydration.

■ Hyperhydration

Hyperhydration is a state of increased hydration from normal, producing a greater than normal body water content. Starting exercise in a hyperhydrated state can improve thermoregulation, improving heat dissipation and exercise performance. However, this area of sports science research needs to be further investigated.

Key term

Thermoregulation The ability to keep the body's temperature constant, even if the surrounding temperature is different.

■ Hypohydration

Hypohydration is a state of decreased hydration from normal, producing a less-than-normal body water content. Hypohydration increases core body temperature, impairs the sweating response and causes skeletal muscle fatigue.

■ Superhydration

Superhydration is a state of hydration achieved by manipulation with the ergogenic aid glycerol. When ingested with large volumes of water (1–2 litres), glycerol has been shown to increase water retention in the body. This reduces overall heat stress during exercise in hot conditions, lowering heart rate and body temperature.

However, not all glycerol studies have shown improvements in hydration or endurance performance

Key terms

Ergogenic Work-enhancing.

Ergogenic aid A substance that improves exercise performance.

and there are side effects to be considered including headaches, dizziness, gastrointestinal upsets and bloating.

Fluid intake

To maintain water balance, a sedentary individual requires around 2–2.5 litres of fluid per day, the equivalent of 6–8 cups. Around 10 per cent of your daily fluid requirements are gained from the metabolic processes that release water within your body. The other 90 per cent is derived from your diet. Approximately 60 per cent of this comes directly from fluids and the rest comes from food, particularly that with a high water content.

During exercise, fluid requirements increase according to the type, duration and intensity of the exercise and the environmental conditions under which it is taking place. Your body's water losses can be very rapid when exercising in hot weather. The longer and harder the exercise, and the hotter and more humid the conditions, the greater the fluid losses that are likely to occur.

■ Pre-event

In an attempt to minimise the effects of fluid loss during training and competition, sportspeople should be encouraged to begin fully hydrated and to drink plenty of water both during and after the activity. Establishing patterns of fluid intake should be an integral part of the training process. Training should be used as the opportunity to practise well-rehearsed fluid replacement strategies that run smoothly in competitive situations. Drinking 300–500 ml of fluid 10–15 minutes before exercise is recommended.

■ Inter-event

Many factors can influence the effectiveness of fluid replacement strategies during exercise. Fluid replacement can be speeded by drinking still, cool drinks of a reasonable volume that are not too concentrated, and they must be palatable to drink. The more intense the activity undertaken, the more the absorption of fluid is slowed. Unpleasant symptoms experienced when drinking during exercise usually mean you have left it too late to start drinking and your body is already dehydrated. Drinking 150–200 ml every 15–20 minutes during exercise is recommended, especially if the exercise lasts longer than an hour.

Post-event

Weight and urine-colour checks can provide a useful and simple way of monitoring fluid status during and after training and competition. A weight reduction of 1 kg is equivalent to 1 litre of fluid loss. Frequent trips to the toilet to pass plentiful quantities of pale-coloured urine are an indicator of good hydration, whereas scant quantities of dark-coloured urine indicate a poor level of hydration. These simple weight and urine checks before and after exercise can provide useful tools to assist in determining fluid requirements post-training or during competition. As a guide, after exercise fluid losses should be replaced 1.5 times within the first two hours of recovery.

Sources

Water

Water is considered to be an adequate fluid suitable for most exercise, but some sports drinks may be useful if running at higher intensities for longer durations.

Sports drinks

Most sports drinks aim to provide three nutrients: carbohydrates to replace energy, water to replace fluid and electrolytes to replace minerals lost in sweat. The carbohydrate in sports drinks is usually glucose, fructose, sucrose or maltodextrins, which are all saccharides that are quickly absorbed. Modern sports drinks often contain a range of minerals and vitamins, but most often include the electrolytes sodium and potassium. Both of these macrominerals are lost in sweat. Sodium promotes the absorption of glucose and water. Magnesium is another mineral lost in sweat, and is present in water and most sports drinks.

Hypertonic

Hypertonic drinks contain over 8 per cent of carbohydrate and have a slower rate of absorption. Although they provide a source of carbohydrate replenishment, they are not ideal for optimal rehydration and may need to be consumed with other fluids. These are best used in the recovery stage after exercise.

Isotonic

Isotonic drinks contain the same concentration of glucose to water as is found in your blood: 4–8 per cent or up to 8 g per 100 ml of water. They usually contain sodium, which makes them quicker to be absorbed into the bloodstream. An isotonic drink is useful whenever exercise has been prolonged or during warmer weather when sweat loss is higher. They can also be used effectively before exercise.

▼ Minimising dehydration is important to performance

Hypotonic

Hypotonic drinks have a lower concentration of carbohydrates and are more diluted than isotonic or hypertonic sports drinks. They contain less than 4 per cent carbohydrate (4 g per 100 ml of water) and are generally easily absorbed and well tolerated. Although water is adequate for non-endurance training or when sweat losses are small, these drinks may encourage fluid replacement through enhanced taste.

Taking it further

Investigate a range of commercially available sports drinks and evaluate their potential use before, during and after exercise.

Activity

Devise a simple five-point plan to ensure that sportspeople maintain an adequate state of hydration. You may choose to use this plan later when formulating your diet plan for a selected sports performer.

Before	During	After
300–500 ml 10–15 minutes before activity	150–200 ml every 15–20 minutes	Based on body mass lost replace losses 150%

Table 10.13 Fluid replacement strategies for exercise

Effects on sports performance

The greater the **frequency**, **intensity** and **duration** of exercise, the more important fluid replacement strategies become and the more likely that sports drinks will have a useful contribution to make in terms of effects on performance and **recovery**, not only by providing a source of fluid but also of energy. Sound nutritional strategies, including those relating to fluid replacement, may have their biggest contribution to make in allowing the sportsperson to train consistently to meet the desired adaptations to training in terms of **specificity** and **progression**.

Taking it further

Undertake your own research into the effects of sports drinks on immune function.

Assessment practice

1. Describe hydration and its effects on sports performance. **P5**
2. Explain the effects of hydration on sports performance. **M3**

Grading tips

Grading Tip P5

You must show knowledge of the relevance of hydration and how it impacts on sports performance. Try to link your answer to the body's energy balance and the digestive process.

Grading Tip M3

Produce a more detailed discussion on how specific sports drinks affect sports performance.

To be able to plan a diet for a selected sports activity, you need to consider the physiological demands of the activity, the phase of training and the individual's needs. These will help you to plan a balanced diet across the food groups that will provide adequate nutrition.

Diet

Food is made of carbohydrates, fats, proteins, vitamins, minerals, non-starch polysaccharide (fibre) and water. The amounts of these nutrients vary from food to food. A balanced diet is one that provides the correct amounts of all nutrients without excess or deficiency.

Balanced diet

Foods that you eat in your diet are popularly classed as good or bad, healthy or unhealthy, with healthy eating often viewed by many as a hardship or a chore. However, there are no good or bad foods, only good or bad uses of food. It is better to look at the overall balance of foods eaten as either healthy or unhealthy.

Healthy eating involves choosing the right foods in the right balance most of the time to provide all the essential nutrients and energy required by your body. The principles of healthy eating aim to reduce the risk of chronic disease such as coronary heart disease, obesity, diabetes and cancer,

but following these principles will also benefit sports performance. Healthy eating principles should form the solid foundations on which sportspeople can build more specific nutritional strategies to support training and competition.

A simple guide to healthy eating:

- eat the correct amount to maintain a healthy body weight
- cut back on your fat intake, particularly fat from saturated sources
- eat plenty of foods with a high starch and fibre content
- don't eat sugary foods too often
- use salt sparingly and reduce your reliance on convenience foods
- ensure adequate intakes of vitamins and minerals by eating a wide variety of foods
- if you drink alcohol, keep within sensible limits
- enjoy your food and do not become obsessed with your diet or dieting.

Fruit and vegetables

Bread, other cereals and potatoes

FLAKES

Milk and dairy foods

Foods containing fat
Foods containing sugar

Meat, fish and alternatives

The balance of good health model ▶

Carbohydrates

Carbohydrates are either starches or sugars. Starchy foods, especially those that are unrefined such as whole grain bread, rice, pasta, cereals and potatoes, provide a steady supply of energy. However, these foods can be filling. To achieve optimal carbohydrate stores, the sportsperson may need to top up with sugary sources that are more rapidly absorbed like sweets, dried fruit, fruit juice, and sugary or sports drinks.

It is recommended that at least 50–60 per cent of your daily calorie intake comes from carbohydrates, and more for those engaged in regular intense heavy training. As a guide, 4–5 g of carbohydrate per kilogram of body weight should be sufficient if you do less than an hour's exercise each day, 5–6 g per kilogram of body weight if you exercise for an hour a day, 6–7 g for one to two hours per day and an intake equivalent to 8–10 g per kilogram of body weight for heavy training exceeding three hours per day.

The best approach is to base all your meals and snacks around starchy carbohydrate foods and eat at regular intervals. Glycogen – your body's store of carbohydrate – is replenished most efficiently within the first half to two hours after exercise.

Fats

Fat provides a concentrated source of energy and is the predominant fuel for low-intensity activity. Eating less fat will allow you to eat more carbohydrate. In the average UK diet, fat accounts for 40 per cent of total calorie intake. To promote good health it is recommended that intake is between 30 and 35 per cent. Those engaging in regular intense activity need to reduce this further to achieve recommended carbohydrate intakes.

Proteins

Many sportspeople believe they need to eat large amounts of protein to build muscle and increase strength, but in most cases it is not necessary to consume a high-protein diet by eating large quantities of meat, fish, eggs, pulses and dairy products. It will not improve performance or increase muscle mass. That can only be achieved by the appropriate training. Some of these foods are also high in animal fats, which should be reduced for long-term health. They may also leave no appetite for carbohydrate foods to provide sufficient energy stores to support training. Eating a normal varied diet and meeting energy (calorie) requirements should automatically provide enough protein.

Normal protein requirements are in the region of 0.75 g per kilogram of body weight per day. The average UK diet significantly exceeds the Dietary Reference Value nutrient intake for protein set at 45 g per day for a female and 55.5 g per day for a male.

Active individuals require greater intakes of protein per kilogram of body weight in order to promote tissue growth and repair. The International Olympic Committee's second Consensus Conference on Nutrition for Sport in 2003 recommended an intake of 1.2–1.7 g per kilogram body weight per day. The lower end of this range should cover the requirements of most endurance athletes, with the upper end meeting the needs of those engaging in more strength and power activities.

Water

Dehydration affects performance and can result in fatigue. Water losses may be up to 1 litre per hour during endurance exercise. Thirst is a poor indicator of dehydration, so drinking before the sensation of thirst is recommended to ensure adequate fluid status. Normal fluid requirements are in the region of 30–35 ml per kilogram of body weight per day, or 1 ml per calorie of energy requirement.

Fibre

Dietary fibre is a carbohydrate that is mainly indigestible. There are two types of fibre: soluble and insoluble. They are both important for maintaining good health. Your daily requirement is 18 g per day. Sportspeople with high carbohydrate requirements will need to manage fibre intake because consuming large quantities of fibre-rich carbohydrate food can make the diet bulky and filling with the potential to limit overall food and energy intake.

Vitamins and minerals

Vitamins and minerals occur naturally in a wide variety of foods. A healthy, balanced and varied diet should provide sufficient intakes. Any increase in requirements as a result of training should be met naturally by increased intake of unrefined starchy carbohydrate foods to meet energy requirements.

Sportspeople often believe they have higher requirements for vitamins and minerals than the average person. There is no doubt that an adequate supply of all the vitamins and minerals is necessary for health, but whether regular exercise increases requirements is a different matter. The scientific consensus is that exercise does not particularly increase the need for micronutrients, although there may be a case for increased requirements of nutrients involved in energy metabolism. Generally, the sportsperson will be eating greater quantities of food to meet increased energy requirements, and as a result will be automatically increasing vitamin and mineral intakes – as long as nutrient-rich foods are chosen.

Assessment practice

1 Create a leaflet targeted at a specific sport to describe the components of a balanced diet to support sports performance. **P6**

2 Produce a short PowerPoint® presentation targeted at a different sport to explain the components of a balanced diet to support sports performance. **M4**

Grading tips

Grading Tip P6

You should consider the importance of carbohydrate, fat, protein, water, fibre, vitamins and minerals.

Grading Tip M4

You should explain the significance of the various nutrients in a balanced diet.

Activities

Different activities require different dietary plans or strategies to optimise performance.

Aerobic

Aerobic or endurance activities will significantly challenge the athlete's energy and fluid stores. The longer and more intense the aerobic training or competition, the more depleted the stores are likely to become. A key goal for aerobic activities should be to maximise glycogen stores. An increase in carbohydrate intake during the two or three days before competition is a useful strategy to adopt. Carbohydrate supplements in the form of energy drinks, bars or gels may be a useful addition to the diet.

All endurance athletes should ensure that they start exercise fully hydrated. The longer the duration of the activity, the more important it is to consume fluids during it. Sports drinks may be a useful consideration as they provide a supply of carbohydrate as well as replacing fluids.

Some aerobic activities may benefit from the practice of carbohydrate loading. The amount of glycogen available for storage in the muscles is related to the amount of carbohydrate consumed in the diet and the level and intensity of activity undertaken. For most sports, eating a diet that consists of 5–10 g of carbohydrate per kilogram of body weight will maintain liver and muscle glycogen stores. However, the aim of carbohydrate loading is to increase the capacity of the muscles to store glycogen above their normal level. This may be useful to sportspeople who compete in endurance events that last longer than 90 minutes, such as marathon running, triathlons and endurance

Remember!

The goal of carbohydrate loading is to increase the capacity of the muscles to store glycogen above their normal level, usually in preparation for an endurance event.

swimming. Although carbohydrate loading does not benefit all sports performers, everyone regularly training and competing in sports should focus on consuming a high carbohydrate diet at all times and will benefit from a carbohydrate-rich meal or snack before training or competition.

Anaerobic

In anaerobic activities, such as strength, power and sprint sports, the key role of nutritional strategies is to support the development of lean body mass (muscle) as well as to meet energy demands. Although carbohydrate requirements are not as great as for aerobic activities, they are still important. Combining carbohydrate with protein post-exercise promotes an anabolic environment and increases protein synthesis that helps to promote muscle development; however, excessive protein intakes should be avoided. Some team sports may fall into this category.

Muscular strength and endurance

Many sports can fall into this category dependent upon the particular physiological demands of the sport. For example, high levels of muscular strength and endurance are required for some team sports such as rugby as well as weight category sports such as judo. Nutritional demands will be dictated by the nature of the individual sport and participant requirements, but key nutrients for consideration in all cases are carbohydrate and fluid.

Flexibility

For sports that require a good deal of flexibility such as gymnastics, diving and figure skating, weight control is a serious dietary issue. Evidence suggests participants in these aesthetic or appearance-orientated sports, where performance is subjectively evaluated by judges, may be more prone to eating-disordered behaviour. Leanness or a specific weight may be considered important for optimal performance, placing greater consciousness on what the sportsperson eats and how they look. However, it is important to remember that the fewer calories consumed, the fewer nutrients consumed. Calcium and iron intakes are reported to be particularly low in studies investigating the dietary intakes of female participants in these sports.

The same healthy eating and balance of good health principles apply to the planning of dietary intakes for these sports but greater emphasis may be placed on a low-fat diet. However, this should not be at the expense of other essential nutrients such as carbohydrate, protein, vitamins and minerals. Adequate fluid intakes and hydration are also essential to maintain concentration for the very technical demands of these sports.

Timing

May sportspeople undertake a periodised programme of training. Periodisation represents the organised division of the training year and has three basic objectives:

- to prepare the athlete for achievement of an optimum improvement in performance
- to prepare the athlete for a definite peak in the competition season
- to prepare the athlete for main competitions within that peak.

Training undertaken within the programme is a form of stress to the body. If it is undertaken properly, the athlete adapts to that stress. Good nutritional practices are important in allowing the body to adapt and to deliver performance improvements.

■ Pre-season

For most sports, pre-season nutritional requirements need to take account of the demands of training in terms of frequency, intensity, duration and specificity. As training progresses – particularly in terms of frequency, intensity and duration – it can be expected that the athlete's energy and nutrient demands will increase, particularly in respect of energy, carbohydrate and fluid requirements. If energy and nutrient demands are not met, the athlete will be put at an increased risk of injury and illness. In addition, reducing post-season weight gain is often a target of pre-season nutritional strategies.

■ Mid-season

Nutritional demands of the mid-season phase are focused on maintaining energy and fluid requirements as the demands of the competition schedule get underway. During this time, less overall nutrition may be required but more attention may need to be placed on pre-event preparation and post-event recovery strategies to remain injury and illness free.

Post-season

Post-season presents a window of opportunity where the athlete can relax dietary intake a little but unnecessary weight gain should be monitored. It is likely during this period that energy and fluid requirements will be at their lowest.

Pre-event

Many of the principles of preparing for a competition mirror those of the training diet. For a competition, the pre-event meal should aim to top up muscle and liver glycogen stores. Therefore, it should be rich in carbohydrate but low in fat and fibre and contain a moderate amount of protein. It should be remembered that larger meals take longer to digest and that nerves can result in delayed digestion.

Competition is not a time to experiment with new foods. The pre-event meal should be made of familiar foods and provide adequate fluids. Solid foods can usually be consumed with comfort up to two hours before an event, but liquid meals or carbohydrate drinks can be consumed up to 30 to 60 minutes before.

Sports performers taking part in events lasting longer than 90 minutes should be advised, where possible, to taper training in the week leading up to the event, include a rest day, and consume a higher than normal carbohydrate and fluid intake.

Activity

Devise suitable pre-event meal strategies for use by sportspeople competing at the following times of day:

- 9.30 a.m. (early-morning competition)
- 2.30 p.m. (afternoon competition)
- 6.00 p.m. (early-evening competition).

Inter-event

During training and competition, fluid loss is a major consideration. During intense training or competition isotonic sports drinks – which assist with fluid replacement and provide a source of fuel – may be consumed. This may be beneficial especially if training or competition lasts longer than 60 minutes. During endurance or ultra-endurance events lasting longer than four hours, solid foods may be required. In these instances, energy bars or gels might be useful as a more concentrated source of carbohydrate.

Remember!

Regular sports performers should be encouraged to practise their fluid and fuelling regimes in training to ensure that they do not run into any unexpected problems during competition.

Post-event

Good nutrition can make its greatest contribution in aiding recovery between training sessions. For the regular sports performer, performance improvements are the product of the body's adaptation to the demands of training. Sound nutrition has its biggest impact in supporting the sports performer in training consistently and effectively to achieve the desired adaptations. To achieve steady improvements, all sportspeople must ensure that their diet consistently meets the demands placed on their bodies by training and competition.

What is consumed, how much and how soon after an intense workout or competition can all influence the recovery process. Refuelling should begin as soon as possible. Sensible choices in terms of food and fluids will allow the sports performer to recover more quickly for the next training session.

It is important to refuel as soon as possible after each workout or competition. The longer refuelling is delayed, the longer it will take to fully refuel. The sports performer may find it easier to have small, frequent meals and snacks at regularly spaced intervals to help to maximise glycogen synthesis.

To refuel efficiently, a high carbohydrate diet is required. Post-exercise carbohydrates that are easy to eat and digest are preferred. Sports performers are advised to consume a high-carbohydrate (at least 50 g) low-fat snack as soon as possible after training or competition, preferably within the first half an hour – when the muscles' capacity to refuel is at their greatest. They should ensure that they eat their next meal, which should be rich in carbohydrate, within two hours.

After exercise, the replacement of fluids lost through sweating should also be a priority. Rehydration should start immediately. Drinks containing carbohydrates will also assist with energy and glycogen replacement. These may be particularly useful if the activity has been very intense and resulted in a suppression of appetite and a reluctance to eat solid foods.

Activity

Jon is competing in a national badminton tournament tomorrow. Suggest a suitable pre-competition meal and provide some advice on how he might ensure that he keeps fuelled and hydrated during the tournament.

Planning diets

Before you can safely and effectively plan and implement balanced eating programmes and nutritional strategies to support training and competition for others, you need to be able to critically evaluate your own eating habits and activity patterns and consider the relationship between them.

Theory into practice

1 To assess your own eating habits, keep a record of all food and drink you consume for at least a three-day period, which should include one weekend day. For a more detailed evaluation, record your intake for a full week.

Write down *everything* you eat and drink. You must be as accurate and honest as possible, and be sure not to modify your usual intake at this stage otherwise you will not be evaluating your typical diet. You will need to carry your record around with you at all times and record food and drink as it is consumed to avoid forgetting any items. Your record should describe the following.

- The type of food and drink consumed and how much. Either estimate the portion size using standard household measures, such as slices of bread, pints of fluid, tablespoons of vegetables, or give the weight.
- The time the food and drink was consumed and where you were when you ate it. These points are useful when assessing external factors that affect your dietary intake.
- Your cooking methods and type of food preparation.
- Any activity or exercise you took part in, including an indication of its duration and intensity, i.e. light, moderate or hard.

2 When you have done this, look at your food record and compare it to the balance of good health model (see page 302). Write short report on your findings.

Taking it further

As well as the types and amounts of food you eat, your food record may give you an idea about how your daily life dictates what, when, where and why you eat. Take another look at your food record and ask yourself the following questions.

- Is your diet better than you first thought or is there plenty of room for improvement? What healthy-eating goals might you not be achieving? Are there any that you achieve with ease?
- Does your diet meet any demands you make on it as a result of sport and exercise?

Optimal performance in sport and exercise requires optimal nutrition. Sportspeople should pay careful attention to foods that can enhance, not hinder, their preparation for participation in and recovery from training and competition. Most sportspeople will obtain all the energy and nutrients they need by eating when they are hungry and choosing a balanced and varied diet.

Good nutrition has a big part to play in aiding recovery between training sessions, allowing the sports performer to realise adaptations in response to the training programme.

The vast array of sports that exist can be categorised into the following groups:

- multi-sprint or team sports, e.g. soccer
- strength sports, e.g. sprinting
- endurance and ultra-endurance sports, e.g. marathon running and the triathlon
- weight category sports, e.g. boxing
- aesthetic sports, e.g. diving.

Each category requires sound nutritional strategies to support successful performance. Winning, avoiding injury and illness, and improving fitness are what matter to most competitive sportspeople. With the intermittent nature of team sports, the intensity at which they are performed can alter at any time. These changes in intensity are irregular and can be random, and may draw significantly on the body's glycogen stores. Performance may be impaired towards the end of a match if glycogen stores are running low. Weight-loss methods and restrictive dietary practices are often used by sportspeople within weight category and aesthetic sports, with potential dangers to both health and performance.

Activity

Choose a sport that is not named in the bullet points above. Consider which category of sport it belongs to and examine the specific nutritional practices and requirements associated with it.

There are a number of methods for collecting information on what people eat and drink. These include the 24-hour diet recall, the diet history or interview technique, daily food records or diaries, weighed food intake records and food frequency questionnaires.

Theory into practice

Work with one of your classmates. Before you start, decide on an appropriate template that could be designed for the purpose of recording all necessary information relating to meal times, types of food and fluid consumed and the cooking methods used.

1 a Take it in turns to interview each other to recall all food and drink consumed in the past 24 hours. Use your template to record the details of your interview.

   b What are the main advantages and disadvantages of this method of dietary intake recording?

2 a Interview the same person again but this time ask him or her to recall everything eaten and drunk in the past seven days. Record the details using the same template.

   b What are the main advantages and disadvantages of this method of dietary intake recording?

You may choose to use this technique in gaining information on dietary intake of selected sports performers. It is important when interviewing people about their dietary habits to adopt a professional approach and to maintain confidentially. It should always be borne in mind that an individual's food intake is a very personal issue, and this information should be handled sensitively. It is also necessary to ask if there are any medical factors such as diabetes or allergies that impact on food habits. These people should always be referred to a qualified professional for dietary advice.

Remember!

Any detailed or complex dietary analysis incorporating major dietary changes, particularly those relating to medical conditions, should always be referred to a qualified state registered dietitian, or an accredited sports dietitian if it concerns an athlete or sportsperson. The usual means of referral to a state registered dietitian are through a general practitioner, consultant or dentist.

- 24-hour diet recall: this method of dietary information collection is quick and easy to use. The interviewer questions the subject to collect information on what he or she usually eats and drinks. This method relies heavily on memory to recall all food and drink consumed. It is useful in assessing the quality of food intake and may reveal obvious dietary imbalances such as a potentially high fat intake. However, it is rarely adequate to provide a quantitative estimate of nutrient intakes to allow for comparison with Dietary Reference Values.
- The diet history or interview: this method is quick and easy to use. The interviewer questions the subject to collect information on what he or she usually eats and drinks, but over a longer time period. This method relies heavily on memory to recall all food and drink consumed in the period specified. Recollections of this kind nearly always underestimate intake and there is the danger of fabrication to impress the interviewer. The method is, however, useful in assessing the quality of dietary intake and may be able to reveal obvious dietary imbalances in the same way as the 24-hour recall.
- Daily food record or diet dairy: this method can give a good overall guide to the types and quantities of food and drink consumed during the recording period. At least three days should be recorded and one of these should be a weekend day to account for any different food patterns at weekends. For a more detailed picture, a seven-day record is recommended. When dealing with sportspeople, the record should include rest and competition days as well as training days.

- Weighed food intake: with this method, individual foods are weighed before consumption. This method is time consuming and intrusive, and could lead to distortion of the overall pattern of foods consumed in order to make weighing and recording easier.

Think it over

Sportspeople face a number of problems in achieving adequate nutritional intakes. Spend ten minutes considering the dilemmas that may face sportspeople in achieving their nutritional requirements.

Assessment of needs

When developing sound eating habits and nutritional strategies to support training and competition, the following issues are important:

- the types of food eaten to support training and competition
- the timing of meals and snacks around training and competition
- ensuring a balanced diet is achieved in respect of all nutrients
- maintaining a sufficient fluid intake
- encouraging an adequate calcium and iron intake, particularly for females
- promoting long-term health and reducing the risk of chronic disease
- the problems of travelling to training and competition venues
- minimising the risk of injury and illness.

The nutritional requirements for different sports and sportspeople will vary according to:

- the type of sport and training methods undertaken
- the intensity of training or competition
- the duration of training or competition
- the frequency of training or competition
- the training status and fitness level of the sportsperson.

The balance of good health principles (see page 302) should be used to plan meals. These principles should form the foundations on which to develop more specific sports nutrition strategies. Sportspeople should be encouraged to eat sufficient carbohydrate and start refuelling as soon as possible after training, when muscle capacity to refuel is at its greatest. This may mean avoiding the restriction of traditional meal times. Eating may need to be fitted in around the training process, with smaller, more frequent meals and snacks being necessary. Snacks and fluids should be carried in the kit bag at all times.

Rest days are also important, and this time should be used to recover from the stresses of training and competition. A high fluid intake should be encouraged. In many sports, post-match alcohol consumption is part of traditional practices, but it is important to rehydrate with other fluids before drinking alcohol after training and competition. Where an injury has been sustained, alcohol consumption may delay the recovery process and should be avoided for at least 48 hours.

Activity

1 Devise a list of simple training and competition guidelines for sportspeople. You may choose to use this list when planning a diet for a selected sports activity.

2 To support this list of guidelines, identify a number of appropriate items for the kit bag that could be used to replenish energy stores and fluid balance after exercise.

■ Weight gain

Weight can be gained in two ways: by increasing the amount of fat or the amount of lean body mass. Both will register as increases in weight on the scales but the results will be very different in terms of body composition.

Gains in fat weight are relatively easy to achieve – as most people wishing to lose weight would testify – but gains in lean body mass can only be achieved as a result of adaptations to a progressive strength training programme, supported by an adequate diet.

■ Weight loss

Most sportspeople are concerned about either attaining or maintaining an optimal body weight. There are some sports in which weight restrictions apply. These are called weight category sports and include body building, boxing, horse racing, martial arts and rowing. The sportsperson must compete within a given weight range.

For some sports it may be crucial to maintain a low body weight, which for some may be below their natural weight. These might be considered as weight-controlled sports, and include sports such as distance running, gymnastics, figure skating and diving. These sports may present challenges in maintaining a nutritionally adequate diet while reducing or maintaining weight. There are a variety of inappropriate weight-loss practices, such as fasting or skipping meals, laxative abuse, bingeing and purging, and intentional dehydration by the use of sweatsuits or saunas. When most athletes talk about achieving weight loss what they are usually trying to achieve is fat loss, as losses in muscle mass may result in unfavourable changes in their power-to-weight ratio.

■ Muscle gain

When the athlete talks about weight gain, what they usually mean is muscle gain. In this case strength training provides the stimulus for muscles to grow while adequate nutrition provides the opportunity for them to grow at an optimal rate.

Rates of weight/muscle gain are dependent on genetics and body type. To gain strength and size, it is necessary to achieve a slightly positive energy balance – somewhere in the region of an extra 500 calories per day – and a protein intake of about 1.4–1.7 g per kilogram of body mass. Eating a high protein diet, or supplementing with amino acids (as is common practice for many sportspeople wishing to gain muscle bulk and size) will not in itself lead to great increases in muscle size or strength. What is more important is achieving an adequate energy intake.

■ Fat gain

In very few instances the athlete may wish to gain fat weight, such as in contact sports were additional body fat may provide extra protection.

Activity

1 What are the nutritional consequences of the unhealthy weight-loss practices identified above?

2 What impact might these practices have on performance in sport?

Nutrition

■ Macronutrients

Performance in and recovery from exercise are enhanced by optimal nutrition. For most sports, carbohydrate requirements are likely to contribute in the region of 55–65 per cent of total energy intake, protein around 12–15 per cent and the remainder coming from fat.

■ Micronutrients

Vitamin and mineral supplementation will not improve the performance of athletes that are already consuming an adequate and varied diet. Those at risk of micronutrient deficiency are people who restrict energy intake, use severe weight-loss strategies or follow a high carbohydrate diet with low micronutrient density. Athletes should aim to consume diets that meet RNI values (see page 286) for micronutrient intakes.

■ Fibre

Athletes should aim to achieve fibre intakes in line with the sedentary population intake target of 18 g per day.

Food groups

The balance of good health model has been adopted as the UK's National Food Guide. It was devised by the Health Education Authority as a new and simplified means of helping people to understand healthy eating. The model attempts to make following a balanced diet easier to implement by identifying the types and proportions of foods required to achieve a healthy, balanced and varied diet, based around the five main food groups.

As you can see on page 302, the model depicts a plate with divisions of varying sizes representing each of these five groups. Those with a larger proportion of the plate should feature in larger proportions in your diet, while those with the smaller shares should be consumed in much smaller quantities or used only as occasional foods.

This UK guide to healthy eating applies to most people in the population, including those who engage in regular exercise and sport. It does not, however, apply to children under the age of five.

The key messages of the model are that you should aim to:

- base all your meals around starchy foods
- eat at least five servings of fruit and/or vegetables each day
- include milk and dairy foods, if possible three servings per day
- eat smaller portions of meat or fish, and try alternatives such as pulses
- limit your intake of foods with a high fat or sugar content.

Table 10.14 shows the recommended daily amounts and nutrients supplied by each of the main food groups.

Activity

Sayeed has recently taken up the triathlon. His usual diet consists of a macronutrient energy distribution of 40 per cent carbohydrate, 40 per cent fat and 20 per cent protein. He is about to enter his first major competition.

1 What effect could this macronutrient distribution have on his performance?

2 What practical advice could you offer to improve his diet?

3 What could Sayeed do in his preparation for the competition to help to delay fatigue?

Food	What is a serving?	Recommended amount per day	Main nutrients supplied
Grains and potatoes			
Bread, rolls, muffins, bagels, crumpets, chapattis, naan bread, pitta bread, tortillas, scones, pikelets, potato cakes, breakfast cereals, rice, pasta, noodles, couscous and potatoes	3 tbsp breakfast cereal, 1 Weetabix or Shredded Wheat, 1 slice of bread, ½ a pitta, 1 heaped tbsp boiled potato, pasta, rice or couscous	These should form the main part of all meals and snacks. About a third of the total volume of food consumed each day	Carbohydrate, NSP (mainly insoluble), calcium, iron and B vitamins
Vegetables and fruits			
All types of fresh, frozen, canned and dried fruits and vegetables (except potatoes) and fruit and vegetable juices	1 apple, orange, pear, banana, 1 small glass of fruit juice, 1 small salad, 2 tbsp vegetables, 2 tbsp stewed or tinned fruit in juice	At least five portions per day. About a third of the total volume of food consumed each day	NSP (especially soluble), vitamin C, folate and potassium
Oils			
Butter, margarine, cooking oils, mayonnaise, salad dressing, cream, pastries, crisps, biscuits and cakes	1 tsp butter or margarine, 1 tsp vegetable or olive oil, 1 tsp mayonnaise	These should be eaten sparingly and lower-fat options selected	Fat, essential fatty acids and some vitamins
Dairy			
Milk, yoghurt, cheese, fromage frais	⅓ pint milk, 1¼ oz cheese, 1 small carton yoghurt or cottage cheese	Two or three servings per day. About a sixth of the total volume of food consumed each day	Protein, calcium, vitamins A and D
Meat, fish and alternative proteins			
Meat, poultry, fish, eggs, pulses, nuts, meat and fish products (e.g. sausages, beefburgers, fish cakes, fish fingers)	2–3 oz lean meat, chicken or oily fish, 4–5 oz white fish, 2 eggs, 1 small tin baked beans, 2 tbsp nuts, 4 oz Quorn or soya product	Two servings per day. About a sixth of the total volume of food consumed each day	Protein, iron, zinc, magnesium and B vitamins. Pulses provide a good source of NSP

Table 10.14 Food groups

■ Sources

The sources of each food group are identified in Table 10.14, together with the main nutrients supplied by each food group.

■ Availability

Several factors influence food availability. These may include physical or environmental factors such as perishability and economic factors such as cost and budgeting priorities. Cooking skills and facilities, and nutritional knowledge, are also crucial factors in the provision and availability of food.

Assessment practice

Identify a sportsperson on whom you can undertake a dietary assessment. You may wish to consider your own diet if you are actively engaged in sport at a competitive level, and use the information you have gathered through the practical activities in this unit. Decide on an appropriate method for collecting dietary intake information from your sportsperson.

1 Analyse the information you have obtained and write a report on your findings which suggests, where necessary, appropriate modifications

or improvements to support their health and performance. Use a combination of manual and computer-based methods of processing and analysing nutrient intake information.

2 Plan a two-week diet for your subject. Include advice on nutritional strategies to support the preparation for, participation in and recovery from training and competition. **P7**

3 Explain the two-week diet plan in terms of your selection of food and nutritional strategies. **M5**

4 Justify your food selection and nutritional strategies. Find ways of supporting your proposals by referring to relevant published material. **D2**

Grading tips

Grading Tip P7

You need to produce an appropriate two-week diet plan for a named sports performer. This should focus on aspects of achieving adequate fuelling and hydration.

Grading Tip M5

Explain your choice of food selection, fuelling and hydration strategies and their likely impact on training

and competition performance. You should carefully consider the status of your sports performer (amateur, semi-professional, elite) in explaining your two-week plan.

Grading Tip D2

You need to justify your selection by being critical and looking for means to support your views. Do this with reference to relevant published material such as the ACSM (American College of Sports Medicine), Position Stand on Nutrition for Athletic Performance or the International Olympic Committee's Consensus on Nutrition for Athletes.

Knowledge check

1 Define the term 'diet'.

2 Define the term Reference Nutrient Intake (RNI). What is the significance of this dietary reference value?

3 Draw and label a simple diagram of the digestive system.

4 Explain the term 'energy balance'.

5 Explain the components and their relative contributions of total energy expenditure.

6 Describe one method for the estimation of energy requirements.

7 List four routes of water loss from the body.

8 Because water losses are greater during exercise, the sportsperson needs to employ sound strategies for fluid replacement. What might be the signs and symptoms of dehydration and how might these be avoided?

9 What are the advantages and disadvantages of high carbohydrate content in a sports drink?

10 Describe the skinfold analysis method of measuring body composition. Why is this method one of the most widely used field techniques for assessing body composition in sportspeople?

11 List two micronutrients for special attention in the diet of athletes. Why might these nutrients be of particular concern in the diets of female athletes?

12 How soon do you need to eat after a hard training session and why is it so important to eat afterwards?

13 Describe the components of a balanced diet.

14 Describe how you might undertake an assessment of the nutritional needs of a sportsperson.

15 What factors need to be taken into consideration when planning a diet for a selected sports activity?

Preparation for assessment

Sports nutrition describes the influence of nutritional strategies on sports performance during the preparation for, participation in and recovery from training and competition. Working with a sports performer of your choice over a number of weeks, this Preparation for assessment is designed to evidence that you can meet all of the learning outcomes for the unit.

1 Select a sports performer willing to participate and likely to benefit from the application of sports nutrition principles in practice. This could be a member of one of your college's sports teams.

2 Describe to the sports performer the importance of nutrition and common terminology associated with it, and developing a good knowledge and understanding of the practical application of sports nutrition principles. You may find it useful to produce a leaflet or information sheet for your sports performer to assist with this task. **P1**

3 In order for the sports performer to understand how the body uses food and extracts energy from it, describe the structure and function of the digestive system. Again, you may find it useful to produce a leaflet or information sheet for your sports performer to assist with this task. **P2**

4 Explain energy intake and expenditure in the context of the physiological demands of their sport, the demands placed on different fuel sources and how they might achieve an appropriate energy intake. Design a clearly labelled poster to help provide suitable evidence of undertaking this task. **P3 M1**

5 Describe and explain energy balance to your sports performer and its importance in relation to successful performance in their sport. Provide suitable evidence of undertaking this task. This could be a review of relevant literature on the energy demands of the sport and the physical characteristics of elite performers in the sport. **P4 M2**

6 Over a suitable time frame, analyse the effects of energy balance on the performance of your sports performer. Present suitable evidence that you have undertaken this task. This could be records of weight or body composition monitoring. **D1**

7 Explain the effects of hydration and appropriate hydration strategies in the context of the physiological demands of their sport and the opportunities it affords for developing before, during and post-training and competition strategies for maintaining hydration. Provide suitable evidence of undertaking this task, such as a report or verbal presentation on the strategies advised. **P5**

8 Describe and explain the components of a balanced diet to your sports performer. For this task you may find it useful to produce a diet plan or timetable. **P6 P7 M4**

Before you embark on this task, you need to be familiar with their usual dietary habits and intake and will need to decide on an appropriate means to record and assess this.

9 Describe and explain the two-week diet plan to your sports performer and provide a copy of your diet plan as evidence of undertaking this task. **M5**

10 Write a short report to justify your two-week plan. This should draw on evidence from relevant authoritative sources. **D2**

Grading tip

In undertaking the tasks listed, you will find it useful to refer back to the Assessment practice activities in this unit for guidance on meeting the pass, merit and distinction criteria.

To achieve a pass grade the evidence must show that the learner is able to:	To achieve a merit grade the evidence must show that, in addition to the pass criteria, the learner is able to:	To achieve a distinction grade the evidence must show that, in addition to the pass and merit criteria, the learner is able to:
P1 Describe nutrition, including nutritional requirements and common terminology associated with nutrition **Assessment practice Page 287**		
P2 Describe the structure and function of the digestive system **Assessment practice Page 289**		
P3 Describe energy intake and expenditure in sports performance **Assessment practice Page 294**	**M1** Explain energy intake and expenditure in sports performance **Assessment practice Page 294**	
P4 Describe energy balance and its importance in relation to sports performance **Assessment practice Page 297**	**M2** Explain the importance of energy balance in relation to sports performance **Assessment practice Page 297**	**D1** Analyse the effects of energy balance on sports performance **Assessment practice Page 297**
P5 Describe hydration and its effects on sports performance **Assessment practice Page 301**	**M3** Explain the effects of hydration on sports performance **Assessment practice Page 301**	
P6 Describe the components of a balanced diet **Assessment practice Page 304**	**M4** Explain the components of a balanced diet **Assessment practice Page 304**	
P7 Describe an appropriate two-week diet plan for a selected sports performer for a selected sports activity **Assessment practice Page 313**	**M5** Explain the two-week diet plan for a selected sports performer for a selected sports activity **Assessment practice Page 313**	**D2** Justify the two-week diet plan for a selected sports performer for a selected sports activity **Assessment practice Page 313**

Psychology for sports performance

Introduction

Sports performers seeking a competitive edge know that sport psychology plays an important role in maximising performance. To understand the importance of psychological preparation and control in both individual and team sports, a number of factors must be explored. This is a relatively new field involving the scientific study of people and how they act in sport environments.

The first stage of developing and using sport psychology techniques with clients is knowing what works and how it works. After we know this, we can begin to identify the practical applications of this knowledge to sport by helping athletes to learn how to use these techniques.

Athletes are continually seeking to improve their levels of performance, and sport psychology has a really important role within this as it can help athletes to have an advantage over their opponents.

After completing this unit you should be able to achieve the following outcomes:

- Understand the effects of personality and motivation on sports performance.

- Understand the relationships between stress, anxiety, arousal and sports performance.

- Understand group dynamics in sports teams.

- Be able to plan a psychological skills training programme to enhance sports performance.

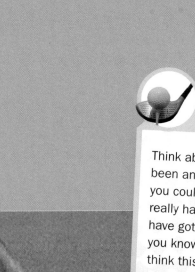

Think it over

Think about when you have played sport. Have there been any times when you have not played as well as you could have done, even though you had trained really hard? Have there been any times when you have got something wrong in a game even though you know how to perform the skill well? Why do you think this could be?

Personality

Personality and the potential effects it can have on sports participation and sports performance has been of interest to sport psychologists and researchers as far back as the late 1800s. However, hard evidence on whether personality affects sports performance is still fairly limited and inconclusive.

Definition

Personality is the sum of those characteristics that make a person unique.

Theories

■ Trait theories

Trait theories suggest that individuals have certain characteristics that will partly determine how they behave.

Key term

Trait A relatively stable and enduring characteristic that is part of your personality.

Traits are relatively stable aspects of personality and early trait theorists such as Eysenck and Cattell argued that traits were mainly inherited. According to Eysenck, there are two main dimensions to personality:

- an introversion-extroversion dimension
- a stable-neurotic dimension.

Introverts are individuals who do not actively seek excitement and would rather be in calm or quieter environments. They tend to prefer tasks that require a great deal of concentration and dislike the unexpected. Extroverts tend to become bored quickly, are poor at tasks that require a great deal of concentration and

constantly seek change and excitement. Extroverts are less responsive to pain than introverts. It has also been argued that extroverts are more successful in sporting situations because they can cope with competitive situations better than introverts and because they can cope better with the distraction from external stimuli such as audiences.

Stable individuals are people who tend to be more easy-going and even tempered. Neurotic (unstable) people tend to be more restless and excitable than their stable counterparts, they have a tendency to become anxious more easily and they are more highly aroused.

The trait approach has been applied to sport by several researchers. Personality traits are enduring characteristics across a variety of situations and the trait approach suggests that the cause of behaviour lies within a person. Therefore, trait theorists say that the reasons someone takes part in sport come from within them and are determined by their personality traits. This approach argues that the environment or situation plays a minimal role.

Think it over

Introverts tend to be drawn to more individual sports such as long-distance running, whereas extroverts prefer team- and action-orientated sports such as football. It is suggested that extroverts are drawn to these types of sport because they offer high levels of excitement and stimulation, and the ever-changing, open and unexpected environments required to keep them interested in the activity. Athletes that are more towards the unstable or neurotic end of the scale tend to experience high levels of over-arousal during the early stages of performance, which can lead to lower levels of performance. Which bracket do you fall into?

Trait theories have been seen as too simplistic in their views and claims. For example, trait theorists have argued that personality traits are more stable and enduring than they actually are, and the theories fail to take into account the significance of the situation the individual may find themselves in. Another limitation of trait theories is that they fail to take into account that individuals can be actively involved in shaping their own personalities.

The conclusion is that personality alone cannot predict athletic success but it can be used to help to explain some of the reasons why people choose some of the sports they do. At best, personality traits can predict a limited amount of behaviour, but traits alone cannot successfully predict behaviour in a particular situation. Personality can be used with physiological and situational factors in order to suggest whether an athlete will be more or less successful in a sporting situation.

Remember!

Although personality traits can be used with physiological and situational factors to try to predict success, there is no single athletic personality that will guarantee sporting success.

■ Social learning theory

Social learning theory suggests that personality is not a relatively stable or enduring characteristic. It is constantly changing and is created as a result of our experiences of different social situations. It is highly unlikely that an individual will behave in the same way in a variety of different situations.

This theory suggests that individuals learn in sporting situations through two distinct processes: modelling and reinforcement. Modelling suggests that individuals are more likely to model themselves on people they feel they can relate to, such as individuals in the same sport or of the same gender, and that as they observe their behaviour, they attempt to copy it. Reinforcement is important because if an individual's behaviour is reinforced or rewarded in some way, it is likely that the behaviour will be repeated.

Bandura, a leading psychologist, identified four main stages of observational learning that demonstrate how modelling can influence personality and behaviour.

1 Attention: to learn through observation, the athlete must have a certain level of respect and admiration for the model they are observing. The amount of respect the athlete has for the model will depend on the status of the model. The model will gain the attention of the athlete observing them more if the model is successful, attractive, powerful and of a high status, and if their behaviour can be seen to have a function or purpose.

2 Retention: for modelling to be effective, the athlete must be able to retain the observed skill or behaviour in their memory and be able to recall it when needed.

3 Motor reproduction: the athlete must be able to physically perform the task he or she is observing. The athlete needs time to practise the skill in order to learn how it should be performed.

4 Motivational response: unless the athlete is motivated, he or she will not go through the first three stages of modelling. Motivation is dependent on the amount of reinforcement (e.g. praise, feedback, sense of pride or achievement), the perceived status of the model and the perceived importance of the task.

■ Situational approach

The situational approach is the opposite of the trait theories approach as it says that behaviour is more dependent on the situation or the environment you find yourself in. It argues that this is far more important than traits. The situational approach draws largely on social learning theory.

Remember!

A situation can influence a person's behaviour but it cannot predict sporting behaviour. To be able to do this, you need to consider the individual's personality traits.

Think it over

An eight-year-old aspiring footballer is watching Wayne Rooney play for Manchester United in his debut in the European Champions League. Wayne becomes a model for the young footballer as he is a powerful model and is similar to the aspiring footballer (same sport and same gender). Wayne is stepping up to take the free kick that led to him scoring his debut hat-trick in Europe and the young footballer pays particular attention to this as he is the free-kick taker for his local football team. The four stages of observational learning are as follows.

1 Attention: the young footballer pays attention to Wayne's approach to the free kick; his confident posture when he picks up the ball and then places it down for the free kick; the confident strike of the ball; the ball going into the back of the net.

2 Retention: the young footballer remembers Wayne's confident approach to taking the free kick; his run-up and body shape as he steps up to take the kick; the strike of the ball; the ball going into the back of the net.

3 Motor reproduction: the next time the young footballer is in the position of taking a free kick for his team, he tries to imitate the actions of the player he has modelled himself on. He attempts to copy the confident approach and displays this by confidently placing the ball down in the spot he is comfortable taking the kick from before striking the ball.

4 Motivational response: the young player feels more confident and as a result becomes more comfortable with his performance. As a result of this change in his behaviour, his performance is reinforced due to his higher levels of self-confidence, which further motivates him to behave in the same way in future situations like this (e.g. free kicks within shooting distance).

This example demonstrates that the aspiring player's personality and behaviour have been shaped by observing the behaviour of people they model themselves on and by the reinforcement experienced. However, it cannot be argued that his increased confidence would be apparent in any other situation, which suggests that it is the situation change, rather than changes in his personality traits, that have shaped his behaviour.

There is some support for the situational approach in sporting behaviour, as individuals may be introverted – displaying characteristics such as tolerance and shyness generally – but may participate in a sport that requires them to be more extroverted and display characteristics such as aggression in the sporting situation.

Therefore, it can be argued that the situation is a more powerful predictor of behaviour than personality traits. However, as with the influence of traits, a situation cannot conclusively predict behaviour.

■ Interactional approach

To more accurately predict behaviour in a sporting situation, you need to consider the interaction of both the situation and the individual's personality traits. This is known as the interactional approach to personality and sport behaviour.

Models like Wayne Rooney keep the attention of observers and make people want to be like them because of the level of skill they display and success they experience ▶

The interactional approach is the view most widely accepted by most sport psychologists when considering behaviour. This theory suggests that when situational factors are particularly strong, for example during competitive sporting situations such as penalty shoot-outs in football, they are more likely to predict behaviour than personality traits. The athlete who tends to be quiet and shy in an everyday situation is likely to run towards an ecstatic crowd screaming if he scored the winning penalty.

Types

Another approach common in sport psychology is the one that suggests that personality traits can be grouped under two headings: type A and type B.

In the sports domain, the main conclusions regarding this theory is that type A individuals tend to be more motivated than their type B counterparts to continue participating in a sport setting when the situation becomes unfavourable or when they are not particularly motivated to take part.

■ Type A

People who fall under the type A personality bracket are those who tend to lack patience, have a strong urge for competition, have a high desire to achieve goals, always rush to complete activities, will happily multi-task when placed under heavy time constraints, lack tolerance towards others and tend to experience higher levels of anxiety.

■ Type B

People in the type B category are those who tend to be more tolerant towards others, are more relaxed than their type A counterparts, are more reflective, experience lower levels of anxiety and display higher levels of imagination and creativity.

Effects on sports performance

There is no direct link between personality type and successful sporting performance. Some research has suggested that certain personality types may be more attracted to certain sports, but little says that your personality will make you a better athlete.

Case study: Interactional approach

Basketball training sessions at a development club have been set up so that players get the opportunity to coach sessions to help with their coach education portfolios. Two players at the club, Jack and Tyreese, have been selected to lead and be assessed in their sessions today.

Jack has a great deal of self-confidence because he knows he is a good coach and has a high level of skill in his particular sport. He looks forward to leading his session because he is aware of his levels of ability and has practised the session a number of times. He is now thinking about a career as a basketball coach. He completes a good session and achieves a good grade for his assessment.

Tyreese, on the other hand, doesn't have a great deal of self-confidence because he is not as experienced or

as skilled as Jack when it comes to playing or coaching basketball, yet he is placed in the same evaluative social situation as Jack. As a result, Tyreese becomes nervous and anxious during his coaching session and is concerned that the assessor and the players are making negative comments about his session. Although Tyreese really likes playing basketball, he finds the situation too stressful and doesn't want to be put in the same situation again.

1   Do Jack and Tyreese behave differently in different situations?

2   How does the interactional approach explain the way Jack and Tyreese behave?

In 1980, Morgan devised an argument relating to the ability of traits to predict sporting behaviour. This argument is called the credulous-sceptical argument. Those who support the credulous view say that personality traits can be used to predict sporting behaviour, whereas people who support the sceptical view say that personality traits cannot be used.

■ Athletes versus non-athletes and individual versus team sports

Previous research suggests that there is no such thing as an athletic personality. This means that when you look at athletes versus non-athletes, there is little difference between personality types. However, if you look closer, some differences start to appear. For example, compared with non-athletes, athletes who take part in team sports tend to be more extroverted. On the other hand, when compared to non-athletes, athletes in individual sports tend to be more introverted. This suggests that in order to study the differences between athletes and non-athletes, we need to consider the sports the athletes play before we can reach any meaningful conclusions.

■ Elite versus non-elite athletes

In the past, it was thought that successful athletes had more positive mental health than athletes who were not as successful or who were unsuccessful. It was also suggested that more successful athletes display lower levels of neuroticism, depression, fatigue, confusion and anger, but higher levels of vigour. However, it has more recently been suggested that evidence which was originally used to draw these conclusions was insufficient, partly because the original work was based on only 16 athletes from one sport, and partly because more recent research has shown that personality accounts for less than 1 per cent of the performance variation.

■ Type A versus type B

Although the type A/type B approach to personality does have some application to sports settings, its greater use has come in the exercise and health psychology through its uses in predicting coronary heart disease. It has been widely suggested that people of a type A

personality are more prone to heart disease because of the amount of stress they put themselves under. In sport, type A individuals are more likely than type B people to continue participating in a sporting setting when the situation becomes unfavourable or when they are not particularly motivated to take part.

Think it over

Can personality traits alone be used to predict both sport participation and performance success?

Assessment practice

1 Describe the effects of personality on behaviour in a sporting environment. **P1**

2 Explain how it has been suggested that personality affects behaviour in sports environments. **M1**

3 Use a range of theories to analyse how personality can affect behaviour in sports environments. **D1**

Grading tips

Grading Tip P1

Give a brief summary to say whether personality alone affects sporting behaviour.

Grading Tip M1

You need to make it clear how personality affects behaviour in a sports setting, if at all.

Grading Tip D1

Use a range of theories to support all of the arguments you make about whether personality affects behaviour in a sports environment.

Motivation

Definition

Motivation has been defined as the direction and intensity of your efforts. Most definitions of motivation refer to having a drive to take part on some form of activity and to persisting in that activity. However, these are general definitions that do not apply specifically to sport. A sport-specific definition is the tendency of an individual or team to begin and then to carry on with the activities relating to their sport.

Motivation is an interesting factor in sport psychology because it is one of the most controllable aspects. There are many examples of when athletes have appeared to be in control of their motivation, often demonstrated when the athletes or teams show an apparent ability to simply change motivation. Think about the 2005 European Champions League final: Liverpool went in at half-time 3-0 down, seemingly having already lost the final. However, the team came out in the second half with a significantly different performance that showed a great deal more motivation and confidence, and ended up winning the match.

Types

There are three main types of motivation: intrinsic, extrinsic and achievement.

■ Intrinsic

Intrinsic motivation is when someone is taking part in an activity without the presence of some form of external reward and/or without the primary motivation being the achievement of some form of external reward. Intrinsic motivation in its purest form is when the athlete participates in his or her sport primarily for enjoyment. When people are asked why they play sport, if they reply with 'for fun', 'because I enjoy it' or 'because it makes me feel good' (or similar responses), they can be said to be intrinsically motivated.

However, be careful when assessing motivation. An athlete may say to you that they play sport because it makes them feel good which, on the face of it, is intrinsic motivation. If you were to probe a little further and ask them *why* playing their sport makes them feel good, and they gave reasons such as 'because I like winning medals', this would actually be a form of extrinsic motivation as it is the external reward, not the feeling good, that is the primary motivator.

There are three parts of intrinsic motivation:

- being motivated by accomplishments – this occurs when athletes wish to increase their level of skill in order to get a sense of accomplishment
- being motivated by stimulation – this refers to seeking an 'adrenaline rush' or extreme excitement

Motivation is the direction and the intensity of your effort and is critical to sporting success

- being motivated by knowledge – this means being curious about your own performance, wanting to know more about it and having a desire to develop new techniques or skills that can benefit performance.

■ Extrinsic

Extrinsic motivation is when someone behaves the way they do mainly because of some form of external mechanism.

The most common forms of extrinsic motivation come through the use of tangible and intangible rewards. Tangible rewards are things that can physically be given to you, such as money, medals and trophies, whereas intangible rewards are non-physical things such as praise or encouragement.

For extrinsic motivation to be effective, the coach needs to make sure that he uses rewards effectively. The coach needs to consider how often the reward is used and the size of the reward offered. If the reward is given too frequently, it will be of little value to the athlete after a period of time, invalidating its potential impact on performance. The coach needs to have an in-depth knowledge of the athletes he

is working with to maximise the effect of extrinsic rewards.

Extrinsic motivation can potentially decrease intrinsic motivation. If the extrinsic motivator is used as a method of controlling the athlete, generally intrinsic motivation will decrease. On the other hand, if the extrinsic motivator is used to provide information or feedback to the athlete, this can benefit intrinsic motivation. The way in which the athlete perceives and understands the original extrinsic motivator determines whether it will benefit or hinder intrinsic motivation.

■ Achievement

The notion of achievement motivation was proposed by Atkinson in 1964, who argued that achievement motivation comes from the individual's personality and is the individual's motivation to strive for success. It is this drive that makes athletes carry on trying even when there are obstacles in their way or when they experience failure. Atkinson grouped athletes into two categories: need to achieve (Nach) and need to avoid failure (Naf). Everyone has aspects of both Nach and Naf, but it is the difference between the two motives that makes up somebody's achievement motivation.

Case study: Extrinsic and intrinsic motivation

A group of young children are playing basketball one day, much to the annoyance of an old man whose house they are playing outside. The old man asks the children to stop playing, but they carry on because they enjoy it so much. After a while, the old man comes out and offers them £5 each to play for him. As the children enjoy playing so much anyway, they gladly accept the offer. The next day, the children come back and play outside the old man's house again. Sure enough, the old man comes out and offers them money to play again, but this time he offers them only £4 each. As the children enjoy playing basketball, they agree to carry on even though the amount is less than the day before. This pattern continues for the next few days until the old man comes out and tells the children

that if they want to carry on playing, they will have to do it free of charge as he has no more money to give them. The children, rather disgruntled, tell the old man that they refuse to play for him again if he doesn't pay them.

1 **What motivates the children to play basketball at the start of the story? Is this intrinsic or extrinsic motivation?**

2 **At the end of the case study, what has been the motivating factor for the children? Is this intrinsic or extrinsic motivation?**

3 **What effect has extrinsic motivation had on intrinsic motivation?**

Attribution theory

Activity

Think about a time when you have taken part in a sport. Read the following statements and write down your reasons to explain them.

- You lost to a player who was better than you.
- You beat a player who was better than you.
- You played badly but beat an opponent.
- You played well but lost to an opponent.
- You lost to a player whom you should have beaten.

Key term

Attribution The reason you give to explain the outcome of an event.

In the activity, you explained each outcome using an attribution. Think about how many times you have said 'we were just unlucky' or 'we were much better than they were; we deserved to win'. These are two examples of commonly used attributions. Attributions can provide thousands of explanations for your successes or failures and fall into one of the following categories:

- stability (is the reason permanent or unstable?)
- causality (is it something that comes from an external or an internal factor?)
- control (is it under your control or not?).

Examples of attributions often given after winning and losing are shown in the table alongside.

Motivation is an essential component for successful sports performance. However, if someone is so motivated that they do not want to stop, this can cause problems.

Positive

The positive effects of motivation are straightforward. Someone who is motivated to play, perform and train at an optimal level will experience increases in performance. It is the role of athletes, coaches, managers and support staff to make sure the athlete is at optimal levels of motivation, without experiencing any negative side effects.

Negative

Being too motivated so that you cannot stop training can be a big problem for athletes. Elite-level athletes are now under so much pressure to perform constantly at a high level, it is easy to see why they feel the need to train more and more. However, over-motivation and a constant gruelling schedule can lead to three things:

Type of attribution	Example
Winning	
Stability	• 'I was more able than my opponent' (stable) • 'I was lucky' (unstable)
Causality	• 'I tried really hard' (internal) • 'My opponent was easy to beat' (external)
Control	• 'I trained really hard for this fight' (under your control) • 'He wasn't as fit as I was' (not under your control)
Losing	
Stability	• 'I was less able than my opponent' (stable) • 'We didn't have that bit of luck we needed today' (unstable)
Causality	• 'I didn't try hard enough' (internal) • 'My opponent was impossible to beat' (external)
Control	• 'I didn't train hard enough for this fight' (under your control) • 'He was fitter than I was' (not under your control)

over-training, staleness and burnout. These factors not only affect players; they can also affect managers, coaches, match officials and team support staff alike, simply because of the work they put into preparing for sport as well.

Key terms

Overtraining This is when the athlete trains under an excessive training load, beyond which they cannot cope.

Staleness This is often a response to over-training. The key sign of staleness is that the athlete is unable to maintain a previous performance level or that performance levels may decrease significantly. Other signs and symptoms of staleness are that the athlete may suffer from mood swings and can become clinically depressed.

Burnout This normally happens because the athlete is trying to meet training and competition demands, and has often been unsuccessful so tries harder. When burnout occurs, the athlete finds they no longer want to take part in activities they used to enjoy. Burnout should not be confused with just dropping out because of being tired or unhappy.

■ Future expectations of success and failure

Expectations of future success or failure are closely linked to attribution theory. You will need to look back at attribution theory on the previous page, but there is a simple rule of thumb to follow. If you attribute to stable causes, you are more likely to have expectations of future success whereas if you attribute to more unstable causes, you are more likely to have expectations of future failure. For example, if you think

Remember!

How you attribute success or failure affects your future expectations of sports performance.

you have won because of your skill level, you are more likely to think you will win again because of your skill level. On the other hand, if you think you have won because of luck, you are less likely to think that you will win again.

Assessment practice

Imagine a coach has asked you to come to speak to a player he is struggling with. The player is completely focused on winning trophies for their team and gets annoyed and frustrated when the team doesn't win. When the team loses, the player says that it was the fault of the other players and bad luck. However, when they win, he makes a point of telling everyone how well he has played.

The player seems to want to play when he is competing against teams he knows he can beat, and he doesn't mind playing against teams he knows will beat them, but he really doesn't like to play against teams with players that are just as good as he is. The coach has asked you to give your opinion on the player's motivation levels.

Your task is to produce a report for the coach that looks at different areas of motivation. In your report you need to include the following details.

1 a Is the player intrinsically or extrinsically motivated?

   b How is this likely to affect his sport performance?

   c What would you need to do to increase his sporting performance?

2 a According to attribution theory, how does the player attribute success and failure?

   b Is the way he attributes success and failure common in athletes?

3 a Would the player fall more under the need to achieve (Nach) or need to avoid failure (Naf) bracket? Explain why.

   b What would this suggest about his performance levels? **P2 M1 D1**

Grading tips

Grading Tip **P2**

Make sure that you define motivation and the different types of motivation. Look at how both intrinsic and extrinsic motivation can affect sporting performance. Describe how having a high need to achieve (Nach) or a high need to avoid failure (Naf) can affect sports performance.

Grading Tip **M1**

Use the attribution theory to discuss how the way people explain success or failure can affect future

expectations of sport performance. Explain how having a high need to achieve (Nach) or a high need to avoid failure (Naf) can affect sports performance and motivation to perform against certain individuals.

Grading Tip **D1**

Evaluate how intrinsic motivation can be affected by extrinsic motivation. Highlight strengths and limitations in the theory of achievement motivation and attribution theory, and say how these affect our understanding of motivation.

16.2 Understand the relationships between stress, anxiety, arousal and sports performance

Stress

Definition

Lazarus and Folkman (1984) provide us with a widely accepted definition of stress: 'a pattern of negative physiological states and psychological responses occurring in situations where people perceive threats to their well-being, which they may be unable to meet'.

Types

The influences of stress on performance are shown in the diagram alongside. Two terms have been introduced in sport psychology that contribute to this explanation: eustress and distress.

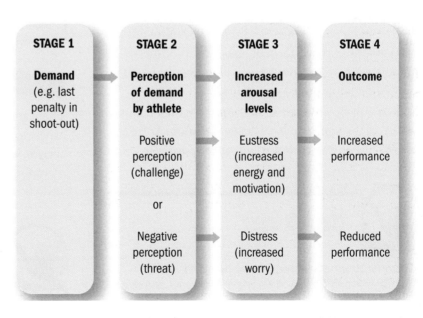

Stress process flow diagram ▲

Key terms

Eustress Known as 'good' stress and is a form of stress that some individuals (mainly in extreme sports) seek out. They feel it benefits their performance, either by helping them to focus or by enhancing intrinsic motivation because they know they have coped with a stressful situation.

Distress This is 'bad' stress and is what you will more commonly know as stress. It is negative, normally viewed as threatening by the individual and is detrimental to performance.

■ Eustress

Eustress is a good form of stress that can give you a feeling of fulfilment. Some athletes actually actively seek out stressful situations as they like the challenge of pushing themselves to the limit. This can help them increase their skill levels and enables them to focus their attention on specific aspects of their chosen sport. The benefit of this is that increases in intrinsic motivation generally follow.

■ Distress

Distress is the bad form of stress and is normally what we are talking about when we discuss the notion of stress. It is an extreme form of anxiety, nervousness, apprehension or worry as a result of a perceived inability to meet demands placed upon ourselves.

At stage 1 of the stress process, some form of demand is placed on the athlete in a particular situation. At stage 2, the athlete perceives this demand either positively

Think it over

How do you think someone who has a high need to achieve (Nach) reacts to having a significant demand placed upon them? How do you think someone who has a high need to avoid failure (Naf) reacts to having significant demand placed upon them?

or negatively. It is this perception that increases the arousal levels of the performer (stage 3) and ultimately determines the outcome of performance (stage 4).

Think it over

When trying to explain the effects of stress on sports performance, the key aspect of the stress process diagram is the perception of the demand. Sports performance itself is a great cause of stress for an athlete. If we use the example of a penalty shoot-out in football in an important event such as the FA Cup Final, the players have a demand placed upon them which they can perceive as either positive or negative. If a player views the demand as positive, he will see this as a challenge which will then motivate him to succeed in his performance. This is known as eustress and generally results in an increased performance – in this case, increasing the player's chance of scoring the penalty. However, if he perceives the demand as negative or too great, he sees this as a threat to his potential performance levels, which increases his levels of nervousness, apprehension and worry and results in a great deal of distress. When levels of distress become too high, they can reduce the chance of a successful performance – in this case, reducing the chance that the penalty will be scored. How do you think you would react in this situation?

Causes

There are a number of causes of stress, but the key aspect to understanding them is knowing that they are specific to the individual athlete. It is common to have a number of athletes in similar situations yet have an entirely different stress response to those situations.

Think it over

What sorts of things cause you to become stressed? Think about things in your everyday life and in a sporting situation.

■ Internal

Internal causes of stress include illnesses such as infections, psychological factors such as cognitive anxiety (worrying about something), not having enough sleep, being overly self-critical or being a perfectionist (e.g. type A personality).

■ External

External causes of stress include the environment in which you find yourself (e.g. too noisy, too quiet), negative social interactions with other people (e.g. somebody being rude to you), major life events (e.g. a death in the family) and day-to-day hassles (e.g. travel to and from games, training schedules).

Remember!

The key difference between internal and external sources of stress is that internal causes of stress are things that we think about whereas external sources come from the environment.

■ Personal

People who are significant in our lives – such as friends, family and partners – can also be a source of stress. Lifestyle factors can also be personal sources of stress. Two common lifestyle sources of stress are health and financial circumstances.

■ Occupational

This relates to your job as a source of stress. It may be that you are unemployed and because of this you suffer from stress. Your boss could be getting at you constantly, which can cause stress. In a sporting situation, it may be that you have had a disagreement with a coach or a manager and you have been dropped as a result of this, causing you to suffer from stress.

■ Sports environments

There are two key aspects of sport performance that can cause stress: the importance of the event you are taking part in and the amount of uncertainty that surrounds it. The more important the event, the more stressful we find it. This doesn't mean that you have to be playing in a World Cup Final or sprinting in the 100m final in the Olympics; the importance of the event can be specific to the individual. For example, someone who is playing their first mid-season game after a serious injury could show the same symptoms of stress as someone who is about to go in to bat in the last innings of a baseball game when the scores are tied and their team already have two outs. On the face of it, the mid-season game against a team you should beat would not be as important as the game-saving situation the baseball player finds himself in, but it is the importance that the individual attaches to the event that is key.

Cognitive, somatic and behavioural effects of stress

When you find yourself in a situation you find threatening, your stress response is activated. The way you respond depends on how serious you view the threat, and the response is controlled by two parts of your nervous system: the sympathetic nervous system and the parasympathetic nervous system.

■ Effects of activating the sympathetic and parasympathetic nervous systems

The sympathetic nervous system is responsible for the 'fight or flight' response in your body. It provides you with the energy you need to either confront the threat or run away from it. In order to do this, the sympathetic nervous system produces the following physiological responses:

- diverts blood to working muscles to provide more oxygen
- increases heart rate
- increases breathing rate
- increases heat production
- increases adrenaline production
- increases muscle tension
- makes the hairs stand on end
- dilates the pupils

- slows digestion
- increases metabolism
- brings about a dry mouth.

Once the stress has passed, the parasympathetic nervous system begins to work. The parasympathetic system helps you to relax. It achieves this by producing the following responses:

- makes the muscles relax
- slows metabolism
- increases digestion rate
- decreases body temperature
- decreases heart rate
- constricts the pupils
- increases saliva production
- decreases breathing rate.

Anxiety

Definition

Anxiety is frequently referred to as a negative emotional state that is either characterised by, or associated with, feelings of nervousness, apprehension or worry.

Types

There are two main types of anxiety: state anxiety and trait anxiety.

Key terms

State anxiety A temporary, ever-changing mood state that is an emotional response to any situation considered to be threatening.

Trait anxiety A behavioural tendency to feel threatened even in situations that are not really threatening, and then to respond to this with high levels of state anxiety.

■ State and trait anxiety

State anxiety is a temporary, ever-changing mood state that is an emotional response to any situation considered

to be threatening. For example, at the start of a show-jumping event, the rider may have higher levels of state anxiety that then settle down once the event has started. State anxiety levels may increase again when coming up to particularly high jumps and then be at their highest level when coming towards the final jump which, if they were to clear quickly and cleanly, would result in a win. There are two types of state anxiety: cognitive state anxiety and somatic state anxiety (see below).

Key terms

Cognitive state anxiety The amount you worry.

Somatic state anxiety Your perception of the physiological changes that happen in a particular situation.

Someone who has a high level of trait anxiety is predisposed to become worried in a variety of situations, whether they are in a situation they should find worrying or not. As the name suggests, trait anxiety is an aspect of personality and is part of an individual's pattern of behaviour. It is argued that somebody who has high levels of trait anxiety will respond to situations they find themselves in with higher levels of state anxiety because of their tendency to worry.

■ Cognitive and somatic symptoms of stress

Cognitive state anxiety refers to the negative thoughts, nervousness and worry experienced in certain situations. The symptoms of cognitive state anxiety include concentration problems, fear and bad decision-making.

When a performer's concentration levels drop, their performance decreases generally because of the number of mistakes they have made. As the performance levels decrease, the levels of anxiety increase further, as do arousal levels. These increased levels of arousal can further lead to increased levels of cognitive state anxiety, which can further increase the number of mistakes made in performance. The performer is now caught in a negative cycle that can seriously harm performance.

Somatic state anxiety relates to the perception of changes in physiological activation, such as increases in heart rate, sweating and increased body heat when you start to play sport. Somatic state anxiety doesn't necessarily mean there are actual physiological changes greater than those you would normally expect; it is more concerned with how the athlete interprets these changes. For example, an athlete could be concerned because they sense an increase in heart rate if they have gone into a game slightly less prepared than normal. This increase in heart rate is nothing different and is actually beneficial to performance, but the athlete can perceive it as something negative. The symptoms of increased somatic state anxiety range from increases in heart rate, respiratory rate and sweating rate to complete muscle tension that prevents the athlete from moving (known as 'freezing').

Effects on sports performance

Anxiety can adversely affect sports performance in a number of ways. It is seen as a negative mental state that is the negative aspect of stress. In skills that require a great deal of concentration such as darts, golf putting and potting a ball in snooker or billiards, anxiety can potentially lead to lower performance levels due to reduced concentration and attention levels, and co-ordination faults. In gross motor skills, anxiety can have a negative effect on performance due to factors such as hyper-elevated muscle tension ('freezing') and coordination faults. These negative effects of stress can lead to lower levels of performance, and as performance levels decrease further this can lead to a significant decrease in self-confidence.

However, some of the symptoms of anxiety can also be beneficial for sports performance, such as increased blood flow, breathing rate and respiratory rate. These symptoms of anxiety are physiologically beneficial for performance, but if the athlete thinks that they are happening because of his or her inability to meet some form of demand, it is the perception of the athlete that will make these symptoms negative.

■ Negative mental state

The definition of anxiety suggests that it is a negative mental state characterised by worry and apprehension.

It is suggested that if this negative mental state becomes too great (i.e. you worry too much), your performance will suffer.

■ Loss of self-confidence and decreased expectations of success

Constantly worrying about an event can make you think that you are not good enough to be successful (decreased self-confidence). This can in turn make you feel like you are less likely to win (decreased expectations of success).

■ Fear of failure

Heightened cognitive anxiety (see page 330) suggests that there is an increase in nervousness, apprehension or worry. One of the main things a lot of athletes worry about is failing. The problem with this is that once you start to worry about it more, you are paying more attention to it. This increases the likelihood of it happening (i.e. if you worry about losing, you are more likely to lose). Heightened fear of failure could result in negative physiological responses such as hyper-elevated muscle tension and lack of movement coordination, which will also negatively affect performance.

Arousal

Definition

Arousal is referred to as a physiological state of alertness and anticipation that prepares the body for action. It is generally considered to be neutral because in itself it is neither positive nor negative. It involves both physiological activation (for example, increased heart rate, sweating rate or respiratory rate) and psychological activity (for example, increased attention). Arousal is typically viewed along a continuum, with one extreme of deep sleep to the other extreme of excitement. Individuals who are optimally aroused are those who are mentally and physically activated to perform.

Theories

The relationship between arousal and performance is demonstrated through a series of theories including drive theory, the inverted U hypothesis, the catastrophe

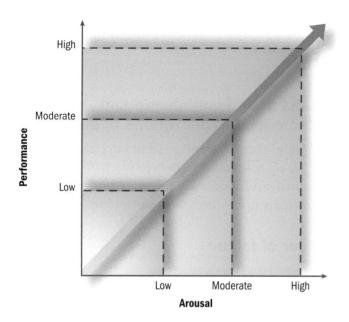

Performance / Arousal

Low, Moderate, High

▲ Drive theory says that 'more pressure leads to greater performance'

Case study: What is drive theory?

An NBA basketball player is at the free-throw line, shooting his second of two free throws needed to tie the game. There are 30 seconds to play in the fourth quarter. He has a good record of free-throw shooting, having hit 87 per cent of free throws through the season, so his team mates are confident of his ability to hit the shot. The player is sweating heavily, his heart rate is very high and his hands are shaking. The player hits the ring and the board with his shot, his opponents win the rebound and score a 3 pointer, giving them a 4 point lead with 10 seconds left to play.

1   **What effect has arousal had on performance in this case?**

2   **Does this case study support or reject claims made by drive theory? Explain your answer.**

theory and the individual zones of optimal functioning (IZOF).

■ Drive theory

This view of the relationship between arousal and performance is that it is a linear relationship. This means that as arousal increases, so does performance. It also suggests that the more 'learned' a skill is, the more likely it is that a high level of arousal will result in a better performance. Therefore, drive theory is often summarised through the following equation:

performance = arousal × skill

However, there is a lot of evidence to suggest that athletic performance is benefited by arousal only up to a certain point, and when you become too aroused your performance decreases.

■ Inverted U hypothesis

The inverted U hypothesis is different to drive theory as it does not suggest that there is a linear relationship between arousal and performance. The inverted U hypothesis argues that at lower levels of arousal, performance will not be as high as it should be because the athlete is neither physiologically nor

psychologically activated to a suitable level (e.g. heart rate and concentration levels may not be high enough). As arousal levels increase, so does performance, but only up to an optimal point. It is argued that at this optimal point of arousal (normally moderate levels of arousal), the athlete's performance will be at its highest. However, after this optimal point, the inverted U hypothesis argues that performance levels will start to decrease gradually. In summary, the inverted U hypothesis suggests that at optimal arousal levels, performance levels will be at their highest, but when arousal is either too low or too high, performance levels will be lower.

Remember!

The inverted U hypothesis states that arousal will only affect performance positively up to an optimal point; after this you will get a steady decrease in performance.

Case study: What is the inverted U theory?

In the Rugby Union World Cup final, a player is getting ready to take a penalty kick that will certainly win his country the tournament. The player is motivated by his coach and other team mates, his heart rate starts to rise, as does his body temperature; but he is able to maintain his levels of concentration and focuses on the aspects of the techniques he needs to concentrate on in order to complete a successful kick. He scores the penalty and his country wins the World Cup.

Does this case study support or reject the inverted U hypothesis? Justify your answer.

The inverted U hypothesis is more widely accepted than drive theory because most athletes and coaches can report personal experience of under-arousal (boredom), over-arousal (excitement to the point of lack of concentration) and optimum arousal (focus on nothing but sport performance). However, there has been some question over the type of curve demonstrated through this hypothesis: does it give an optimal point, or do some athletes experience optimal arousal for a longer period of time?

■ Catastrophe theory

Catastrophe theory is based on a similar theory to the inverted U hypothesis, but it introduces an important concept called cognitive anxiety.

Key term

Cognitive anxiety The thought component of anxiety that most people refer to as worrying about something.

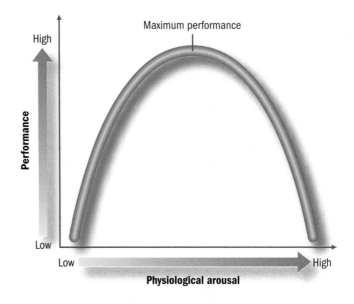

▲ The inverted U theory, which starts like drive theory but predicts a point where increasing arousal decreases performance

▼ Catastrophe theory: (a) low cognitive anxiety (worry) and (b) high cognitive anxiety

Catastrophe theory suggests that performance is affected by arousal in an inverted U fashion only when the individual has low levels of cognitive anxiety. If the athlete is experiencing higher levels of cognitive anxiety, and arousal levels increase up to the athlete's threshold, the player experiences a dramatic

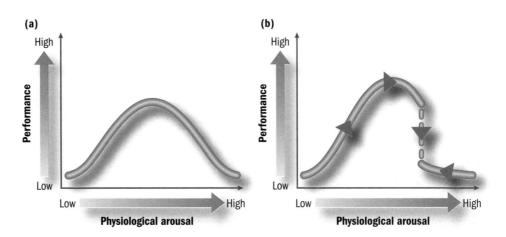

(or catastrophic) drop in performance levels. The key difference between catastrophe theory and the inverted U hypothesis is that the reported drop in performance does not have to be a steady decline when arousal levels become too high.

However, catastrophe theory does not argue that cognitive anxiety is completely negative. The theory actually suggests you will perform at a higher level if you have a certain degree of cognitive anxiety because your attention and concentration levels increase; it is only when levels of cognitive anxiety are combined with hyper-elevated levels of arousal that performance levels decrease dramatically.

Activity

Discuss with a group of classmates the different theories of arousal. Which do you think is most likely to explain the effects of arousal on performance? Can you think of any occasions when you have been playing your sport that would provide examples of each of the theories?

■ Individual zones of optimal functioning

Individual zones of optimal functioning (IZOF) works along similar principles to the inverted U hypothesis. It agrees that at low levels of arousal, performance will be lower; at optimal levels of arousal, performance will be at its highest, and when arousal levels increase further, performance will decrease again. The main differences between the inverted U hypothesis and IZOF are as follows.

- Where the inverted U hypothesis sees arousal at an optimal point, IZOF sees optimal arousal as a scale that differs from athlete to athlete.
- Where the inverted U hypothesis sees every athlete's optimal point at a mid-point on the curve, IZOF suggests that the optimal point varies from person to person.

IZOF and the inverted U hypothesis are similar in that they both propose that, after the optimal point of arousal, performance decreases gradually.

Think it over

What are the key differences between drive theory, the inverted U hypothesis, catastrophe theory and IZOF?

Activity

In pairs, produce a poster presentation explaining the four theories of arousal. Make sure you include the following information:

- a diagram and explanation of each theory
- a note about which theory you think is the most likely to explain the relationship between arousal and performance
- practical, sport-based examples of each theory to develop your points.

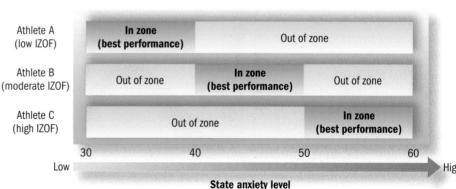

Individual zones of optimal functioning

Arousal influences attention and concentration by narrowing your attentional field during heightened states of arousal. This means that the more aroused you become, the lower the number of relevant cues you can concentrate on. For example in a game of netball, when at optimal states of arousal the centre will be able to focus on the opposing player in possession of the ball as well as her position on the court and the position of other players around her. During heightened states of arousal, the centre may be able to focus only on the opposition player who has the ball and may simply disregard other important cues. Just as a heightened a state of arousal can narrow the player's attention, it can also broaden it to the point where performance is decreased. In this scenario, the netball player would be concentrating not only on all the relevant game cues; she would also concentrate on a lot of irrelevant information such as crowd noise.

Improvements and decrements in performance level

Arousal does not necessarily have a negative effect on sports performance – it can be positive depending on the perception of the athlete. If the performer interprets the changes due to arousal as positive, this can have a positive effect on performance or prepare the athlete for their event (psyching up the performer). However, if the performer views these changes as negative, this can negatively affect performance or preparation for performance (psyching out the performer). Work by Jones, Swain and Hardy in the 1990s suggests that if a coach can get the athlete to view the symptoms of anxiety and arousal as excitement rather than fear, performance will generally be facilitated.

Changes in attention focus

As with most other areas, arousal and state anxiety can affect attention focus and concentration either positively or negatively. If an athlete is under- or over-aroused, they may find that they attend to irrelevant aspects such as crowd noise, which will negatively affect performance. However, at optimal arousal levels, athletes will find that they can focus their attentional field and concentrate primarily on relevant aspects of sports performance, such as the position of the other players on the pitch or court.

Increases in anxiety levels

Increases in arousal levels can lead to an increased awareness of symptoms of state anxiety, which in turn leads to increases in both somatic and cognitive state anxiety. Whether this becomes a positive or negative influence is then dependent on how the individual reacts.

Choking

Choking occurs in high-pressure situations, such as important events like waiting to putt in the Open. It is an extreme form of nervousness that negatively affects performance. It can be more apparent in the presence of significant others (e.g. parents, peers, husband or wife) or large audiences.

However, choking is not just the behaviour of the observed poor sports performance. It is the process that has led to the poor performance. For example, in 1993 Nideffer highlighted that important events or evaluation by significant others potentially leads to physical and psychological changes. These changes can reduce performance by increasing the onset of fatigue, negatively affecting movement coordination or making them rush the performance. All of these factors can be potentially detrimental to performance.

Remember!

Choking is the whole process that leads to decreased performance, not just the decreased or poor performance.

Assessment practice

Imagine you are working with a sprinter, whose coach has contacted you because the sprinter is becoming aroused on a regular basis. The coach thinks this may be affecting performance in different events. The coach has asked you to give some feedback after your initial meeting. You have spoken to the sprinter, who has said they don't mind you giving feedback to the coach.

Write a letter to the coach, in which you answer the following questions.

1   What are the causes of arousal in a sports setting?   **P3**

2   What are the effects of arousal on sports performance?   **M2**

3   Using the different theories of arousal, analyse how arousal can affect sport performance.   **P3** **M2**

Grading tips

Grading Tip   P3

Define arousal and include a range of causes of arousal. Name and describe the theories that try to explain how arousal affects performance.

Grading Tip   M2

Use all of the different theories to explain how arousal affects performance. Then tell the coach which is most likely to explain the relationship between arousal and performance. Make sure you discuss how arousal can be both positive and negative.

16.3   Understand group dynamics in sports teams

Group processes

Groups or teams

For a collection of individuals to be classed as a group, there must be interaction between the group members. This is normally characterised by communication over an extended period of time. The individuals need to get on with each other (interpersonal attraction) and there needs to be some form of collective identity – the members of the group must perceive themselves to be a distinct unit that is different to other groups. The group must also have shared goals and targets, norms and values, and be prepared to achieve these goals collectively.

All of these characteristics are common in teams, but for the group to become a team there are some key differences. The main difference relates to the pursuit of shared goals and objectives, both team and individual. For a group to be classed as a team, the members can

▲ Teamwork is an essential component of successful sport performance

depend on each other and offer support to each other in order to try to achieve the team goals, and the members interact with each other to accomplish these goals and objectives.

Stages of group development

A collection of people in the same place does not necessarily make a team. In order for a group of people to become a team, they must go through four developmental stages (Tuckman, 1965). These are forming, storming, norming and performing. All groups go through all stages, but the time they spend at each stage and the order in which they go through the stages may vary.

Once a team has progressed through the four stages, it does not mean that they will not revert back to an earlier stage. Teams often go through each stage on a number of different occasions. For example, if key members of the team leave, it is common for the team to revert back to the storming stage as the members of the team begin to vie for position within the team.

■ Forming

During the forming stage, group members familiarise themselves with other group members, get to know each other and try to decide whether they feel they belong in that group. During this stage, group members will start to assess the strengths and weaknesses of the group members, as well as starting to test their relationships with others in the group. Individuals within the group will try to get to know their roles within the group and will start to make decisions about whether or not they feel they can fulfil (or want to fulfil) their role within the group. Formal leaders in the group tend to be directive during the forming stage.

■ Storming

During this stage, conflict begins to develop between individuals in the group. It is common for individuals or cliques within the group to start to question the position and authority of the leader, and they will start to resist the control of the group. Often, conflicts develop because demands start to be placed on the group members and because some individuals start to try to acquire more important roles within the group. During the storming stage, the formal leader in the group tends to take on more of a guidance role when it comes to decision-making and helps the team to move towards what is expected in terms of professional behaviour.

■ Norming

During the norming stage, the instability, hostility and conflict that occurred in the storming stage is replaced by cooperation and solidarity. The members of the group start to work towards common goals rather than focusing on individual agendas, and group cohesion begins to be developed at this stage. As group cohesion develops, group satisfaction increases (mainly due to satisfaction from achieving tasks) and levels of respect for others in the group start to increase. In the norming stage, the formal leader will expect the group members to become more involved in the decision-making process, and will expect the players to take more responsibility for their own professional behaviour.

■ Performing

The performing stage involves the team progressing and functioning effectively as a unit. The group works without conflict towards the achievement of shared goals and objectives, and there is little need for external supervision as the group is more motivated. The group is now more knowledgeable, and is able to make its own decisions and is responsible for those decisions.

Steiner's model of group effectiveness

Steiner's model was put forward to explain group effectiveness. It is described as:

$$\text{actual productivity} = \text{potential productivity} - \text{losses due to faulty group processes}$$

Actual productivity refers to how the team performs (the results they get and the level of performance they put in). Potential productivity refers to the perfect performance the team could produce based on the individual skill and ability of each athlete in the team and the resources available. According to Steiner's model, if a basketball team contained the five best players in the world, the team would be the best team in the world. This is because each player's skills and ability are the most important resource for the team. Losses due to faulty group processes relate to the issues that can get in the way of team performance, preventing the team from reaching its potential performance. Losses are normally due to two main areas, motivational faults/losses and coordination faults/losses.

Key terms

Motivational faults/losses These occur when some members of the team do not give 100 per cent effort.

Coordination faults/losses These occur when players do not connect with their play, the team interacts poorly or ineffective strategies are used. Generally, sports that require more interaction or cooperation between players are more susceptible to coordination faults or losses.

Case study: Motivational and coordination losses

In a volleyball team, two players seem to be putting in little effort. When they are setting, they don't appear to be on the same wavelength as the other players on the team, and when they are blocking they don't seem to be putting a great deal of effort into their jumps. The other players on the team appear to be working harder to try to make up for this. However, despite their efforts, there is little interaction between spikers and setters.

1 Where are the coordination losses in this scenario?

2 Where are the motivational losses in this scenario?

3 What do you think would be your role as the coach to improve these faults?

Ringelmann effect

The Ringelmann effect is a phenomenon whereby as the group size increases, the individual productivity of the people in the group decreases, by as much as 50 per cent in some cases. It has been widely assumed that the Ringelmann effect is caused not by coordination losses but by motivation faults or losses. This means that the Ringelmann effect can occur when people are not as accountable for their own performance – as the group gets larger, athletes can 'hide' behind other athletes and not get noticed.

A rowing team was being assessed on its rowing performance by researchers looking at the effects of team size on rowing performance. They found the following information.

One rower gave 100 per cent effort, but when two rowers performed together they put in only 90 per cent effort each. When this was doubled again to four people, each person's individual effort reduced to just 80 per cent. When this was doubled again to eight people in the rowing team, each person's effort reduced to 65 per cent.

■ Social loafing

Social loafing refers to when group members do not put in 100 per cent effort when they are in a group- or team-based situation. This is generally due to losses in motivation. Losses in motivation that cause social loafing are most evident when the individual contributions of group members are not identified or are dispensable. It can also occur when some players seem to be working harder than other players. Individuals who display social loafing often lack confidence, are afraid of failure and tend to be highly anxious. It is often also the case that players who display social loafing do not feel they can make any form of useful contribution to overall team performance, which can be the reason why they don't want to participate.

During a football match when the ball is with the right winger in an attacking play, the winger's team mate, who plays at left wing, may not work too hard to get in position because he knows that most of the attention will be focused on the right winger. However, if the left winger knew that his performance would be noticed (for example, if the national team manager had come to watch them play a club game), he would work harder to make sure he was contributing to the game more fully.

Interactive and coactive groups

Interactive teams require team members to work directly with each other in order to achieve a successful performance. Their performance is dependent on interaction and coordination between members for performance to be successful.

Coactive teams require individuals to achieve success in their individual games, events or performances in order to achieve overall team success. There is no direct interaction between team members during the performance.

Activity

For the following sports, say which type of team they are and explain your answers:

- 100m relay
- football
- cricket
- ten-pin bowling
- basketball
- Ryder Cup golf
- baseball.

Cohesion

Definition

Cohesion is defined as a dynamic process that is reflected in the tendency for a group to stick together and remain united in the pursuit of its goals and objectives.

Task and social cohesion

Task cohesion is how much group or team members work together to achieve the group's common goals and objectives. Although both types of cohesion influence performance to a certain degree, task cohesion is more closely related to successful sporting performance.

Social cohesion is how well the team members get on with and enjoy each other's company. For example, in recreational sport all of the players may get on well with one another and enjoy playing the game regardless of whether they win or lose.

Task and social cohesion are independent of each other. It is possible that team members may not get on particularly well with one another, but they are successful because they are focused on achieving the task. The team could be said to have a high degree of task cohesion but a small degree of social cohesion. A team that gets on really well while not being very successful can be said to have a high level of social cohesion.

Creating an effective team climate

The team climate is a term that is used to describe how well the different players in the team get on with each other. The key part about the team climate is that it is how the players perceive the relationships within the team that will ultimately determine how effective the team climate is.

The coach has an important role to play in building an effective team climate, but the first stage of doing this is to assess it. The two most common ways of assessing it are through the use of sociograms and questionnaires like the group environment questionnaire.

- Sociograms are used to find out who likes whom in different teams to help the coach prevent people from being left out or to prevent the formation of cliques. They are produced by asking different questions to the team members, such as 'Who do you most like spending time with away from competition and training?'. The responses to the questions then tell the coach who is more or less popular. Sociograms are drawn with the most 'popular' person (the most frequently selected) placed in the middle of the diagram, with all the other team members placed around the outside. The names are linked by arrows, with the direction of the arrows showing who likes whom.

- The group environment questionnaire looks at how attractive the group is to the members within the group. The more the individuals are attracted to the group, the higher the levels of team cohesion and the more effective the team climate.

Factors affecting cohesion

Carron's conceptual model of cohesion was put forward to explain the factors effecting cohesion. It suggests that four main factors can affect team cohesion:

- environmental
- personal
- leadership
- team.

■ Environmental

Groups that are closer to each other (in terms of location) tend to be more cohesive as this gives members greater opportunities to communicate with each other and to develop the group as a whole. The size of the group is also important. Think about when you are in a big group and when you are in a small group. In smaller groups, you will have the opportunity to speak to other people more. The same applies to sports teams: the smaller the team, the greater the opportunity to interact with others and to form relationships.

■ Personal

The individual characteristics of the group members are an important factor in group cohesion. If players are motivated to achieve the group's aims and objectives, are from similar social backgrounds, have similar attitudes and opinions and similar levels of commitment, you are more likely to be satisfied with the group members and the group is more likely to be cohesive.

■ Leadership and team

The main leadership factor that affects group cohesion is the leadership style that the leader adopts. Three main leadership styles are commonly used: autocratic, democratic and consultative (see page 343). Another key leadership factor that affects cohesion is how the leader communicates with the team about different aspects of performance such as goals, player roles and tasks that need to be completed.

If the team can stay together for a long period of time, this allows relationships to develop between the group members. A more productive group is also likely to be more cohesive, especially if the members have been involved in the decision-making process regarding what is considered as productivity for the group. Another important consideration is what the group has been through together. Group cohesion is greater (and is maintained for longer) in groups who have experienced a range of successes and failures together over a period of time. This is known as shared experiences.

Relationship between cohesion and performance

It is easy to say that the greater the level of cohesion, the higher the level of performance. However, some research has shown that cohesion has little or no effect on performance. When we think of interactive sports – such as football, basketball and volleyball – these require a greater deal of direct interaction and coordination between players. Coactive sports, on the other hand, require little, if any, direct interaction or coordination. Therefore, cohesion has a greater influence on performance in interactive sports than it does on coactive sports such as bowling, archery or golf.

Leadership

Qualities and behaviour

The best leaders can match their styles, behaviours and qualities to the different situations in which they find

Think it over

Think about different leaders you have worked with. What qualities do you think make a good leader?

themselves. The following qualities will contribute to making a good leader.

- Patience: not everything will work the first time you try it. A good leader is able to give athletes the necessary time to be able to develop their skills.
- Self-discipline: if the leader expects players to display professional standards at all times, the players expect the same of the leader. The athletes will expect the leader to lead by example.
- Intelligence: a good leader is expected to be able to come up with ideas and formulate plans to improve team performance. This could include the ability to introduce new tactics and discuss ideas with the team.
- Optimism: the leader needs to remain positive and enthusiastic at all times, even when everything else is negative. This is one of the essential aspects of a good leader, as it helps to motivate team members. It can be very demoralising to see a down-beat and pessimistic leader.
- Confidence: if you want to build confidence in your players and others who work with you, you must first display confidence in yourself. A good leader needs to give the people they work with the responsibility and the capabilities to make decisions, and to support them in these decisions.

Prescribed versus emergent leaders

Leaders are either prescribed or emergent.
- Prescribed leaders are those who are appointed by some form of higher authority. For example, Steve McClaren was appointed England manager by the FA in 2006.
- Emergent leaders are those who achieve their leadership status by gaining the respect and support of the group. These leaders generally achieve their status through showing specific leadership skills or being particularly skilful at their sport. For example, David Beckham emerged within the team and became the leader of the England national team before he was appointed to captain it. He emerged because of his impressive performances, gaining the respect of other players.

Theories of leadership

The three main theories of leadership are trait, behavioural and interactional.

■ Trait approach

Trait approach (often referred to as the great man theory) suggests that there are certain personality characteristics that predispose an individual to being a good leader. It suggests that leaders are born, not made. This theory says that leadership is innate and that a good leader would be a good leader in any situation, not necessarily just the domain he or she is currently working in.

This approach has not had a great deal of support since the late 1940s and it is now generally accepted that there is no definitive set of traits that characterise a good leader.

■ Behavioural approach

Behavioural theories of leadership argue that a good leader is made, not born, and suggests that anyone can be taught to be a good leader. The behavioural approach has its roots in social learning theory (see page 319), so it suggests that people will learn to be good leaders by observing the behaviours of other good leaders in a variety of situations, reproducing those behaviours in similar situations and then continuing them should they be reinforced.

Theory into practice

An assistant coach of a rugby union team is watching the head coach deal with a disagreement between two players in training. The head coach deals with the situation well and the conflict is resolved. Imagine you are the assistant in this situation and have witnessed how the coach dealt with the situation. How do you think you would handle a similar situation? Why would you act in this way?

■ Interactional approach

Trait and behavioural approaches to leadership place a lot of emphasis on the personal qualities of a coach. The interactional approach considers other factors that could affect the effectiveness of leadership, mainly the interaction between the individual and the situation in which they find themselves. Two main types of leader are identified through the interactional approach: relationship-orientated leaders and task-orientated leaders.

- Relationship-orientated leaders: these leaders are focused on developing relationships with the people in the group. They work hard to maintain communication with members; always help to maintain levels of social interaction between members and themselves; and develop respect and trust with others. Relationship-orientated leaders are generally more effective with experienced, highly skilled athletes.

- Task-orientated leaders: these leaders are more concerned with meeting goals and objectives. They tend to create plans; decide on priorities; assign members to task; and ensure members stay on task, all with the overall focus of increasing overall group productivity. Task-orientated leaders tend to be more effective with less experienced, less skilled performers who need constant instruction and feedback.

Different athletes will have a preference for task-orientated or relationship-orientated leaders. In principle, it is getting the right balance between providing a supportive environment and focusing on getting the job done that makes the most effective leader. It is a leader's role to get to know their performers so they know in which area to concentrate.

Multidimensional model

The multidimensional model states that the team's performance and the team's satisfaction with their leader will be highest if the leader's required behaviours, preferred behaviours and actual behaviours all agree. This means that if the leader is required to act in a certain way in a certain situation and does so, and the group like the way the leader has acted, the group or team are more likely to be happy with their leader and

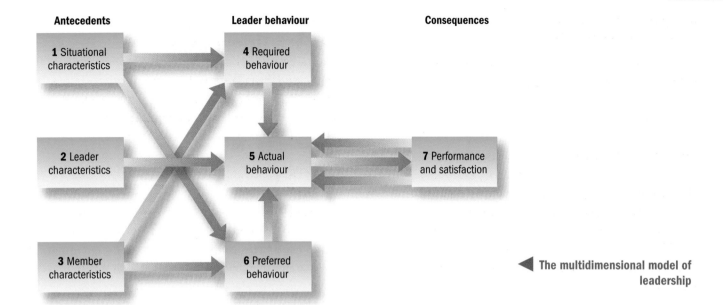

The multidimensional model of leadership

higher levels of performance are likely to occur. This is shown in the diagram above.

- The behaviour required by the leader at the time is generally determined by the situation the leader is in and should conform to the norms of the group.
- The preferred behaviour is mainly determined by the people within the group or team. The preferences of the people in the group are generally determined by factors such as personality of the athletes, experience of the athletes, skill/ability of athletes and non-sport related aspects such as age and gender.
- The actual behaviour is determined by the characteristics of the leader, the situational factors and the preferences of the group.

Styles

■ Autocratic

Think about when you have been working with a coach, tutor or manager who is says things like 'do this', 'do it like this' or 'do it how I said'. These are all examples of how autocratic leaders approach the people they work with.

Autocratic leaders have very firm views about how and when things should be done. They tend to be inflexible with their approach to the group. This type of leader dictates to the group who does what tasks and when to do them, and they often dictate how the task should be done. The views and comments of the people within the group are not sought and it is rare that the leader gets involved on a personal level with the members of the group. This means group members tend to be passive. When working with this type of leader, group members can stop working or work more slowly when the leader is not there, and they have a tendency to become aggressive towards each other.

■ Democratic/consultative/group

Think about when you have been working with a leader who has used questions such as 'How do you think we can do this?', 'Do you think this could work?' or 'How do you feel about doing it this way?'. These questions are commonly used by democratic (consultative) leaders. This type of leader makes decisions only after they have been through a process of consultation with the group members. They actively encourage the involvement of the group, tend to adopt a more informal and relaxed approach to leadership and listen to ideas relating to the prioritisation and completion of goals and objectives.

Democratic leaders maintain their status as the leader by making the final decision based on all the information collected from the group members and their own thoughts and ideas. Generally, when the leader is not present, group members tend to continue working towards agreed goals and do not become aggressive towards each other when things start to go wrong.

16.4 Be able to plan a psychological skills training programme to enhance sports performance

Although it is important for developing sports performance, some people don't practise their psychological skills as much as their physical skills. Have you ever walked off the field of play in disgust, having lost a game you thought you should have won? Have you ever turned up to a game and thought to yourself, 'I can't be bothered today'? Have you ever got to a crucial point in a game and your performance has sunk without you being able to explain why? These are all situations where effective psychological skills training (PST) programmes might have helped you.

PST is the acquisition and development of a range of psychological skills that are designed to improve performance over a period of time. PST programmes involve three main phases:

- education (teaching the athlete why PST is beneficial)
- acquisition (learning different psychological skills)
- practice (providing opportunities to use techniques in competition).

PST programmes require you to conduct baseline assessments, plan the programme, take part in the programme, conduct reassessments and review the programme.

Key term

Psychological skills Qualities that the athlete needs to obtain through the PST programme.

Remember!

Planning and reviewing the PST programme on a regular basis are crucial to making the programme effective.

▼ To help sports performance, many coaches and sport psychologists use psychological skills training (PST) programmes

Plan

Assess

Before deciding on the aims and objectives of the PST programme, you need to carry out an initial assessment of the psychological strengths and areas for improvement in your athlete. This can be achieved through:

- interviews – semi-structured interviews are often best
- questionnaires – these assess levels of different psychological factors in sport and the athlete's current psychological skills (see pages 346–348)
- other methods such as performance profiling (see page 353) and decision balance sheets.

A good way of assessing your client's current psychological strengths and areas for improvement is to use a combination of all three methods. The use of self-assessment questionnaires is particularly useful because motivation and adherence problems can occur if the athlete does not have an input into the PST programme at all stages. Therefore, performance profiling is strongly recommended when obtaining an athlete's self-evaluation of their current levels.

■ Psychological strengths and weaknesses of the individual

As part of your PST programme, you need to carry out an initial assessment to identify the current strengths and areas for improvement for the athlete you will be working with. There are four methods you could use.

1 The Athletic Skills Coping Inventory (ACSI) is a questionnaire that rates an athlete's psychological skills. It shows the athlete's psychological skills in a number of areas including coping, peaking, goal setting and mental preparation, concentration, confidence, achievement motivation and coachability. The ACSI is useful for sport psychology consultants wanting to get to know the psychological skills of their athletes, but it is important to tell athletes that it will *not* be used for the purposes of team selection – would *you* answer it honestly if you thought your answers could get you kicked off the team?

Activity

1 Complete the following ACSI questionnaire by reading each statement and circling the response you most agree with. As with other inventories, read each statement carefully, remember that there are no right or wrong answers, and do not spend too much time on any one statement.

2 Work out your score for each subscale (see page 348). Each scale has a range from 0 to 12, with 0 indicating a low level of skill in that area and 12 indicating a high level of skill in that area. After working out your score for each subscale, add up all of your scores to get a total score for psychological skills. Your total score will range from 0 to 84, with 0 indicating low levels of psychological skills and 84 signifying high levels of skill.

---

1 On a daily or weekly basis, I set very specific goals for myself that guide what I do.

Almost never	Sometimes	Often	Almost always

2 I get the most out of my talent and skill.

Almost never	Sometimes	Often	Almost always

3 When a coach or manager tells me how to correct a mistake I've made, I tend to take it personally and can get upset.*

Almost never	Sometimes	Often	Almost always

4 When I am playing sports, I can focus my attention and block out my distractions.

Almost never	Sometimes	Often	Almost always

5 I remain positive and enthusiastic during competition.

Almost never	Sometimes	Often	Almost always

6 I tend to play better under pressure because I can think more clearly.

Almost never	Sometimes	Often	Almost always

7 I worry quite a bit about what others think of my performance.*

Almost never	Sometimes	Often	Almost always

8 I tend to do lots of planning about how I can reach my goals.

Almost never	Sometimes	Often	Almost always

9 I feel confident I will win when I play.

Almost never	Sometimes	Often	Almost always

10 When a coach or manager criticises me, I become more upset rather than feel helped.*

Almost never	Sometimes	Often	Almost always

11 It is easy for me to keep distracting thoughts from interfering with something I am watching or listening to.

Almost never	Sometimes	Often	Almost always

12 I put a lot of pressure on myself by worrying about how I will perform.*

Almost never	Sometimes	Often	Almost always

13 I set my own performance goals for each practice.

| Almost never | Sometimes | Often | Almost always |

14 I don't have to be pushed to practise or play hard. I give 100 per cent.

| Almost never | Sometimes | Often | Almost always |

15 If a coach criticises or yells at me, I correct the mistake without getting upset about it.

| Almost never | Sometimes | Often | Almost always |

16 I handle unexpected situations in my sport very well.

| Almost never | Sometimes | Often | Almost always |

17 When things are going badly, I tell myself to keep calm and it works for me.

| Almost never | Sometimes | Often | Almost always |

18 The more pressure there is during a game, the more I enjoy it.

| Almost never | Sometimes | Often | Almost always |

19 While competing, I worry about making mistakes or failing to come through it.*

| Almost never | Sometimes | Often | Almost always |

20 I have my own game plan worked out in my head long before the game begins.

| Almost never | Sometimes | Often | Almost always |

21 When I feel myself getting too tense, I can quickly relax my body and calm myself.

| Almost never | Sometimes | Often | Almost always |

22 To me, pressure situations are challenges that I welcome.

| Almost never | Sometimes | Often | Almost always |

23 I think about and imagine what will happen if I screw up.*

| Almost never | Sometimes | Often | Almost always |

24 I maintain emotional control regardless of how things are going for me.

| Almost never | Sometimes | Often | Almost always |

25 It is easy for me to direct my attention and focus on a single object or person.

| Almost never | Sometimes | Often | Almost always |

26 When I fail to reach my goals it makes me try even harder.

| Almost never | Sometimes | Often | Almost always |

27 I improve my skills by listening carefully to advice and instruction from coaches and managers.

| Almost never | Sometimes | Often | Almost always |

28 I make fewer mistakes when the pressure is on because I concentrate better.

| Almost never | Sometimes | Often | Almost always |

Use the following scale to calculate your skills.

- For statements that *do not* have an asterisk (*) next to them: Almost never = 0, Sometimes = 1, Often = 2, Almost always = 3.
- For statements that *do* have an asterisk (*) next to them: Almost never = 3, Sometimes = 2, Often = 1, Almost always = 0.

Subscales

Coping score: *add up your scores for statements 5, 17, 21 and 24.* The higher your score on this scale, the more likely you are to be able to remain calm, positive and enthusiastic when things start to go badly. You are also more likely to be able to overcome setbacks in a performance situation.

Coachability score: *add up your scores for statements 3, 10, 15 and 27.* The higher your score on this scale, the more likely you are to be receptive to instructions and guidance from coaches and managers and be able to concentrate on using these instructions to benefit your performance, rather than getting upset and taking the comments personally.

Concentration score: *add up your scores for statements 4, 11, 16 and 25.* The higher your score on this scale, the less likely you are to become distracted by different things and the more likely you are to be able to focus on important aspects of your sport performance.

Confidence and achievement motivation score: *add up your scores for statements 2, 9, 14 and 26.* The higher your score on this scale, the more likely you are to give 100 per cent in both competitive and practice situations. You are also more likely to be confident in your skills and abilities and be motivated by challenges.

Goal setting and mental preparation score: *add up your scores for statements 1, 8, 13 and 20.* The higher the score on this scale, the more likely you are to set yourself effective goals and produce appropriate plans to foster goal achievement. You are also more likely to plan out your sport performance effectively.

Peaking under pressure score: *add up your scores for statements 6, 18, 22 and 28.* The higher your score on this scale, the more likely you are to find high-pressure situations challenging and use them to help performance, rather than viewing them as threatening and allowing them to hinder performance.

Freedom from worry score: *add up your scores for statements 7, 12, 19 and 23.* The higher your score on this scale, the less likely you are to put pressure on yourself by worrying about performance, making mistakes or what other people think about your performance (particularly if you perform badly).

Total psychological skills score: *add up all your subscale scores.* The higher your score on this scale, the higher the level of psychological skills you have.

2   Martens, Vealey and Burton (1990) developed a self-report questionnaire based on the multi-dimensional anxiety theory that measured levels of anxiety on three different scales: cognitive state anxiety, somatic state anxiety and self-confidence. This questionnaire is known as the CSAI 2 and looks specifically at anxiety in a competitive situation. Each of the scales (cognitive anxiety, somatic anxiety and self-confidence) range from a score of 9 to 36, with 9 indicating low levels of anxiety or confidence and 36 indicating high levels of anxiety or confidence.

Activity

The form on the following page shows a number of statements that athletes have used to describe their feelings before competition. Read each statement and then circle the appropriate number next to each statement (1 = Not at all; 4 = Very much so). You need to indicate how you feel now. There are no right or wrong answers. Do not spend too long on any one statement but choose the answer that best describes your feelings.

		Not at all ← → Very much so			
1	I am concerned about this competition.	1	2	3	4
2	I feel nervous.	1	2	3	4
3	I feel at ease.	1	2	3	4
4	I have self-doubts.	1	2	3	4
5	I feel jittery.	1	2	3	4
6	I feel comfortable.	1	2	3	4
7	I am concerned I may not do as well as I should.	1	2	3	4
8	My body feels tense.	1	2	3	4
9	I feel self-confident.	1	2	3	4
10	I am concerned about losing.	1	2	3	4
11	I feel tense in my stomach	1	2	3	4
12	I feel secure.	1	2	3	4
13	I become agitated in a competitive environment	1	2	3	4
14	My body feels relaxed.	1	2	3	4
15	I am confident I can meet the challenge.	1	2	3	4
16	I am concerned about performing poorly.	1	2	3	4
17	My heart is racing.	1	2	3	4
18	I am confident about performing well.	1	2	3	4
19	I am worried about reaching my goals.	1	2	3	4
20	I feel my stomach sinking.	1	2	3	4
21	I feel mentally relaxed.	1	2	3	4
22	I am concerned that others will be disappointed with my performance.	1	2	3	4
23	My hands are clammy.	1	2	3	4
24	I am confident because I mentally picture myself reaching my goal.	1	2	3	4
25	I am concerned I won't be able to concentrate.	1	2	3	4
26	My body feels tight.	1	2	3	4
27	I am confident of coming through under pressure.	1	2	3	4

To calculate your scores, add up all of the numbers you circled for the scores as outlined below to get a score for each scale. Statement 14 is reverse scored (e.g. score 4 points if you circled 1, 3 points for answer 2, 2 points for answer 3 and 1 point for answer 4).

Cognitive state anxiety score: *add up your scores for statements 1, 4, 7, 10, 13, 16, 19, 22 and 25.*

Somatic state anxiety score: *add up your scores for statements 2, 5, 8, 11, 14, 17, 20, 23 and 26.*

Self-confidence score: *add up your scores for statements 3, 6, 9, 12, 15, 18, 21, 24 and 27.*

3 The Sport Competition Anxiety Test (SCAT) was designed by Martens in 1977 to assess levels of competitive trait anxiety. Although SCAT has been shown to be a useful measure, it is still a personality measure that should not be used without taking into account the situation that the individual is in as well. If you score high on the SCAT, this is an indicator that you are less likely to control anxiety well and you are more likely to become nervous in competitive situations. If you score low on the SCAT, you are less likely to become nervous in competitive situations and you are more likely to be able to cope with anxiety symptoms.

4 Smith, Smoll and Shutz (1990) used the multi-dimensional model of anxiety to produce the Sport Anxiety Scale (SAS), which measures levels of trait anxiety. The SAS measures worry and concentration disruption (cognitive anxiety) as well as somatic anxiety to give you a total trait anxiety score.

Grading tips

Grading Tip P5

You will need to assess the psychological strengths and weaknesses of your client before you can produce an effective plan for your six-week programme.

Grading Tip M4

Make sure you explain what will be needed on a daily and weekly basis and explain to your client the different techniques you have selected so that they know how to do them.

Grading Tip D3

Your performer will want to know why they are doing what they are doing, so make sure you give your reasons for selecting the different techniques, saying how they will be of benefit to your client.

Assessment practice

You are now going to start fulfilling some of the roles of a sport psychologist. The activities in this section are linked, so make sure you keep all your work.

In pairs, one of you will take on the role of the sport psychologist and the other is the athlete. Using a range of techniques, assess the psychological skills of the athlete. Remember, it is good practice to include an objective assessment (such as the ACSI), a subjective assessment (such as performance profiling) and an interview. When you have completed the task, swap roles. **P5 M4 D3**

After you have completed your initial assessments with the athlete, you should complete a needs analysis. This is a written document that outlines what the athlete's main strengths and areas for improvement are; what you can offer the athlete to help them to improve; and some initial suggestions of what they can do to improve. The needs analysis allows you to make your PST programme more effective by personalising it according to your athlete. From this needs analysis, you can start to put together the aims and objectives of the PST programme in conjunction with the athlete, managers, coaches etc. The needs analysis document should be given to the athlete in the second one-to-one meeting you have with them. Make sure the session is long enough for you to explain the needs analysis form to the athlete and for the athlete to ask you any questions about it.

Needs analysis

Client's name _____

Sport psychologist's name _____

The following initial assessments were undertaken (*name the assessment methods and state what they were used for*):

1 _____

2 _____

3 _____

Results from assessment 1: _____

_____

_____

Results from assessment 2: _____

_____

_____

Results from assessment 3: _____

_____

_____

Your main strengths are _____

_____

Your main areas for improvement are _____

_____

You could improve your performance using the following techniques: _____

_____

_____

_____

_____

_____

_____

Assessment practice

Using the initial assessments you completed for the Assessment practice on page 350, produce a needs analysis for your partner using the example on the previous page to help you. Remember to report the results of your initial assessments to highlight the athlete's strengths and areas for improvements. **P5 M4 D3**

Psychological	Physical	Attitudinal/character
Confidence	Strength	Weight control
Concentration	Stamina	Discipline
Relaxation	Endurance	Determination
Visualisation	Flexibility	Will to win
Emotional control	Power	Positive outlook
Motivation	Speed	
	Balance	
	Reaction time	

Table 16.1 Examples of qualities

■ Identifying psychological demands of sports

Before you can start to plan your PST programme, you need to identify the demands of the particular sport you are looking at. Performance profiling is one way of doing this.

Performance profiling is an aspect of psychology known as personal construct psychology and it is based on two main assumptions.

- Everyone has a way of making sense of their experiences.
- In order to understand an individual's viewpoint of their experiences, you must look at things from their perspective.

Performance profiling has five main stages.

- *Stage 1: Identify and define key qualities for performance* – introduce the idea by asking the client what attributes they think are important for top performance. This is sometimes known as eliciting constructs, but it is often best not to use this term as it is quite a scary one! Many athletes prefer to think of this as simply assessing their performance. When using performance profiling in a sports setting, the athlete could be asked to think of an elite performer and try to write down what qualities the athlete possesses. Table 16.1 highlights some prompts that can be used with different clients.

It will be useful for the client to record the qualities necessary for performance and their definitions in a table. This helps both the client and the practitioner to develop an understanding what the terms mean. To avoid any misunderstanding,

make sure the definitions used are those devised by the client. There is no limit to the number of qualities that can be identified initially, but the list should be narrowed down to 20 key qualities. When identifying and defining the various qualities, it is important that the client is made aware that there are no right or wrong answers and this process is not a test.

- *Stage 2: Profile the practitioner's perceptions of the client's levels and profile the client's perceptions of their levels* – this is an assessment by the practitioner and the client of the current level of performance. The practitioner and the client write the 20 key qualities in each of the blank spaces around the outside of the circular grid. Each quality is given a rating from 0 to 10, where 0 means that the client/practitioner feels there is no evidence of that quality in the client, and 10 means that the client/practitioner feels that the client possesses high levels of that quality.
- *Stage 3: Discuss the practitioner's and the client's profiles* – in this stage, you are using the results. This involves interpreting the results of the performance profiles by identifying areas of perceived strength and areas of perceived weakness. When looking at the differences between the two profiles, if the difference is small you could suggest that the practitioner and the client are on the same wavelength. However, if the difference is large this would suggest that the working relationship is

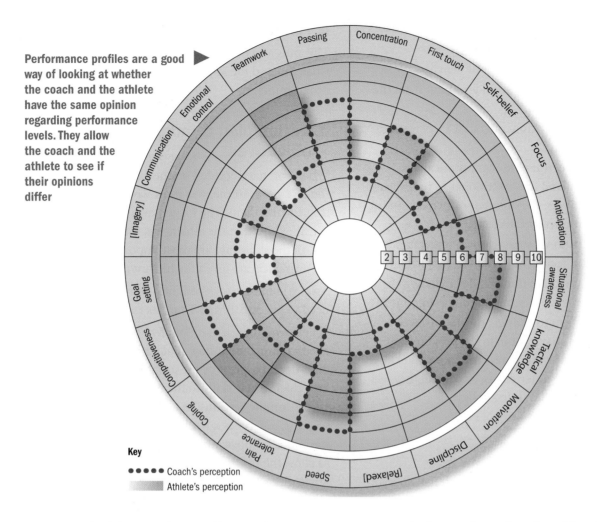

Performance profiles are a good way of looking at whether the coach and the athlete have the same opinion regarding performance levels. They allow the coach and the athlete to see if their opinions differ ▶

Chart segments (clockwise from top): Concentration, First touch, Self-belief, Focus, Anticipation, Situational awareness, Tactical knowledge, Motivation, Discipline, [Relaxed], Speed, Pain tolerance, Coping, Competitiveness, Goal setting, [Imagery], Communication, Emotional control, Teamwork, Passing

Scale: 2 3 4 5 6 7 8 9 10

Key
● ● ● ● ● Coach's perception
▨ Athlete's perception

not so good. If there are large differences between levels (a large difference is classed as two points or more), this should lead to a discussion between the practitioner and the client about why the different levels have been given.

Activity

Using the profiles in the diagram above, identify which qualities have a mismatch in terms of the client's (athlete's) and the practitioner's (coach's) opinions of performance levels.

- *Stage 4: Agree on goals and how they will be achieved* – the practitioner and the client agree on what they would like the client to have achieved (i.e. set the benchmarks for each of the qualities). The results

are used to set the goals to be achieved through the PST programme. Normally, each of these desired benchmarks will be at level 10 – any target level below this on the client's behalf would suggest that there is some form of resistance to achieving the ultimate level of performance.

- *Stage 5: Repeat the profiling to monitor progress* – performance profiling can be repeated on a number of occasions to assess the client's progress. The aim is that the client will gradually progress further towards the outside of the scale (closer to the rating of 10). If the client does not make the desired progress, the practitioner and the client need to discuss why progress is not being made. Usually this is because the training programme did not take into account a particular quality (errors in design of programme), the client and the practitioner have different views on the importance of a quality (errors in communication and understanding) or the client has not put in the effort to achieve the improvements in performance.

Performance profiling has a number of benefits.

- It allows the practitioner to consider things from the client's perspective.
- It encourages the practitioner to tailor their work to the needs of the client.
- It provides an opportunity for communication between the client and the practitioner to resolve any discrepancies between the opinions or perceptions of either the practitioner or the client.
- It helps the practitioner to develop an understanding of what the client feels is important to performance.
- It enables both the practitioner and the client to have an input into the design of the training programme.
- It commits the client to training due to the level of investment they have put in to the programme design. The client's levels of intrinsic motivation also increase due to the greater degree of control they feel they have had over the training design.

Plan

The planning stage of a PST programme comes after you have conducted your needs analysis with the athlete. The strengths and areas for improvement you have identified will help you to decide on the aims and objectives of the PST programme. During the planning stage of the PST programme, you need to consider the aims and objectives, targets, content, resources required and any other considerations relating to the athlete's personal circumstances.

■ Current situation

The current situation of the athlete can be assessed through a number of ways including inventories and questionnaires (such as ACSI, see page 345, CSAI 2, see page 348, SCAT and SAS, see page 350), performance profiling and interviews. All of these (normally together) help the consultant to get an overall picture of the athlete's current situation, which can then be summarised in the needs analysis form.

■ Aims and objectives

The aims and objectives of the PST programme are what you and the athlete want to achieve through the programme.

■ Action plan to address aims and objectives

When you have decided on the aims and objectives of the PST programme, you must work with the athlete to prioritise them. The biggest areas for improvement (i.e. the skills that the athlete has the lowest level of skill in), or the skills that are most important to the athlete's performance, are given the highest priority.

After you have prioritised the aims and objectives, you need to produce SMART targets (see page 157).

When producing a plan for any PST programme, you need to think about how much time needs to be spent on different aspects of the programme. If you are introducing new skills to the PST programme, then 15–30-minute sessions, in addition to physical practice sessions, 3–5 times a week are beneficial. Gradually, the aim is to move away from needing distinct sessions to allow the psychological skills to be integrated with normal practice, but this becomes possible only when athletes become more proficient in their new skills.

■ Daily and weekly content of the plan

The daily and weekly content should be decided by the consultant, coach and athlete together. This means the daily and weekly content has been decided on objectively and takes into account the different perspectives. Including the athlete in the decision of the daily and weekly content also increases their motivation to adhere to the programme, as they will have had to invest time and effort in its design. The athlete will feel like they are more in control, which will benefit motivation. Another important reason behind the inclusion of both the athlete and the coach is to ensure the daily and weekly content is manageable. You can also show how the PST programme fits with the normal training routine.

Assessment practice

Based on the initial assessments and needs analyses you have conducted for the Assessment practices on pages 350 and 352, produce a six-week plan for a PST programme. Explain the programme to your client and justify why you have selected the different PST activities. **P5 M4 D3**

Psychological skills

Motivation

Helping the athlete to increase their motivation to optimal levels is one of the most important aspects of the consultancy role of a sports psychologist.

■ Goal setting

There are two main types of goal: subjective and objective. A subjective goal is a general statement of intent such as 'I want to have fun' whereas an objective goal is a measurable statement that relates to the achievement of some form of standard normally within a designated period of time (e.g. 'I want to lose 2 kg in a month'). See page 411 for more information on goal setting.

■ Performance profiling

You should consider the use of performance profiling within any psychological skills training programme you design as it is one of the most widely used and effective techniques within sport psychology. See pages 352–353 for more information on performance profiling.

Arousal control

■ Progressive muscular relaxation

Muscle tension is one of the most uncomfortable and devastating symptoms of an over-aroused state and can severely hinder performance due to losses in coordination (and therefore disruption to technique). It

can also lead to an increased risk of injury due to vastly decreased flexibility.

Progressive muscular relaxation (PMR) is an easy-to-use technique that can help to reduce muscle tension. It is a useful technique because it increases an individual's awareness of their levels of muscle tension and, through the relaxation phase, helps the individual to distinguish between what is a state of tension and relaxation.

The technique involves tensing and relaxing groups of muscles in turn over the whole body. The process involves tensing a muscle group for five seconds, releasing the tension for five seconds, taking a deep breath and repeating. It is called progressive muscular relaxation because the athlete progresses from one muscle group to the next until all muscles have been tensed and relaxed.

■ Mind to muscle relaxation

The aim of mind to muscle relaxation is to train the muscle to be able to recognise tension so that it can be released and a relaxed state can occur. Common examples of mind to muscle relaxation techniques include imagery, PMR and autogenic training.

■ Autogenic techniques

Autogenic training is a type of self-hypnosis that you do to try to develop feelings of warmth and heaviness. In this programme of self-hypnosis, you use a series of sentences, statements or phrases to focus your attention on the different feelings you are trying to produce.

A normal autogenic programme has six stages:
- heaviness in the arms and legs, e.g. my left leg feels heavy
- warmth in the arms and legs, e.g. my right leg feels warm
- regulation of cardiac activity, e.g. my heart rate is normal
- regulation of breathing, e.g. my breathing rate is normal
- abdominal warmth, e.g. my abdomen feels warm
- cooling of the forehead, e.g. my forehead is cool.

Autogenic training is not used as widely as other techniques of arousal regulation simply because it takes several months to learn how to use effectively and each session can last for an hour.

■ Breathing control

When you start to experience increased pressure in sports situations, an automatic tendency is to hold your breath a little. Unfortunately, when you do this, it increases factors that can be detrimental to performance such as muscle tension. The best time to use breathing control is when you are in a sporting situation that allows you to take a break.

Theory into practice

Practise inhaling, breathing in as deeply as you can, making sure that you raise your shoulders a little as well so that you fully expand your chest and rib cage. Do this for 2–4 seconds. Hold your breath for a few seconds. Now make sure that you exhale fully, making sure you lower your shoulders and fully lower your chest cavity and rib cage, and pull in your abdomen. Do this for about 4–8 seconds. Working to the ratio of 1:2 for inhalation and exhalation will deepen your state of relaxation. This process helps with your arousal levels and gives you a greater feeling of core stability.

■ Psyching up techniques

Psyching up techniques are techniques that are frequently used to increase arousal levels for competition. Some of the more common techniques are discussed below.

- Acting energised: how many times have you seen an American football player butt helmets with a team mate? What about when a tennis player wins a key point in tennis and screams at the crowd? These are examples of a technique known as acting energised. These actions have different common characteristics and generally involve the combination of quick and forceful movements, positive thinking and strong emotional releases.
- Energising imagery: in the same way that imagery can be used to reduce arousal and anxiety, it can also be used to increase arousal. This can be achieved through the use of high-energy images of competition (e.g. a hard tackle in rugby), playing well (e.g. crossing the finish line first in a race) and high levels of effort (e.g. being able to lift a new weight in the gym).
- Using music: the use of music has been shown to increase arousal in a number of ways. By narrowing a performer's attention, music can divert attention away from sensations of fatigue. Another benefit is that music that people consider to be exciting can increase body temperature, heart rate and breathing rate, all of which will improve sporting performance.

Imagery

Imagery is a polysensorial and emotional creation or recreation of an experience that takes place in the mind. It should involve as many senses as possible, as well as trying to recreate emotions experienced through the activity you take part in. The most effective imagery uses kinaesthetic, visual, tactile, auditory and olfactory senses.

There are two main types of imagery in sport and exercise: internal and external.

Key terms

Polysensorial Involving as many of your senses in the imagery process.

Kinaesthetic You concentrate on the feel of the movement.

Visual You concentrate on the different things that you can see during the movement.

Tactile You concentrate on your sense of touch throughout the movement.

Auditory You concentrate on the different sounds that you associate with a sporting movement (e.g. hitting the sweet spot on a cricket bat).

Olfactory You concentrate on the different smells that you associate with a sporting action (e.g. the smell of freshly cut grass on the first game of the season for your football team).

Internal imagery Imagining yourself doing something and concentrating on how the activity feels.

External imagery Imagining yourself doing something as though you are watching it on a film so that you can develop an awareness of how the activity looks.

■ Mental rehearsal

Mental rehearsal is one aspect of imagery. It is a strategy for practising something in your mind before actually performing the task. The difference between mental rehearsal and imagery is that mental rehearsal does not take into account how the skill is rehearsed or what senses and emotions are used throughout the skill. It is the cognitive rehearsal of a skill without any physical movement.

There are a number of ways in which mental rehearsal is used including skills practice and rehearsal, practising for events, competition practice, practising 'What if…?' scenarios, replaying performance and performance routines.

Using mental rehearsal in the lead up to, during and after competition, as well as in practice settings, has been shown to benefit skill practice and development. It gives the performer the opportunity to practice 'what if' scenarios (e.g. What if I did it this way?) to assess whether something different would work in the same scenario. This is often combined with replaying performance in your mind, where you go through previous performances and detect errors in performance using the mental rehearsal.

A link can also be made here between mental rehearsal and pre-performance routines (see page 358) as mental rehearsal can allow the performer to rehearse how they want to complete an activity before they actually start the performance. The use of mental rehearsal of future performance ensures that athletes take time to review physical, technical and mental aspects of the activity and produce strategies that will help individuals to meet its demands.

Although it is not as effective as physically practising a skill, mental rehearsal is more beneficial than not practising the skill at all. It actually helps to develop neuromuscular patterns associated with different movements. It is important for the performer to rehearse both good and bad movement patterns so that they can get to know the difference between the two to develop the appropriate neuromuscular responses.

A tennis player might use mental rehearsal as part of a pre-performance routine when waiting to play an important serve. Think about how many times you have seen a player stand on the service line, close their eyes, take a deep breath, open their eyes and bounce the ball before the serve. What do you think they will have been doing when they have their eyes closed? Often, they are mentally rehearsing the skill, running through the finer points in their mind so that they are focused on the key aspects of the skill (e.g. getting the toss right, getting a full back scratch with the racquet, hitting the ball on the sweet spot and then seeing the ball hit the court where they intended).

■ Controlling emotions

A cricket player is preparing to go out and bat in the Ashes Test series. He starts to visualise situations in the past where he has been bowled out against Australia and then starts to breath deeply and change the image from being bowled out to successfully striking the ball and scoring combinations of quick singles, 4s and 6s. One of the benefits of using imagery is that you can imagine things that have gone wrong in previous performances (such as missing penalties, being bowled out, experiencing poor officiating). Then you can imagine yourself coping with these negative influences in a number of ways and being able to perform the task successfully.

■ Concentration

A golfer is waiting to putt to win the Masters at Augusta. He concentrates on the feel of the putter in his hand, the distance between the ball and the hole, the changes in the ground, the feel of the movement when he goes to stroke the ball and the smell of the green. He closes out any noises from the crowd so that he can listen to the contact of the club on the ball. A key aspect to concentration is being able to focus on relevant cues in your environment (e.g. things that directly affect your sports performance) and being able to close out factors that don't directly effect your sport performance (e.g. crowd noise and banners). By imagining what you want to achieve and what you need to be able to do to achieve it, you can prevent your attention from focusing on irrelevant aspects and focus instead on relevant aspects.

■ Relaxation

A sprinter is in the start position in the final of the women's 100m at the Olympic Games. In this example, the athlete would imagine emotions associated with relaxation and, together with other techniques such as breathing exercises, could more effectively control anxiety, arousal and stress levels.

■ Pre-performance routines

These are routines that performers go through before a competition to help them (among other things) focus attention, increase arousal or decrease arousal. Think about when you have seen a tennis player at Wimbledon before an important game serve. You will see them close their eyes, take a deep breath, bounce the ball and then start the serve. This is an example of a pre-performance routine.

Confidence building

A football player has been taking penalties for his team on a regular basis but keeps missing them, which has knocked his confidence in his ability to score penalties. The sport psychologist could work with the player, asking him to remember having a strong support foot placement, striking the ball hard and true, thinking about where exactly he wants the ball to go, seeing the ball hit the back of the net and thinking about the elation experienced at successfully scoring a goal. The sport psychologist would do this because seeing yourself perform well in your mind is a good way of increasing a sense of mastery. It increases your belief in your ability to perform a task.

■ Self-talk

The main focus of self-talk is to convince yourself that you are good enough to play or perform well. Self-talk helps the athlete to build self-confidence. It is something we all do quite frequently. Think about when have been playing your sport – how many times did you said to yourself 'Come on!' or 'You can do this!'? Everyone does this at some point and it can be effective.

A cricket player is stood at the crease and is having a very unsuccessful innings. Every ball he goes for he hits incorrectly or misses, and he finds himself leaving balls he would normally attempt. The player starts to say to himself 'Think back to when you scored 100 against Australia. You concentrated on the flight of the ball, you watched the spin, you took into account the position of the fielders and you struck the ball well most times.'

■ Positive thinking

This is often used with other techniques such as imagery and PMR (see page 355) in order to increase the confidence of athletes during PST sessions. It is also used regularly by athletes in different sports during the event to improve their performance.

A golfer has a problem missing putts during important events and this has greatly knocked his confidence. He seems to miss most putts that are more than about six inches. When he approaches the shot the next time in competition, he automatically thinks 'Oh no, I hope I don't miss this one as well.' Positive thinking would be good here because the athlete would change the negative thought into a positive one. He could do this by thinking more about times when he had been successful in performance. Using phrases such as 'I *can* do this, I've done it a million times before. Relax.' After the event, the golfer could use imagery techniques to imagine putting from distances while using the positive thoughts to further enhance confidence.

Changing self-image through imagery

Imagery can be used to change self-image through increasing confidence. Through imagery, the athlete will be able to experience success and will be able to come up with strategies as to how they can be successful in performance. As the performer sees that they can complete the performance successfully (if only in their minds), their levels of self-confidence will increase.

Knowledge check

1 What is personality and how does it affect sports participation and performance?

2 What are the main theories that have tried to explain the relationship between personality and sports participation and performance?

3 What are the main arguments of each of these different theories and which is the most widely supported?

4 What is motivation and what are the different types of motivation?

5 What is the attribution theory and what are the different types of attributes we give?

6 What is stress and what are the different sources of stress?

7 What is the stress process?

8 What is arousal and what are the different theories that try to explain how arousal affects performance?

9 What is anxiety and what are the different types of anxiety?

10 What are Tuckman's stages of group development?

11 What is cohesion? Explain the key factors that can affect team cohesion.

12 What are the two main ways that team cohesion can be assessed?

13 What are some of the tools that you can use to plan and review a PST programme?

14 What are some of the different skills that you can incorporate in a PST programme and which areas of psychology will they benefit?

Preparation for assessment

Sports psychology is a relatively new area within sport. Some people are still resistant to using sport psychologists because they don't really understand any of the concepts within sports psychology. Your task is to produce an illustrated leaflet that can be used as an educational tool for coaches. Your leaflet needs to be split into four sections.

- *Section 1 – Personality*: say what personality is and whether it can affect sports participation and performance. Use different theories to analyse how personality can affect sports performance. **P1 M1 D1**

Grading tips

Grading Tip P1

Give a brief outline to say whether personality affects sporting behaviour or not.

Grading Tip M1

Make it clear how personality affects behaviour in a sports setting, if at all.

Grading Tip D1

Use a range of theories to support all of the arguments you make about whether personality affects behaviour in a sports environment.

- *Section 2 – Motivation*: say what motivation is and discuss the different ways people are motivated. Discuss how motivation can affect sports performance. Use a range of theories to explain how motivation can affect sports performance. **P2 M1 D1**

Grading tips

Grading Tip P2

Make sure you define motivation and the different types of motivation. Look at how both intrinsic and extrinsic motivation can affect sports performance. Describe how having a high need to achieve (Nach) or a high need to avoid failure (Naf) can affect sports performance.

Grading Tip M1

Use attribution theory to discuss how the way people explain success or failure can affect future expectations of sports performance. Explain how having a high need to achieve (Nach) or high need to avoid failure (Naf) can affect sports performance and motivation to perform against certain individuals.

Grading Tip D1

Evaluate how intrinsic motivation can be affected by extrinsic motivation. Highlight strengths and limitations of the theory of achievement motivation and attribution theory, and say how these affect our understanding of motivation.

- *Section 3 – Arousal, stress and anxiety*: describe arousal, stress and anxiety and their causes. Explain the symptoms of arousal and anxiety. Explain the positive and negative effects of arousal and anxiety on sports performance using different theories. Name and explain different sources of stress. **P3 M2**

- *Section 4 – Group dynamics*: define groups and teams. Discuss how a group becomes a team. Explain at least four different factors that can affect how the team functions. Analyse how these factors will affect how the team functions. **P4 M3 D2**

Grading tips

Grading Tip **P3**

Define arousal and include a range of sources of arousal. Name and describe the theories that try to explain how arousal affects performance.

Grading Tip **M2**

Use all the theories to explain how arousal affects performance, then say which is most likely to explain the relationship between arousal and performance. Make sure you discuss how arousal can be both positive and negative.

Grading tips

Grading Tip **P4**

Describe the different group dynamics such as leadership, group processes and cohesion.

Grading Tip **M3**

Say how the different group dynamics have affected the team performance you have observed.

Grading Tip **D2**

Say why the different group dynamics will affect performance.

To achieve a pass grade the evidence must show that the learner is able to:	To achieve a merit grade the evidence must show that, in addition to the pass criteria, the learner is able to:	To achieve a distinction grade the evidence must show that, in addition to the pass and merit criteria, the learner is able to:
P1 Describe personality and how it affects sports performance **Assessment practice Page 322**	**M1** Explain the effects of personality and motivation on sports performance **Assessment practice Pages 322, 326**	**D1** Evaluate the effects of personality and motivation on sports performance **Assessment practice Pages 322, 326**
P2 Describe motivation and how it affects sports performance **Assessment practice Page 326**		
P3 Describe stress, anxiety and arousal, their causes and their effects on sports performance **Assessment practice Page 336**	**M2** Explain the effects of stress, anxiety and arousal on sports performance **Assessment practice Page 336**	
P4 Describe group dynamics and how they affect performance in team sports **Assessment practice Page 344**	**M3** Explain how group dynamics affect performance in team sports **Assessment practice Page 344**	**D2** Analyse how group dynamics affect performance in team sports **Assessment practice Page 344**
P5 Plan a six-week psychological skills training programme to enhance sports performance for a selected sports performer **Assessment practice Pages 350, 352**	**M4** Explain the six-week psychological skills training programme for a selected sports performer **Assessment practice Pages 350, 352**	**D3** Justify the six-week psychological skills training programme for a selected sports performer **Assessment practice Pages 350, 352**

Technical and tactical skills in sport

Introduction

All sport requires a certain amount of technical ability. Tactics are required also in order to use your technical ability. Some skills belong to all sports such as running, throwing, catching and jumping. Other skills belong just to that specific sport, for example a tennis serve, a golf swing or discus throw. Tactics are actions and strategies which are incorporated into sport and used to achieve a goal, which is usually to win.

All great athletes and players have tactical awareness. They will think about factors such as the opposition, and even the importance of the game or event. You should always be looking for ways to improve, and this can be done by observing elite performers and how they work with their coaches.

In this unit you will look at the technical skills and tactics associated with different sports and elite individual sports performers. You will then consider your own abilities during competition and over a period of time.

Finally, you will think about your development, technically and tactically by producing a plan that aims to help you optimise your own sports performance.

After completing this unit you should be able to achieve the following outcomes:

- Understand the technical skills and tactics demanded by selected sports.

- Be able to assess the technical and tactical ability of an elite sports performer.

- Be able to assess your own technical and tactical ability.

Think it over

This unit will provide you with the knowledge and understanding of why all sports require some form of technical skill: continuous skills – walking, running, swimming, rowing; serial skills – high jump, triple jump, pole vault, dribbling in football; discrete skills – golf swing, snooker shot, putting in golf or a throw-in when playing football.

You will examine tactics related to selected sports such as positioning, choice of strokes and shots, and use of space. By assessing the technical ability of an elite sports performer you can learn and improve your own technique.

In this unit you will prepare an observation checklist and observe an elite performer. This can be a professional athlete, a national representative or an international champion. Using all the information gathered you will be able to assess your own technical and tactical ability by keeping a four-week log. You can then use the log to identify your strengths and weaknesses.

- Consider your favourite sports person. Have you ever wondered how they have achieved their level of performance?
- Explore the background to the development of this sports performer and build up a profile of this player.

In this section we are going to examine technical skills and how they can be classified under continuous, serial and discrete, with examples from a wide variety of sports. We will then, through the examples of volleyball, tennis and basketball, cover skills appropriate to those sports and the tactics involved, considering positioning, choice of stroke, variety, conditions and use of space.

There are many physical actions in any sport. A coach has to break down these actions into various parts and improve the technique in the correct sequence. In order to understand technical analysis you need to know the types of skills which are present in sport.

Think it over

Individually, consider your favourite sport. Write a short paragraph about your skill level.

- Think about how well you execute a skill.
- Do you use space well?
- Are you well coordinated?

Think it over

What skills do you expect to see in sport? Would you consider the following to be skills?

- A batsman running between the wickets to score a run.
- A tennis player focusing on the strengths of an opponent.
- A footballer mentally rehearsing the skill of taking a penalty.

Technical skills

Skills in sport are the movements and actions which are needed to perform shots, strokes, jumps, throws etc. Coordination is the skilful interaction of these movements. Balance is being able to maintain equilibrium.

Taking it further

Compare your skill level with a sports professional you have seen live or on television. Here are some points you may have noticed in the professional.

- Efficient movement: precision, balance and coordination.
- Positive use of energy at the right moment.

Key terms

Motor skills Skills associated with the movement of the body. There are two types of motor skills: gross motor skills and fine motor skills.

Gross motor skills Involve a low level of expertise and large muscular movements, such as the muscular movements of a sit-up with a low level of coordination needed.

Fine motor skills Highly controlled skills such as drawing and writing. The movements are small and precise, take a long time to perfect and improve over a number of years.

Cognitive skills To perform a cognitive skill you need to use your brain. You have to think about what you are doing. In sport you have to apply tactics, make decisions quickly, and plan and select how to play. In team sports verbal skills are used to encourage and motivate everybody.

Perceptual skills Information comes into the brain through your senses and this is the process by which you interpret that information. From this, you will choose what is relevant and then act. If you are going to perform a skill effectively, then it must be practised both individually and also in a game situation.

Activity

1 Think about a football player who is taking a free kick. Describe how that person would use the following:

- motor skills
- cognitive skills
- perceptual skills.

2 Are all three of these skills used at the same time?

Taking it further

1 Select any sport and choose two motor skills that are used in this sport.

2 Identify the cognitive skills and perceptual skills that would be associated with the movement.

A physical movement always has a beginning and an end. This is not always clear. Skills, therefore, can be divided into categories depending on how clearly the beginning and the end of the movement are defined.

The categories are:

- continuous skills
- discrete skills
- serial skills.

Continuous

This skill has no obvious beginning or end and has a regular rhythm. Examples of technical skills under this heading include walking, running, swimming, rowing and cross-country skiing.

■ Walking

There are two phases of walking: brisk walking; and walking at a comfortable pace.

■ Running

The skill of running can be divided into three phases: support; flight; and support. The support phases can be divided into front support and drive. Flight is divided into recovery, front swinging and back into support. This is a rhythmical continuous skill.

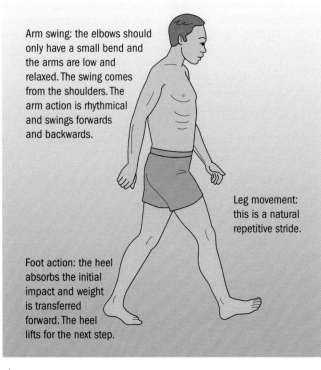

Arm swing: the elbows should only have a small bend and the arms are low and relaxed. The swing comes from the shoulders. The arm action is rhythmical and swings forwards and backwards.

Leg movement: this is a natural repetitive stride.

Foot action: the heel absorbs the initial impact and weight is transferred forward. The heel lifts for the next step.

▲ The actions for walking

During recovery the trunk is upright and the arms are relaxed. When the foot leaves the ground the driving leg bends and the heel is brought close to the sprinter's body.

Front swing: the body is upright and the thigh of the front leg is brought high and parallel to the ground and extends in preparation for touchdown.

During the drive the hip, knee and ankle joints of the support leg are strongly extended. The opposite arm is driven back so coordinating and balancing the drive leg.

When the forefoot is planted there is minimal sinking of the knee; the support leg is only slightly bent in order to maintain the power to drive.

▲ The actions for running

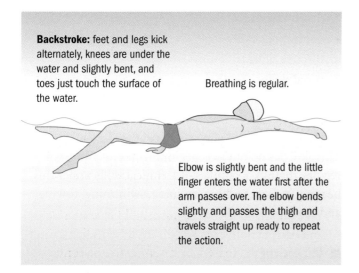

Backstroke: feet and legs kick alternately, knees are under the water and slightly bent, and toes just touch the surface of the water.

Breathing is regular.

Elbow is slightly bent and the little finger enters the water first after the arm passes over. The elbow bends slightly and passes the thigh and travels straight up ready to repeat the action.

▲ The actions for swimming

■ Swimming

A stroke in swimming has an arm action and a leg action; you must also consider the line of the body in the water and the timing of breathing.

■ Rowing

The actions of rowing occur in a smooth continuous cycle. The stroke can be divided into four sections: the catch – the last part of the recovery where the oars are placed into the water; the drive – when the oars are in the water and the power is applied to move the boat; the extraction – when the oars are out of the water; and the preparation for the catch.

The actions of rowing ▶

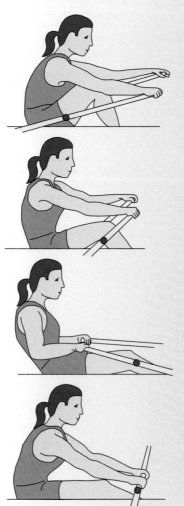

The catch: this phase is when the rower connects the blade to the water. This is performed by moving the feet away from the seat.

The drive: the rower drives both the legs and back together. The aim is to reach maximum force when the legs are about two thirds down and the body is vertical. The rower draws the handle by maintaining the pressure which has been generated on the handle. From the point that the legs are flat the pressure in the fingers is maintained through to the end of the stroke. The rower thinks about moving the boat and not accelerating the oar.

Extraction: the blade is extracted by the handle coming into the rib cage and the rower begins this by a slight push down with the outside hand. When the blade is out of the water there should be no excess movement.

Recovery: the hands stretch away from the body, putting the handle as far from the body as possible keeping the outside hand grip. The recovery sequence does not end until the blade enters the water.

■ Cross-country skiing

1 Stick the poles in the snow at your side and slide the skis back and forwards while remaining in a stationary position to become used to the skis.

Put your hands through the pole straps.

2 Put one foot in front of the other letting the skis slide as if you were walking across an ice rink.

Plant your poles in a rhythmical manner, placing the left one in the snow at the end of a right foot glide and vice versa.

Gradually increase the speed and the gliding distance.

▲ The actions of skiing

Activity

1 Name three other continuous skills.
2 Describe these skills and explain why they are called continuous.

Serial

These are made up of both discrete and/or continuous skills. This is a series of skills which follow each other in quick succession in an orderly sequence to become one movement.

Examples of serial skills would be high jump, triple jump, pole vault, dribbling in football and the 400-metre hurdle race.

■ High jump

This can be divided into four phases: approach, take off, flight and landing.

- Approach: this run is J-shaped, straight for the first 3–6 strides and then curved for 4–5 strides. For the initial stride, the foot plants on the ball of the foot, the body leans slightly forwards, speed increases throughout the approach, the body leans naturally into the curve and the body is lowered in the penultimate stride.
- Take off: the foot plant is quick and flat with a 'down and back' action. The take off leg is bent slightly and the knee of the free leg is driven up to horizontal and stopped. The body is vertical at the end of the take off.
- Flight: as the body gains height, the take off position is held. The leading arm reaches up, across and over the bar. By arching the back and lowering the head and legs, the hips are raised over the bar. The head is brought up towards the chest to bring the legs clear of the bar.
- Landing: the head is drawn up towards the chest. Performer lands on the shoulders and back, with the knees apart.

■ Triple jump

This can be divided into four phases: approach, hop, step and jump.

- Approach: this can vary between 10–20 strides. The running technique is similar to sprinting. Speed is increased throughout the approach. The stride is increased towards the end of the approach. The foot is planted actively and quickly with a 'down and back' motion.
- Hop: take off is forwards not upwards and the thigh of the free leg is brought to the horizontal position and then the leg is drawn backwards. The take off leg is close to the jumper's body and then cycled forwards to extend and prepare for landing. The trunk is kept upright.
- Step: the thigh of the free leg is brought forwards and upwards to be horizontal or higher. A double arm swing is used and the trunk is kept in an upright position. The free leg is extended forwards and

downwards. The foot is planted quickly with a 'down and back' motion.

- Jump: the take off leg is extended and a double arm action is used, if possible. The body position is upright. The hang technique is used in the flight and the legs are extended before landing and then collapse at contact.

■ Pole vault

There are five phases to the pole vault: approach and plant, take off, flight, flight off the pole and landing.

- Approach and plant: the pole is held with the hands shoulder-width apart, the upper hand being opposite the take off leg. Both arms are bent with the upper arm close to the hip. The tip of the pole is higher than head height at the start. Approach length is between 10–20 strides and the tip of the pole is lowered in the last third of the approach. A forward push of the pole commences the plant on the two steps out. The upper hand is raised quickly and the body is upright.
- Take off: the foot plant is quick and active, the body is completely stretched with the upper arm fully extended. The upper hand is directly above the take off foot and the thigh of the free leg is driven forwards.
- Flight: the body acts as a long pendulum and the lower arm pushes forwards and upwards. The upper arm is fully extended. Both legs are bent and drawn to the chest as the vaulter swings forward. This leads to the rock back phase when the feet are almost above the head. Both arms are extended. The vaulter is then in an inverted position.
- Flight off the pole: the push off the pole is with the upper hand. The bar is crossed in a bent position.
- Landing: the vaulter positions his body for bar clearance and landing. The body straightens and landing is on the back.

■ Dribbling in football

There are several types of dribbling.

- Stop and go: jog slowly with the ball, when the defender is alongside burst pass the defender.
- Cut back: cut the ball back behind the body with the inside of the right foot. Plant the left foot to the side

of the ball and then bring the right foot up to cut the ball back.

- The fake shot: bring the leg back as if to shoot. This can buy time.
- Inside outside: carry the ball a little to the inside with the inside of the foot on the ball. When the defender looks off balance or not ready, make a dash for the outside. This gives more space to cross the ball, make a pass or shoot.
- Sole of the foot: pull the ball back with the sole of the foot and burst away with a change of speed.
- Scoop: lift the ball over the defender's foot after making to go one way and then moving in the other direction.

■ 400-metre hurdle race

There are four phases: sprinting, take off, clearance and landing.

- Sprinting: athletes adjust the stride well before the take off.
- Take off: upright posture and forward drive. The hip, knee and ankle joints of the take off leg are fully extended and the thigh of the lead leg swings quickly to the horizontal position.
- Clearance: take off well in front of the hurdle. The lead leg is extended towards the hurdle with the foot flexed, shoulders are square and the lean depends on the height of the hurdler. The knee of the trail leg is kept high as it is pulled through and is brought down as quickly as possible after the hurdle.
- Landing: landing is on the forefoot, hips are over the landing foot. Contact with the ground is quick and the first stride away from the hurdle should be dynamic.

Activity

Select two sports of your choice.

1 Write six skills associated with each sport and place the skills into the following categories:

- continuous
- discrete
- serial.

2 Select one skill from each category. Compare and contrast these skills. Explain the similarities and differences.

This is the opposite of a continuous skill and has a clear beginning and end. It is performed in one clear movement. An example of this would be a golf swing, snooker shot, board diving, putting in golf and a throw-in in football.

■ Golf swing

This can be broken down into stance, arm swing and body movement (the pivot).

- Stance: feet should be shoulder-width apart, knees flexed and posture established by bending forwards from the waist (at your hips), so that arms drop down from your body.
- Arm swing: with palms together, swing arms back and forth, keeping arms in front of chest, first pocket to pocket, hip to hip, shoulder to shoulder, make a bigger swing – arms will follow body in a circular motion.
- Body movement (the pivot): put hands on hips and turn body to the right side (left side for left-handed players), target knee and hip should move slightly towards centre but not beyond, weight should transfer back onto rear heel, turn forwards now and the opposite weight transfer should occur, continue turning until you face the target.

■ Snooker shot

Keep your body as still as you can when you are playing the stroke and concentrate on the cue brushing your chin as you push the cue through to strike the cue-ball. Keep your eyes fixed on the spot where you have aimed the centre of the cue-ball to be when it strikes the object-ball, and you will see if you have hit it where you intended.

■ Board diving

- Start with an erect and relaxed stance at the back of the board – three big steps from the edge.
- Make a three-step approach. As your third stride reaches the end of the board, keep your head up, your arms relaxed at your sides, and your eyes fixed on the tip of the board.

- Make your third step slightly larger than the first two and feel the board flexing beneath you. Concentrate your weight on the foot you step off from.
- Swing your arms forward and up over your head to give yourself forward and upward momentum.
- Lift the knee of your other leg (the leg your weight is off) and leap up from the board off your right leg (your jumping leg).
- Bring your feet together in the air. Straighten your legs and keep your arms extended above your head.
- Drop down on the end over the springboard, landing toes first and then heels. Bend your knees to cushion your impact. Swing your arms down past your sides and then begin to swing upward again. Fix your eyes on the opposite end of the pool. Your landing will push the springboard down.
- Spring up and out, swinging your arms up and feeling the springboard pushing you upwards, adding to your lift. This will project you up and out into the air.
- Bend slightly at the waist as your body begins to fall. Bring your hands together above your head and point them down towards the water.
- Enter the water hands first and let your body follow. Your body should be streamlined with legs extended behind you.

■ Putting in golf

- Arms hang loosely and hold the putter lightly so both hang like a pendulum from the shoulder to achieve a smooth swing.
- Set up with the ball near the front foot, the club face square to the target line and eyes over the ball. It is important to keep your hands level.
- Move the putter away smoothly, the arms hingeing from the shoulders not the elbows or wrists. Keep the putter head as low to the ground as possible. Keep the putter on a line square to the target as you swing it back and then forth. Maintain your tempo through the swing, accelerating slightly into the ball.
- Watch the putter head strike the back of the ball on the upswing, feeling almost as if the palm of your right hand is striking it towards the target. Follow through to the hole with your club, not your eyes.

■ Throw-in in football

- Secure the ball with both hands having the index fingers and thumbs as close as possible.
- Bring the ball over the head behind the ears with your arms loose and elbows bent and out.
- Feet should be a little more than shoulder-width apart, with one foot in front of the other.
- Face the pitch.
- Bring your head, neck and trunk back, bending at the knees.
- Thrust the ball forward and this will result in the whole body going forward. Parts of both feet must remain on the ground at all times.
- Release the ball as it just goes past the head.

Activity

List three different discrete skills. Explain these skills in detail.

Tactics

In this section we will examine three sports, look at examples of skills for these sports and the tactics covering positioning, choice of strokes and shots, variation, conditions and use of space.

Appropriate to selected sports

These are plans which are set up for a specific purpose during a performance or match. Tactics are involved in all sports. They can be discussed before a game situation and be part of the winning formula. However, the performer must be able to carry them out successfully. An example of a tactic in tennis would be to move your opponent around the court. A tactic in football might be the system you are to play. A player or team will go into a match with a strategy and the tactics will have been planned and be employed to meet the objectives of the strategy. Of course, the player or team has to be allowed by the opponent to carry out the tactics.

Think it over

Do you play in a team? Have you ever discussed tactics before a match? Describe the tactics and when you might use them.

Sport 1: Volleyball

There are many words used in sport which are specific to that sport. In volleyball you will find words such as block, dig, set, as well as words found in other sports such as attack, defend, smash and volley. Volleyball is a sport in which you are not allowed to control the ball and move with it. Every contact is a rebound action.

All skills in volleyball begin with a mental process (cognitive skill) because before you can perform you must decide what action is required and then choose how to achieve this action. As you have learnt already, all technical skills are actions and you learn the basic mechanics of these actions. Having done this, the player is then exposed to a game situation where you gather information and make tactical decisions. A player might have to access the flight of a ball and then make a decision whether to use a volley or a forearm pass. To perform a skill well in volleyball the player has to be in the right place at the right time. If you are out of position, you cannot control the ball.

■ Positioning

There are several skills that can help you be in the right place at the right time.

- Being ready: you must be ready to move quickly from your base position to the ball. This posture shows physical and mental alertness and is an essential skill in volleyball (and indeed all sports).
- The 'ready' position:
  - feet shoulder-width apart
  - knees bent and inside the line of the toes
  - weight forward slightly over the knees
  - the spine straight
  - hands out in front of the body.

All movement in volleyball will begin with this 'ready' position. The hips and the eyes should remain parallel in order to judge the flight of the ball when it is moving. While travelling forward you will need to stop quickly by using a breaking step (skip check) to control you body weight. Make the front foot your brake by turning it in

Think it over

▲ 'Ready' position in volleyball

Stand in the position shown in the diagram.

1 Can you move efficiently in any direction?

2 Can you think of other sports which would use the same 'ready' position?

3 What other similarities are there in these sports relating to skills?

45° from the direction you were travelling. There are five essential skills for the game of volleyball. These are:

- the volley
- the forearm pass
- the serve
- the smash
- the block.

■ Choice of strokes and shots

The volley is a two-handed pass above the forehead. The flight is high and slow and, therefore, a beginner has a chance of assessing the flight of the ball and can move to make efficient and correct contact. The volley is an accurate pass.

This pass is used to set up an attack. The ball is set high and close to the net and the attacker can then attempt to win the point from this shot. It is also used if a player wants to pass a slow moving ball to a team mate.

- Player should be in the ready position.
- Player should watch the ball and judge where and when it will be at its highest point.
- Player should position their body behind and under the ball. The ball will now be above the player's hair line.
- Player will approach the ball with their hands in the air and arms slightly bent.
- Contact should be made with the ball above the player's hair line exactly in line with their body.
- On immediate contact, the player's knees should bend further then extend from the knees with the arms pushing through the ball in the direction the performer wants the ball to travel.
- Player should then recover and be ready for the next movement.

Remember!

A consistent contact point will come from:

- being ready
- being able to correctly judge the flight of the ball
- good flexibility of the knees upon ball contact
- knee extension
- using the whole body to complete the action.

The serve is used to start a game. This is a closed skill. A closed skill is one where the environment will not change. Whereas an open skill is one where the environment will always be different. For example, when a goalkeeper makes a save, the angle of the shot

Think it over

With a partner, decide whether the volley is a continuous, discrete or serial skill. Practise the skill and describe the technical demands the skill is making upon the performer. Does this resemble a skill in other sports?

and the position of defenders and attackers will always be different. A serve is the only skill in volleyball over which the player has complete control. An accomplished volleyball player will put pressure on the opponents through their serve by using more power or tactics. There are several different serves:

- the underarm serve
- the overarm serve
- the overarm float serve
- the overarm topspin serve
- the jump serve.

The player chooses a position behind the baseline, behind the serving zone on the right-hand side of the court. The following describes the underarm serve.

- The player's feet should be shoulder-width apart, with the left toe pointing towards the target.
- The right foot should be behind and to the side of the left foot. The player's weight should be mostly on the right foot with knees bent. The ball is held in the player's appropriate hand, the elbow bent and in front of the hip.
- The hitting hand can be closed in a fist or open.
- The hitting arm will swing through close to the player's hip.
- Finally, the player's body weight is transferred from the back to the front foot as the hitting arm swings forward and the ball is struck.

■ Variation

The smash is the principal attack shot in volleyball. The player runs in and jumps above and close to the net to hit the ball with one hand down into the opposite court. Variations that can be used include the following.

▲ The principal attacking shot in volleyball

- Smashing a high set cross court, or down the line.
- Smashing a quick set.
- Hitting the ball off the block and out of court.
- Tipping the ball just over the block (similar to a drop shot in tennis).

■ Conditions

Conditions can be internal and external in character. Internal conditions may depend on the importance of the match in relation, for example, to your team's position in a league or whether it is a cup game. Another factor could be that you are coming back from injury or there may be key members of your team

injured. External conditions would include the state of the court.

Activity

With a partner, practise the volleyball serve. Once you have accomplished the underarm serve, if you are experienced in this sport, experiment with the other serves.

1 List the technical demands of the serves.

2 What classification of skills would the serves be?

■ Use of space

Developing tactics should go along with technical skill in any sport. In volleyball you will need to think about where and how it is best to attack and where you should stand in order to have the best opportunity to defend. The main aim of the defence is to stop having the ball smashed down the centre of the court. The defence can stop this attack option when the block is used to defend the middle of the court against a powerful smash. Powerful attacks in volleyball are made from above the height of the net and close to it. By being in this position, the attacker opens up the options for attacks and gives the minimum amount of time for defenders to play the ball.

Activity

1 In groups, select one of the essential skills in volleyball. Classify this skill. One person in the group must then describe exactly how to perform the skill. What are the technical demands of this skill?

2 Devise a practice for this skill. What tactics could you introduce into the practice that consider positioning, choice of shots, variation and use of space?

A tennis player will always have good balance. Without this, the athlete will not be able to play at the top level. When a tennis player moves from being balanced to unbalanced, a sprinting action begins because the tennis player is forced to move their feet otherwise they would fall. When a tennis player swings a racket, another part of the body, usually the arm, comes across to counter the movement of the racket arm. The player then retains control over the body keeping the centre of gravity over their base of support. When a tennis player serves, the centre of gravity moves in the direction of the arm that is swinging upwards to toss the ball.

■ Positioning

Tracking the ball is important in tennis and you have to follow the movement of the ball in order to position yourself properly in relation to the ball. This is very difficult to do if the ball is moving quickly or is very high or low. Throwing and catching the ball following a gentle arc pathway is the best way to initially follow the

ball. A player can then be encouraged to move to catch the ball at either side making sure that their body gets behind the ball before catching it. As this skill develops, the starting position can be moved further away and a bounce introduced.

Activity

1   Devise a small game which would reinforce the skill of tracking the ball.
2   Classify this skill.

When a player is developing their strokes and techniques, they often run too far from the ball or too close. You can begin by hitting the ball from a stationary position with a tennis racket. By moving the ball further away from the player they have to adjust their body and travel towards the ball before making contact with it. Many players who are looking to approach the net will hit their shot into the corners of the court to give themselves more time to position themselves at the net. However, an opponent who moves and reads the game well will be able to position themselves in order to return the shot or even drive the ball past you. If you hit the ball deep but down the middle of the court, this will stop your opponent from hitting their return by using angles created by the approach. Therefore, hitting deep into middle of the court will cut off the options available to your opponent.

■ Choice of strokes and shots

The technique used by the less skilled tennis player is the straight backswing.

▼ Example of a straight backswing

However, few professionals use a straight backswing because it is difficult to hit a ball with high velocity because the racket stops before it starts to move forward. The most common swing used by professionals is the small loop backswing. The body must prepare for the backswing by moving into the correct position. The foot on the racket side turns outwards and the hips and shoulders rotate. The back foot then pushes forwards. The upper limbs control the stroke but the power comes from timing and the lower limbs. The arm and the racket must generate speed before impact occurs in order to successfully hit through the tennis ball.

If a player stops their swing at impact, they will lose control of the shot and probably cause damage to themselves. Therefore, a good follow through is necessary for the following reasons:

- to make an effective shot
- to avoid injury.

Activity

1 In small groups, select any three skills essential to playing tennis. Classify these skills.

2 Carry out some research on these skills with fellow members of your group. Prepare a short presentation explaining the technical demands of the skills you have selected.

Every shot you make should have a purpose. You should always have a plan of action when playing any sport. Waiting for your opponent to make a mistake is not always the best strategy. Your plan may be to get to the net at every opportunity, or to keep your opponent away from the net. You should always approach a tennis match with a plan of action in mind.

■ Variation

- A forehand topspin drive: when the player wants to attack they will hit the ball deep with topspin in order to push their opponent back, making it difficult for the opponent to return the ball.

- A defensive lob: used when a player is out of position on the court. It involves hitting the ball high into the air and deep into the court. This will give the player time to recover their position on the court and be ready for the next shot.

■ Conditions

Conditions can affect technical and tactical demands, as these examples show.

- Grass court: a grass court is quick and the bounce is low.
- Clay court: a clay court is very slow, players can slide into their shots and the bounce is high.
- Environment/weather: the player may have to adjust their shot selections in order to cope with the glare of the sun or the direction of the wind.

■ Use of space

- An attacking tennis player will approach the net at every opportunity.
- They will need a good level of anticipation in order to know what their opponent will do next.
- Advanced players will quickly identify the strengths and weaknesses of their opponent and try to focus on these by making them hit as many shots in areas on the court they are least comfortable with. If this is successfully done, it will pressurise the opponent and affect their rhythm and concentration.

Activity

1 You are invited to play a tennis game. You know your opponent well. Describe some possible tactics you may use in order to give yourself the best chance of beating your opponent.

2 Draw diagrams to explain your reasoning.

Basketball is a non-contact sport and, therefore, possession is important. The technical demands are strongly based around passing the ball.

- Passing must be accurate and you need to consider the direction of the pass and the effective use of movement and space.
- The speed of the pass is important. By aiming the pass for optimum speed your opponent has less time to intercept.
- A lob pass will allow a team mate time to move their body into a position to receive the pass.
- You will need to disguise your intentions when passing a ball. This will come from the technique of 'fast release' of the ball. You will use both the wrist and fingers and the minimum movement from your arms.

Name of pass	Description
The two-handed chest pass	Position your arms as if you have just caught the ball, elbows tucked in and fingers at the side of the ball. Then extend your arms and push the ball away from you with your fingers. If you step forward into the pass, you will release the ball with more power.
The two-handed overarm pass	This is a direct pass made from a high point. It is excellent for when a taller player is passing over a shorter opponent. It can be used if you are closely marked. The ball is passed with a vigorous snap of the wrist and fingers. When using this technique you should not take the ball behind the shoulders.
The bounce pass	This is similar to the chest pass but you should lean forward slightly as you release the ball. The ball should bounce two thirds of the distance between the passer and the receiver.

Table 26.1 Examples of the passes made in basketball

The bounce pass should bounce two-thirds of the distance ▶ between passer and receiver

In basketball the ball often remains in play after a missed shot. This is called the rebound. A defender has two roles in these circumstances and needs to know about the technique of blocking out the opponent.

- The defender does this by gaining the inside position between the basket and the attacker. The defender should be in a ready position, feet shoulder-width apart, knees slightly bent, elbows out and hands in front of the chest.
- The defender also has to jump for the rebounding ball from a position on the court which allows them to claim the ball.

Dribbling is a technical skill used in basketball for several reasons:

- to advance the ball up the court
- to move away from a crowded space
- to allow a player to travel with the ball
- to find a good position on the court to make an effective pass
- to get close to the opponent's basket.

The skills demanded in dribbling in basketball include the following:

- pushing the ball firmly towards the floor using the hands, wrist and arm
- controlling the height and speed of the bounce
- keeping your hand firmly on top of the ball
- being aware of the position of both opponents and team mates on the court
- protecting the ball by keeping your head and body between the ball and your opponent.

■ Positioning

Most play in basketball is tactical and you will need good footwork. Always position yourself between your opponent and the basket so that the attacking player cannot take a straight route to the basket. Watch your opponent to see which way they might move and then block their path by positioning yourself in their pathway. Defensive tactics in basketball include man-to-man marking or zonal defending. In zonal defending, individual defenders are responsible for certain areas on the court. The tallest player in the team operates close to the basket. In every game the majority of free ball opportunities occur after a shot has been taken

and missed. Success in gaining possession will depend upon gaining an advantageous position by blocking out opponents and jumping for the ball.

■ Variation

Dribbling with changes of hand and direction are used to dribble around a defender. You can switch the ball from one side of your body to the other, moving it from hand to hand. A change of hand goes with a change of direction. A high dribble is used to move from one end of the court to the other quickly. This is the same technique but a more upright stance. A low dribble is used when the player needs to avoid losing the ball. A roll is a change of direction used by an offensive player to escape from a defender.

■ Conditions

Conditions would include team injuries, the pressure surrounding the game and the playing facilities.

■ Use of space

This is important for defending. The defender has to move quickly in order to cover the attacker as rapid changes of direction are made. Full court defences are called presses and the aim is to get more possession than the other team by forcing them into hurried shots and misplaced passes. If the attackers do get past the frontline defenders, then these defenders must use the space and sprint back to pick up their team mates again. Space can be created by pivoting. This is when you have the ball and want to take or keep the ball away from a close guarding defender. Take a step to the left on your left foot, your right foot remaining on the ground. Lift your left foot again and move it to the right away from the defender. Now you can dribble to the right and past the defender.

Activity

1 Watch a basketball game on video or DVD. Identify the technical skills used specific to this sport.

2 Explain the technical demands of these skills and the tactics used.

Assessment practice

1 You have been asked to give a presentation to a group of young sports performers from the local sports academy. They have been studying various sports, particularly the factors relating to skills. Their tutors, therefore, would like you to explain the technical skills and tactics used in a variety of sports. You may select the sports of your choice.

It would make the presentation more interesting if you could provide diagrams, demonstrations of performance technique and video clips. During your presentation you must cover the following.

- Select three contrasting sports.
- Describe the technical and tactical demands of these sports. **P1**

2 Having told your audience about the technical and tactical demands of three contrasting sports, explain in more detail the wider range of skills and tactics required. **M1**

3 Your student audience has received a wealth of information from you about each sport. To make the presentation more interesting, identify the fact that many skills belong to most sports but some skills are very specific to a sport. Likewise, the tactical demands of the sport may be very similar or very different.

a Complete your presentation by identifying the main factors that apply in three or more of the sports.

b Explain the similarities and differences in relation to the technical and tactical demands of your three chosen sports. For example, explain the similarities and differences in shots, defence/attack and positioning. **D1**

Grading tips

Grading Tip P1

To achieve a pass grade, your description must include all the relevant features of the skills used in three different sports, clearly identifying each specific technique. The tactical demands should also be described. Think of painting a picture in words, for example describe the essential skills and the tactics used when defending and attacking.

Grading Tip M1

To achieve a merit grade, the learner must provide detailed explanations and examples of the skills and the reasons why certain techniques and tactics are adopted in that sport, for example selection of shots and tactics adopted for defensive play.

Grading Tip D1

For a distinction, you need to compare and contrast the skills.

In this section you are going to learn how to produce an observation checklist for player analysis. This checklist will be used to assess the technical and tactical ability of a performer in a selected sport. By using an observation checklist you will be able to identify the strengths and weaknesses of the performer.

Observation checklist

There are many different factors to think about when preparing a checklist. In order to assess the technical and tactical ability of a performer the checklist will cover the following.

- **Technical skills.**
- The performer's **selection of skills.**
- **Application of skills.**
- The performer's **tactical awareness.**
- **Application of tactics.**
- The performer's **ability to defend** and **attack.**
- The performer's **shot selection.**

There are several stages which you will now be taken through.

- Producing a checklist.
- How to use the checklist to identify the player's strengths and areas for improvement in their sport.
- To explain these strengths and areas for improvement.
- To justify the development suggestions for your chosen player.

Tables 26.2 and 26.3 are examples of checklists for a sport. Many of the sections are transferable from one sport to another. The criteria can be marked from 1–3 as in Table 26.2 on page 382.

By using a checklist you are able to focus on the key aspects of a competitive match. The checklist gives you specific objectives to assess when viewing, especially if it is a video and you can use playback, pause and 'slow'. You can assess the performer during live competition, training sessions or through video or televised events. Through observation you can identify the strengths and weaknesses of the performer. The advantages of a checklist are that it is inexpensive and information can be processed quickly and used to analyse and inform. However, you must record what is seen without bias. If you are analysing live matches, it is difficult to observe every movement because of the speed of the game/sequence and you may miss important movements. It may also be poor weather conditions.

You may have a smaller checklist which is associated with a specific area you want to assess, for example key skills and tactics (see Table 26.3) below. The observation could be focused on a particular period of time during the competition.

Having completed the checklists, you can then identify the strengths and areas for improvement.

5 = Almost always; 4 = Often; 3 = Sometimes; 2 = Rarely; 1 = Hardly ever.

Ball watch in attack	4
Ball watch in defence	2
Look up and then decide whether to pass, run with, dribble or shoot the ball (**shot selection**)	3
Make conscious pass to retain possession (**applying the skill**)	3
Kick the ball towards the opposing goal (**tactical awareness**)	3
Make a run to the opposing goal (**ability to attack**)	4
Defend by running back towards own goal when possession is lost (**ability to defend**)	3
Intercept the pass (**technical skill**)	4
Deny the opponents space, close down and mark (**application of tactics**)	3

Table 26.3 Checklist to assess key skills

1 = Good; 2 = Very good; 3 = Excellent.

Player's name	Observer grade	Sport: football	Observer grade
Physical abilities:		**Technical skills:**	
Pace		**Heading:**	
Balance		Attacking the ball	
Endurance		Timing	
Work rate		**Shooting:**	
Tackling		Accuracy	
Jockeying		Selection	
Aggression		Technique	
Agility		**Receive and control:**	
Shielding and holding the ball		First touch	
Mental abilities:		Different surfaces of feet	
Motivation and determination		Open body on back foot	
Composure		Both feet	
Concentration		Shielding on front foot	
Awareness including tactical		Different parts of the body	
Creativity		**Passing:**	
Decision-making		Accuracy	
Attitude		Weight	
Self-confidence and belief		Timing	
Footwork:		Communication	
Both feet		Both feet	
Ball juggling		Different surfaces	
Turning skills		Selection of pass	
Dribbling skills		**Ability to defend:**	
Ability to attack:		Is the defender brave?	
Can the attacker exploit the defensive weakness?		Does the defender clear strongly?	
Can the attacker take opportunities to score?		Can the defender counter attack?	
Can the attacker deliver good passes?		Can the defender take responsibility?	
Shot/stroke selection:		**Application of skills:**	
Pass, dribble, shoot when possible		Retain possession	
Create attacking moves		Support other players	
Tactical awareness:			
Make effective use of set play			
Vary the pattern of play			
Recall patterns of play			

Table 26.2: An example of an observation checklist

Activity

1 Using the ideas presented to you, design an observation checklist. Form groups if several of you are designing a checklist for the same sport.

2 On completing the checklist, ensure that the following areas have been covered.

- Technical skills.
- Selection of skills.
- Application of skills.
- Tactical awareness.
- Application of tactics.
- Ability to defend.
- Ability to attack.
- Shot selection.

3 Observe a colleague and practise analysing their skills by completing your designed checklist. Does the checklist give you all the information you need for assessing your chosen performer?

Assessment practice

Your coach would like to encourage you to be aware of how a sports performer can develop through assessment and feedback. For this reason, he would like you to design a checklist that could be used to assess an elite performer in your selected sport. **P2**

Grading tip

Grading Tip **P2**

Ensure that your checklist can assess your performer's skills, how the skills are applied to the game, the performer's tactical awareness, how the tactics are applied, the performer's ability to defend, ability to attack and ability to select the right shots.

Elite performer

Professional athletes

A professional athlete is a performer who plays in front of an audience and gets paid for doing so. They must perform their job to the highest level at all times because, if they do not, people will not want to pay to watch them.

Professional athletes spend a good part of their lives training. There are many professional performers in the world of football, rugby, cricket, tennis, snooker, athletics, golf and other sports. Young elite performers are those who perform at the highest level.

National representatives

National representatives are athletes who perform for their country in competitive situations. Elite performers would include national team members who have achieved or broken records in their sport.

National champions

National champions are the winners of those competitions. The competitions may be for professional performers or amateur performers.

International champions

International champions are winners of worldwide competitions such as the Olympics. The Olympic Games are the world's greatest festival of sport. International champions can be professional and amateur sports performers.

Assessment

This next section will help you assess your elite performer by taking you through the steps that will assist you in identifying the strengths and areas for improvement of your selected elite performer, and how to advise them on development.

Competitive situation

If you analyse an elite performer in a competitive situation, you will have a more balanced picture of that particular player because they are being put under pressure physically, psychologically and socially. Analysis gained in competitive situations can be used to provide feedback for the performer, which then leads to improved player performance.

Use of observation checklist or performance profiling

You have produced an observation checklist and this checklist is now going to be used to identify the strengths and areas for improvement of your selected elite performer. You may wish to use a performance profile.

Performance profiling allows the performer and coach to focus on goals which improve performance. Why use a performance profile? A performance profile:

- highlights perceived strengths and areas for improvement
- monitors change
- identifies any mismatch between the perceptions of the coach and the player
- analyses performance following a competition.

Think it over

If you were to select just six qualities that an elite performer must possess, which qualities would you choose and why?

Experienced performers should select 6–8 goals to work on. Once the goals are identified from the performance profile, strategies would be put into place to achieve the goals.

Strengths

This section will assist you in identifying the strengths in the technical and tactical ability of an elite performer.

■ Specific skills

Elite performers are those athletes who are at the highest level in their sport. They can be defined as those in the top 5 per cent of their group.

- An elite performer has an innate ability in their sport and their technical and tactical ability is very strong.
- They are confident performers and have high levels of energy, speed, strength and power.

Activity

1 Complete a list of as many qualities as possible that you feel are essential for elite sports performance in your selected sport. Qualities may include technical, tactical, physical, mental and lifestyle factors. Examples are shown in Table 26.4.

Technical	Tactical	Physical	Mental	Lifestyle
Passing	Creating space	Speed	Determination	Diet
Shooting	Closing down	Stamina	Concentration	Hydration
Tackling	Communication	Flexibility	Setting goals	Positive attitude
Smash	System of play	Strength	Mental rehearsal	Preparation
Serve	Ability to play different systems	Power	Mental toughness	Punctuality

Table 26.4 An example of a performance profile

- When things go wrong, elite performers persevere. Regular cardiovascular exercise raises their ability to cope.
- They are disciplined people and should be high in self-control. Their tactics are planned and executed.
- An elite performer can put tactics and ideas into practice; they can experiment and dismiss movements that are not working.

When assessing an elite performer's skill level, you would identify qualities which show mental toughness – qualities such as the ability to deal with pressure and anxiety. There must also be a great desire within them to achieve. Their focus and concentration will be strong. They will be highly skilled. An example of a specific skill might be a footballer who has a talent for dribbling with the ball. This skill would unsettle defenders, lead to crossing and shooting opportunities and create a positive attitude in the team. Another performer may have a powerful tennis serve or another a strong golf swing.

Activity

1 Name the sports performer who possesses all of the identified strengths.

2 There are many professional sports performers who are termed elite performers but who do not possess all of the identified strengths. Name a sample of these from different sports and discuss their strengths and weaknesses.

■ Specific techniques

Technique is the way the action is carried out. Many elite sports performers carry out the same skill with a different technique. Skills can be executed in a variety of ways. Technical requirements in sport include passing, shooting, receiving a ball, the golf swing, rowing and bowling in cricket. You will assess a performer's technique on the results it brings them. If the technique is successful for them, then the performer will stay with the technique.

Activity

1 In small groups, choose a skill, for example a serve in tennis. Research the skill and discuss the differences in technique.

2 Select a skill which is related to the elite performer you have selected. Examine this skill.

3 Compare and contrast the same skill with another elite performer. Define the differences.

■ Tactical awareness

Tactical awareness is the ability to make the correct choice of strategies and tactics relative to the strengths and weaknesses of the opposing player or team. Through having a game plan, the performer can:

- control the structure of the game
- exploit the opposition's defensive weaknesses
- reduce the likelihood of conceding goals, points or runs
- avoid wasting energy
- increase the attempts on goals/opportunities to score points
- create more attacking moves
- make effective use of set plays
- vary the game.

When assessing an elite performer's tactical awareness you will consider the above factors. How successful is the performer at varying the game, creating attacking opportunities and making use of set play and dead balls?

■ Fitness levels

In order to determine sports performer's fitness levels it is necessary to carry out a series of fitness tests. Once fitness has been evaluated, the performer and coach can consider several factors:

- the effect of the present training programme
- whether the performer needs to train harder
- the feedback between the player and the coach
- the objectives of the training programme

- the level of the competition the performer is being prepared for
- the revising of the training programme.

Tests will not, however, predict what level of performance the elite performer will achieve in the competitive situation. The results of fitness tests can motivate performers to train harder and may also assist coaches and managers with decisions about bringing players back into full training or into competitive situations.

When observing and assessing an elite performer's fitness level, you will be aware that each sport makes different demands on the player. When cycling, swimming and running the energy level is constant. In football and other sports it varies in intensity because there are periods of jogging, walking, moderately paced running and short bursts of speed. When assessing your performer you will assess, for example, the continuous bursts of speed and how quickly the performer can recover. The greater the performer's aerobic and anaerobic power, the quicker the player can recover from high intensity bursts and repeat the high intensity sprint again.

Taking it further

1 Research exercises that will improve aerobic power for a specific sport.

2 Research exercises that will improve anaerobic power.

3 Why would interval training benefit a sport such as football?

4 In a 100m sprint, which systems would you need to develop most – aerobic or anaerobic? Explain your answer.

■ Ability to read the game

Elite performers will have an ability to read a game. This is a perceptual ability rather than a visual one. Elite performers can:

- anticipate the opponent's movement direction or the pass or stroke which is to be made
- predict what would be likely to happen in a range of different situations based on previous experience

– for example, the performer will recognise the potential passing/stroke/shot option to the player in possession
- recall patterns of play.

Through observation you will assess how your elite performer reacts, for example, under pressure. Under pressure elite performers can pick up a situation by recognising the body shape of an opponent and can anticipate what happens next. They can pick out players who are less of a potential threat to current play and identify the critical players in a given scenario. During competition, elite performers are aware of defensive and offensive patterns used by opponents and can recognise the evolving patterns. Does your elite performer fulfil all these functions?

Areas for improvement

This next section will assist you when assessing areas for improvement in the technical and tactical ability of an elite performer. You will need to consider all the following factors and decide whether your selected elite performer needs to improve in the following areas.

■ Attacking

When attacking, does the performer take on the responsibility or pass it to someone else? Does the performer take every opportunity to attack? Areas for improvement may be in set play situations. Consider whether performers fulfil their roles, for example is the attacking player protected from a defender in order to have a clear shot on goal. Do the attacking players create space and when they pass is it a quality pass?

Attacking performers will:

- score points/goals
- create chances to score points/goals
- deliver good shots
- deliver good passes
- attempt to be the first to the ball
- shoot or attempt to win a point at every opportunity
- select the right shot/stroke
- be aware of team mates.

Defending

You may wish to consider the roles and responsibilities of defending such as marking, challenging and blocking. There may be little understanding between the defenders. A player may have to spend more time developing defensive shots. Therefore, think about the following.

- Does the defender get caught out or is the opponent stopped from playing attacking strokes/shots?
- Is it man-to-man marking or zonal marking?
- Are the defenders brave?
- Are the clearances strong?
- Can the performer counter attack?
- Does the performer take responsibility during set play?

Activity

1 Design a checklist that concentrates only on attacking and defending.

2 Watch a video or DVD of an elite performer and assess that player considering the checklist criteria.

Specific skills

An important function for coaches is to advise performers on how to perform skills correctly. It is a process that requires a good knowledge of the specific skills and analysis based on observation and assessment of these skills. Through correction of specific skills, the player's performance will be enhanced.

Specific techniques

Having identified the specific skills for improvement, a coach would break down the skill to assess the technique. Most skills have four identifiable phases.

- Initiation phase: this is sometimes called the 'approach' or the 'getting ready' phase. This is the position adopted in order to begin the skill and to prepare for the next phase.

- Preparation phase: this is sometimes called the 'wind up' phase or 'withdrawal' phase. This is the specific action required to prepare execution.
- Execution phase: this is the 'action' or 'motion' phase. It refers to the actual production of the skill.
- Follow through phase: this is sometimes called the 'recovery' or 'completion' phase. This refers to the movements which ensure that the skill is properly finished off. Techniques are improved by identifying sub-phases but the sub-phases are integral parts of a phase.

Fitness

All sports performers benefit from fitness training programmes. Many sports are physically demanding and are characterised by activities such as running, jumping, turning, throwing or serving. Fitness training can help the performer meet the physical demands of their chosen sport and, therefore, maintain the technical abilities throughout a match, game or performance. Every performer, no matter what level they are at, can benefit from a fitness training programme. There are three different types of fitness training:

- aerobic training
- anaerobic training
- specific muscle training.

These areas are covered under Training in the Development section.

Development

In this section you will consider factors which will assist you with assessing the development of the technical and tactical ability of an elite performer.

Training

The principle of training dictates that training should be specific to the sport. Nevertheless, there are circumstances in which components of performance must be taken from a game context for particular targeted training. This is the case with strength training. For example, footballers and tennis players do not have to change their body shape like rugby players and body builders.

Training should also focus on tactical needs. The choice of practices will give the coach and performer the opportunity to concentrate on detail. In this case, there would be four phases to the practice.

- The practice is shown as a whole.
- The tactics are clarified, focusing on the specific element which needs working on.
- The practice is shown again.
- The performer practises while the coach gives feedback.

Training may be to develop a specific skill. Here, the coach will give a lot of feedback to the performer regarding any problems.

Training may also develop strength and power. Strength refers to the neuromuscular system to apply forces. Power is 'speed strength' – that is, the ability to apply force quickly. Muscles will become stronger if they are exposed to a higher level of stress above that to which they are accustomed.

The exposure of muscles to overload can be changed through:

- the amount of training, e.g. the number of repetitions, sets and training days
- the rest interval between sets and exercise
- the intensity of training, that is, the load or weight used.

The development of muscle strength is an important requirement for sports performers. Muscle strength contributes to the development of power in running, jumping and kicking activities, as well as providing stabilisation of limbs and joints.

Resistance training should be included in training programmes to enhance muscle strength, and continue in order to retain this strength. In order to achieve quick results, the muscles used in individual sports will be trained specifically. This training is called specific muscle training.

Muscle relaxation exercises involve alternate tensing and relaxing of muscles starting with your forehead and extending to your feet. Through this system you can learn to relax specific muscle groups on command and to differentiate increases and decreases in muscle tension.

Aerobic training can be divided into three components:

- aerobic high-intensity training
- aerobic low-intensity training
- recovery training.

The aims of aerobic training are to increase the capacity of the oxygen transporting system and to increase muscle capacity during long periods of training. Aerobic training will also help the performer to recover quickly after a period of high-intensity exercise and put more effort into the next competition.

As the performer does not tire so easily, the technical performance will not deteriorate and concentration can be maintained throughout performance. Elite players are required to have a high level of physical fitness. The fitness of the performer can be assessed in a variety of ways. This can be through observation during performance, performance tests, and physiological measures during simulated performance. You would assess the performer's fitness by the level of fatigue at the end of a match. The aerobic system contributes most when the activity is low to moderate intensity. That is jogging and running below maximum.

Anaerobic fitness training increases your ability to act quickly and produce power during high-intensity exercise, and also to increase your capacity to continuously produce power and energy through the anaerobic system. It is also important for recovery after a period of high-intensity exercise. The benefit to performers would be found in acceleration, sprinting, tackling, jumping, shooting and serving. The types of training can be divided into speed training and speed endurance training.

Speed is important to performers for three reasons.

- To perceive situations that require an immediate response.
- To take appropriate action immediately.
- To increase their ability to take this action.

For example, during certain situations a player has to produce force to perform an activity such as sprinting and a quick change in direction. You could assess the performer's change of activities: how often does the player sprint and for how long? Does the player recover quickly?

▲ A player has to produce force to perform an activity

Agility is the ability to change direction rapidly and is dependent on factors such as strength, speed, balance and coordination. Due to the dynamic nature of many sports it is important that performers possess good levels of agility. How many times does your performer rapidly change direction? In what skill do they display coordination and balance? What is the strength displayed when playing attacking shots?

Training can be used to increase competitiveness. When training, factors such as whether the performer or team is in a long run of defeats or wins would be considered. Either situation would contribute to the content of a training programme.

Activity

1 What would you introduce into a training programme for a team that has had a long run of defeats?

2 Explain why you would introduce this type of training.

A coach should break the monotony of training and introduce surprises, but it is also important that performers go through well-known routines to strengthen areas in which they excel.

■ Competition

Performers develop through competition. Competition can be introduced through training and matches. Elite performers gain knowledge of their sport, which allows them to solve sport-related problems under pressurised game situations. In competitive situations, as well as technical and tactical skills being important, an elite player will be assessed on psychological factors also, such as concentration, confidence and attitude.

Top-level competitive performance has to be supplemented with a strength and conditioning process. To assist with all-round fitness, elite performers seek out coaches, nutritionists, fitness experts and psychologists to help them perform with maximum efficiency. Endurance training in all sport activities is now being recognised as important, regardless of whether it involves sprinting, is slow skilled or of an endurance nature. Exercise must be specific to the type of strength required. You would assess strength by observing the power your elite player possesses, for example kicking, throw-in, passing, strokes/shots, bursts of speed etc.

■ Specific coaching/coaches

The coach is responsible for creating the learning situations in a performer's development. Their training programme and methods should always be interesting, stimulating and exciting for the performer. There may be many setbacks for the performer and one of the many skills of the coach is to motivate the performer in spite of these setbacks. The coach has two main roles.

- To educate the performer to make the correct decision.
- To equip the performer with the necessary skills to do this.

A coach will design effective ways to explain important points to their performers. For example:

- What needs to be practised?
- When will it be practised?
- Where will it be practised?
- Who will be involved in the practice?
- How will it be practised?

In a study by Dubois (1981) of youth coaches, there was a strong link between coaches who gave a lot of support and team performance. If a coach, therefore, gives their player/team a high level of support, you would expect that performer/team to have:

- increased levels of self-satisfaction
- a desire to remain in the game/sport longer
- lower anxiety levels
- higher levels of self-esteem
- higher levels of performance.

A coach should have a high level of knowledge of their sport and it is the application of this knowledge and skill which separates the excellent coach from the average one. A coach can be assessed on their qualifications and past experiences but it will be on the results of their performers by which they will be judged. If the performance of a sports performer is to be enhanced, it is how the coach facilitates the learning in that player that is important. A coach should receive feedback about their coaching strategies and methods. Most are looking for new ideas. When assessing an elite performer, a training session observation would identify strengths and areas for development of the coach.

A coach must be able to adapt to all kinds of different situations and scenarios. The emphasis on training is the biggest factor that will determine their effectiveness. Another factor which affects the development of performance is the influence the coach has over the performer. What style do you recognise in a coach?

- An autocratic style: here, the coach will play a leading role in the decision-making process and will expect the performer to follow their set plan.
- A democratic style: here, the performer will be involved in the decision-making process and play a far more active role in the plan.

■ Observational analysis

Performers develop and improve through analysis of their performance. The characteristics of their game are examined alongside sports-specific assessments. Their strengths and areas for improvement can be identified and assessed as a means of improving the player's development. Research on elite performers includes the following:

- physical development
- psychological development
- sociological development.

These three factors need to be integrated and explored to find out what separates an elite sports performer from their counterparts.

Competitive performance can be examined through observation. Data is collected by the use of video analysis of the performer during competitive matches. Video evidence is valuable because it can be rewound,

Tactics are discussed before a game ▶

paused and slowed down, and this makes analysing performance easier.

Research is concerned with either quantitative or qualitative techniques depending on the proposed nature of the research.

Think it over

How many sports on television record and analyse match statistics for their viewers? This type of data is quantitative. On your first viewing of a televised match, pay close attention to what the commentators say and this will help you with observation techniques.

Video analysis provides a means of collecting quantitative and qualitative data to assess the characteristics of individual and team performance. Their performance can then be developed through feedback. Observation can provide a wide range of data from the modern computer tracking systems to the handwritten notation system. Through observation, you can assess the performer's physical performance ranging from low-intensity movements (e.g. walking or jogging) to high intensity ones (e.g. sprinting). Assessment from observation can play a vital role in assessing fitness and, thus, implementing specific training regimes. This may be broken down into skill and technique activities for the performer. The success rate of important match actions, for example serves, can be analysed and the ensuing consequences of the results could mean a specific coach spending time with the performer developing this action.

Remember!

Video evidence provides a permanent record of tactical and technical performance.

Qualitative data was analysed at an international competition based on the successful execution of techniques performed. The players were grouped as defenders, midfielders, attackers and goalkeepers. There were also comparisons made between successful teams and unsuccessful ones. The test was used to compare the differences in technical ability between the positions in the successful and unsuccessful teams. The results of the study showed that when analysing a football player, a coach must take into account the skills required by each position and, therefore, select players whose role is within that position in the team.

Think it over

Do you think a training session must accurately meet the needs of the individual and their position within the team? Think about how often a football player is played out of position due to the tactics the coach adopts. Does this have a negative effect on that particular individual's performance? Discuss.

Activity

Observe 30 minutes of a competitive match.

1 Track a player, observing their technical and tactical skills and record your findings in any form of notation.

2 Form groups and discuss your findings.

3 Explain to each other your method of recording.

4 In your group, design a checklist that you could use for assessing an elite performer.

■ Assessment

Both an observation checklist and a performance profile can be used as coaching tools for assessing a performer's strengths and areas for improvement and, from these, training strategies can be designed to improve performance. Mental skills can be learnt in much the same way as physical ones. Athletes may put hours into training but then attribute their failure to mental factors. A performer's state of mind influences their performance.

Assessment consists of tests and observations that are used to assess how well you have achieved the objectives or goals that have been set for you. There are several techniques used for assessing performance. Some of the techniques are described below.

Self-assessment – this is a widely recognised form of assessment. When using this form, you must identify clearly the goals that you have in mind and how to achieve the criteria for assessment for each of your goals.

- Identify what you need to improve.
- Decide how you are going to improve.
- Which criteria will you use to measure that improvement?

Performance profiling is not an assessment technique in itself. Profiling can be used during a plan when assessing what improvements can be made by providing a basis for action. Performance profiles can be very structured and related to the objectives, or much freer.

A checklist is when you mark with a tick or cross whether you did or did not carry out the specific features of the task. This is not the most complex form of observation but is the most accurate. It has a high degree of structure. Performance profiling and checklists will assist you with identifying strengths and weaknesses, opportunities for improvement and threats which may hinder you from achieving.

Below is a section of a checklist for a tennis player that would be used to assess the player's mental training needs while on court.

	Place a cross or a tick
Eyes well controlled	☐
Rituals for serve good	☐
Rituals for serve return good	☐
Excellent pace	☐
Very good breathing during points	☐
High positive intensity	☐
Manages mistakes well	☐
Strong, confident image	☐
Good self-talk	☐
Positive attitude	☐

Activity

During a competition, ask a friend or your coach to observe you and complete the following performance profile with comments.

Name:	Sport:
What technical skills did you use?	
Did you select the skills wisely?	
Did you apply the skills well?	
Where you tactically aware?	
How did you apply tactics?	
What is your fitness level?	
Did you read the game well?	
What areas do you need to improve?	

Activity

1 Study the checklist above. Draw up a similar checklist for your chosen sport. Ask a coach or team mate to observe you and complete the checklist. You could even assess yourself.

2 Identify the areas for improvement.

3 How do you think your coach could help you improve your weaker areas, for example imagery exercises, breath control, relaxation exercises?

▲ **Can mental attitude influence your performance?**

Taking it further

1 Ask your coach, team mate or teacher to observe you in a competitive situation. A checklist and/or performance profile can be used.

2 From the findings you are given, complete the following SWOT analysis. Identify your strengths, weaknesses, the opportunities you may have to improve performance, for example coaches, courses etc. and what may hinder your progress, for example finance and travelling distance.

Strengths	Weaknesses
Opportunities	Threats

Think it over

Have you ever started a training session or competitive match and really felt that you were not in the correct state of mind? Describe how this has influenced your performance. Have you been trained in mental skills?

Following assessment, the purpose of evaluation is to give feedback to the performer. The feedback should not be a list of what went wrong but could be detailed diagrams, photographs or video evidence of how the specific technique could be improved. Too much feedback overwhelms a performer and can lead to discouragement and then the analysis becomes worthless. A detailed checklist, therefore, should not address too many issues relating to one skill, for example a significant number of problem areas in a tennis player's swing. To improve the swing, you would target one or two errors at a time and begin by working on the beginning of the stroke.

Activity

1 Refer back to the player you tracked in Activity 1 on page 391. Select one skill and two factors about that skill you believe you could improve in that player.

2 Is there such a person as a perfect model in sport?

■ Nutritional guidance

An athlete may want to lose weight or gain weight in order to improve performance. If an athlete is overweight, then a dietitian would recommend a diet that would be lower in fats and carbohydrates. If an athlete wants to increase body weight, it is to gain lean body tissue or muscle mass which can provide a competitive advantage. However, appropriate training strategies are needed as well as nutrition to decrease

▲ A balanced diet is essential for a performer to meet the demands of sport

or increase body weight. To increase lean body weight, increased energy intake in the form of carbohydrates and suitable amounts of protein are required.

An athlete's diet must contain all the nutrients needed for general well-being and also the extra stresses of training and competition. The essential nutrients include carbohydrates, protein, fat, vitamins, minerals and water. A performer needs a diet that will provide enough energy for the demands of their sport. Part of a development process could involve examining the performer's intake of food and fluids. Different sports require certain types of food. Also, the amount of food an individual needs varies from person to person. Once a performer has identified the amount of calories used in a day, they can then balance their food intake to equal this. To lose weight you would bring into your diet fresh fruit juice, cereals, yogurts, brown bread, lean meats, salads, fresh fruit and vegetables.

Carbohydrates are a major source of energy. Carbohydrates are broken down by the body into

glucose molecules. The muscles need glucose for energy and any glucose that is not used is then stored as glycogen in the muscles and the liver. The body stores enough glycogen for 90–120 minutes of exercise.

Think it over

During a professional game of tennis, what kinds of foods do you see the players consume?

Foods that contain a larger proportion of carbohydrate include breads, pastas, rice, fruits, potatoes and vegetables. Around 60 per cent of a performer's diet should be made up of carbohydrates and this would be increased during intensive training and competition days.

Protein is essential in a performer's diet to build and repair broken tissue. Exercise breaks down protein. Therefore, if an athlete trains intensively and not enough protein is eaten to compensate for this, their performance will be affected. Protein should make up 10–15 per cent of an athlete's diet. This is found in foods such as meat, fish, poultry, cheese, eggs, milk, nuts and bread.

Common foods that are rich in fat include butter, oils, meat, milk, chocolate, ice-cream and cakes. Fats can be divided into the following.

- Saturated fats: animal fats – these lead to bad cholesterol levels and heart disease.
- Polyunsaturated fats: vegetable oils and plant sources – these are the good fats and are needed for good cholesterol levels.

If there is too much fat in an athlete's diet, their digestion is delayed and their aerobic power diminishes. This will lead to underperformance.

Vitamins are essential for health and tissue growth. With a healthy diet performers should obtain all of their vitamin requirements and not need supplements. The performer will only benefit from a supplement if there is a deficiency in that vitamin.

Minerals include calcium, sodium, potassium and iron and are essential for the functioning of nerves and muscles. They are also important for bones and skin. In a balanced diet a performer should meet their daily requirements.

Athletes regularly become dehydrated during exercise or competition and this impairs their performance. Water regulates body temperature and transports nutrients and hormones throughout the body. It also removes waste from the body. Water is obtained from drinking and also from the foods we eat, such as vegetables and fruit. When you exercise you lose fluid through sweating. Extra fluids should be taken the day before a competition and also with the pre-performance meal. If fluid loss is as little as 4 per cent of the body weight, the performer can expect to achieve 20 per cent less than their capacity for exercise. This could make the difference between winning and losing.

There is significant evidence from research to show that a high carbohydrate meal eaten within 3–4 hours before exercise can improve performance. The amount of carbohydrate in the pre-match meal should be approximately 4 g per kilogram of body mass. For a 70 kg athlete this is around 280 g of carbohydrates.

The total amount can be consumed incorporating high carbohydrate drinks and eating dried fruit, such as raisins or having jam or honey in a dessert. Other nutrients would be some protein and low amounts of fat. Meat or fish should be grilled. Athletes often eat pasta dishes but the sauces should not be fatty or served with fatty mince.

A marathon runner would follow a seven-day diet before competition. The pattern would be as follows.

- Days 7, 6 and 5: strenuous exercise and a low carbohydrate intake.
- Days 4, 3 and 2: exercise is gradually decreased and the carbohydrate intake increased.
- Day 1: no exercise but the performer would eat a high quantity of carbohydrate.
- The competition: after completing this eating plan, research has shown that the amount of glycogen stored has increased and the performer can exercise at higher intensity for longer.

Nutritious meals for athletes

Starter:
- Soup

Main meals:
- Lean grilled steak, boiled potatoes, vegetables
- Grilled or poached fish
- Skinned boiled chicken, potatoes, vegetables
- Pasta or rice
- Baked beans on toast

Desserts:
- Apple pie
- Ice cream
- Fruit
- Yoghurt

Drinks:
- Sports drinks
- Fruit drinks
- Skimmed milk

Think it over

What comments could you make about your elite performer's diet? Does the performer need to lose or gain weight? Can the performer sustain energy levels throughout the game/contest? If the performer tires, what might be the problem? What nutritional guidance would you give the performer?

Activity

1 Write down all of the foods you ate yesterday and categorise them under the headings: carbohydrates; protein; and fats.

2 Plan three meals for a sports performer of your choice for a specific day in their lives, for example competition or training.

3 Explain how the foods you have suggested meet the daily requirements for the sports performer.

Taking it further

In small groups, prepare a pre-match meal for one of the following performers:

- tennis player
- footballer
- marathon runner
- middle-distance runner
- weightlifter.

■ Psychological guidance

Psychological guidance can be incorporated into a training programme and lead to enhanced performance. However, you cannot observe what is going on in a player's mind and sometimes performers do not want to discuss certain issues. Performance profiling can be used for assessing psychological factors as well as

Case study: Giving psychological guidance

Ben plays tennis for his county and, along with his coach, he is using performance profiling to enhance his performance. Ben finds it hard to remain cool when under pressure. This affects his level of concentration. Recently, Ben has not been performing as he would like and his results have been on a downward spiral over the last few months. Ben and his coach would like you to study his method of performance profiling and help him to improve his performance. (Earlier in this section you learnt about performance profiling.)

Ben would like you to use a scale of 0–10 to assess each performance variable (see Table 26.5).

	Ideal state	Ben's state	Difference	Multiply difference by 10 to form a %
Confidence	10	7	3	30
Concentration	10	8	2	20
Motivation	10	8	2	20
Refocus after errors	10	5	5	50
Relaxed attitude	10	7	3	30
Enjoyment	10	6	4	40
Awareness	10	7	3	30
Arousal	10	8	2	20
Attitude	10	6	4	40
Anxiety	10	6	4	40

Table 26.5 Ben's performance profile

1 a How important is confidence to an elite player? Ben believes that this should be 10. What do you think it should be?

  b What would Ben's ideal state be for concentration? He believes it should also be 10. What do you think it should be?

  c How does Ben rate his confidence at the moment? He believes that it is only 7.

Do you think this is the correct figure? Give reasons for your answer and suggest how Ben could improve his mental attitude.

2 Identify the major areas that Ben needs to work on in order for his performance to improve. Suggest how he can develop these areas and explain why you have made these suggestions. How will your suggestions improve Ben's performance?

physical attributes. Profiling can evaluate strengths and areas for improvement and identify long-term goals for development.

The aims of a performance profile are the following:

- to identify a weakness and the appropriate action to be taken
- to motivate the performer to remain on task in their training programme
- to evaluate and monitor the progress over a period of time
- to involve the performer.

Think it over

What are the key psychological qualities of an elite performer?

The key psychological factors of an elite performer are:

- confidence
- concentration
- motivation
- attitude
- arousal
- refocus after errors
- awareness and vision
- anxiety
- enjoyment
- having a relaxed attitude.

There are several psychological factors associated with sports performance.

- Confidence: this is when you expect success because of your previous accomplishments. You have a positive interpretation of anxiety.
- Concentration: you have a good focus of attention and can select the important signals from the unimportant ones. Concentration is the ability to avoid distractions, which could mean blocking out the actions of your opponent, bad refereeing or umpiring, and fatigue.

- Motivation: great performers are highly motivated and they tend to be optimistic. Sports psychologists have attempted to indicate the importance of motivation by suggesting that
performance = skill × motivation.

An elite performer's motivation is either intrinsic or extrinsic. Intrinsic motivation comes from within. They want accomplishment, achievement and challenge. Extrinsic motivation comes from outside the individual in the form of financial gain, trophies, rewards, fame and glory.

Think it over

Identify an elite player in six different sports. Order the players in terms of their motivation – performing for the achievement and challenge through to performing for reward.

- Anxiety: we can overcome tension by improving our confidence level. Confidence gives positive feelings and a high level of confidence brings less stress in competition. Excess anxiety can produce underachievement. Why does a player miss an open goal? Why does a player succeed at certain skills in training but not in competition? It is because their muscles tense up when they are anxious.
- Arousal: this can be defined as the level of excitement a performer reaches. There is an ideal level and this optimum level allows players to perform at their best. If the player is highly skilled, arousal will make them respond positively but, if they not highly skilled, then arousal will reduce their skill level further and consequently produce a poor performance. This explanation can be refuted because some players who perform very complex movements in their sport, for example a snooker player might find that a high arousal level could damage their performance.

- Imagery: this is used to develop top-class professionals. This is the visualisation of situations that can be used to practise skills, instil confidence and motivate the performer for competition or for coming back from injury. Through imagery you can re-create positive experiences or picture new events to prepare for performance. Imagery can become part of a training routine. Examples of imagery are as follows.

  - Images: you re-create the movements of the skill in your mind.
  - Positive focus: you focus on a positive outcome, e.g. winning the point.
  - Video: watch the replays of yourself performing successfully.
  - Execution and outcome: you can imagine the act and see the result.
  - Real time: the images you go over in your mind should be played out real time.

    'Before every shot I go through the movies inside my head. Here is what I see. First, I see the ball where I want it to finish, nice and white and sitting up high on the bright green grass. Then I see the ball going there, its path and trajectory and even its behaviour on landing. The next scene shows me making the kind of swing that will turn the previous image into reality. These home movies are a key to my concentration and to my positive approach to very shot.'

    (Jack Nicklaus, 1976)

Activity

1 Rehearse in your mind the image of a moment in a sports competition that you really enjoyed.

   - Make the image as vivid and as colourful as possible.
   - Bring your senses into the image to make the scene clear and realistic.
   - Include emotional feelings in your image and begin to be aware of the whole picture.
   - Is it possible to break the image into smaller parts by identifying how you are breathing, the action of your arms, legs, feet, head and trunk, and your facial expression?

2 Write the basic story of the image, for example the preparation, the ball toss, the impact and recovery, the ball flight and the ball landing just where you planned.

3 Now add the colour, the detail and exactly how you feel. Refine the script until you feel that it is really happening to you. Remember this moment.

▼ The image of my shot turns into a reality

When assessing the psychological attributes of your elite performer, you will consider situations in which the performer shows confidence or lack of it. Does the player communicate well with other players and motivate themselves and others? Are there lapses in concentration or does the performer remain totally focused?

Goal setting can be used to improve the long-term performance of an elite performer. Goal setting develops a performer because setting goals:

- draws attention to the important elements of the sports performer
- encourages the performer to focus their efforts
- makes the performer persist with their efforts
- encourages the development of new learning techniques.

Activity

1 In groups, select an elite sports performer who has had a dip in form. Discuss the areas of weakness that may have led to this underachievement.

2 If you were the performer's coach, what three short-term goals would you set?

3 How do you think goal setting will improve the long-term performance of the individual?

■ Fitness guidance

A sports performer has to give 100 per cent. You will have often seen an athlete at the end of a race, a match, a contest with nothing left. They are exhausted. The main reason for this is a fall in glycogen stores in muscles. Performers should not train the day before competition. Those who do not train the day before a competition have a higher level of muscle glycogen throughout a match/competition and appreciable levels still at the end of a race/game/contest. Fatigue brings on a drop in performance capability and this can be an advantage to any opponent. Performers become slower in returning to positions and the work rate slows down.

Coaches identify and guide performers through fitness programmes specific to their needs and the needs of a team. For example, a coach may identify the need for a performer to develop muscle strength as this contributes to the development of power in, for example, running or jumping. The coach would guide the performer towards resistance training to enhance muscle strength and to continue to maintain this strength.

Assessment practice

1 In order to improve your performance, your coach would like you to observe an elite sports performer of your choice. You may decide to watch this performer live, on television or on video or DVD.

  a Using the checklist which you designed to assess the technical and tactical ability of an elite performer for your selected sport on page 383, identify realistic strengths and realistic areas for improvement. You may observe your performer as many times as you wish.

  b Verbally describe to your tutor in a one-to-one discussion the strengths you identified in the performer and also the areas for improvement. You must do this working from your checklist. Give as many relevant features as possible and think about what your performer could do to play a better game/contest. **P3**

2 Having completed the above task, your tutor would like you to go further and explain the strengths and areas for improvement you have described. Present your findings to your tutor or group of students, explaining your methods of assessment and using diagrams, photographs and/or video to clarify the points you wish to make.

In your recommendations, make suggestions relating to performer development. This will mean providing details with reasons to clearly support these recommendations. The findings should then be presented to your coach in the form of a short report. **M2**

3 Now extend the presentation and report by explaining why you have made the above recommendations. Using the evidence you have collected from your observations, what conclusions have you reached about the benefits to your elite performer if he or she were to include your recommendations into their training plan? Give reasons or evidence to support your conclusions. **D2**

Grading tips

Grading Tip **P3**

Ensure that you describe the elite performer's strengths including their level of skill, techniques, tactical awareness, fitness levels and their ability to read the game. When you talk about the areas for improvement, do not forget to describe how the performer could improve attacking, defending, certain skills and techniques and fitness.

Grading Tip **M2**

You must clearly explain the elite performer's strengths and areas for improvement covering all the areas for P3 above. Also, make suggestions relating to development considering the performer's training, competition,

specific coaching and the coaches the performer works with. You must also suggest how the performer could improve performance through observational analysis, nutritional, psychological and improved fitness guidance.

Grading Tip **D2**

Having explained the suggestions for development, justify your suggestions by explaining why you made the suggestions and what positive results this would have on the performance of the elite performer. How will your ideas and suggestions for improvement develop this player?

26.3 Be able to assess your own technical and tactical ability

This section will assist you to identify and select methods of self-assessment for your own sport. Through writing a log book, you will be able to identify strengths and weaknesses in your own technical and tactical ability. These findings will then be used for your personal development plan.

Assessment

Competitive situation

There are several levels at which you can participate in sport.

- Foundation level: at this level you would participate mainly through school activities.

- Participation level: this is when you participate regularly in sport by belonging to a team and playing for enjoyment and fun through competitive situations.

- Performance level: at this level you would compete for a club, your county or at regional level. You will have been identified as having talent and will have been selected to play at representative level.

- Elite level: now you are at the highest level and may be a national team player, an Olympic competitor, champion or a professional.

Competitive situation	Examples	Mark 1–10
Technical skills Do you understand the roles of your position? For example, if you are a defender do you combine with other players to progress play from the back, do you support your team mates? Can you interchange positions, for example defender, midfield, attacker? Can you distribute the ball over short and long range? Can you mark, challenge, block and defend, head, control, receive, dribble, shoot, turn, cross the ball and communicate with team mates?	*I operated as an attacker when coming forward from the back.*	6
Selection of skills Do you observe how the ball is coming to you? Do you know where your team mates and the opposition are placed? Do you select the right skill to use? Is the timing of the skill correct, and the pace and weight? Why have you made that choice considering the tactical objectives?	*The cross led to a goal.*	
Application of skills Do you run and dribble with the ball, maintain possession and penetrate the defence, create attempts on goal, shoot, cross the ball frequently?	*I scored a goal.*	
Tactical awareness How good are you at choosing the correct action in a game? Are you able to see the whole situation around you, evaluate and then make the right choice of action? Can you decide quickly which skill to use, the technique, where, when, how to use this skill and why your choice was the best option?	*My free kick went into the wall.*	
Application of tactics Do you know how to prepare instantly to move from attack to defence and defence to attack? Can you move quickly from one system to another or adapt positions when a substitute is used?	*I changed positions when the substitute came on.*	

Table 26.6 An example of an observation checklist

Strengths

This section will assist you in identifying the strengths in your own technical and tactical ability. You will assess your skill level, technique, tactical awareness, your ability to read a game and your fitness.

■ Specific skills

Because you are continuing to develop and change through growth, fitness levels and learning, your skill level can continue to develop. To continue to reproduce a skill by repeating an identical movement sequence would result in static and inflexible behaviour. In a quick and lively team game it is important that the performer continues to improve specific skills. A tennis player, for example, would assess their basic coordination pattern for a tennis volley and then practise movement patterns that would improve variables such as speed and force.

■ Specific techniques

When assessing your technique you are considering how the skill is performed. You might ask yourself whether the action was successful and how it can be improved. There are four phases to each action:

- initiation phase
- preparation phase
- execution phase
- completion phase.

By breaking down the skill, you can identify your strengths.

■ Tactical awareness

Tactics mean actions in specific situations. Before a match the performer will have discussed and decided upon a tactical plan. It may be that tactical changes have to be made, for example as a result of an injury or a player being sent off. During a match situation the performer has a choice of action and, therefore, they must make decisions. During your training sessions you will gain an insight into the tactical opportunities available during game situations. The performer can assess their strengths and acquire an in-depth understanding of the use of tactical skills through theoretical examination. By recording competitive situations the player is able to observe their own game and assess specific tactical situations. This will develop their understanding of tactical awareness.

■ Fitness levels

Playing a match or game is the best overall test for a sports performer. It is, however, difficult to assess fitness during a game. Therefore, it is easier to assess fitness levels while training because they can be evaluated while performing defined activities related to the specific sport. If fitness tests are to be reliable, the performer should be well rested, thoroughly warmed up and have clear instructions on how to perform the test. The tests should be performed at least once before a test result should be considered.

Ability to read the game

It is important during competitive situations that you have the ability to read the game. Through video analysis the performer can assess how successful they are at reading the game. When assessing this ability, the following factors should be observed.

- Does the performer keep their head up and observe what is going on around them and where players are in relation to each other?
- Do they look before receiving the ball: do they anticipate the next pass and do they think ahead?
- Do they maintain a stance that allows them to see what is going on around them?
- Can the performer control the ball/pass/shot and move the ball away from pressure and create space?

The ability to read the game means having the imagination to know how your team mates or opponent(s) will react following each touch/shot/pass. The performer should assess their own insight into how various techniques can be used to control and play a shot/pass into different spaces.

Areas for improvement

This next section will assist you when you are assessing areas for improvement in your own technical and tactical ability. Think about the sports you play and the skills and techniques which could be improved.

Attacking

When identifying areas for improvement under this heading the performer can consider individual attacking options and those of the team. For example, a basketball player might want to improve shooting, passing, getting free to receive a pass, creating space to allow players time to perform skills and moving to receive a return pass. In volleyball the player might want to improve a specific attacking skill, such as a smash or tip which is a soft attack shot when the attacker plays the ball with the fingers just over the top or around the block similar to a drop shot in tennis. Some performers like their opponents to attack. For example, in tennis, players will often make a mistake when they are continually forced to take the initiative in a rally.

An attacking system in football would mean playing the ball quickly up to strikers so that the game is taken into the opposition's 'defensive' area.

Defending

Defending is a skill and when assessing the player's defensive attributes there may be weaknesses in the following areas:

- one-to-one situations
- preventing shots
- providing effective covering
- getting the ball back up the court/field quickly
- not applying enough pressure on the opponents
- cutting off opponents' paths.

It is important that the performer gets back to their defensive position quickly to avoid attackers beating them.

Specific skills

There may be many reasons why a performer has to improve specific skills. It may be that the performer has not mastered a complex skill and, therefore, needs to master a more basic skill first. Some performers may not have developed sufficient strength levels or have the range of flexibility to execute certain skills. Their coach having identified the areas for improvement would encourage practising the skill with regular reminders of the key points. The coach also, when assessing areas for improvement, needs to consider the physical development of a performer, as well as their technical development.

Specific techniques

The player or coach will observe and analyse performance in order to identify which phases of a technique need to be improved. Therefore, it is necessary to have a good understanding of the techniques required in the specific sport. Improving technique will come through identifying the differences between how the performer executes the technique and how it should be performed. It will be necessary to observe the technique several times before assessing how improvements can be made. Often a skill is not 100 per cent technically correct but will still be very effective. A cricketer would have to correct a bowling technique if the arm action suggests throwing, however, other top performers have unorthodox techniques but are very successful at their sport.

■ Fitness

Fitness training will help you to endure the physical demands of your sport and also maintain your technical ability. Fitness training can be divided into:

- aerobic training: high-intensity training, low-intensity training and recovery training
- anaerobic training: speed training and speed endurance training.

Specific muscle training can be divided into:

- muscle strength, e.g. training biceps using some form of external resistance
- muscle speed endurance, e.g. training the abdominal muscles using several repetitions of an appropriate exercise
- flexibility training, e.g. stretching the hamstrings.

You should improve your fitness in a games situation. In this way the specific muscle groups in the sport are trained. Also the performers develop the technical and tactical skills similar to those needed in a competitive match. This form of training also provides greater motivation for the performers. The physical demands made on you during a competitive match will influence your fitness training programme, for example striker, defensive player, tennis player etc.

A good coach will continue to observe performers even after they have learnt and mastered skills and techniques. On-going observation and analysis of performers will enable the performer and the coach to identify strengths and areas of improvement.

Activity

Select your strongest sport.

1 Identify strengths and areas for improvement in your chosen sport.

2 What two short-term goals could you set yourself that would encourage you to focus on your weaker areas?

3 What could your coach build into your training that would lead to an improved performance?

4 What does a checklist or performance profile provide for the performer and the coach?

Log

Diary of specific training sessions

The log book is a diary of specific training sessions that the performer has attended over a period of time. In the log book the performer will include the following:

- details of specific training sessions
- competition analysis
- areas for improvement
- specific practices.

The following information below and on pages 405–410 will assist you with the log book. There are also examples of entries and performance profiles and match analysis game sheets.

Training sessions for talented young people

You have been accepted on to a football academy training plan and have been asked to keep a log book for four weeks. Your log book has to include the following:

- skills you have learnt
- the techniques and tactics you have covered
- your strengths and areas for improvement identified during competition and training
- some coach analysis after competition and training.

Your log book will also include areas for improvement such as:

- defending
- attacking
- fitness
- examples of specific practices that can be used to improve your performance.

Skills

Today, my coach observed me in a training situation. He was assessing key skills in order to target areas for improvement. My coach observed me for 30 minutes. This was divided into three ten-minute periods. The session was a training match between those invited on to the course and the academy players. I have included the data the coach collected about me in Table 26.7 below.

▲ Extract 1 from log book

The following five-point rating indicates the frequency of the key skills:

5 = Almost always; 4 = Often; 3 = Sometimes; 2 = Rarely; 1 = Hardly ever.

Activity

1 Design a front cover for your log book which identifies you, your sport, club and level of participation. Write words associated with your specific sport on the first page of the log book.

2 Reproduce a key skills chart for your favourite sport similar to Table 26.7 below. Ask your coach to complete it by observing you in a training situation and giving marks for each category.

The coach recommended that this player intensified training relating to 'Make a conscious pass to retain possession' and 'Ball watch', particularly relating to attack.

	Time period		
	2–11 minutes	20–29 minutes	50–59 minutes
Ball watch: in attack	2	2	3
Ball watch: in defence	4	3	4
Look up and then decide whether to pass, run with the ball, dribble or shoot	4	3	3
Make a conscious pass to retain possession	2	2	3
Kick the ball towards the opponent's goal	3	4	4
Make a run towards the opponent's goal	3	3	4
Defend by running back towards own goal when possession is lost	4	4	3
Attempt to intercept passes	4	4	4
Deny the opposition space: close down, mark tightly	4	3	3

Table 26.7 Key skills chart. Did the player perform the above skills?

	Initiation phase	Preparation phase	Execution phase	Follow-through phase
	Run up	*Retraction of kicking leg*	*Forward swing of kicking leg and contact*	*Follow through*
Key observational features	Run up used to gain speed Used an angled approach Normal running with arms used to balance	Body leans to the back and side Arms used to balance Kicking leg retracts to open out hip Arm on side of kicking leg is brought forward Eyes on ball	Twist is created in the trunk by counter-rotating the shoulders on the hips from a forward position to a backward position At contact, the knee is slightly flexed but extends through contact On contact, the foot is plantar flexed	The leg is raised for a high follow through gradually slowing down

Table 26.8 The penalty kick

■ Techniques and tactics covered

Today, our coach targeted shooting as a specific training point. I was in the group which concentrated on taking penalties. The penalty kick is a very important skill in football in which gaining high ball speed, as well as accuracy, is necessary. The coach showed us a video of an expert penalty performer and he encouraged us to watch the whole body movement and how the body is used to help the movement. The coach gave us some notes which I have included in Table 26.8 above.

▲ Extract 2 from log book

Activity

Select a skill from a chosen sport and detail how you might improve that skill and what technical skill your coach would be looking for.

Today was a theory lesson about match tactics. The coach had a match analysis game sheet to go through with us. The data had been collected during our previous competitive game. It was interesting to discuss this data. I have included just a section of this game sheet in Table 26.9 below.

▲ Extract 3 from log book

	Team	First half	Second half	Total
Entries into the attacking third	A B	21 26	22 30	43 56
Regained possession in the attacking third	A B	6 6	4 6	10 12
Effective crosses	A B	1 3	2 1	3 4

Table 26.9 A section of a match analysis game sheet. Team A: talented group on the course; team B: academy players

Activity

1 Devise a match analysis game sheet suitable for your sport.

2 Ask your coach to complete the sheet and, from analysis, explain areas for improvement in tactics.

Competition analysis

It is difficult to reproduce the stress of competition on the performer during normal training conditions. Therefore, it is important in training to focus on games with a strong competitive element. This can prepare the performer for competitive situations.

■ Strengths and weaknesses during a competitive match

I really enjoyed myself today. My passing was brilliant. The practice really paid off. My crosses were accurate and we won. I ran and dribbled with the ball more frequently and the whole team was able to put more passes together. We created a lot more attempts on goal. I was really tired about 20 minutes before the end and I could work on my endurance in order to improve my performance levels.

▲ Extract 4 from log book

5 = Excellent; 4 = Very good; 3 = Good; 2 Average; 1 = Poor.

Specific skills	5	4	3	2	1
Specific techniques	5	4	3	2	1
Tactical awareness	5	4	3	2	1
Fitness levels	5	4	3	2	1
Ability to read the game	5	4	3	2	1
Attacking	5	4	3	2	1
Defending	5	4	3	2	1

Table 26.10 Match analysis – a sample

This form of self-assessment shown in Table 26.10 can be used to identify your strengths and areas for improvement and what you need to work on before the next game.

Activity

1 Why would you tire 20 minutes before the end of a game?

2 How would you improve this area of weakness?

3 What specific training associated with your own sport could you do to improve speed and endurance?

4 Explain your areas of strength in a selected sport.

5 Explain why you think specific areas in this sport need improving.

■ Coach analysis after competitions and training

The coach has asked me to include a profile checklist which he completed after competition and training (see Table 26.11).

▲ Extract 5 from log book

5 = Excellent; 4 = Good; 3 = Satisfactory; 2 = Signs of weakness; 1 = Unsatisfactory.

Technique	4
Fitness levels	3
Awareness of others	2
Ability to play as part of a team	2
Attitude and behaviour	4
Motivation	5
Speed	3
Ability	4

Table 26.11 Profile checklist

Coach's comments

Areas of strength: the performer is technically gifted with good levels of natural ability. The performer is very motivated and tries very hard to please.

Areas for improvement: the performer tends to play as an individual and needs to learn that football is a team game. In the training plan for this player speed can be worked on.

Performer's statement:

I accept the comments and will endeavour to work hard in the future to turn the above areas for development into key strengths.

Grading tips

Grading Tip P4

Ensure that your checklist covers technical skills, selection of skills, application of skills, tactical awareness and application of tactics. When you describe your strengths, give some examples of certain skills and techniques and also examples of your tactical awareness, fitness levels and ability to read the game.

Grading Tip M3

Remember that you must assess yourself in a competitive situation. When you explain your strengths and weaknesses and areas for improvement, support your explanations with evidence.

Activity

1 Ask your coach or team mate to complete a profile similar to Table 26.11 assessing your own performance.

2 Add your own comments about the marks you receive. If you were to assess yourself, would your marks be different?

Assessment practice

For this assessment you will need to ask your coach/tutor or team mate to video a sample of your performance in either training or competition to enable you to complete a self-analysis.

1 Consider the checklist you designed for the Assessment practice on page 383.

   a Adapt the checklist for your own sport.

   b Use the checklist to assess your own technical and tactical ability. Watch the video of your performance as many times as you wish.

   c From this analysis, identify your strengths and areas for improvement. Describe these to your coach/tutor or team mate. When you describe your strengths, include as many strengths as possible. Look at the video carefully and consider all the factors on the checklist that you did well. What did you perform that could

have been better? Describe these to your coach/tutor. **P4**

2 For this task you will need to ask a coach/tutor or team mate to video a sample of your performance in a competitive situation.

   a From analysis, explain the strengths and areas for improvement that you have identified in your own sport.

   b Present these findings in the form of a short presentation to your group or coach using the video evidence to support your argument. When you give your explanation, provide details of your strengths and reasons to support your decisions. Also, clearly explain your areas for improvement and state why you think these areas should be improved. **M3**

Theory into practice

Your log book can be used for recording information by both you and your coach. This will help you to identify strengths and areas for improvement by assessing your technical and tactical ability in your own sport.

In your log book you could keep the following:

- details of training sessions
- technical details of your performance
- tactical development points identified and agreed by you and your coach
- performance profiles
- self-evaluation and reflections of your performance in both training and competition
- feedback from performance tests, observations, team mates and coaches
- your training and performance goals
- necessary drills to improve areas of weakness (both technical and tactical).

Areas for improvement

Your log book will assist you in identifying areas for improvement. By considering Extract 6 from a log book, you can examine the areas the performer and coach wished to develop.

Date: March

Place: Local tennis club

Event: Club Junior Championships

My opponent for this match was the club champion. I have played him twice before and lost both times. My game plan was to try to serve well in order for me to win my service games easily. If I managed to do this, I could then really attack on my opponent's service games and try to break their serve. I would concentrate on serving to their weakness rather than their strength.

Match result: Lost 2 sets to love. 6/5 – 6/5.

▲ Extract 6 from log book

The performer competed well for the majority of the time. This was reflected in the close score line. The plan succeeded in that they managed to hold serve but lost in two tie-break sets. They tried to impose their game rather than react to their opponent's game by trying to be the one who was dictating the rallies.

■ Attacking

At times, the performer was over-attacking and this led to some unforced errors creeping into their game. They must try to practise choosing the right time to attack the ball and learn to realise that, if the time is not right, to wait for the correct opportunity.

■ Defending

The performer needs to be a little more consistent in their defence. At times, they were caught out of position on the court. This was due to fatigue.

■ Specific skills

They must work a little harder on their return of serve. Although they held their serve, which was the game plan, the performer was not successful at breaking their opponent's serve. This must be implemented more effectively for performance to improve.

■ Specific techniques

The performer must learn not to become nervous in tight game situations. This lost them the match because the opponent handled the situation better than them, particularly during the tie-breaks.

■ Fitness

The reason the performer was caught out of position was because they were tiring. The aim should be to increase fitness levels, particularly aerobic training.

■ Specific practices that could improve your own performance

This practice will improve aerobic capacity.

- Warm-up: light jogging and specific stretching.
- Key factors: accelerate, receive the ball, play it back, spin and accelerate again.
- Cool-down: jogging and stretches.

Activity

Devise an aerobic exercise plan to improve aerobic capacity for your preferred sport.

This practice will improve crossing.

- Warm-up: light jogging, side to side, stretches, jog high knees, flick heels, specific stretches.
- Key factors: position of the goalkeeper, eye on the ball, relaxed at the point of contact, and head over the ball, eyes on the ball.
- Cool-down: light jog with specific stretches.

Activity

Devise an exercise in order to develop defensive tactics.

This practice will improve your competitive edge.

- Use one half of a pitch.
- Use two full-sized goals.
- Play 8 × 8.
- After four minutes of play in the fourth period, the side in the lead at the end of the third period has a goal taken away from them every two minutes until the losing team scores.

In this way, the intensity is maintained and the team behind is still motivated to prevent further scoring.

Activity

Devise a similar practice for your favourite sport.

Assessment practice

1 Complete a four-week log book while participating in your chosen sport. Design a front cover for your log book that identifies you, your sport, club and level of participation. Write words associated with your specific sport on the first page of your log book.

The log book needs to include as much detail as possible regarding your technical and tactical ability. You must identify both your strengths and areas for possible improvement. **P5**

2 a Having completed your log book in the above task and identified your strengths and areas for development, explain each strength stating why it is a particular strength in your chosen sport.

b Explain the impact improving your areas for development will have on your all-round performance.

This is a written task. Within your explanations, present evidence to support your opinions regarding your strengths and areas for improvement in a selected sport. **M4**

Grading tips

Grading Tip **P5**

Ensure that you include in your log book evidence in training sessions of your own technical and tactical ability in a selected sport that covers the skills, techniques and tactics that you have covered at these training sessions. You must also show that you have evidence of assessments that identify your strengths during a competitive match. Ask your coach to assess you after a competition and in training and include these assessments in your log book. What areas can you improve? Identify these under the headings of attacking, defending, skills, techniques and fitness. Finally, include in your log book practices which could improve your performance.

Grading Tip **M4**

Ensure you have identified and explained in detail the strengths and areas for improvement of your own technical and tactical ability in a selected sport.

Development plan

How can you reflect on your performance and obtain feedback? This can be achieved through a development plan.

This is a structured plan that will be undertaken by you so that you can reflect upon your own performance and plan your personal development. This plan will identify your goals and objectives and evaluate your progress in order to become a better sports performer. Having a development plan will:

- improve your performance
- give you a deeper understanding of how you can become a better performer
- encourage you to remain positive during your development.

Goals

You have identified where you are now by assessing your strengths and areas for development. Now you need to plan exactly where you want to get to, what skills you need to get you there and how you will acquire the opportunities to do this. Putting your development plan into practice will mean recording and identifying your progress. When you have achieved your goals you can then reflect on your personal achievements and consider where you want to go next. You will do this by setting yourself goals.

There are three main types of goals.

- Outcome goals: here, you focus on particular events such as Wimbledon or wining a race.
- Process goals: these are short-term goals for use during training and competition.
- Performance goals: these encourage performers to play to their potential.

When designing your development plan it is essential to use the SMART principle:

- **S** – **s**pecific
- **M** – **m**easurable
- **A** – **a**chievable
- **R** – **r**ealistic
- **T** – **t**ime-bound

■ Specific

This means that your development plan states a specific objective. For example, if a tennis player has a specific weakness with their backhand you could say that movement and racket preparation before ball impact is a weakness.

■ Measurable

This is how your performance will be measured. If, after training for the above example, your backhand percentage increases, then one can see that the training has worked.

■ Achievable

What you set out to achieve must be possible. You would not expect a beginner in tennis to quickly master the art of the topspin backhand.

■ Realistic

It must be realistic to achieve your set goal. Your goals are written down and a contract is made between you and the coach.

■ Time-bound

There should be enough time to complete the set development plan.

Key term

Monitoring and evaluation You will only improve performance if you continually monitor and evaluate your performance. Through observation, you can analyse your performance and identify areas for improvement. Monitoring is recording your progress towards achieving the set goals in your development plan and evaluation is about reaching conclusions and what you would then recommend for further improvement in future performances.

Key terms

Feedback This will inform you about how you are progressing and whether your objectives have been met. It will also inform you whether or not your choice of objectives was correct. If you are not meeting your goals, then your training plan may be inappropriate. You can gather feedback from performance tests, competitive results, peers, your coach and assessments. Records of these could be added to your log book.

Self-evaluation This is when you use feedback from observation, performance tasks, your results and questionnaires to determine how well you have achieved your goals and objectives. If you have not achieved your objectives, then you can make meaningful changes. Through self-evaluation you can identify what you want to achieve and the appropriate methods of training to enhance performance.

Resources

■ Physical

When considering your development plan you will take into account the opportunities and equipment available at high-quality and safe facilities within travelling distance from where you live.

■ Human

The performer will take into account the opportunities available for coaching. Who is at their club with the knowledge and experience to develop their performance, or can lead them towards better coaches? Are there coaching awards that they might access that would improve their technical skills?

■ Fiscal

A performer needs money to participate in sport. Club fees and also match fees can be high. The performer also needs money for equipment such as tennis rackets, tennis shoes, football boots, and for travel. There could be funds available for them and their club in the form of grants.

As the performer progresses and becomes involved in more competition, finance is very important. Elite performers are often sponsored and win prize money. Sponsorship at local level means that nearby businesses would sponsor performers but for this to happen the performers would need to have been identified as having ability. Over two billion pounds from the government and National Lottery has been dedicated to sport over the next three years. Through the Awards for All scheme any organisation can attract funding. This enables individuals to have access to high-quality and safe facilities and high-quality coaching, allowing performers to progress to their best ability and to compete at the highest level. Performers can then improve performance.

Activity

1 Research the coaching opportunities and facilities within travelling distance that may provide you with better coaching opportunities.

2 Research the coaching awards available to you in your selected sport in your local area.

  a Which level of this award would you choose to access in order to improve performance?

  b Which facilities are running these courses and how would you fund the course?

  c Are there grants available?

Assessment practice

1 You must produce a development plan in the form of a report. Your report will be sent to the head coach of your sports club. This will enable you to plan around your specific needs.

In the report, identify your strengths and areas for development. Your plan will include current strengths and areas for improvement. This plan should include your targets, specific sport practices, courses which you can attend, competitions you can become involved in and coaching practice. **P6**

2 After completing your development plan in the previous task, explain how the targets set, practices, courses and coaching are closely related to identified strengths and areas for improvement in your own technical and tactical ability and will make you a better performer. **M5**

3 You have made suggestions in your personal development plan on how to enhance your own performance in your selected sport. Now do the following.

a Review the information and make recommendations on how your development plan can be met.

b Explain how the targets, practices, courses, competitions and coaching are to be attainable.

c Assess the timescale that the plan should be completed in and reviewed.

d Give reasons or evidence to support your recommendations on how the development plan can be met and show how you arrived at your conclusions.

e Will your development plan improve personal performance? **D3**

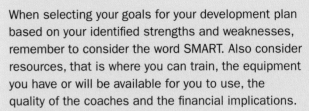

Grading tips

Grading Tip P6

When selecting your goals for your development plan based on your identified strengths and weaknesses, remember to consider the word SMART. Also consider resources, that is where you can train, the equipment you have or will be available for you to use, the quality of the coaches and the financial implications.

Grading Tip M5

When preparing your goals and considering your resources, relate your plan closely to your needs. What strengths and areas for improvement in your own technical and tactical ability have you identified? Think about them and build the development plan around these strengths and areas for improvement.

Grading Tip D3

Ensure that you justify the suggestions that you have made in your development plan and show examples of how the suggestions can be met and how they could be attainable. Why, and how, do you think your goals will improve performance?

Knowledge check

1 Describe the differences between continuous, serial and discrete skills. Give an example of each skill. Describe the skill and state why you have selected the specific skill to be classified as continuous, serial or discrete.

2 What do you mean by the word 'tactics'? If you were giving a team a talk before a match, what might you say to the players about tactics?

3 Why is the ready position so important in sport? Give an example of three sports in which the performer returns frequently to the ready position.

4 Why is positioning important in sport? Discuss positioning when defending and attacking.

5 Every shot/pass/stroke should have a purpose. Select a skill from sport and explain when you would use that skill – what is the purpose of the skill? Explain when you would consider the skill to be successful and when you would consider the skill to be unsuccessful.

6 The purpose of observation analysis in sports is to improve performance. Why would you use a checklist or performance profile to assess the technical and tactical abilities of a sports performer?

7 What do you mean by an elite performer? Name your favourite elite performer and explain the qualities possessed by this person which puts them into this category. Do you believe these qualities can be taught?

8 What factors would a coach and sports performer consider when discussing a training programme?

9 Discuss the roles and responsibilities of defenders and attackers in sport.

10 What is meant by aerobic and anaerobic training? Give examples of sports that would emphasise either or both training systems and explain why.

11 Why is competition so important in the development of sports performance?

12 What is the role of the coach in developing sports performance? Does knowledge alone make a good coach?

13 Why is video analysis so widely used by elite sports performers to develop performance?

14 How does nutrition affect sports performance?

15 What is the best way for you to improve sports performance? Is it through assessment? How does assessment help in your development plan?

Preparation for assessment

You have enrolled in a sports summer school for two weeks. To qualify for a place you have to play a sport to club level and have an all-round interest in the technical and tactical demands of sport. During the two weeks you are going to learn about the technical and tactical demands of a variety of sports, learn how to assess the technical and tactical ability of an elite performer and, finally, be able to assess your own performance ability. You will keep a log book during your stay and continue this for a further two weeks when you return home. This will assist you with identifying your own strengths and areas for improvement and the writing of a development plan.

1 Your initial sessions involve tasters of contrasting sports. You will learn about the technical and tactical demands of these sports. At the end of this section of the course the coach would like you to do the following.

   a Choose three contrasting sports.

   b Give a presentation to your group in which you describe the technical and tactical demands of three contrasting sports. Consider factors such as continuous, serial and discrete skills with examples from your chosen sports. Also describe the positioning, choice of strokes, variations, conditions and use of space involved in these sports. You may have taken photographs that will help you with your description or have images that will enhance the main points that you are making. Perhaps you are good at drawing and can include diagrams? **P1**

   c Another group at the summer school has not been taking part in these sessions and does not play the sports you have identified as your three contrasting sports. Therefore, more detail is required. Explain the technical and tactical demands of the three contrasting sports. It would help if you can provide relevant examples with practical demonstrations. Use diagrams and plans to demonstrate tactics and carefully identify and explain the main features to support your presentation. **M1**

   d Finally, as part of your presentation, compare and contrast the technical and tactical demands of your three contrasting sports. You can do this by identifying the main factors that are the same in the three sports and explain their similarities and then conclude by explaining the differences. **D1**

2 The summer school has been invited to attend a training session at a famous club. While observing this session, you have been asked to track an elite performer by observing them with the view to

▲ A training session at the summer school

assessing that performer's technical and tactical ability. In order to do this, you will have to design an observation checklist.

Produce an observation checklist that can be used to assess the technical and tactical ability of your selected performer in the sport of your choice. Think about dividing your checklist under specific headings such as technical skills, selection of skills, application of skills etc. **P2**

3 Your coach at the summer school has the training session that you attended on video and also further videos of your elite performer in competitive situations. The group members are all interested in each other's findings and would like to see the observational assessments. The plan is to design a poster giving information about your chosen elite performer.

a On your poster show how you used the observation checklist to assess the technical and tactical ability of your elite performer in a selected sport. Identify the strengths and areas for improvement. You could do this by displaying the checklist and the results. From the results, you can identify the strengths by making a list and using photographs and diagrams to illustrate your results. To complete the poster, identify the areas in which your elite performer can improve. Once again, make a list and use drawings. **P3**

b Each poster will be backed up with a short report. This report will be sent to the head coach at the summer school who is in charge of the sport played by your selected elite performer.
Explain your conclusions in the poster. Explain the assessment. Why do you think, for example, the performer reads the game well, still has energy left at the end of the contest or is completely exhausted? What areas need improving? Explain these areas. **M2**

c To complete the report, review the information and give reasons for the development suggestions.

Why do you think your development suggestions will improve the performance of your elite performer? **D2**

4 During the second week of the summer school you will have coaching sessions. Assess your own technical and tactical ability in competition or training situations. By identifying your strengths and areas for improvement you will be able to produce a development plan when you return home. During your training sessions and competitive matches you will be encouraged to work with a media student who will take photographs and video your training and matches. This observational evidence will be used by you for analysis and assist you when assessing your own technical and tactical ability.

a Using your observation checklist and photographs, create a second poster that shows your assessment of your own technical and tactical ability in your selected sport. You will identify your strengths and areas for improvement. **P4**

b The coach at the summer school has studied your poster and wants more information about you in a competitive situation.
Explain your strengths and areas for improvement in your own technical and tactical ability in a competitive situation. Identify your strengths and areas for improvement and then explain in detail to your coach/tutor your strengths and areas for improvement. You could consider factors such as the pressure of competition, confidence, concentration, as well as the physical factors. **M3**

c Select a specific sport and explain to your coach /tutor the strengths and areas for improvement in your technical and tactical ability that you have identified. Consider factors relating to skills, tactics, reading the game etc. Give reasons to support your opinions. **M4**

5 While you have been at the summer school you have been keeping a log book. In this diary you have recorded specific training sessions, checklists and

performance profiles that have helped you analyse competitive and training situations and helped you identify strengths and areas for improvement. Now that you are at home and continuing to train at your local club, you should continue with this log book for a further two weeks.

Complete a four-week log book. Remember to identify strengths and areas for improvement throughout the log book. **P5**

6   At the end of four weeks you have a meeting with your coach. The coach would like you to write a development plan. In the development plan you are to consider short-, medium- and long-term goals and think about the word SMART.

a   Produce a development plan of your own technical and tactical ability based on your identified strengths and areas for improvement. **P6**

b   Show that you have related your plan to the identified strengths and areas for improvement in your own technical and tactical ability. Show that

your goals are associated with the areas in which you want to improve and that they are specific, measurable, achievable, realistic and time-bound. **M5**

c   Justify the suggestions made in the development plan. That is, state why you have suggested your goals, and how you can achieve them in the suggested time. Are the opportunities and resources available for you to achieve all you wish to achieve? Explain why you need to improve in these areas to enhance your own performance. **D3**

Grading tips

Ensure that you look back at the grading tips for previous assessment practices. These will assist you when completing the preparation for assessment.

To achieve a pass grade the evidence must show that the learner is able to:	To achieve a merit grade the evidence must show that, in addition to the pass criteria, the learner is able to:	To achieve a distinction grade the evidence must show that, in addition to the pass and merit criteria, the learner is able to:
P1 Describe the technical and tactical demands of three contrasting sports **Assessment practice Page 380**	**M1** Explain the technical and tactical demands of three contrasting sports **Assessment practice Page 380**	**D1** Compare and contrast the technical and tactical demands of three contrasting sports **Assessment practice Page 380**
P2 Produce an observation checklist that can be used to assess the technical and tactical ability of a performer in a selected sport **Assessment practice Page 383**		
P3 Use an observation checklist to assess the technical and tactical ability of an elite performer, in a selected sport, identifying strengths and areas for improvement **Assessment practice Page 399**	**M2** Explain strengths and areas for improvement, in technical and tactical ability, of the selected elite sports performer, and make suggestions relating to development **Assessment practice Page 399**	**D2** Justify development suggestions made for the selected elite sports performer regarding areas for improvement **Assessment practice Page 399**
P4 Use an observation checklist to assess own technical and tactical ability, in a competitive or training situation for a selected sport, identifying strengths and areas for improvement **Assessment practice Page 408**	**M3** Explain strengths and areas for improvement, in own technical and tactical ability in a competitive situation **Assessment practice Page 408**	
P5 Complete a four-week log of own technical and tactical ability in a selected sport, identifying strengths and areas for improvement **Assessment practice Page 410**	**M4** Explain identified strengths and areas for improvement of own technical and tactical ability in a selected sport **Assessment practice Page 410**	
P6 Produce a development plan of own technical and tactical ability, based on identified strengths and areas for improvement **Assessment practice Page 413**	**M5** Relate development plan to identified strengths and areas for improvement in own technical and tactical ability **Assessment practice Page 413**	**D3** Justify suggestions made in personal development plan **Assessment practice Page 413**

The athlete's lifestyle

Introduction

The aim of this unit is to introduce the concept of how the athlete's lifestyle can affect physical performance and future success. It is aimed at those who have a realistic chance of achieving excellence in their chosen sport. The unit examines various aspects of the athlete's lifestyle, both within and outside of the sporting community.

Being successful in sport is no longer simply a case of preparing physically, mentally, tactically or technically. Athletes must now consider the importance of how they spend their leisure time, plan their financial futures and employment after sport, and how they deal with the media.

There are many areas that athletes must consider in order to be successful. The roles and responsibilities of modern athletes must be understood, as well as the duties they are expected to undertake as part of their professional role. The emerging athlete will face many pressures when developing their talents, such as pressure on time to train and compete. Personal and financial sacrifices will be made along the road to success. Athletes must also consider their behaviour on and off the field.

With the recent growth of the media, it is now common for the lifestyles of elite athletes to come under close scrutiny by the public. Being able to cope with such scrutiny is invaluable. Clear planning for a long and successful career is vital. A full understanding of your responsibilities as an athlete, as well as how the many aspects of your life will impact on others, is paramount if your goals and aspirations are to be achieved.

After completing this unit you should be able to achieve the following outcomes:

- Understand how lifestyle can affect athletes.
- Understand the importance of appropriate behaviour for athletes.
- Understand how to communicate effectively with the media and significant others.
- Understand factors involved in career planning.

Think it over

David Beckham is considered to be one of the world's best footballers and is rewarded for his talents with a huge salary, sponsorship deals and endorsements. This has allowed him to lead a glamorous lifestyle with several homes and sports cars. However, in return, his every move is scrutinised by the media and his private life is often reported in the press. He has photographers following him wherever he goes, including simple tasks such as taking his children to school or going shopping. Although Beckham's lifestyle may seem glamorous, such intrusion into his private affairs must be frustrating.

Consider how you would cope if you were in his position. Would you be able to deal with the pressures? Would you be happy having your personal life reported in the media rather than your sporting achievements? Being an elite athlete brings many rewards, but it can also bring enormous pressures and responsibilities.

Lifestyle factors

Being a successful athlete involves a huge commitment and many personal sacrifices. It is important that the athlete understands how lifestyle can play both a positive and a negative role in achieving this success.

Leisure time

Leisure can be defined as time available for ease and relaxation or the freedom to choose a pastime or enjoyable activity. This means time where the athlete can choose what he or she wishes to do. Athletes are advised to spend leisure time doing things that are appropriate, such as rest and relaxation. However, some people might choose to spend their leisure time inappropriately, doing such things as gambling or smoking.

■ Appropriate activities

Rest

Rest allows the athlete to unwind and is therefore important. Not only does it allow the body time to recuperate, it also offers mental relaxation away from the pressures of training and competition. Realistically, however, an emerging athlete has to combine their sport with education or working to pay the bills in order to fund future financial security. This might have a significant impact on the amount of leisure time available to the athlete, and it is common to 'juggle' their time to fit everything into daily lives.

Relaxing

People find different ways of relaxing. Relaxation can be either active, such as yoga or Pilates, or it can be sedentary or non-active, such watching television or listening to music. Either way, it is important that the athlete finds the time to relax and 'switch off' from their training or competition programme. This allows the mind and body time to relax, helping athletes to be prepared and focused when competing or training.

The athlete will have started like all sports people. They are likely to have taken up sport as a hobby, and progressed as the hobby becomes a career and the career a way of life. As the hobby progresses into a career, the athlete will often have a hectic lifestyle combining training, competition and travel with work or education. Therefore, they might have limited leisure time in which to relax or socialise. This is particularly important when trying to switch off from the rigours of their sport. It is therefore important that athletes carefully plan when and how they choose to rest, relax and unwind.

Activity

1 Keep a diary for a week to investigate how much time you spend relaxing per day. Record activities such as:

- sleeping
- cooking and eating
- personal hygiene
- watching television
- listening to music
- reading
- using the computer.

2 Draw a large table with two columns. List examples of positive ways and negative ways of spending leisure time.

Education

From your own experiences, you might be aware of how difficult it can be to train, compete and study. Training often takes place after a hard day at school and you might feel tired and unable to fully commit yourself to the session. Compulsory education means that much of your time is spent at school studying for your exams, with homework taking up much of your evenings. An athlete's career can be a relatively short one and it is therefore essential that education is considered in order to gain future financial security.

Combining education with training and competition can be difficult, so a flexible approach should be adopted. You may already be trying to combine study with your sport or considering further qualifications in order to prepare for your future. Fortunately, many courses and qualifications can be studied full or part time and will give you a better understanding of sport and performance.

This should not only improve your understanding, it is likely to enhance your future performance too.

Remember!

It is essential that any learning you undertake fits in with your sporting commitments and is realistically manageable in terms of effort and time.

Theory into practice

The English Institute of Sport (www.eis2win.co.uk) has developed an initiative called Sport and Study. Its aim is to offer the athletic student a valuable insight into the opportunities available as they make one of the biggest decisions of their life: which academic institution best matches their high-performance sporting skills. The website is designed for university and college applicants who are also talented sportspeople. Discuss with your tutor or coach the options available to you and what you need to do to achieve your goals.

Case study: Rob Ferley

Rob Ferley is a professional cricketer with Nottinghamshire County Cricket Club. Having played cricket at county and international level since a young age, Rob has dedicated his time to achieving his goal of being the best left-arm spinner in the UK. This has involved a huge amount of commitment and hard work and he has made many sacrifices throughout his career. As cricket is a summer sport, Rob has to spend most of his time in the winter training. This time is spent working on his own game, including technique and fitness as well as coaching and advising younger players. He also helps out in local schools with PE lessons and encouraging youngsters to play cricket.

During the season, Rob spends much time travelling around the UK and he is away from friends and family. Due to the nature of cricket, he has to spend time waiting to play because of the weather. It is during this time that he has to remain focused as there are many distractions that may have a negative effect on his performance.

Because Rob is a high-profile, professional cricketer, he is aware of the need to behave in an appropriate manner at all times, both on and off the field of play. He realises that he is an ambassador to the sport of

cricket and that he may be a role model to youngsters. He is keen to promote a positive image of himself and of the game of cricket.

Through his dedication, Rob has managed to combine his cricket career with further study and has completed a degree in sports science and a number of coaching awards in preparation for life after cricket. He is fully aware that cricket (and sport) can be a short career and is already considering the future.

1 **Describe five lifestyle factors that may have a negative affect on Rob's cricketing performance.**

2 **Rob is a role model in cricket. Explain the importance of appropriate behaviour for athletes.**

3 **As a cricketer, Rob may have to deal with the media. Describe two methods of communication and the importance of these.**

4 **Identify careers that county cricketers may undertake at the end of their sporting careers. What qualifications will they need?**

■ Inappropriate activities

Relaxation away from sport can come in many forms, most of them positive. However, there are certain activities that can be described as inappropriate, especially for the elite or emerging athlete. Activities such as smoking, drinking alcohol – especially to excess – and gambling are considered to be such pastimes. These pursuits are known as vices, which means they are likely to be viewed as bad habits. There is the danger of an elite athlete, who has both time and money, to undertake in these activities to excess. You are probably aware of a number of high-profile sportspeople who have had their lifestyles reported by the media, often with a focus on any negative or inappropriate behaviour.

Alcohol, drug and tobacco use among young people have increased significantly in the past ten years. The Information Centre carried out a survey in 2005 of 9,000 secondary schoolchildren. The survey found that around 11 per cent of 11–15-years-olds had taken drugs in the last month, 9 per cent had smoked at least one cigarette a week and 22 per cent had drunk alcohol in the last week.

Web links

For more information on the Information Centre's survey, go to their website at www.ic.nhs.uk/pubs/drugsmokedrinkyoungeng2005.

Alcohol

Alcohol is often used as a social tool and in sport it is sometimes used to celebrate a victory. It is also common for alcohol manufacturers to use sport as a marketing tool through sponsorship.

Unfortunately, alcohol can have a negative side. Drinking to excess presents both short- and long-term problems. Drinking too much alcohol can lead to unruly and inappropriate behaviour, with crimes sometimes committed when drunk. In the long term, excessive alcohol use results in liver damage and can prove to be fatal.

◄ Alcohol companies are keen to promote themselves via sporting success. What problems might there be with this?

▲ Being caught using performance-enhancing drugs – even unintentionally – can have serious consequences, with a ban from sport common (skier, Alain Baxter)

Drugs

Drugs can be divided into two main categories:

- recreational drugs
- performance-enhancing drugs.

Key terms

Recreational drugs Taken for social or recreational purposes and generally alter the mind and body. Such drugs include tobacco, alcohol, cannabis, cocaine and heroin.

Performance-enhancing drugs Used by athletes to improve performance and are strictly forbidden in sport. Examples include anabolic steroids, nandrolene and diuretics. Athletes may be tempted to use performance-enhancing drugs in order to achieve success.

Common recreational drugs such as marijuana, cocaine or heroin are extremely dangerous. Their use can have major consequences for the athlete. Not only will performance be affected in the short term, with success unlikely, the risk of long-term damage to health is considerable. All athletes exposed to such drugs should say No as there is no benefit to their use. It is now common for athletes to be tested for both performance-enhancing and recreational drug use. If

found guilty, athletes are likely to be banned from their sport for a long time, as well facing the risk of police prosecution.

Doping refers to using performance-enhancing drugs, which is forbidden. Their abuse has been well publicised, with many high-profile cases of athletes found using them. Some athletes take these drugs to gain an unfair advantage in their sport, with the aim of achieving sporting success. However, the consequences can have both long-and short-term health implications, as well as resulting in a ban from the sport.

Think it over

UK Sport's athlete-centred programme aims to increase understanding of drug-free sport among the whole sporting community. The organisation does this through high-quality, relevant information on anti-doping. It also promotes the positive attitudes and values of sportspeople in the UK who have competed successfully in sport drug-free. Why is a knowledge of anti-doping important to athletes and to sport?

Gambling

Gambling means to bet money on an activity that has an uncertain outcome. By its very nature, sport has many

▲ Horse racing is a multimillion-pound gambling industry and has wide appeal

cases where famous sports stars have gambled enormous amounts of money at sporting events. Attention is often focused on the amount they have bet and the amount of money lost.

Online betting has made gambling even more accessible. It is possible to gamble with people from the entire world via the Internet. Some of these companies are now sponsoring British sports teams.

Betting is risky because sport is uncertain and it is easy to lose large amounts of hard-earned money. Athletes must consider how best to spend their money. Proper financial investment is a much better option.

Smoking

The dangers of smoking are widely publicised. In recent years the government has spent large amounts of money on campaigns aimed at preventing smoking among young people. Many young people are attracted to smoking as it is (wrongly) considered fashionable. There might be peer pressure to join in with friends, which is often given as a reason why people start smoking. Other reasons given are that smoking alleviates or reduces stress and so can help relaxation.

uncertainties and gambling on sport is a multibillion-pound industry. Some sports, such as greyhound and horse racing, are dominated by gambling.

The Gambling Act 2005 sets out the laws that must be followed in order to gamble. For example, athletes are not allowed to gamble on events in which they are involved. This is to prevent accusations of match fixing, where the result is determined not by skill but by cheating.

Web links

There is more information on the Gambling Act on the Gambling Commission's website at www.gamblingcommission.gov.uk.

High-earning athletes often gamble on a variety of sports in order to get the same thrill of winning that they get when they are successful in their own performance. You will probably be familiar with a number of media

Theory into practice

A recent government campaign encourages young adults to give up smoking. The campaign, known as Motivations that Matter, has separate adverts for men and women. The message to men is that they risk their ability to perform sexually. The campaign highlights to females the damaging impact smoking can have on their appearance and attractiveness. In small groups, discuss why young people are attracted to smoking.

As an athlete, the effects of smoking will have a negative effect on sporting performance. This means that training will be harder and success in competition unlikely. The long-term effects of smoking will not only impair sporting performance, they can also be fatal. See Unit 1: The Body in Action for more information on smoking.

Unruly behaviour

The athlete who is regularly in the media spotlight also needs to consider their role as a sporting ambassador whom many young people will aspire to be like. If media pictures show them smoking or behaving in an unacceptable or anti-social way, there is a possibility that children will copy them. Even amateur athletes should consider their behaviour during sporting competition and training, as well as away from the sports ground. Any behaviour that is deemed unruly will be drawn to the public's attention in the media. This will have a negative effect on the image of the athlete and the sport.

Activity

1 In pairs, find examples and images from the media to investigate three athletes whose behaviour can be described as inappropriate. This can be in their social lives, in training or while competing. Create a PowerPoint® presentation to show your findings to the rest of your group.

2 Discuss what you think the consequences of the athletes' actions are.

Pressures

■ Peers

There are many pressures on the athlete's time. Work, education, training and competition commitments mean that there is often little time left to socialise with friends. What time there is might leave the athlete too tired to commit to other activities. However, the emerging or young athlete will feel pressure to meet with friends. Combined with the pressure to achieve success through training and competition, the athlete's life can be stressful. It is important to realise how an athlete must make sacrifices to be the best and to maintain a healthy and rewarding social life. An athlete often has both the time and the money to relax with friends. However, in order to achieve this success, the emerging

athlete has to work hard and train hard. Understanding and supportive friends are important if the athlete is to feel confident in their commitment.

■ Social life

The athlete will have many pressures that affect the amount of time available to socialise with friends and family. However, it is important that time is spent relaxing in their company, away from the pressures of training and competition. Periods should be built in to the training programme to allow the athlete time to relax and socialise.

Activity

Look at your own daily life and record how much time you spend socialising. What activities do you undertake as part of your social time?

■ Training

Pressure will be put on the athlete to perform, both in training and in competition. Such pressure might come from coaches, tutors, parents or spectators. One of the main reasons why athletes drop out of sport is stress. This is often the result of well-intentioned parents or coaches, who might set unrealistic expectations or goals. For example, athletes should be told that mistakes are part of the learning process and should not be feared. Another way athletes face too much stress is when goals are set that are not within their control. Pressure might even come from the athlete themselves who has set targets that are too difficult to achieve.

Being able to deal with this is important if the athlete is to perform to the best of their ability. Training or performing when unwell or injured is likely to have a long-term damaging effect and should be avoided. Likewise, overtraining will be unproductive and significantly increases the risk of injury. A successful athlete will have pre-determined coping strategies that have been developed through experience and through discussion with their coach, tutor or parents.

■ Competition

The athlete is likely to experience high pressure during competition. The desire to win – combined with factors such as spectators, the venue and other athletes (or the opposition) – all play a part in putting stress on the athlete. Being able to deal with this is important if the athlete is to compete to the best of their ability.

Activity

Consider a stressful situation in your sport. How did you deal with it and what was the outcome?

Think it over

Athletes will have their personal lives scrutinised by the media. Do you think the press should be allowed to report athletes' lifestyles and not just their sporting performances?

Financial

■ Spending

It is common for the emerging athlete to have to work in order to fund their sporting aspirations. Many sports can be expensive, with the costs of equipment, travel and accommodation having to be met by the athlete. Lottery funding might be available to provide the essential support services, such as coaching, training camps, competition and sport science. UK Sport also offers money to help with the essential personal living and sporting costs incurred while training and competing as an elite athlete. This is called an Athlete Personal Award (APA).

The athlete is likely to combine work with their sport in order to reach their targets. A key area that must be considered is gaining experience of how to control income and expenditure, especially when sports careers can be relatively short. Many young, high profile athletes will spend their money on the trappings of success such as sports cars or jewellery. However, considering how best to invest money for the future is important for financial security.

Remember!

Many young, prominent athletes have very high salaries but find their careers cut short through injury or loss of form.

■ Saving

The career of an athlete can be a relatively short one, with second careers often undertaken at the end of a competitive career. It is essential that the athlete saves some of their income so that they have a source of money in the future. Savings accounts vary greatly, with some allowing tax-free investment while others offer immediate access to your money. Either way, it is vital to have savings you can fall back on. Savings accounts can be set up and managed online, saving a great deal of time.

■ Investing

Investments are forms of saving designed for longer periods of time. The money is invested in the hope of making a profit on it. Investments can come in many forms such as buying shares in a company or buying property.

■ Sponsorship

Sponsorship is where a company or individual gives money or equipment to an athlete or team. This can be a valuable source of income, as it allows the athlete to concentrate on their training rather than having to work full time to support themselves. The influence of sponsorship on the modern development of sport has been massive. Sport is now big business, with large companies spending millions of pounds to sponsor events or individuals.

▲ David Beckham has a multimillion-pound contract with Adidas to promote its products. Why is Adidas keen to do this?

Many companies want a high-profile athlete to endorse their product or company so that they gain media attention and, ultimately, sell more products. Companies such as Nike and Adidas invest millions of pounds into teams and individuals so that they wear their clothes. Such companies have been partly responsible for creating sporting icons such as David Beckham.

Commercial companies recognise that elite sports stars can be fashion icons and role models. Such organisations use these sportspeople in their advertising campaigns. This is particularly true of sports wear, which is now a fashion product rather than a sporting one!

On a smaller scale, a Sunday league football team might gain sponsorship from a local business in order to pay for their kit or match fees.

■ Tax

Paying tax on income can be stressful for the young athlete. A knowledge of what is required and how to do it is important. If you are on a fixed salary, tax should be deducted automatically before you receive your money. Any additional private work or self-employment involves declaring your income to the Inland Revenue.

An athlete in receipt of an Athlete Personal Award (APA) does not have to pay tax. However, if the government feels you are a professional athlete making a profit from sport, you will be taxed. If your sole income from sporting activities is your APA, you will not be considered to be a professional athlete, so your Award is not taxable. If, however, you have another source of income you might be liable for tax. This is especially important if you receive money through sponsorship. In this case, you might be taxed on your entire income.

■ Insurance

Athletes need to consider buying insurance to protect themselves and their equipment. Insurance can protect a number of things such as life, injury or property. For example, athletes may wish to protect their expensive equipment against theft or damage. This means they will pay a fee or premium to a company, which in return pays to repair or replace the equipment if it is broken or stolen.

Web links

Further information can be found from UK Sport (www.uksport.gov.uk), which gives advice on supporting the athlete financially.

Think it over

Consider how you might handle your own budget.

Income
Income is the money received and paid into a bank account. It may come from a variety of sources:

- salary
- sponsorship
- grants
- donations
- private work
- state benefits.

Expenditure
Expenditure is the money paid out of a bank account. It includes the following:

- rent
- mortgage
- council tax
- water rates
- electricity
- gas
- car: petrol, insurance, servicing, road tax, loans
- television licence
- travelling expenses
- food
- clothes
- telephone (landline and mobile)
- outings and entertainment.

The money that is left over is called disposable income. Disposable income = income less expenditure.

Assessment practice

Imagine you have been approached by a coach working with emerging, young athletes who have the potential to reach a high performance level in their sport. The coach knows the importance of training and preparation, but is becoming increasingly concerned about how outside lifestyle factors are affecting the athletes' performance. Your task is to prepare a short PowerPoint® presentation as follows.

1 Describe the main lifestyle factors that can affect performance. **P1**

2 Explain five of these factors. **M1**

3 Analyse why you think these five factors can have an effect on sporting performance. Use relevant examples you have read about in the media. **D1**

Grading tips

27.2 Understand the importance of appropriate behaviour for athletes

The way athletes conduct themselves during competition and training will influence sporting success. A positive attitude towards themselves and others is important if personal goals and targets are to be achieved. In this section, you will examine how appropriate behaviour both on and off the field of play is essential for sporting success. You will also look at a variety of situations in which you might find yourself and discuss how you would cope with them.

Behaviour

Conduct during competition and training

■ Adherence to rules

Ethics and values underpin all sporting performance. Ethics are moral principles or codes of conduct. In sport, these include the idea of playing to the spirit of the rules of the game. Values are ideals that form beliefs and actions. In sport, these might be enjoyment, personal satisfaction and health.

Key terms

Ethics In sport, it is ethical to recognise when you have inadvertently broken a rule without anybody noticing. For example, a cricketer would tell the umpire he has not caught a ball cleanly or has carried it over the boundary.

Values Athletes try to perform at their best in order to achieve success for their country or team. By recognising that they are competing not just for themselves, they are playing with positive values.

It is important to note that an athlete should uphold these ethics and values in both competition and training.

■ Respect for peers and others

An athlete's behaviour often comes under scrutiny from team mates, coaches and spectators. Behaving professionally and respectfully not only shows your own personal values, but also that you value those around you. Sport can be frustrating, especially when you are performing below your best or when results are not favourable. Such frustration can cause the athlete to react badly to a refereeing decision or comments from spectators. However, this will have a bad impact on the athlete's image and the sport.

They must always follow the rules and respect their peers and others. Sportspeople should never argue with officials, team mates, peers or spectators.

Remember!

Athletes should consider how they behave at all times, especially in training and competition.

■ Appropriate clothing

It is important that the athlete wears appropriate clothing and that the equipment used is suitable and safe. Presenting the correct image is essential when it comes to sporting success.

Activity

1 In small groups, identify a code of conduct that could be followed by participants in your chosen sport.
2 Explain why these rules are important.

Equal opportunities

Equal opportunities involve treating everybody equally and fairly regardless of race, gender, age, disability or religion. Clear legislation is set out to prevent discrimination. As an athlete, you must treat everybody equally and fairly.

Sports equity is about fairness in sport, fairness of access, recognising inequalities and taking steps to address them. It is about changing the culture and structure of sport to ensure that it becomes equally accessible to all members of society.

Web links

Sport England's website at www.sportengland.org.uk has more information about equity and inclusion in sport. You can also find out about its national initiative, Sporting Equals, which promotes racial equality in sport.

Clear and detailed guidance on equal opportunities is available from the Equal Opportunities Commission (EOC). The key discrimination laws are as follows.

- The Race Relations Act 1976 make it illegal to discriminate either directly or indirectly on the grounds of race, religion, colour, nationality, or ethnic/national origin.
- The Sex Discrimination Act 1975 make it illegal to discriminate either directly or indirectly on the grounds of someone's gender or marital status.
- The Disability Discrimination Act 1995 make it illegal to discriminate against disabled people.

Theory into practice

In sport, there are some exemptions to the above Acts.

- Selection for sports teams based on nationality or place of birth is exempt. In other words, you can only represent your country based on strict selection criteria.
- Private sports clubs are exempt from the Disability Discrimination Act and the Sex Discrimination Act. There are many examples where women have fewer rights than men in private golf clubs.
- Section 44 of the Sex Discrimination Act also states that any sport can be restricted to one sex where the physical strength, stamina and physique of the average women would put her at a disadvantage to the average man.

In small groups, discuss the implications of these exemptions to sporting provision.

Web links

For more information on key legislation, explore the following websites: the Equal Opportunities Commission (www.eoc.org.uk); the Commission for Racial Equality (www.cre.gov.uk); the Disability Rights Commission (www.drc-gb.org).

Appropriate role models

In recent years, we have seen a rise in media coverage and the sponsorship of sports stars. These athletes must conduct themselves in the correct manner at all times, as they come under intense press scrutiny. Their private lives are often considered more newsworthy than their sporting successes. Sports stars can be positive ambassadors to their sports. They play an important role in introducing children to the sport and so increase participation. Children copy their heroes, both in the way they play and also in the way they behave on and off the field of play. Athletes should consider that their actions can have both positive and negative consequences, for which they must be responsible.

Think it over

In cricket, the 2005 Ashes series versus Australia saw the emergence of Andrew 'Freddie' Flintoff as a national hero. Since then, children have become increasingly involved in cricket at grass-roots level, some even modelling the way they dress and their appearance to look like Flintoff.

However, children can also copy negative behaviour. A child who witnesses a premier league footballer arguing with the referee and being aggressive might believe that this is acceptable and copy his behaviour. The child might think that because the player has a high status, it is acceptable to behave in such a manner.

You do not have to be famous to be a role model! Younger and inexperienced athletes might look at you and wish to copy your performance or style. Therefore, it is important that you conduct yourself in the right way. Poor behaviour is often recognised and people might view you negatively.

Think it over

Identify a personal role model. What is it that you admire and why? How does their behaviour reflect what you do?

▼ Andrew 'Freddie' Flintoff was highly praised for his sportsmanship following Australia's defeat in the 2005 Ashes

Sports ambassadors

High-profile athletes often work within their local communities to provide encouragement to children and to act as sporting ambassadors. This is not only a positive experience for youngsters wishing to progress their sport further, it also reflects well on the athlete. It is usual for the media to report such occasions, raising the profile of both the athlete and the sport. These sessions might happen on a local basis, with local athletes working in schools and helping out with coaching. Alternatively, they might take place on a national basis, with athletes endorsing specific nationwide campaigns.

Celebrities

Many athletes have become sports stars or celebrities away from their sport. This means they are widely recognised by the general public and so their behaviour might be scrutinised. It is important that these celebrities behave in a positive manner at all times.

Enhancing the status of sport

All athletes can enhance the status of their sport by conducting themselves in a positive manner, both on and off the sports pitch. The media often report the behaviour of athletes and it is vital that their behaviour enhances the image of the sport. By behaving positively and working with the local community, the athlete can raise or enhance the profile of the sport via the local or national media. This in turn attracts children to the sport and can increase participation at grass-roots level.

Encouragement of young performers to reach excellence

An athlete who has achieved sporting success is an excellent source of advice and information for up-and-coming athletes. They will be able to share their experiences as well as give training and competition advice. The elite athlete can also act as a motivator or coach and will further enhance the opportunities given to young performers.

Increasing participation for all

A positive role model in sport will have a positive effect on sports participation. Youngsters might try to copy their favourite sports stars and participate in the same sport, such as the Wimbledon Tennis Championships where the profile of tennis is raised via the media. People, especially children, see tennis stars and wish to copy their performance at their local tennis courts. Such an increase in participation potentially means an increase in the elite sports stars of tomorrow.

Coping and management strategies

Being able to cope with a hectic and varied lifestyle is essential for sporting success. Athletes might find themselves in a wide range of situations, both on and off the field. They will have to develop coping strategies to be able to deal with these situations as they arise. Failure to be able to cope might result in an increase in stress and could have a detrimental effect on performance. Factors that might need to be considered by the athlete will include:

- opposition
- spectators
- injury
- training and competition
- environment.

Each of these factors might have an affect on the athlete. Therefore, they should be addressed in advance so that a coping strategy can be developed.

Activity

On your own, write down factors that affect your own performance in training and competition. Then get into small groups and discuss your findings, identifying any similarities and differences. How do you cope with these?

Research indicates that athletes must develop a range of cognitive and behavioural coping skills to manage the competitive stresses they face. Unit 16: Psychology for Sports Performance outlines coping with such stressors in more detail.

Mentoring and coaching

A mentor is an experienced and trusted tutor or coach. A coach will not only teach technical and tactical skills, they will also be able to understand their individual athletes. Being able to talk to an experienced athlete or coach helps the emerging athlete in understanding sporting performance as well as how to deal with different situations. A good coach listens to the athlete and shares experiences while giving objective advice. It should be possible to allocate time to work through and discuss problems with the coach so that a strategy can be developed. Being able to discuss problems with your coach means that preventative measures can be adopted. The coach and athlete can discuss past, current or future performances and their concerns. It is important to be reflective and honest if the strategies are going to be successful.

For more information on mentoring in sport, especially for new coaches, read *A Guide to Mentoring Sports Coaches*, published by Sports Coach UK (www.sportscoachuk.org). Your local sports development offices will also offer a wide range of courses and information on this important area.

Group and one-to-one discussions

To raise sporting performance, it is essential to be able to discuss problems openly and honestly. The coach needs to have the awareness and skills to be able to understand both the individual athlete's needs and those of the team or group. Individual discussions are important so that the athlete can discuss private or confidential information that might be affecting them. Likewise, airing experiences or feelings as part of a group or team aids team cohesion and sporting performance. Group discussions or seminars allow athletes to express any problems, and coping strategies can be shared among the athletes or team members. Open discussions allow

the coach to identify factors that might be affecting the team or individual performance.

Change of lifestyle

Athletes make many sacrifices in order to reach their potential. Commitment to sport often leads to a pressure on other aspects of their lives, such as family, friends, work or education. This feeling of lack of time or control can result in stress. Athletes will not be able to perform effectively if these feelings exist. Therefore, it is important that athletes consider how they are going to be able to cope with time pressures within their daily lives.

Change of routines

Sport involves changing routines, so planning can be difficult. Fixtures or competitions can involve travelling both in the UK and abroad, and it is normal to stay overnight in hotels. Athletes need to have a flexible approach in order to deal with their daily lives. Likewise, they might experience an injury that will prevent them from training and competing, causing frustration and worry. Commitment and support from family, friends and employers significantly helps the athlete in coping.

Situations

As an athlete, you are likely to find yourself in a variety of situations. These situations may occur during competition or training, or they may happen away from the sports arena. Being prepared to deal with these effectively means you can focus on your own performance, with the aim of producing a successful result. Situations likely to occur can involve a wide variety of people and organisations. These may include:

- team mates or colleagues
- coaches or managers
- opposition players
- spectators
- the media
- sponsors.

In small groups, discuss who is involved in your chosen sport. What contact do you have with these people and how do you deal with them? Try and think of specific examples of how you dealt with difficult situations.

On and off the sports pitch or area

An athlete will often be at their happiest when they are actually participating in their sport. Too often, however, they have to spend time dealing with situations away from the field of play or travelling to or from the sports pitch. People such as journalists might want to ask about the results or past or future performances, so valuable time has to be spent in answering these questions. This can cause frustration, as athletes are under pressure to either train or gain successful results. It is important to be able to deal with these situations in a professional way, as being accessible and friendly enhances the reputation of the athlete and the sport.

On the field of play, the opposition might try to affect your performance through negative comments or actions. 'Sledging' is a term used to describe the exchanging of words with an opposition player to put them off their usual game. This is an attempt to 'psych out' an opponent. It is thought that sledging can lead to an unexpected decline in performance. However, it is not in the spirit of the game.

Key terms

Sledging A term devised by the Australian Cricket team in the 1970s. It describes the use of comments towards opposition players with the intention of distracting them from their performance.

Psyching out The use of psychology to interfere with an athlete's or team's preparation is well known. Psyching out is an attempt to intimidate an opponent or team by making personal remarks, intimidating body language or threatening behaviour. Each of these is designed to have a negative effect on the opposition's performance.

Likewise, players might play aggressively with the intention of physically hurting the opposition. The rules or laws of the sport are designed to prevent this, with punishments to deal with offenders. You are probably aware of examples where players have reacted to a bad challenge. This can have a negative effect on the player and the team as a whole. Likewise, the media regularly focus on the negative aspects of players' performances and behaviour, with strong images shown around the world.

◀ Is it common for footballers to confront referees over decisions? What image does this give to fans?

During competitions

It is important that athletes behave in an appropriate manner during competition. Sport can be frustrating at times, but sportspeople must remember to conduct themselves in the correct manner. Officials might make decisions that you disagree with or the opposition might make derogatory remarks, but you must always conduct yourself appropriately.

During training

Training is a time when you can practise with a coach or other team members. When certain situations occur that frustrate you, such as poor performance or a decision you disagree with, you might react badly. However, working with your team mates and coaches rather than criticising them will enhance your performance and reputation.

Travel to and from sports pitch or area

Many people might wish to speak to an athlete and this might be on the way to training or competition. Sportspeople are often at their happiest when they are actually playing their sport, so having to speak to people can prevent them from reaching the sports pitch or area. To deal with this, athletes should allow a set amount of time to be interviewed before or after training or competition. During this time, they should answer questions in a helpful and professional manner.

Dealing with the media

There are many different forms of the media, including television, radio, newspapers and the Internet. They are important to athletes as they give a valuable opportunity to promote themselves and their sport. It is important to be able to deal with the media effectively and professionally so that opportunities can be maximised.

There are three key reasons why an athlete will deal with the media:

- to promote themselves or to raise their personal profile
- to promote or raise the profile of the sport
- to promote a sponsor.

A press conference is a way of briefing the media on major issues, such as the aims of a forthcoming competition or the reaction to events that have taken place. Press conferences could take place before, during or after a competition, depending on the circumstances.

Athletes are likely to encounter the media in two main forms:

- broadcast, such as on television or radio
- written, such as in newspapers or magazines.

Many retired sportspeople have careers in both the broadcast and written media, offering their opinions on current issues and events.

Activity

Using a selection of newspapers, identify ex-sportspeople who now work as journalists. Why do you think newspapers are keen to print their stories?

Television

Television offers the athlete the strongest opportunity to get their message across because sound and vision are the best methods of delivering a point of view. Like radio, television can be an immediate outlet. It relies on many of the same techniques to deliver its messages, such as satellite links and studio editing.

Television interviews can take place in the studio or at a venue as part of the outside broadcast unit. They are either live or pre-recorded, depending on deadlines and the accessibility of technical equipment.

Television covers sport across the same basic areas as radio and operates across the following formats:

- live coverage
- pre-recorded coverage
- studio-based items
- outside broadcast items
- news bulletins
- documentary programmes.

There are two main areas of television that the athlete is likely to deal with:

- terrestrial television, such as the BBC or ITV
- satellite/cable television, such as Sky Sports or Eurosport.

With the arrival of digital broadcasting, there will be an ever-increasing number of television stations starting up over the next few years.

■ Radio

Radio is a flexible medium that operates 24 hours a day. It is also immediate because of its ability to turn around interviews and features quickly.

Radio covers sport in three basic forms:

- live coverage of events
- news bulletins
- magazines and documentary programmes that look behind the scenes.

Radio gives minor sports a great opportunity to gain coverage, especially through local and regional radio.

■ Press

The written media includes local newspapers, national newspapers and magazines. There is also an increasing number of specialist sports magazines coming on to the market, which offer athletes the chance to gain additional coverage. Sportspeople may also appear in more general lifestyle publications.

Roles in the written media can be broken down into four main areas.

- News reporters, who are looking for an eye-catching story. These writers often have a variety sports to report and so will not be dedicated to only one area. They may be sent to a local charity or sports event, or to an international event such as the Olympic Games, for their story. These stories might focus on a scandalous or negative aspect of performance rather than the achievements of the athlete or team.
- Sports reporters, who are generally supportive of athletes and their sport. They will not report on failures, but they will usually have a balanced approach with the interest of sport at heart. Sports reporters may be well known to the athlete as they will be a regular at events. It is not in the reporters' interest to 'rubbish' the athletes or the sports because they need to have a good on-going relationship with both. Therefore, athletes should try to build a good relationship with these writers as their articles can influence the public's perceptions of them.
- Columnists, who are looking for an overview. Columnist are journalists who write regular features about sport. The subjects covered vary greatly, but normally include issues within sport or a specific team or individual performance. The role of the columnist is to give their opinion and to provoke thought and debate.

- Feature writers, who cover the sport or the athlete in depth. Feature writers examine the sport or the athlete in greater depth than sports reporters. If the athlete is a known winner or has a good story, feature writers may look to do a piece with the athlete before a competition. On the other hand, feature writers may write afterwards if the athlete has emerged as a champion or something extraordinary has happened to them.

Key terms

Tabloid Commonly known as 'red-top newspapers' and include the *Sun*, the *Mirror* and the *Star*. These newspapers tend to cover gossip, sensational stories and images. Sports stories normally focus on negative behaviour rather than actual performance and results. Common sports covered by tabloids are football, cricket, boxing and horse racing.

Broadsheet These newspapers include *The Times*, the *Telegraph* and the *Independent*. They report factual news items and sports events and tend not to report celebrity or gossip. Broadsheets do not sensationalise a sports event and simply attempt to report the facts.

Activity

Investigate a selection of reports from tabloid and broadsheet newspapers. Look at how sporting events are reported and the style of writing used for each type of newspaper.

1 Discuss the ways in which the reporting styles differ.

2 Why do you think reports for the same event differ?

3 What aspects of the event or match are actually reported? Explain why.

Dealing with the public

Athletes often have to deal with members of the public as part of competition and training. They also have to deal with fans, who might be aggressive or hostile towards them or their team. On the other hand, fans can be supportive of the athlete, which often leads to improved performance. It is important that the athlete deals with these in a professional and effective way. With practice and experience, athletes will develop the art of being able to deal with confrontation. This will further enhance their reputation.

Many clubs employ a public relations (PR) officer who is responsible for dealing with the public and the media. Public relations means managing communication between an organisation and the public to build, manage and sustain a positive image. The PR officer usually makes sure the club is seen in a positive light.

■ Disruptive and aggressive fans

Unfortunately in sport there are some spectators who behave in an inappropriate or aggressive way towards either the opposition's fans or the players themselves. Athletes can be subjected to personal verbal abuse, which in turn may affect their performance. It is essential that sportspeople learn to ignore such comments and behaviour, and to focus on their sporting performance. Athletes should never engage with disruptive or aggressive fans as this may provoke them further.

Dealing with others

There are many other people and organisations athletes have to deal with as part of their sport. These may include employers, match officials, managers, sponsors, agents and team colleagues. Being able to communicate and behave appropriately is fundamental to achieving sporting success.

■ The athlete and work

Working with an employer in a professional and open manner allows the athlete to develop their career fully. The support of an employer, who understands the needs of the athlete, means additional time can be spent on training, travel and competition. A flexible and open approach is beneficial to both parties: the employer has a dedicated worker while the athlete feels valued in their work.

■ Referees

Match officials are an essential part of sport. Without officials sport could not exist in the form that it does today. Match officials are in charge of the decisions within the competition in which the athlete is involved. Their decisions are final and must never be questioned by athletes. Behaving in a way that puts pressure on an official to make a favourable decision is known as gamesmanship and is unacceptable in sport. Sportsmanship, on the other hand, means conforming to the rules of the sport.

As an athlete, you should never question the authority of match officials, even if you are frustrated with your own performance. They are an essential part of sport and should be treated in a positive and supportive way.

Key terms

Gamesmanship A term used to describe 'bending' the rules or cheating in sport in order to gain an unfair advantage over an opponent or team. Examples of gamesmanship include time wasting, intimidating officials, shirt pulling or feigning injury.

Sportsmanship Describes playing by the rules and following the ethics of the game. Playing for enjoyment rather than trying to win at all costs is an example of sportsmanship. Other examples include helping an opposition player who is injured, respecting an opponent and congratulating winners at the end of competition.

Think it over

The media often show images of players arguing with the referee's decisions. Discuss the implications of this and your own behaviour when competing or training. Are there any similarities?

■ Coaches

Successful athletes work with a number of coaches in their pursuit of excellence. You may have worked with coaches at a variety of levels as your sporting career has developed. Athletes need to understand what each of these coaches demands and expects in order to reach collective sporting goals. Behaving in a professional manner will help you in your pursuit of success.

■ Third party representation

Athletes may feel that they need to have an agent as part of their support team. An agent would help them with the following issues:

- commercial and sponsorship opportunities
- contract advice
- managing external commitments.

Think it over

The need for an agent arises when an athlete feels that the management of their business and lifestyle concerns is becoming too much of a burden. How does an athlete know when this is the case?

First, it is important that the athlete understands what an agent could do for them. Then the athlete needs to consider how the work of an agent could have a positive impact on their performance and their life outside their sport. Once the athlete has decided that they do need to take on an agent, who should they approach?

The British Olympic Association (BOA) and UK Sport have lists of sports agents and their profiles, which are available to athletes. The data on the agents includes their contact information, athletes they have worked with in the past, and the type of service provided. This enables the athlete to meet with a selection of agents before deciding on the most appropriate. Think of a list of requirements that you would want to discuss with a prospective agent.

■ Manager relationship

A team manager is in charge of making team selections, organising fixtures, and preparing kit and equipment prior to training and competition. As an athlete, you are supported by a manager who will help you as part of your training. The manager organises a variety of opportunities to help you improve, such as additional coaching or injury rehabilitation. The manager also decides on competition tactics before and during an event, and these decisions might affect you as an athlete.

It is important that a manager is treated with respect and honesty, even if you feel that a decision is affecting you personally. Managers have to make difficult but considered decisions that they feel are going to benefit all those concerned in the competition. This is especially true for team sports.

■ Sponsorship

Sponsorship is a formal relationship between the athlete or team and a company. The business deal should be mutually beneficial to the sponsored individual and the sponsoring company.

Most companies seek a return on their support or investment, ranging from goodwill within the community to increased media awareness of their products.

A successful sponsorship deal can be long-lasting and beneficial. It involves the athlete building strong, positive relationships with the sponsor. The longer the relationship lasts, the greater the value that can be gained from it.

The sponsor might make demands on the athlete's time in reward for publicity and money. The athlete should behave in a way that is likely to benefit the sponsor and portray them in a positive way, enhancing their reputation or company. Negative publicity through poor behaviour is likely to result in the sponsor withdrawing or cancelling their contract.

Gaining sponsorship can be hard work. It involves time, effort and luck on the part of the athlete. Normally, athletes only get one chance to impress, so it is vital that they know exactly what they want to achieve from the arrangement.

Remember!

Athletes should treat sponsors with respect, commitment and loyalty.

Activity

Examining different forms of the media, give examples of positive and negative sporting behaviour. Explain how these actions might affect any sponsorship deals.

Web links

UK Sport has set up its own website, called Get Sponsored!, which is dedicated to athletes seeking and securing personal sponsorship. For more information, go to sponsorship.uksport.gov.uk.

■ Teammates and peers

Being part of a team is a vital ingredient in many sports such as cricket, rugby and football. Taking collective responsibility for success and failure is also part of being in a sports team. Working closely and striving to achieve the same goals for success allows a team to bond and perform at the optimum level. Therefore, as an athlete you should not blame team mates or individuals for bad results or mistakes. You need to be able to identify how to improve and develop as a team.

Assessment practice

Modern athletes often have their lives scrutinised by the media. This includes both their sporting performances and their personal lives. Your task is to prepare a short PowerPoint® presentation as follows.

1 Outline examples of positive and negative behaviour in sport. Describe the importance of appropriate behaviour. **P2**

2 Explain why behaviour is important to athletes and their chosen sport. **M2**

3 Consider how athletes are expected to deal with a variety of situations in their sporting careers. Describe at least three of these situations. If you were a coach, describe how you would deal with these situations. **P3**

Grading tips

Grading Tip P2

Choose a number of high-profile sports or sports you are involved in. You should be able to give at least five examples of positive and five examples of negative behaviour. Remember to describe why this behaviour occurs and what the implications of it are. Use images to highlight behaviour and remember to describe what is going on and to explain the background to the picture.

Grading Tip P3

Describe what causes a player to behave inappropriately. Consider your own performance and how you have reacted to comments or other players' behaviour. Outline the consequences of negative behaviour and how clubs deal with it. As part of your presentation, you should also consider how athletes are expected to deal with a variety of situations in their sporting careers and explain the importance of appropriate behaviour.

Grading Tip M2

Explain why good behaviour is important in sport and consider the role of the media in portraying behaviour. You need to explain the long-term effects of negative behaviour on the image of the player and their sport. Highlight the role of sponsorship and how negative behaviour may affect this.

Grading Tip

Use a variety of media – newspapers and television provide valuable images of behaviour. Record matches and review these with your friends. Discuss examples of positive and negative behaviour. Use a wide variety of sports.

27.3 Understand how to communicate effectively with the media and significant others

It is important that athletes can communicate clearly and appropriately. They are required to speak to many people and organisations in their pursuit of success. These may include the media, sponsors, managers and coaches. Communication skills are therefore vital in a developing career so that sporting potential can be fully maximised. This section gives you an understanding of communication skills and why they are important. It also gives practical advice and tips so that you can communicate with a wide variety of people in preparation for achieving your own sporting goals.

Communication

Communicating accurately and clearly

There are verbal and non-verbal forms of communication. We communicate using speech, writing, body language or gestures. By communicating, we are giving information or knowledge. Being able to do this accurately and clearly is essential for effective communication. It is a skill that can be developed with practice and has a significant effect on the learning process and sports performance.

Key terms

Verbal communication Includes talking, explaining, asking questions and giving commands.

Non-verbal communication Includes body language, gestures and listening.

■ Active listening skills

If you do not have listening skills your performance will suffer because you do not have the knowledge of what is expected in a task or situation. In sport, this might lead to confusion, frustration or injury. Clear lines of communications must be open between people who rely on one another to get good results.

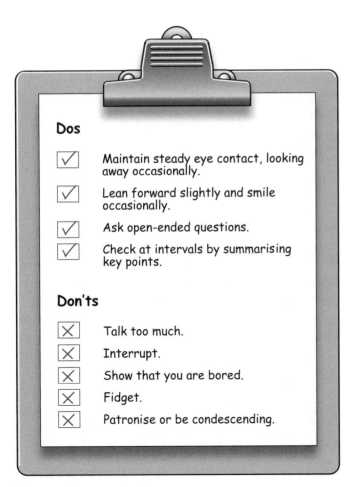

Dos

☑ Maintain steady eye contact, looking away occasionally.

☑ Lean forward slightly and smile occasionally.

☑ Ask open-ended questions.

☑ Check at intervals by summarising key points.

Don'ts

☒ Talk too much.

☒ Interrupt.

☒ Show that you are bored.

☒ Fidget.

☒ Patronise or be condescending.

▲ **Tips for successful listening**

You must be able to listen carefully if you are to perform to expectations, avoid conflicts and misunderstandings, and succeed in any arena.

People speak at between 100 and 180 words per minute, but they can listen to between 550 and 800 words per minute. However, as only a part of the brain is paying attention, it is easy to let your attention wander, thinking about other things while listening to someone. Therefore, try practising active listening skills. This involves listening with a purpose. It might be to gain information, obtain directions or instructions, understand others, solve problems or show support.

Pretending to listen is an easy skill, although *really* listening is much more difficult. The checklist highlights the dos and don'ts of successful listening.

Activity

Listen to a TV broadcast of a recent sports event without looking at the screen. Then compare this with a radio broadcast.

■ Asking questions

What someone says and what we hear can be amazingly different! We might make assumptions that can distort the information. It is useful to ask relevant questions, both to gain knowledge and to confirm understanding. Being able to ask such questions in an open and honest way will clarify key points as well as show that you have an understanding of what is expected from you. Asking questions will also help develop your understanding of personal performance and allow you to discuss your short- and long-term goals with others.

Questions can be open, where more information is gained. They normally start with words such as why, what, how, where or when. A closed question is where a simple yes or no answer is sufficient.

■ Writing clearly and effectively

There are times when athletes have to write to people such as sponsors, managers, the media or coaches. Many people are intimidated by having to do writing.

However, there are times when it is the best way to communicate, and there are other occasions when it is the only way to communicate. Remember that once something is in written form, it cannot be taken back. Communicating through words can be more concrete than verbal communication, with less room for errors and mistakes. This means that you must use accurate writing skills, and think about your spelling, grammar, punctuation, writing style and choice of words.

Remember!

It is important that you write in a clear and effective way so that you can express yourself properly.

Today's technology makes letter writing and other written forms of communication easier by providing reliable tools that check and correct misspelled words and grammar use.

Always check a letter or email thoroughly when you have finished writing it. Even when you think it is exactly what you want, read it through again before sending it. Check that there is nothing in the writing that could be misinterpreted.

Discussions

Throughout your sporting career, you will have discussions with others covering a wide range of subjects such as results, personal or team performance.

■ With coaching staff, managers, advisers, other athletes

You might find yourself having conversations with coaching staff, managers, advisers and other athletes. Such discussions allow you to share ideas and opinions, and can often be a useful tool in identifying how to improve performance. Discussions may also form part of contract or sponsorship negotiations, which means they are important. The key to a successful discussion is to be prepared, know what you want to say in a clear way

and be able to listen to others. It is also important that you respect others, with everybody having the chance to put across their thoughts and ideas.

Preparation for communication

The old saying 'fail to prepare; prepare to fail' is true when discussing coaching, performance and communication. It is important that you are prepared well in advance so that you know what to expect. Preparation might include research, scripts, prompt sheets and rehearsals. Using these should prevent any poor or unexpected performance. This is essential when preparing to deal with the media, especially as part of a press conference or live broadcast interview. Athletes need to be able to convey information in a clear and concise manner to aid understanding and avoid any embarrassing or controversial moments.

Knowing what you want to say or rehearsing the questions you are likely to be asked will help. Researching the content of the area to be discussed will also give you confidence in your ability to deal with the situation.

Being prepared might include asking yourself the following questions.

- What questions will I be asked?
- How should I respond to these questions?
- How should I present myself at the interview?
- What should my appearance be at the interview?
- Who can I seek help and advice from?

■ Purpose and content

Knowing what the purpose of the interview is beforehand will allow you to prepare in advance. This involves researching what questions are likely to come up, and what the answers should be. You should also prepare for the unexpected so that you are fully aware of the content of the interview or presentation.

■ Audience

Being aware of your audience means you can prepare a suitable presentation. The size and level of knowledge within the audience means you can talk at the correct level and aid the understanding of those people.

■ Rehearsals

A good way of improving your presentation skills is to rehearse in advance. Read through your notes and presentation, so that when you have to do it for real you are familiar and confident with its content.

■ Scripts and prompt sheets

Scripts and prompt sheets can be used to refer to during a presentation. This will give you confidence in case you feel that you might forget something during the presentation. However, do not rely solely on these as you may end up simply reading a script rather than presenting the information.

■ Research

Research into the area that you have to present will give you valuable knowledge. This allows you to have the confidence to answer any additional questions that may arise. Having a thorough understanding of the information also allows you to concentrate on your presentation skills.

■ Resources and information gathering

Before you undertake a presentation, gather as much information as possible in advance. This research might involve investigating the subject matter, as well as speaking to experts or people who can give specific advice. Remember to use all the resources available to you to prepare a professional and clear interview or presentation.

Activity

1. On your own, prepare a set of possible questions that a journalist could ask.

2. In pairs, ask each other the questions you have devised and try to give clear answers.

3. Then repeat the activity. Was it easier next time around? If so, explain why.

Extracting key points from written material

It is important that you can extract the key points from written material. This is a valuable skill that will save you a great deal of time. You need to focus on the relevant information and use it appropriately. This means you can spend more time preparing other aspects of an interview or presentation. There are three main styles of quick reading.

- Skimming means focusing on the introduction, first line and main paragraph. This will give you a 'flavour' of the text.
- Scanning is used to identify a key piece of information within the text, such as a quote.
- Searching is used when you know the exact phrase or words you are looking for within the text.

Personal delivery

The ability to communicate effectively depends on many factors, including body language, style of communication, vocabulary and tone. Communication might also be affected by your appearance and the timing of your delivery.

Whether you are giving an interview or a presentation, speaking to an audience can be fun and exciting. However, lack of preparation or not defining the purpose of the presentation can make even the best-intended presentation a poor experience. To ensure you are effective, ask yourself the following questions.

- Why am I giving this presentation or interview?
- What do I want the audience to take away from the presentation?

You also need to know your audience. Their familiarity with the presentation or interview topic should determine how you make your presentation. The media will be familiar with the sport or subject areas, so pitch your presentation at the right level.

Find out in advance how long you will have to make your presentation. Take this time and break it into smaller parts, with each part tackling a specific task. All of the elements should reflect the overall objective of the presentation. For example, the first part should be an introduction to the subject. Here you could give an overview of your presentation or a short summary of your speech, explaining the topic, why you are covering it and what you hope to accomplish.

Keep your presentation short and simple. Your audience will not remember every point of your presentation, so highlight the most important parts.

Remember!

The longer the presentation, the higher the risk of boring the audience.

■ Communication styles and body language

Your style of communication will vary depending on who you are communicating with, what message you are giving and the situation you are in. You are no doubt aware of your own style of communication. There are three main styles of leadership:

- passive, where you put the needs of others before your own and minimise your own self-worth
- assertive, where you stand up for your rights while maintaining respect for the rights of others
- aggressive, where you stand up for your rights but in doing so violate the rights of others.

Each of these styles has a direct effect on how athletes communicate, as well as how they are perceived by others.

Remember!

Consider which style of leadership you are most likely to use and how this will affect your communication with others.

Body language is the term used for forms of communication using body movements or gestures as well as verbal communication. These may include hand gestures, smiling or nodding. The use of body language can help communication and shows whether somebody understands or is acknowledging what you are saying. It is important to understand the use of body language and how it affects the way you might be perceived. For example, yawning can show disinterest, while keeping your arms crossed might indicate a lack of openness. Personal gestures should be kept to a minimum so that they are not a distraction.

Activity

In pairs, try discussing an issue in sport without using any hand gestures. What does this show you?

■ Language

It is essential when presenting information that you use the correct language. Your voice should be clear and words should be pronounced properly. Any difficult or unfamiliar words should be practised beforehand. You should avoid slang and swearing during a presentation.

■ Speech
Use of technical vocabulary

Sport uses many technical terms and specialist language to describe performance and techniques. If you are talking to other athletes, they are likely to understand what you are saying. On the other hand, a non-sportsperson might be confused by technical jargon and so in this case it should be avoided. Terms should be described and explained in their simplest forms to ensure that the entire audience understands what you are trying to say. This can also be true in training and competition if a coach uses too many technical terms. Athletes may be unsure about what is required, leading to confusion and poor performance.

Pace

For a presentation to be successful and to ensure that the audience remains involved and interested, consider the pace at which you talk. If you talk too fast, people will not be able to follow what you are saying. If you talk too slowly, people may become bored.

Intonation and clarity

What you are saying might be affected by the intonation and clarity of your verbal communication. Intonation is the pattern and pitch of your voice, and clarity means how clearly you speak. You may be aware of people who speak very slowly in a non-expressive voice. This can be difficult to understand and uninspiring. Alternatively, someone with a lively, fast-paced voice is difficult to understand as they speak too quickly. You must use your voice in a way that creates interest and is easy to listen to. This ensures that your communication is heard and understood.

Appearance

When you meet someone, remember that first impressions count. In a short time, an opinion of you will be formed, based on your appearance, body language, mannerisms and dress.

These first impressions can be nearly impossible to change, making such encounters important. They set the tone for the whole relationships that follows. This is often conveyed by the way you look. It is vital for successful communication that you look professional and act professionally. There is a phrase that says that 'a picture paints a thousand words'. The person you are meeting for the first time does not know you, so your appearance is usually the first clue they have to go on.

The way you dress is important. In a sports setting, appropriate attire may be training wear, kit or even a suit or blazer worn with a shirt and tie.

You should also consider your grooming. A clean and tidy appearance is appropriate for most occasions. Hair should be clean and tidy, with long hair tied back and jewellery kept to a minimum. A professional appearance involves a clean shave for men and discrete make-up for women. Clean and tidy clothes and shoes are essential in making the right impression. Make sure your grooming is appropriate and helps make you feel 'the part'.

Timing

As an athlete, you may well be an ambassador or role model. Make sure you always go to appointments on time and well prepared. Plan to arrive a few minutes early and allow flexibility for possible delays in traffic or taking a wrong turn. Arriving early is much better than arriving late, and it is the first step in creating a great first impression.

Media

Local and national television and radio

The media give the athlete a valuable opportunity to promote themselves and their sport. Making sure that communication is clear and open is a skill that develops with practice and experience. Athletes may have to give interviews with journalists working on televisions, radio stations and newspapers. Athletes might have to attend press conferences to give their views on individual or team performances.

It is important to understand how to communicate verbally and non-verbally in a professional way. This will raise the profile of the athlete and their sport, and present them in a positive light. The British Olympic Organisation (BOA) produces an information sheet that gives athletes advice when dealing with the media. This advice not only gives tips to budding Olympic athletes, it also applies to athletes in any sport who may have to deal with the media. Here is a summary of the main points.

- Be yourself.
- Show how you feel.
- Think before you speak. Before the interview, think what possible issues could arise. What do you want to say? Make sure you have a clear view as to how to tackle difficult issues. Ask the interviewer beforehand what the questions will be. If there is a difficult issue, do not avoid it. If you are not willing to give your views, someone might make them up for you.
- Be natural. Do not be over prepared as you will come across false.
- Have a conversation with the person giving the interview. Forget about the audience listening and watching. Listen carefully and answer each question. This is the best way to come across naturally.
- Speak clearly and not too fast, even if you are excited.
- Look the interviewer in the eyes – you will come across as a sincere, believable person.

- For television and radio, answers should not be too short, i.e. not one word, but do not ramble. Journalists might only have a short time slot and you can cover several points.
- Sponsor coverage should be subtle – any blatant logos may be edited.
- Do not alienate the media. Be open and available for interview and it will report favourably. Build relationships with sports journalists.
- Enjoy it! People want to know about you, so sell your sport.

Internet

The last ten years have seen a massive growth in communication in the form of the Internet. It is now possible to communicate and send images instantly over the web. This form of media will continue to expand and, as such, sport can now be seen all over the world. This does not only include sporting performance; it might include interviews, press conferences, discussions and debates. Being able to communicate in a manner that is clear to different cultures is a skill that has to be learnt and practised.

Specialist magazines

In recent years, there has been a massive increase in sports specialist magazines, ranging from athletics through to activities such as climbing and mountain biking. Magazines regularly feature specific athletes who give exclusive interviews informing the public of their achievements and hopes for the future. They also report on poor sporting behaviour, so it is important that the athlete acts professionally at all times, both on and off the field of play.

Club magazines

Club magazines are produced to inform athletes and sport club members of recent events, results and sport-specific news. These magazines interview successful athletes and question them on areas such as training, competition success and lifestyle away from sport.

Requirements of different media types

Different media types require different information about the athlete. This might range from immediate post-match interviews through to lifestyle guides. Some forms of media – such as newspaper or radio interviews – allow athletes to prepare their responses in advance. Others put the athlete on the spot during live interviews that can be broadcast around the world. Sportspeople must be prepared and confident in their ability to communicate with the many forms of media that exist in the twenty-first century.

Significant others

Employers

Emerging athletes are often employed outside their sporting careers and need a positive relationship with their employers. These athletes should communicate openly, professionally and with respect. They might need the employer to be flexible with their conditions of work in order for them to train, travel or compete.

Match officials

Match officials are an essential part of competitive sport. Athletes must respect the officials' decisions during and after competition. Communication should be clear, open and respectful, both in terms of verbal and non-verbal communication.

Club/regional/national coaches

Successful athletes work with a number of coaches. You have probably worked with coaches at a variety of levels as your sporting career has developed. Athletes need to understand what each of these coaches demands and expects in order to reach collective sporting goals. Communicating in a professional way will help you in your pursuit of sporting success. It is important that your relationship with your coaches is honest and open so that important goals and performances can be discussed and developed.

Agent

An agent normally looks after the personal affairs of the athlete, such as contracts and sponsorship deals. The agent also organises events that athletes need to attend in order to raise their profile. For this to be successful, athletes should consider how to communicate with their agents. It is important that they can express what they want to ensure that the agent is clear of the goals and aspirations the athlete has.

Manager

The manager is responsible for the athlete's or team's sporting affairs and should be treated with respect and consideration. The manager often has to make difficult or unpopular decisions, such as selecting a team or dropping a player who has been under-performing. This may cause frustration on the part of the player, but he or she must remember to communicate their concerns or worries in an open and constructive manner.

Sponsors

Individual or event sponsors are an important source of income for the athlete or sport. Athletes may be required to attend meetings with sponsors, so they should present themselves in the best light. They must be courteous and professional at all times and ensure that they communicate appropriately. This communication should be both verbal and non-verbal. It should show that the athlete is interested and values the contributions the sponsor has made.

Other team colleagues

Being able to communicate openly and honestly with team colleagues is an important part of sporting team success. All members should feel valued and that they are able to raise concerns or specific points with team mates, managers and coaches. An environment where open communication and discussion should be developed, and encouragement should be given to any players that might be under-performing. Athletes should never criticise other team members as this will have a negative effect on performance.

Evaluation

Strengths and weaknesses

As an athlete you must be able to evaluate both your sporting performance and your personal, lifestyle performance. Your evaluation should investigate your strengths and weaknesses, as well as how you can improve. The media judge you not only on your sporting success but also on your lifestyle and the ability to communicate with different parties. Self-evaluation will give you the confidence to recognise your personal strengths and any weakness you might have, so that you can do your best to change these in the future. Think about how to evaluate yourself and how others are able to help you improve your communications skills.

Use of feedback

Feedback can come in many forms and from a variety of areas. It may even come from you. Being able to interpret the feedback so that it provides constructive advice and support is essential. Any feedback should come from valued people and give clear and direct advice on the positive and negative aspects of performance. It should highlight the strengths and weaknesses in order for improvement plans to be devised.

Peer and tutor feedback

An athlete's peers, tutor and family are likely to be valued, so their feedback should be sought. Having these people involved in sport will give valuable information on how to improve both in terms of sporting performance and in communication skills. In the past, you have probably asked for feedback or advice from friends or family. Using this information, you might have developed a personal strategy to improve.

Video analysis

Another area or tool that can used to improve performance is the use of video equipment. The benefit of this is that time can be spent individually or with others to reflect on a specific situation. Video analysis can highlight areas that you may not be familiar with, such as hand gestures or facial expressions. Being aware of non-verbal communication aids future presentations or interviews, and generally improves the communication process.

The evaluation process provides the athlete with many opportunities to improve or modify performance. The process should always be honest and open, and it should be ongoing with time allocated to review performance.

Modifications to improve and/or change performance

The purpose of evaluating performance is so that improvements can be made in the future. This may involve changing training or techniques, or simply modifying existing practices. By using feedback and analysis, it allows the athlete to gain valuable information on areas of weakness. It is important that such information is utilised using an open and honest manner rather than worrying about criticism.

Activity

1   Using a camcorder, video yourself and a friend giving a short interview or presentation.

2   Review the recording and note any non-verbal communication. How do these affect or influence the presentation?

Assessment practice

Imagine an inexperienced group of athletes wish to improve their communications skills as they have an important presentation to give in the near future. As an experienced coach, they have approached you to give them specific advice on how to communicate with the media. You have identified the main methods of communication and set them the following task to practice.

In a small group, prepare a ten-minute presentation on a sports-related subject. Using detailed research, the group should present using appropriate aids such as slides or handouts for the rest of the class. Focus should be made on non-verbal and verbal communication. **P4**

Grading tips

Grading Tip   P4

Practise the presentation in front of friends and family and ask them for comments. Remember to consider non-verbal communication. Watch a television interview and turn down the sound. What body language do you see and what does this tell you? Prepare cue cards to help you but do not read from them. Each group member should rehearse and concentrate on difficult or unfamiliar words. Remember that your appearance is important. Speak to tutors and ask them for their advice when making a presentation.

Factors

Being a successful athlete does not happen by chance. Athletic careers are usually well considered and well planned, with short- and long-term personal goals identified by the athlete and coaching team. Progress may be made from club to regional and national teams or competitions. This brings many aspects that will support success, as well as considerations about post-athletic careers when factors such as injury or loss of form might result in secondary careers being undertaken.

Goal setting

Just as you set goals in your sport, it is important to set targets for yourself in terms of career planning. These targets provide clear direction so that you can achieve the things that will bring you success. When setting goals, you should have a detailed plan, commit to that plan, and then take action. This may sound easy, but goal setting should be well considered and a systematic approach is necessary.

■ Short-term

To successfully achieve a long-term goal, set smaller, short-term goals that build towards the long-term goal. Focus your efforts and energy into achieving these small goals. Remember to bear in mind the larger, long-term goal. If you are not sure how to do this, seek advice from experts and coaches. Talking to experienced athletes enables you to gain an invaluable insight into how these

Remember!

Goal-setting plays an integral role in achieving success, so it is important to take the time to set some goals.

athletes have achieved success in the past. Coaches should help their athletes set career and performance goals, as well as encouraging them to achieve short-term goals.

Short-term targets are the stepping stones along the way. As you achieve each short-term goal, your confidence will grow and you will be closer to the next one.

■ Medium-term

Medium-term goals usually last for between one month and six months and are a progression of short-term goals.

■ Long-term

The first thing that an athlete needs is a long-term goal. This is an objective statement about a specific achievement that can be measured. What is it that you want to achieve? Examples of this might be 'to finish tenth or above at the end of season' or 'to have a batting average of at least 50 at the end of the season'. When most athletes are asked what their goal is, they typically reply, 'I want to win' or 'I want to be the best.' These

Key terms

Short-term goals Goals that are set with the immediate future in mind. These might last from a day to a month, and they might include what you hope to achieve in a session. However, it is more usual for short-term goals to last for about a month.

Medium-term goals These goals normally last between one and six months, and they form the progression from short term goals to long-term goals.

Long-term goals These are the final goals that the athlete wishes to achieve. They are usually set for one season, although some long-term goals last the entire career.

statements tell you little about how to achieve this, and they do not direct your behaviour. Therefore, athletes and coaches need to have a long-term goal in mind, especially when considering the career of the athlete.

Being able to appraise yourself honestly is the foundation to future success and achievement. What are you trying to achieve specifically? It is important for long-term success that athletes are clear in their minds on what they want to achieve before identifying how to accomplish this. You might find there is a gap between performance and what you want to achieve. You should identify how you are going to bridge this gap.

■ SWOT analysis

It may be useful for athletes to perform a SWOT analysis. Originally a SWOT analysis was a business concept used to plan and evaluate the Strengths, Weaknesses, Opportunities, and Threats involved in a project or in any situation requiring a decision. Being clear and identifying each of these key areas will allow you to set long- and short-term goals both in terms of performance and also long-term athletic career planning.

Strengths
What are your strengths?

Weaknesses
What are your weaknesses or areas that you wish to develop?

Opportunities
What are the opportunities for employment in your local area?

Threats
What competition is there that may act as a barrier to your career planning?

▲ A SWOT analysis diagram

■ Short- and long-term career goals

Goal setting should follow the SMART principle:
- **S** – **s**pecific
- **M** – **m**easurable
- **A** – **a**chievable
- **R** – **r**ealistic
- **T** – **t**ime-bound

Use this method to define exactly how you are going to achieve your career successes. (SMART is covered in more detail in Unit 4, on page 157.)

■ Technical and practical skills

Within your sport, you possess a number of important technical skills. These may be your ability to serve a tennis ball or kick a ball accurately. Through practice, training and analysis, these skills will improve so that you can gain success either individually or as a team. Identifying the specific practical skills required will enable you to focus on how to improve. This is true for basic or key skills that will be important as part of your future career. You need to learn how to communicate to individuals or groups of people and how to deal with the media. In order to do this, you can seek specialist advice from experts or even enrol on college courses that specialise in a variety of communication or public-speaking courses.

■ Key and basic skills

Key and basic skills may include communication, interpersonal and organisational skills. These can be developed within sport as well as outside, and are an important part of development. The skills learnt will help athletes in both their sport as well as their careers after their competitive sports careers have finished. Skills such as numeracy and literacy should also be learnt and developed as these are essential in all areas of life and work.

Before we discuss athletic career planning, it is important to identify your current sporting expectations. If you want to be the best, how are you going to achieve this? This will involve athletic training and life skills. Being able to identify practical skills that can be used to achieve personal targets is important to the athlete. Clear and time defined planning is also important as this will indicate how and when such targets are achieved.

■ Current expectations as an athlete

As an athlete, you will no doubt have expectations of yourself and others in terms of sporting performance and how you see your sporting career developing. Being able to clearly identify specific expectations will help you to plan you career and set defined targets.

■ Key review dates

It is vital that athletes set clear and defined dates to review their career plans. Such targets or goals will help in identifying specific targets and whether these have been achieved or not. Key dates must be realistic, although they can be flexible if it is unlikely they are going to be achieved due to unforeseen circumstances.

■ Transitions

Athletes experience many transitions and changes throughout their careers. These might include a change in coach, a change in club or location, and a change in national or international status. There will also be the significant transition from participating in sport to the secondary, post-sport performance career. This can be a difficult time as athletes face the change from a sports career, and they may feel regret, anxiety and a loss of identity that can accompany retirement.

Change of coach

There may be times during an athlete's career when they will have to change coach. This may be due to career progression or when representing different teams. It is important that athletes accept this transition and are able to continue to perform at their best levels.

Change of club

Changing club can be a difficult time for an athlete. The athlete may be leaving friends or family and feel like they are the new person in the club. There are likely to be many unfamiliar faces and the prospect can seem daunting at first. Therefore, athletes must be able to deal with this process while still focusing on their own performance and training.

Achieving national and international status

As an athlete's career progresses, they may be fortunate to be selected to represent their region, county or country. This involves communication and working with a wide range of people including coaches, managers and the media. Being able to recognise how to achieve national and international status allows the athlete to identify key targets and how these targets can be achieved.

■ Contingencies

Sport can be a career with many uncertainties. Clear and definitive planning does not prevent an unexpected occurrence happening, such as long-term or permanent injury, an accident preventing participation or illness. You should consider what options are available after a performance career has ended and what skills and qualifications are required.

Illness

An unexpected illness will prevent an athlete from performing or training. It may also act as a setback in terms of competition preparation.

Accident

As the nature of sport is often uncertain, accidents will occasionally happen. If this happens, it is important that there is a contingency in place. Accidents must be dealt with promptly and you should evaluate the impact this has on future training practices and performances.

Permanent injury

Unfortunately, many sports careers are cut short due to permanent injury. If this happens, the athlete may feel uncertain of their future as most of their lives may have been dedicated to training and competition in their sport. It is important that athletes have a contingency plan in case this happens and they have a future career plan in place.

Second career planning

Being faced with planning a career away from sport can often be a daunting and stressful experience for athletes. For most of their adult lives, they will have been training and competing, and an uncertain future can lead to anxiety and stress. However, many of the skills gained in sport can be used in other occupations. Athletes tend to be highly motivated and committed: valuable traits in any industry. Teamwork and leadership skills are also important skills found in both sport and industry. Identifying which careers are available and the qualifications and experience needed will give athletes the direction needed in planning for the future.

■ Qualifications and experience

Most jobs or careers require you to have qualifications and experience. As part of your career planning, you should identify the careers you are interested in and the qualifications required to undertake these jobs. A valuable insight into jobs can be gained by work experience, where you take on a job for a short period of time to see whether it is an area in which you would enjoy working.

■ Career options inside and outside professional sport

Careers after sport can be found both within professional sport and also outside it. The skills found within sport can be transferred easily to many employment areas. There are also many careers found alongside current athletes. These can involve physiotherapy, sports nutrition, coaching and teaching, working in the media or sports development. Each of these key areas still involves close contact with sport and competition, and tomorrow's emerging athletes can benefit from the retired athlete's experience.

Coach

It is a natural progression for athletes to continue in their sport as a sports coach. There are opportunities to coach at all levels, from grass roots through to elite. A number of specific and progressive coaching courses are now available.

Case study: Careers after sport

Austin Healey recently started training for life after rugby. 'Four months ago I was quite concerned about what I was going to do,' he said. 'Would I take the easy way and go into coaching or find employment elsewhere?'

His answer was to consult Careers After Sport (www.careersaftersport.com). This organisation was set up in 2005 by Jon Sleightholme, the former England wing, and two partners from the world of recruitment, Alan Dickenson and Russell Yeomans. It helps elite sports people – not only from rugby – to make the transition to what Healey calls the 'real world'.

1 **Which skills do you think can be transferred from sport to a second career?**

2 **Which skills do you have that are important to both your sport and your future career aspirations?**

3 **Analyse the factors that you need to consider to pursue your chosen career after sport.**

Teacher

Teaching can be undertaken at schools, colleges or university. It is natural for sports teachers to have an active interest in sport and they often compete outside work. To be a teacher you must study to degree level in sports science or physical education and also hold a certificate in education. Study normally lasts for a period of three years in higher education.

Media

There are many jobs in the media such as a journalist or reporter. To undertake a career in this field, you should have a good command of written and spoken English and it is normal to study up to degree level.

Sports development

Sports development is concerned with getting various groups involved in sport. This may include the elderly, children or disabled people. Local authorities normally target groups that are under-represented in sport and offer schemes or sessions to get them actively involved. Sports development officers normally have a sports-related qualification as well as a wide range of coaching awards.

Physiotherapist

Athletes are often keen to become physiotherapists as they may have experienced injury during their careers. There are a number of courses available throughout the UK, but competition for places is stiff. A physiotherapist has to study to degree level and the course will involve working in general physiotherapy at a local hospital. The study of sports injuries and rehabilitation is not undertaken in a physiotherapy undergraduate degree course.

Sports science support

The area of sports science is expanding as we try to improve athletic performance. Areas of sports science include biomechanics, psychology, fitness testing and physiology. Each of these areas is designed to offer athletes support and to improve their performance. Sports scientists normally study at university and often continue their studies afterwards in the form of research.

Theory into practice

There is a wide range of careers in sport that can be undertaken by athletes of all abilities. There is also a huge variety of sports science-style courses available at college or university. Each of these has its own areas of specialism within sport and can be rewarding. Discuss your career aspirations with a tutor or careers adviser, who will be able to identify the best course of action for you.

Assessment practice

Imagine as a coach you are aware that an athletic career can be uncertain in terms of success or length. You feel that as part of your commitment to your athletes it would be useful to prepare a presentation to identify future career options. Your task is to prepare a short PowerPoint® presentation as follows.

1 Outline the factors that should be considered when planning a career both in sport and beyond a competitive career. **P5**

2 Explain each of the factors you have identified. **M3**

3 Analyse how these key factors might influence an athlete's career planning. **D2**

Grading tips

Grading Tip **P5**

Identify at least five sporting careers that interest you. Research what qualifications and experience you would need for each one. What factors will influence your future career? Discuss these careers with a teacher or careers adviser. Identify clear targets on how to achieve your sporting and career goals.

Grading Tip **M3**

For each factor identified (at least five should be noted), you should explain how these can affect your future career. Explain who can help you to overcome problems you may encounter. Research where you can undertake both academic and coaching courses. What are the

costs and entry requirements of these? Discuss these options with your parents and tutor or coach.

Grading Tip **D2**

You should fully analyse how these key factors will influence an athlete's career planning. Choose at least five factors and fully investigate how these will influence your career choices. Analyse who will be able to help you in deciding the best career for you. Contact people who are already working in the area and discuss how they achieved their success. Arrange an interview with a professional athlete and ask how they manage their careers. Speak to successful coaches and get advice on how to succeed in sport.

Knowledge check

1 Describe how athletes can use their leisure time, explaining how some of these activities can be either appropriate or inappropriate.

2 Using examples, outline how lifestyle can affect athletic performance.

3 Explain the importance of financial management to the athlete.

4 Name five activities that must be considered by athletes when planning their time management.

5 Explain the importance of appropriate behaviour during competition and training.

6 Why are athletes considered role models and what does this mean in terms of their behaviour?

7 How can athletes enhance the image of their sport and what does this mean to participation of young people?

8 Where may pressure come from for athletes?

9 How can a coach help an athlete in coping with the pressure?

10 Give examples of how an athlete would deal with aggressive fans.

11 Give examples of verbal and non-verbal communication.

12 Why is communication with the media so important and how should an athlete prepare for this?

13 Explain the different types of media and their individual requirements.

14 Explain the difference between short-term, medium-term and long-term goals.

15 Research the factors that can influence athletic career planning.

Preparation for assessment

1 You have been selected to coach and mentor a group of emerging athletes. As part of this role, you are expected to highlight the different lifestyle factors that can affect athletes. You should prepare a five-minute presentation based on the title 'Lifestyle factors that can affect athletes.'

   a Choose relevant examples from the media of both appropriate and inappropriate behaviour.

   b Describe at least five different lifestyle factors relevant to sport.

   c You may choose a particular sport or athlete as an example, but you must consider positive and negative factors.

   d Consider using pictures to highlight key points and remember to make your presentation interesting. **P1**

To help you meet the M1 and D1 criteria you should read the following grading tips.

2 Following your presentation, the head coach feels that the emerging athletes would benefit from information regarding the importance of behaviour. It has come to his attention that a number of these athletes are behaving in an inappropriate manner both during training and competition and also away from their sport. You have been asked to prepare a code of conduct that should include the following helpful hints:

   • conduct during competition
   • conduct during training
   • respect
   • adherence to rules
   • dealing with the media
   • dealing with significant people.

The code of conduct should describe fully the importance of appropriate behaviour for the athletes. **P2**

Grading tips

Grading Tip M1

You need to take the examples used in your presentation and explain how each of these will affect the athlete. You should consider how appropriate factors such as rest and relaxation can help the athlete's performance, whereas inappropriate factors such as gambling and alcohol may have a negative effect on sporting performance. You should also explain the importance of financial management and pressure and how these can affect the athlete.

Grading Tip D1

You should analyse how your identified lifestyle factors will affect the athlete. This means you should give the plus and minus points and write about your own judgement on why these can influence performance and the athlete. For example, you might consider socialising with friends as a positive way of relaxing although this can also be considered negative if it has a detrimental effect on performance.

To help you meet the M2 criteria you should read the following M2 grading tip.

Grading tips

Grading Tip **M2**

You should further explain each point raised as part of your outlined code of conduct. It may be useful to present the code of conduct to the athletes so that they are able to ask pertinent questions and you can provide answers.

- Explain why good behaviour is important in sport.
- Consider the role of the media in portraying behaviour.
- Explain the long-term effects of negative behaviour on the image of the players and their sport.
- Highlight the role of sponsorship and how negative behaviour may affect this.
- Use a variety of media – newspapers and television provide valuable images of behaviour.
- Record matches and review them with your friends. Discuss examples of positive and negative behaviour.
- Use a wide variety of sports.

3   Your code of conduct has been warmly received by both the athletes and the head coach. The athletes now understand how they are expected to behave both on and off the sports field and the importance of this to them and their sport in general. However, a number of the emerging athletes are still concerned that their behaviour can be influenced by other people or different situations they find in sport. Therefore, you have offered to prepare a report that describes key strategies that can be used to help the athletes deal with different situations in which they might find themselves.

a   Look at three different situations that can be used by the athletes.

b   Consider high-profile sporting situations and think how you would cope in that situation.

c   Analyse televised sporting events and describe different situations that occur during that event.

d   In small groups, discuss how others can have positive and negative effects on performance.   **P3**

4   The head coach has just informed you that your athletes are to be involved in a high-profile competition. It is likely that the media will be present, so they will want to interview a number of the emerging athletes. You feel, however, that at present the athletes have little experience of communicating with the media or dealing with significant others.

The head coach and you decide to hold a media training day in which to teach the athletes of the importance of communication. You should produce an information pack to be used by the athletes, which describes the methods of communication that can be used when dealing with the media and significant others.

a   Make sure your information pack is clear and easy to read.

b   Use pictures to highlight examples of athletes communicating with the media.

c   Analyse television interviews and note the good points and describe the bad points.

d   Use at least two methods of communication.

e   Consider both verbal and non-verbal communication.

f   As part of the introduction, describe the different types of media.

g   In small groups, practise interview techniques and identify areas that each of you could change.   **P4**

5   At the sports event, one of your athletes suffers a severe injury. This makes you realise that, as a coach, you need to advise emerging athletes and their parents or carers of the importance of career

planning. You arrange a presentation that outlines the factors that should be considered when planning a career both in sport and beyond a competitive career.

a Identify at least five sporting careers that interest you.

b Research which qualifications you require for each one and what experience is needed.

c What factors will influence your future career?

d Discuss these careers with a tutor or careers adviser.

e Identify clear targets on how to achieve your sporting and career goals. **P5**

To help you meet the M3 and D2 criteria you should read the following grading tips.

Grading tips

Grading Tip M3

Explain each of the factors you have described to achieve the P5 criteria. This explanation should include the use of goal setting, SWOT analysis and the importance of second career planning. Investigate examples of sports-related careers and explain the qualifications needed to undertake these careers.

Grading Tip D2

Analyse how the key factors you have described will influence the career planning of the athlete. You should evaluate fully the importance of career planning and explain what an athlete should do to prepare for a career in sport and afterwards.

- Choose at least five factors and investigate fully how these will influence your career choices.
- Analyse who will be able to help you in deciding the best career for you.
- Contact people who are already working in the area and discuss how they achieved their success.
- Arrange an interview with a professional athlete and ask how they manage their careers.
- Speak to successful coaches and get advice on how to succeed in sport.

To achieve a pass grade the evidence must show that the learner is able to:	To achieve a merit grade the evidence must show that, in addition to the pass criteria, the learner is able to:	To achieve a distinction grade the evidence must show that, in addition to the pass and merit criteria, the learner is able to:
P1 Describe five different lifestyle factors that can affect athletes **Assessment practice Page 430**	**M1** Explain five different lifestyle factors that can affect athletes **Assessment practice Page 430**	**D1** Analyse five different lifestyle factors that can affect athletes **Assessment practice Page 430**
P2 Describe the importance of appropriate behaviour for athletes **Assessment practice Page 441**	**M2** Explain the importance of appropriate behaviour for athletes **Assessment practice Page 441**	
P3 Describe strategies that can be used by athletes to help deal with three different situations that could influence their behaviour **Assessment practice Page 441**		
P4 Describe two methods of communication athletes could use when dealing with the media and significant others **Assessment practice Page 450**		
P5 Describe factors involved in career planning for an athlete **Assessment practice Page 455**	**M3** Explain how the factors identified influence career planning for an athlete **Assessment practice Page 455**	**D2** Analyse how the factors identified influence career planning for an athlete **Assessment practice Page 455**

Index

Page number in *italic* type refer to illustrations and tables, those in **bold** type refer to key terms.

A

accident book **85**
acromion **20**
Act of Parliament **61**
adaptive thermogenesis (AT) 295
adenosine triphosphate (ATP) **18**, 43, *43*, 44
Adventurous Activities Licensing Act 59–60
Adventurous Activities Licensing Authority (AALA) 66
advisory **202**
aerobic endurance 93, *93*, 102, **233**
aerobic respiration **18**, 44
agility 95, **95**
alveoli 38
amino acids 279
anaerobic endurance component **108**
anaerobic glycolysis 44
anaerobic respiration **18**
anal canal 288
anatomical terms 7, *8*
antioxidant vitamins 282
anxiety 330–1
appendicular skeleton **4**, 5–6, *5*
arousal 331–6
    effects on sports performance 335–6
arteries 31, *31*
arterioles 32
articular (hyaline) cartilage **11**
articulation **8**
athletics 97–8
attribution **325**
auditory **356**
axial skeleton **4**, 5, *5*

B

balance 95–6, **95**
balanced diet **276**
barriers to participation 186–8, **186**
behaviour for athletes 431–42
    adherence to rules 431
    coping and management strategies 434–5
    respect for others 431–3
    situations 435–41
        during competitions 437
        during training 437
        during travel 437
        media 437–9
        other people 439–41
        other team colleagues 441
        public 439
benchmark scores **261**
body composition 93, 94–5, *95*, **239**
body mass index (BMI) 256–7
bones 4–10
broadsheet **439**
bronchi 38
bronchioles 38
buccal cavity 287
burnout **326**

C

calcaneus **20**
calorie **289**
capillaries 32, *32*
carbohydrates 277–9
cardiac muscle **17**
cardiovascular system 29–36
    blood vessels 31–3
        arteries 31, *31*
        arterioles 32
        capillaries 32, *32*
        veins 32, *32*
        venules 32
    functions 33–4
    heart 29–31
    response to exercise 34–6
career planning 451–6
    athletic career planning 452–4
    goal setting 451–2
    second career planning 454–5
    self-need analysis 452
cartilage
    articular (hyaline) **11**
    costal **8**
    fibrocartilage **11**
child protection 143–4
chronic adaptation **115**
chyme 288
coaches 82, 136–7
    coaching process 161
    code of conduct 78
    delivering coaching sessions 170–6
        components 171–2
        demonstrations 171
        feedback 172
        health and safety considerations 171
        resources 171
        responsibilities 170–1
        roles 170
        sequencing 172
    planning sessions 162–9
        aims and objectives 164
        components 167–8
        health and safety 166–7
        participants 164–5
        resources 165–6
        responsibilities 164

roles 164
  sequencing 168
  skills and techniques 168–9
  targets 164
responsibilities 143
  equal opportunities 148
  health and safety 147
  knowledge of coaching environment 148–9
  legal obligations 143–5
  professional content 146
reviewing coaching sessions 173–5
  aims, objectives and targets 173
  areas for improvement 174
  development 174–5
  feedback 174
  formative and summative reviews 173–4
  strengths 174
roles 137–43
  educator 141–3
  friend 139
  innovator 137–8
  manager 139–41
  role model 141
  trainer 141
skills 150–4
  analysis 153
  communication 150–2
  evaluation 153
  organisation 152–3
  problem solving 153
  time management 153–4
techniques 154–60
  adapting to individual needs 159–60
  developing performer diaries 159
  fitness assessment 156–7
  goal setting 157–8
  modelling and demonstration 158
  observation analysis 156
  performance profiling 156
  practice session design 160
  simulation 158
  technical instruction 158–9
codified systems **62**
cognitive anxiety **333**
cognitive skills **366**
cognitive state anxiety **330**
combat sports 99
communication 442–50
  evaluation 449–50
  media 447–8
  significant others 448–9

confidentiality **249**
contractile proteins **42**
Control of Substances Hazardous to Health (COSHH) 55–6
coordination **95**, 96
costal cartilage **8**
cross-cutting agendas 184–6, **185**, 199

D
dance 99
dehydration 298–9
diaphragm 38
diastolic **254**
diet **276**
dietary fibre 282
dietary thermogenesis (DT) 294
digestion
  functions of digestive system
    absorption 288
    digestion 288
    excretion 288
  structure of digestive system 287–8, 288
digestive juices 288
direct delivery **202**
distress **328**
dorsal surfaces **8**
duodenum 288

E
enabling **202**
energy intake and expenditure 289–97
  energy balance 294–7
    basal metabolism 295–6
    physical activity 296–7
  measures of energy 289
    body composition 290
    body weight 292
    direct and indirect calorimetry 292, 293
    lean body mass 290
    percentage body fat 290–2
  sources of energy 290
energy systems 42–4
  recovery periods 47
equipment for sports 82
ergogenic **299**
ergogenic aid **299**
essential amino acids (EAAs) 279
ethics **431**
eustress **328**
exercise **15**
expiration 39

expiratory reserve volume 40
external imagery **356**

F
facilitating **202**
fats 280–1
fat-soluble vitamins 281–2
fatty acids 280
fibrocartilage **11**
fine motor skills **366**
Fire Safety and Safety of Places of Sport Act (1987) 59
first aid 82
fitness 92–102
  components 92–6
  sporting activities 97–102
    athletics 97–8
    combat sports 99
    dance 99
    gymnastics 98–9
    invasion games 99–100
    net/wall games 100
    outdoor activities 101
    striking and/or fielding games 100–1
    swimming 98
    target games 101
fitness testing 230–44, **230**
  advantages and disadvantages of tests 241–4
    cost 241
    equipment requirement 242
    facility requirement 242
    reliability 243–4
    skill of tester 243
    time 241–2
    validity 243
  aerobic endurance 233–5
    maximal treadmill protocol 235
    multi-stage fitness test 233–4
    step test 234–5
  analysing results 265–9
    accepted health ranges 266
    elite athlete norms 266
    performer norms 265
    population norms 265
  body composition 239–40
    bioelectrical impedance analysis 240, 291
    hydrodensitometry 240
    skinfold callipers 239–40, 291
  communicating results
    fitness levels 268
    recommendations 269

strengths and areas for
improvement 269
   test results 268
   tests carried out 268
   verbal 267
   written 268
conducting tests 258–64
   1RM 258
   bioelectrical impedance analysis 260
   grip dynamometer 259
   health and safety considerations 263
   hydrodensitometry 260
   maximal treadmill protocol 258
   multi-stage fitness test 258
   one-minute press up and sit up 259
   preparation 260
   recording results 264
   skinfold callipers 260
   sprint test 259
   step test 258
   terminating tests 264
   test protocols 262
   test sequence 262
   vertical jump 259
   Wingate test 259
flexibility 230–1
   sit and reach 230–1, *231*
muscular endurance 238–9
   one-minute press up 238
   one-minute sit up 238–9
power 236–7
   vertical jump 236–7
   Wingate test 237
selecting tests 260–2
   pre-test procedures 261
   purpose 261
   reliability 261
   validity and practicality 261
speed 235–6
   sprint tests 236
strength 231–3
   1RM 232
   grip dynamometer 232, *232*
fitness training evaluation 125–8
   monitoring 125–6
fitness training methods 102–11
   aerobic endurance 107–9
      continuous training 108
      Fartlek training 108
      interval training 108–9
   flexibility training 103–4
      ballistic stretching 104
      proprioceptive neuromuscular

facilitation (PNF) stretching 104
   static stretching 103–4
speed 109–11
   interval training 110
   sport-specific speed training 110–11
strength, muscular endurance and
power 104–7
   circuit training 105
   core stability 107
   free weights 106
   medicine balls 107
   plyometrics 106–7
   resistance machines 105
fitness training planning 112–24
   information collecting 112–14
   periodisation 120–2
      individual sessions 121–2
   principles of training 114–20
      frequency, intensity, time and type
        (FITT) 119–20
      individual differences 116–18
      overload 114–15
      progression 116
      reversibility 118
      specificity 115
      variation 118
   training diaries 123–4
flexibility **93**, 94, 102
food **276**
food groups 311–12, *312*
franchise **198**

G

gall bladder 288
gamesmanship **440**
gaseous exchange **30**
glucose 278
glycogen 278
gross motor skills **366**
group dynamics in sports teams 336–44
   cohesion 339–41
   leadership 341–4
gymnastics 98–9

H

hazard idientification 71–2
Health and Safety (First-Aid) Regulations
   (1981) 56–7
Health and Safety at Work Act (1974)
   52–4
Health and Safety Executive (HSE) **54**, 64
health screening 244–57, **244**
   procedures 245–52

client confidentiality 249
client consultation 245–8
coronary heart disease risk factors
   251
informed consent 249–51
listening 248
medical referral 251–2
non-verbal communication 249
questioning 248
questionnaires 245, *246–7*
tests 253–8
   blood pressure 253–5
   body mass index (BMI) 256–7
   heart rate 253
   lung function 255–6
   waist to hip ratio 256, *256*
health surveillance **56**
healthy eating **276**
heart 29–31
hyaline cartilage *see* articular cartilage
hydration 298–301
   dehydration 298–9
   effects on sports performance 301
   fluid intake 299–300
      inter-event 299–300
      post-event 300
      pre-event 299
   hyperhydration 299
   hypohydration 299
   sources
      hypertonic drinks 300
      hypotonic drinks 301
      isotonic drinks 300
      water 300
   superhydration 299
hypertrophy 28

I

iliac crest **20**
innominate bone **6**
insertion **20**
inspiration 39
inspiratory reserve volume 40
intercostal muscles 39
internal imagery **356**
intestines 288
invasion games 99–100
isometric contraction **104**

J

joints 10–16
   fixed 11, *11*
   movement types 12–15, *13*, *14*

response to exercise 15–16
slightly movable 11
synovial 11–12, *12*
joule **289**
jurisdiction **61**

K

kilocalorie **289**
kilojoule **289**
kinaesthetic **356**

L

lactic acid 43–4
large intestine 288
larynx 37
leader of sporting activities 81
legal factors 60–4
   case law 62
   civil law 61–2
   duty of care 62–4
   higher duty of care 64
   loco parentis 62
   negligence 64
   statutory law 60–1
legislation **52**
legislative factors 52–60
   Adventurous Activities Licensing Act
      59–60
   Control of Substances Hazardous to
      Health (COSHH) 55–6
   Fire Safety and Safety of Places of
      Sport Act (1987) 59
   Health and Safety (First-Aid)
      Regulations (1981) 56–7
   Health and Safety at Work Act (1974)
      52–4
   Management of Health and Safety
      Regulations (1999) 57–9
   Manual Handling Operations
      Regulations (1992) 57
   Personal Protective Equipment 2002
      (PPE) 55
   Report of Injuries, Diseases and
      Dangerous Occurences Regulation
      (RIDDOR) 54–5
lifestyle factors 422–31
   leisure activities 422–3
      alcohol consumption 424
      drugs, recreational 425
      education 422–3
      gambling 425-6
      relaxation 422
      rest 422

smoking 426
   unruly behaviour 427
   pressures
      competition 428
      financial 428–30
      peers 427
      social life 427
      training 427
ligaments 16
litigation **54**
liver 288
long-term goals **451**
lungs 38

M

macrocycles 120, **120**
macronutrients **276**
Management of Health and Safety
   Regulations (1999) 57–9
Manual Handling Operations Regulations
   (1992) 57
maximum heart rate **109**
medium-term goals **451**
mesocycles 120, **120**
microcycles 120–1, **120**
minerals 282
mitochondria **18**
motivation 323–7
   achievement 324
   effects on sports performance 325–6
   extrinsic 324
   intrinsic 323–4
motor skills **366**
multicultural **185**
muscles 17–28
   fibre types 18–20, *19*
   major muscles 20–3, *21, 22*
   movements 23–7
      antagonistic pairs 24–5
      contractions 25
      sliding filament theory 27
   origin **7**, **20**
   response to exercise 27–8
   types 17–18, *17*
muscular endurance **93**, 94, 102, **238**

N

nasal cavity 37
net/wall games 100
non-starch polysaccharide (NSP) 282
non-verbal communication **443**
nutrition 276–87, **276**
   dietary planning for sport activities

302–4
   activity-based 304–5
   appropriateness for activity 308
   appropriateness for performer 308–9
   assessing needs 309–10
   balanced diets 302–4
   carbohydrates 303
   fat gain 310
   fats 303
   fibre 303
   inter-event 306
   mid-season 305–6
   muscle gain 310
   post-event 306–7
   post-season 306
   pre-event 306
   pre-season 305
   proteins 303
   vitamins and minerals 303–4
   water 303
   weight gain 310
   weight loss 310
dietary requirements 283–7
   carbohydrates 283–4
   fats 285–6
   proteins 284–5
fibre 282, 311
macronutrients **276**, 311
   carbohydrates 277–9
   fats 280–1
   proteins 279–80
micronutrients 311
   minerals 282
   vitamins 281–2
terminology
   Estimated Average Requirments
      (EAR) 287
   optimum level 286
   recommended daily allowance (RDA)
      286
   Safe Intake (SI) 287

O

occipital bone **20**
oesophagus 287
olecranon process **20**
olfactory **356**
operational **202**
origin **7**, **20**
osteoporosis **16**
outdoor activities 101
overtraining **326**

P

pancreas 288
perceptual skills **366**
performance-enhancing drugs **425**
Personal Protective Equipment 2002 (PPE) 55
personality 318–22
   effects on sports performance 321-2
   interactional approach 320–1
   situational approach 319–20
   social learning theory 319
   trait theories 318–19
   Type A 321
   Type B 321
pharynx 37
physical activity **15**, 294–5
planning safe sporting activities 81–6
   equipment 82
   insurance 84
   participants 83–4
   reviews 84–6
   roles and responsibilities 81
      coaches 82
      first aid 82
      leader 81
      site 83
polysensorial **356**
power **93**, 94, **95**, 96, 102, **236**
proteins 279–80
psyching out **436**
psychological skills **345**
psychological skills training (PST) to enhance performance 344–58
   planning 345–55
   techniques 355–8
pubic crest **20**

Q

quality **208**
quality systems **208**

R

reaction time **95**, 96
recreational drugs **425**
rectum 288
regulatory bodies 64–8
   Adventurous Activities Licensing Authority (AALA) 66
   governing bodies of sport 66–7
   Health and Safety Executive (HSE) 64
   local authorities 64–5
   local education authorities 65
   police 65
reliability **243**
Report of Injuries, Diseases and Dangerous Occurences Regulation (RIDDOR) 54–5
residual volume 40
respiratory system 36–42
   breathing mechanism 39
   components 37–9
   functions 39
   respiratory volumes 40–1
   response to exercise 41–2
resting metabolic rate (RMR) 294
Ringelmann effect 339
risk assessments 68–74, 75–6
risk avoidance **58**

S

safety in a sports environment 74–80
   communication 77
   emergency procedure protocols 76
   first aid 76–7
   procedures and protocols 77–80
   risk assessments 75–6
   staff development 75
   staff training 75
saturated fatty acids 280
short-term goals **451**
skeletal muscle *17*, **17**
skeletal system 4–10, *4, 5*
   functions 6–7
   major bones 7–10
   response to exercise 15–16
sledging **436**
sliding filament theory of muscular contraction 27
small intestine 288
SMART targets 164
smooth muscle **17**
somatic state anxiety **330**
speed **93**, 94, 95, 103, **235**
spine 10
sport **15**
sports development
   barriers to participation **186**
      cultural 187
      economic 187
      educational 187–8
      historical 187
      social 187
   benefits
      cross-cutting agendas 199
      healthy lifestyles 199
      opportunity 199
      performance improvement 199
   current initiatives 216–23
      2012 Olympics 216
      areas of activity 221
      Awards for All 217
      Big Lottery 218
      effectiveness 222
      governing body sports development 220
      local authority sports development 219
      local programmes 218–19
      partnerships 220–1
      private sector programmes 218
      voluntary clubs 220
   key concepts 182–92
      appropriateness 184
      cross-cutting agendas 184–6, **185**
      excellence 184
      foundation 182–3
      participation 183
      performance 183–4
      purpose 184
   key providers 193–200
      governing bodies of sport (GBSs) 196–7
      local autorities 194–5
      private sector providers 198
      professional providers 198
      Sport England 193
      Sports Coach UK 193–4
      voluntary organisations 197–8
      Youth Sports Trust 194
   quality measures 208–15
      advantages 213
      benchmarks 208
      Charter Mark 210
      Clubmark 211
      disadvantages 214
      external audits 212
      internal (self-assessment) 212
      Investors in People (IiP) 209–10
      national governing body schemes 213
      purpose 213
      Quest 208–9
   roles 202–7
      providers 202–6
      sports development officers 206
      volunteers 207
   structure 200–2
      committees 200
      consultation groups 201

forums 201
working groups 200
target groups 188–92, **188**
50+ participants 189–90
black and ethnic minority groups
(BMEs) 190-2
disabled people 190
women 188–9
young people 189
sports development continuum **182**
sports nutrition **276**
sportsmanship **440**
staleness **326**
Steiner's model of group effectiveness
338
stomach 287
strategic **202**
strength **93**, 94, 102, **231**
stress 327–30
striations **17**
striking and/or fielding games 100–1
stroke volume **35**
sugars 278
swimming 98
systolic **254**

tabloid **439**
tactile **356**
target games 101
target groups 188–92, **188**
technical skills 366–72

assessing performers 381–400
nutritional guidance 393–6
observation checklist 381–3
psychological guidance 396–400
assessing personal abilities 400–12
areas for improvement 403–4
competition analysis 407–10
competitive situations 400–2
development plan 411–12
log books 404–7
strengths 402–3
continuous
cross-country skiing *369*
rowing 368
running 367
swimming 368
walking 367
discrete
board diving 371
golf swing 371
putting in golf 371
snooker shot 371
throw-in in football 372
serial
dribbling in football 370
high jump 369
hurdles 370
pole vault 370
triple jump 369–70
tactics 372
basketball 378–80
tennis 376–7

volleyball 373–5
tendons 16
test protocol **262**
thermoregulation **33**, **299**
tidal volume 40
total lung capacity 40
trachea 38
training see fitness training
trait **318**
triglycerides 280

unsaturated fatty acids 280

VO_2 maximum **108**, **233**
validity **243**
values **431**
veins 32, *32*
venules 32
verbal communication **443**
vertebral column 10
visual **356**
vital capacity 40
vitamins 281–2

water-soluble vitamins 282

xiphoid process **20**